Genetics of the Dog

Also by the author:

The German Shepherd Dog: its history, development and genetics

Genetics of the Dog

Malcolm B. Willis BSc (Dunelm), PhD (Edin)

Senior Lecturer in Animal Breeding and Genetics, Faculty of Agriculture, The University, Newcastle upon Tyne

HOWELL
BOOK HOUSE
New York

Howell Book House
A Simon & Schuster Macmillan Company
1633 Broadway
New York, NY 10019

First published in Great Britain 1989
by H. F. & G. Witherby

© Malcolm B. Willis 1989

Library of Congress Cataloging-in-Publication Data

Willis, Malcolm Beverley.
    Genetics of the dog/by Malcolm B. Willis.—1st ed.
        p.   cm.
    Bibliography: p.
    Includes index.
    ISBN 0-87605-551-X
    1. Dogs—Genetics.   2. Dogs—Breeding.   I. Title.
SF427.2.W55   1989
636.7'0821—dc19   891871
                                                       CIP

10 9 8 7 6 5

Typeset in Great Britain by
Rowland Phototypesetting Ltd, Bury St. Edmunds, Suffolk
and printed and bound in Great Britain by
Biddles Ltd, Guildford and King's Lynn
Illustrations originated and printed by
BAS Printers Ltd, Over Wallop, Hampshire

Contents

List of Tables

List of Figures

List of Plates

Acknowledgments

This book had its conception in an idea from my then publisher Dennis Kelsey-Wood following the successful launch of my book on the German Shepherd Dog which we found being read by enthusiasts of other breeds seeking genetic guidance. In preparing this present volume I have been aided by a number of people and organisations without whose cooperation the end product would have been much poorer.

Parts of the manuscript have been read by my colleague Dr R. J. Thomas MRCVS and by Miss Lorana Sullivan, Mrs Margaret Thomas MRCVS and Mrs T. B. Willis DMV. All have made suggestions that have improved the work and any deficiencies that remain must be laid at my door.

Photographs have been provided by Doctors E. Andresen, K. C. Barnett, S. M. Fletch, G. A. Hegreberg, P. W. Ladds, J. E. Lund, K. M. Myers, J. R. Pick, V. J. Selmanowitz, Mr J. Richardson and Mr H. Teall. I am grateful to all these people as these visual aids have been an invaluable help.

Permission to reproduce copyright material has been given by the Kennel Club, the British Veterinary Association, Lea and Febiger, Dr D. F. Patterson, W. B. Saunders & Co, Dr M. W. Strickberger and the National Foundation March of Dimes, as well as by the editors of the following scientific journals: *American Journal of Cardiology*, *Cornell Veterinarian*, *Hereditas*, *Journal of the American Veterinary Medical Association*, *Journal of Dermatologic Surgery and Oncology*, *Journal of Heredity*, *Journal of Small Animal Practice*, *Laboratory Investigation* and *Veterinary Record*. I am grateful to all these people and organisations as well as to the many scientists whose work has been utilised in this book. I am also grateful to the Institut für Tiermedizin und Tierhygiene mit Tierklinik, Universität Hohenheim, for permission to reproduce thesis material of Dr Viktoria Richter. Also to Mrs Jo Royle for the gift of the British Boxer Club record book which was used in the inbreeding study.

Finally I must thank the German Shepherd Dog League of Great Britain and the British Briard Club. I act as Honorary Geneticist to these two bodies which are beginning to compile the sort of data which will be of value both to their members and the canine world in general. Some of their material is reproduced in this book and hopefully more will be available for future editions, by which time other breed clubs in other countries may have started to copy their example. Only by pooling our knowledge can we hope to increase the speed of our progress in the search for better dogs and a reduction of the incidence of defects. It is the enthusiasm of the more ardent members of these and other breeds which has encouraged my own optimism in the canine world and it is to be hoped that this book will stimulate others to follow in the example of the pioneer breed clubs.

M. B. WILLIS

Newcastle upon Tyne
March 1988

Introduction

The breeding of livestock for specific purposes—be these the production of food, specialised work, sport or merely exhibition—is a very old occupation but it did not take on any real scientific significance until the eighteenth century when the pedigree breeding of cattle and sheep was first established in Britain. In the canine field Britain must rank as the pioneer, having set up the Kennel Club in 1873. For many decades Britain was regarded as the stock farm of the world and this applied to dogs no less than to farm livestock. But, as in so many fields, the pupils have not been slow to profit from the example of their mentors and Britain can no longer claim any intrinsic right to supremacy. This is certainly the case in dogs where changing fashions have led to fluctuations in the popularity and numerical strength of individual breeds, which in turn is reflected in the quality of those breeds.

The British Isles can still claim to rank at the top in many breeds—but not in all. Dog breeding has become a much more international business than was once the case and in particular breeds the advantage has been gained by other countries. This is certainly true of America and Germany but in most developed countries of the world, and in some developing ones, an interest in dog breeding has advanced to the stage at which it involves many thousands of people and massive amounts of capital. Registrations are numbered in hundreds of thousands and many thousands of dogs are exported from one country to another at not inconsiderable prices.

Dog breeding is 'big business' involving not only the breeders themselves but all the resultant service industries: the pet food companies, the veterinarians, boarding kennels, professional handlers, judges and the like. Research is undertaken into more effective ways of feeding dogs and into better ways of preventing or combating disease and yet very little indeed is spent on the ways in which the genetic principles of dog breeding might be more clearly understood.

Dogs serve man in a host of different ways, they are used by the hunter seeking sport or food, by the police to combat crime, by the armed services to perform military duties, by farmers to round up sheep or cattle, by the blind to act as eyes or simply as companions to those whose lives might otherwise be less full. The multiple uses of the dog have resulted, over the centuries, in a myriad assortment of breeds which, by accident or design, have been found suitable for some specific task. Indeed it can be argued that the dog, more than any other species, is the supreme example of what can be achieved by genetic selection. No other species shows such differentiation of size and shape, character or range of activities. It is, one might say, the geneticists' dream and yet it is the one species sadly neglected by the geneticist.

Genetics is a young science since it really dates back only to the rediscovery of Gregor

Mendel's work around the year 1900. In the past three-quarters of a century many advances have been made but the basis of genetic material—the genetic code as it is called—was not understood until the 1950s. Genetics is the science of life itself and we have clearly much to learn but, for all that, vast strides have been made in our understanding of genetic principles as they apply to farm livestock. In dog breeding we are greatly retarded. Few universities in the world despite their numerous genetic departments occupy themselves, even in some small way, with the genetics of the dog.

One obvious reason for so little interest stems from shortage of funds but it also relates to a basic lack of interest in the subject among dog breeders themselves. To many people dog breeding is a hobby; even those whose livelihoods depend upon their ability to breed and sell dogs have found it all too easy to succeed, in some degree at least, with the production of saleable stock. Too many breeders work in an empirical fashion and their failures are quickly buried or, more frequently, sold to the uninitiated and unsuspecting public seeking a pet. Many breeders, even some of the more successful ones, make disparaging or cynical remarks about genetics whenever the subject comes up. Yet, if the truth were known, the most successful breeders operate along reasonably sound genetic lines. Were this not so they would not have found the success they have.

The cynic may argue that the differentiation seen in dogs was obtained without the help of geneticists. This is undoubtedly true but the time scale cannot be ignored. Many breeds may have existed in pedigree terms for less than a century but the differentiation has existed for much longer and has taken centuries to achieve. A modern dog breeder needs quicker results than that and he will not succeed in the true sense of the word 'success' unless he understands something about animal breeding.

As befits any subject with a large number of devotees, the dog breeder has had a plethora of books telling him how to go about his activities. There are books on training, feeding, mating, whelping, health, judging, individual breeds and a host of fringe subjects. There is no real shortage of books on breeding but I make no apologies for adding to the list because I am convinced that it is in the area of breeding and genetics that the dog breeder is most deficient and that, in the main, the existing books on dog breeding are sadly lacking in scholarship.

Any intelligent breeder will, in time, pick up a good deal of the basic principles of breeding from canine books on the subject but generally such books are written by experienced breeders. As a trained geneticist who makes his living from the breeding field of farm livestock but who has been a dog man all his adult life, I find most dog breeding books oversimplify the issue. All too briefly the crucial aspects of polygenic inheritance are dismissed yet, as will be seen, these are the most important areas of the business controlling all the main traits of type, construction, character and the like. In all of these aspects the environment plays a crucial role as well which makes for complexity—a complexity not helped by the tendency among dog breeders to record and measure very little. Few breed organisations bother to compile statistics—even the most rudimentary ones—that would be considered essential in other fields of animal breeding. Too often breeders work from fallible memory and from isolated incidents they draw generalisations which are too frequently erroneous.

A lack of information may not have prevented some breeders from gaining great fame in their breed but who is to say that given greater knowledge of facts fame might not have been gained by many more? Indeed how much of the fame of a 'great' breeder rests upon the well-remembered names of a few outstanding show dogs while innumerable animals from the same kennel achieved nothing and did nothing for the breed beyond increasing its numbers? Given greater statistical control who can say whether or not hip dysplasia or progressive retinal atrophy might have been maintained at lower and less damaging levels?

In a listing of inherited traits in man that were of relatively simple origin McKusick (1971) could cite 866 disorders of known mode of inheritance and a further 710 with the mode of inheritance not yet conclusively determined. In contrast, a similar study in the dog by Patterson (1974) had corresponding figures of 33 and 18. The fact that some 26 to 30 times as many simple genetic traits have been reported in man as compared to the dog does not indicate any greater intrinsic susceptibility in man but rather reflects a higher degree of medical scrutiny and awareness.

The very shortage of information on the dog has not made my task in writing this book any easier. An almost total absence of canine data has necessitated taking my illustrations in some areas from other species. In doing so I may have made my reader's task no easier but it is preferable to try to deal with complexities, however inadequately, than to brush them aside as being too difficult to bother about.

This book will not, at times, be easy. It requires some effort on the part of the reader (particularly those with no mathematical bent) if the full grasp of the subject is to be gained. If I have genuinely failed to put over my points in an intelligible fashion then the fault is mine, not the subject of genetics. There is, however, a physical limit to the size of any book and one has to assume that breeders are intelligent beings capable of mental effort or one is forced to write at the level of a school primer. I have chosen to believe the former and have written accordingly.

My own breed is the German Shepherd Dog and in the thirty-five years or so that I have been a devotee of that breed I have amassed a large quantity of information about it. In the absence of data on other breeds I have drawn on material from my own. There is, however, no attempt to make this a breed book in any sense and I have cast the net as widely as possible. If any breed appears more frequently in this book it tends to reflect rather that there were more data about it than that it was my own personal preference. Those who support breeds other than those used in specific examples may feel impatient but it is clearly impossible to illustrate every principle with examples from every breed. Though dogs may differ in their physical appearance the principles discussed apply over a broad field.

The breeds discussed are found in many regions of the world and since genetics knows no national boundaries the material presented should have a wider appeal than just my own country. It is not, however, a general dog book. There is nothing about feeding, exhibiting, judging, mating, whelping or training other than insofar as these various factors may influence genetic action. Many of the illustrations and examples used to demonstrate certain phenomena are the result of investigations by scientists and have been published in scientific journals not readily available to breeders. I have cited references in the normal fashion of a scientific text. This may interfere with the flow but it is done deliberately because it is high time dog breeders started to appreciate that you must cite chapter and verse for your views or ideas. Too many opinions circulate around show rings that have no basis in fact. In this book if you do not agree with what I say or with my interpretations of the data then you can check the original work and examine its validity.

The book is not aimed at any particular section of the dog breeding public, nor at any nationality. Novice and expert alike will find something of value between the covers if they seek it out. The trained geneticist with no specialised knowledge of dogs will find the text of use as a reference source though he may admittedly find the genetics aimed at a level below his own. Veterinary surgeons will also find this book a guide to the genetics of defects they encounter on a regular basis. It is not an attempt at a veterinary text but there is an increasing need for veterinarians to understand animal breeding principles on which there is only minimal emphasis in most veterinary courses.

The book itself is basically in three sections. Chapters one and two form the basic introduction to genetic principles as they apply to dogs. The next eleven chapters deal with the mode of inheritance of specific traits met with in dogs. Finally, chapters fourteen to seventeen deal with selection and methods of mating. I hope that sufficient data are given to enable a breeder to apply the ideas expounded to his own breeding operations. Technical terms are explained on first usage but a glossary is also given (see page 405).

The final chapter deals with recording systems in the hope that breeders and organisations might move in this direction and thus make available better records for those who follow on. The more we are prepared to share our knowledge and to publicise our failures the more our breeds will benefit. If we want to understand how a particular problem occurs and how to be rid of it we have to cooperate or we will achieve nothing.

It must not, of course, be assumed that a knowledge of genetics will result in a sudden upsurge of champions even if you are unwise enough to equate breeding prowess with the number of winners produced. Success in the show ring is not only dependent upon breeding ability but also the size of one's purse, the number of breeding bitches, the numerical strength of the breed, the quality of judges, the time one can spend exhibiting and, in great measure, luck. No genetic text can serve as a kind of recipe book for success because the ingredients in terms of breeds, genes and environments are too numerous to cover in so limited a space. If this book should serve to stimulate an interest in the subject and give you a greater insight into the many problems that do or will beset you then it will have served its purpose. If you actually breed better dogs as a consequence that will be a rich reward indeed.

We are the custodians of our chosen breeds during the relatively short period of our dog breeding lives. It behoves us to hand over the material we breed with in a better state than when we received it or we have achieved nothing and the breeds we profess to love will be the sufferers. 'The good of the breed' is the most oft quoted lie in dogdom. This book was written to make it a truism.

Chapter 1

Basic Genetic Principles

The Cell

Any dog, like every other animal, is made up of innumerable minute cells which, when studied under an electron microscope, can be seen to consist of two basic components. The major area of the cell is the cytoplasm which contains various structures of no immediate concern to us here and which is largely made up of proteins. In the middle of the cytoplasm is a darker area known as the nucleus. It is here that the principal genetic material is located.

The nucleus contains a series of structures called chromosomes. In any species the number of chromosomes is constant for every member of that species and in every body cell of that individual (except for the sex cells which are discussed later). In the dog, of whatever breed, there are 78 chromosomes just as there are in wolves and coyotes, jackals have 74, man has 46, cats 38, horses 64 and so on. The number is always even and closer examination reveals that although chromosomes come in different shapes and sizes there are two of every particular kind. Thus it is more correct to speak of 39 pairs of chromosomes in the dog rather than 78 chromosomes. Chromosomes belonging to a pair are known as homologous chromosomes, one member of each pair having been derived originally from each parent of the individual animal.

Along the length of each chromosome are situated the genes. It has sometimes been likened to a string of beads with the string representing the chromosome and the genes being indicated by the beads. The analogy is not theoretically correct since genes are essential and integral parts of the chromosome whereas beads are not part of the string. However, as an illustration the analogy will serve the purpose at this stage.

Chemically the gene is made up largely of deoxyribonucleic acid (DNA) and it is through this that all the myriad of complex genetic information and instructions that are the basis of heredity are passed on. The gene is the unit of inheritance and like chromosomes genes are paired. Thus the genes in the same position (locus) in homologous chromosomes will influence the same character or characters in the dog. Since one member of the homologous chromosomes derived from the sire and one from the dam it follows that one member of each gene pair derived from each parent.

Although the genes at a particular locus of a specific chromosome influence the same character they can influence it in different ways. If alternative ways of influencing the character exist then these are called alleles of a gene. There can be many alleles of a gene, as we shall see in colour inheritance, but in any individual animal there can only be two alleles at any locus because there are only two chromosomes bearing that locus. If the two alleles are identical, that is, they influence the character in the same way, then the individual is said to be homozygous for that locus. If the two alleles are different —influence the character in different ways—the animal is said to be heterozygous for that character.

Cell Division or Mitosis

As a dog grows older it becomes larger in size. This is achieved by what is called somatic division or mitosis. At conception the dog is a single cell and from that point onwards we have an almost constant process of cell division and multiplication until death. A cell divides into two and these two divide to give two more so that we have a continuous increase in cell number. Yet each cell remains a more or less exact copy of the original, complete with cytoplasm, nucleus, 39 pairs of chromosomes and all the necessary genes still identical with those of the original cell. The process is illustrated in Figure 1 using only three chromosome pairs for simplicity.

The process of mitosis need not concern us in great detail since it does not advance our understanding of animal breeding very far. However it is necessary to understand that during the cell division operation each chromosome divides into two so that where we originally had 78 chromosomes we have 156 for a temporary period. At this point divided chromosomes go to opposite ends of the cell so that 78 are at one end and an identical 78 at the other. The cell then splits into two identical parts.

Not all body cells continue to grow in this fashion throughout life. During the process of development of the foetus certain genetic instructions are transmitted through the individual and some cells develop into brain cells, others into blood cells and so forth. Certain of these, like brain cells, may not grow beyond a particular point while others are continually being renewed.

Sexual Reproduction or Meiosis

Somatic growth explains what happens to the cells in the same animal but of greater interest to the animal breeder is the mechanism by which genetic material is passed from

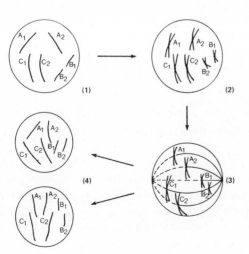

Figure 1   Mitosis. For purposes of simplicity only three chromosome pairs are shown. These split lengthways to give a duplicate number (2) and then are drawn to opposite sides of the cell (3) which then splits forming two new cells each with the original number of chromosomes (4). This type of division occurs in normal growth.

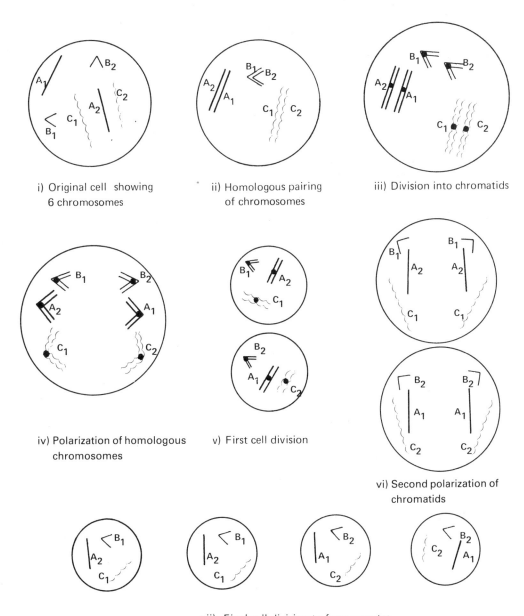

i) Original cell showing
6 chromosomes

ii) Homologous pairing
of chromosomes

iii) Division into chromatids

iv) Polarization of homologous
chromosomes

v) First cell division

vi) Second polarization of
chromatids

vii) Final cell division to form gametes

Figure 2 Meiotic division. Showing how gametes are produced so as to contain a random sample of chromosomes but with at least one coming from each pair.

one generation to the next. It was stated earlier that each cell had 39 pairs of chromosomes. However, in sexual reproduction the sperm of the male is united with the ovum of the female. If sperm and ovum each have 39 pairs the resultant progeny would have 78 pairs or 156 chromosomes. Clearly, if chromosome number is to stay constant in a species then some reduction in number must occur at some stage.

The process which brings this about is the meiotic division. Like mitosis this is a rather complex operation of which only a simplified explanation is given here and illustrated in Figure 2.

In mitosis each chromosome divides in two to provide identical cells. In meiosis chromosomes also divide but when the sperm or ova are being produced the reproductive cells arrange for one chromosome of each homologous pair to go to opposite ends of the nucleus. When the final division occurs four cells result in each of which there are 39 chromosomes, one from each homologous pair. Thus when the sperm (with 39 chromosomes) contacts the ovum (with a matching but different 39) the resultant zygote, from which the new animal is to be formed, has 78 chromosomes in 39 homologous pairs.

The four final gametes shown in Figure 2 have received their chromosomes from different sources. Thus one has $A_2B_1C_1$ while another has $A_1B_2C_2$. If the suffixes 1 and 2 are used to represent the paternal or maternal origin respectively, then we can see that some element of randomness or chance occurs. On average the most likely division is one whereby half the chromosomes in any gamete stem from the sire of the animal and half from the dam but all possibilities will exist ranging from 100% of paternal origin to 100% maternal. With 39 pairs of chromosomes it is apparent that the number of possible combinations is vast. Herein lies the element of chance which a breeder ignores at his peril. Since the allocation of which chromosome to which gamete is purely random (except that each gamete must have one member of each homologous pair) it is equally obvious that the genes carried by a particular gamete will depend upon the chance allocation of the chromosomes. There is then the further element of chance as to which male gamete (sperm) will meet up with which ovum.

There is no known way by which man can control this random sorting of chromosomes and their genes and this is what makes genetic predictions fascinating and difficult. This does not mean that we must adopt a fatalistic approach and assume that all breeding is mere chance. Clearly chance plays its part but, as we shall see in later chapters, a breeder can, by careful selection of breeding stock and subsequent planning of their mating, increase his prospects of obtaining what he seeks. The better he is at selecting, the better his knowledge of specific genetic factors, then the greater his chances. But he can never be totally sure of anything and the breeder who is eager to boast about his breeding success had better beware.

Crossing-over and Linkage

Thus far it has been assumed that chromosomes were transmitted as whole units. In many instances this is true but it is an over simplification to assume that this is always the case. Sometimes a piece of one chromosome may, at the chromatid stage of development (see Figure 2), become transposed with a similar piece from its homologous partner. At the subsequent division into gametes these two pieces will now go in separate ways as shown in Figure 3.

Crossing-over of chromosomes is fairly frequent and it means that alleles carried on a

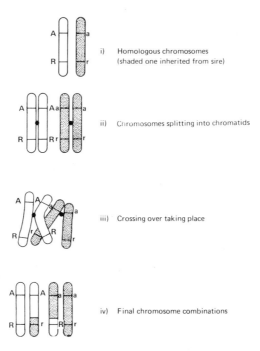

i)   Homologous chromosomes
     (shaded one inherited from sire)

ii) Chromosomes splitting into chromatids

iii) Crossing over taking place

iv) Final chromosome combinations

Figure 3   Crossing over. Although an animal must transmit the full quota of chromosomes it can transmit parts of one linked to a corresponding part of its partner.

particular chromosome inherited, let us say, from the sire, can become separated from those carried elsewhere on the chromosome and instead become linked up with those which originally stemmed from the dam.

When genes are carried on the same chromosome they are said to be linked. If they affect different characters then this may lead to specific traits being frequently seen together in the same dog. However, the phenomenon of crossing-over will gradually break up specific linkages. The closer together genes are situated on a certain chromosome then the less the chance that they will become separated. Conversely the farther apart they are the greater the chance of separation.

The Inheritance of Sex

In the opening to this chapter it was stated that the dog carried 39 pairs of chromosomes and that members of a pair were of similar shape. We can now modify this slightly to introduce the concept of sex chromosomes and autosomes.

In the cell the chromosomes are all jumbled up in the nucleus but under microscopic examination pairing can be done. In the male one pair are not identically shaped, while in females this pair would be of matching size. We call this pair the sex chromosomes and the other 38 pairs are called autosomes.

In the female the two identical sex chromosomes are called XX whereas in males there is only one X and another one which is called Y. Thus all females are XX and all males XY and this is true of all animals but is the reverse in birds.

Since parents pass on only half their chromosomes to each sex cell or gamete it follows that all female gametes or ova must carry an X. In contrast male gametes or sperm can carry either an X or a Y. These will be produced in equal numbers but it will depend which kind of sperm reaches the ovum first as to which kind of sex is produced. If the Y gets there first then the resultant individual will be XY and male whereas if an X gets there first the resultant animal will be XX and female.

Sex determination is shown diagrammatically in Figure 4. In theory there ought to be an equal number of males and females conceived because all ova are X and the sperm are 50% Y and 50% X. In actual practice many animal species have a situation in which the Y-bearing sperm is either faster at reaching the ovum or else the ovum itself has some predilection for Y-bearing sperm. At all events more males (XY) are conceived than females (XX). But from conception onwards there is some kind of natural reaction against males so that more are stillborn and hence at birth the sex ratio is less heavily weighted towards the male. Estimates of sex ratios vary in dogs and are discussed in more detail later (see page 49).

Gene Action—Complete Dominance

We have already learned that genes are made up of DNA and a whole section of genetics exists that is devoted to DNA and how it works. As animal breeders we are less concerned with what is going on at the biochemical level and more with the biological expression of all that activity. However it is important to realise that the biological variation which we see and can measure is the final result of what may have been a series of complex biochemical reactions. A dog does not inherit a gene which produces, let us say tan coloration. What it does inherit are specific DNA structures which will, in the right circumstances, and depending upon what is going on in some other part of the DNA, bring about tan pigment.

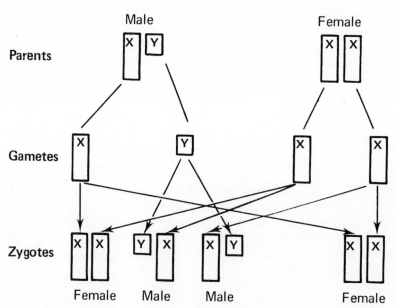

Figure 4   The inheritance of sex showing the way in which the sex chromosomes are transmitted.

If things go wrong en route or if the other DNA structures act to prevent this happening then we may not have tan colour . . . we may not even have a dog. For simplicity genes will be referred to as though inheritance is a fairly straightforward operation rather than the complex and intricate mechanism it so obviously is.

The concept of alleles of a gene at a given locus has already been outlined. Here we are concerned with the different ways in which alleles may act. If a specific allele acts in such a way that even when present in a single dose (that is, on only one chromosome), it can totally mask the other allele carried on the other chromosome then the first allele is said to be dominant and the allele which is masked is termed recessive. It follows from this that the dominant allele can be present either singly or in duplicate but the external effect will be the same. In contrast a recessive allele must be present in duplicate for the animal to reveal that by its appearance.

The underlying genetic structure is termed the genotype while the external expression of this—that which we see or can measure—is termed the phenotype. The number of different phenotypes for a specific character may be fewer than the number of genotypes.

If we are dealing with a single gene whch has only two alleles, one of which is dominant and the other recessive then we have three genotypes and two phenotypes. It is relatively easy to predict the outcome of various matings provided that one is not working with very small numbers. To illustrate this Figure 5 uses the example of the B series controlling colour in the dog.

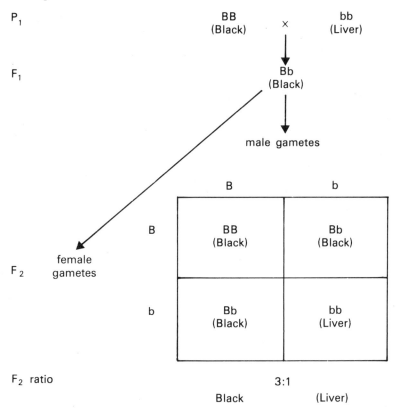

Figure 5 Monofactorial inheritance—B series.

In the B series there are two alleles: B which allows black pigment to be formed in the coat and b which permits liver or red colour to be formed. Black is totally dominant to liver and is thus designated by an upper case letter while liver is given a lower case letter.

With two alleles there are only three possible genotypes which are BB, Bb and bb but since B is dominant to b the BB and Bb types are identical in phenotype, namely black. The bb genotype is expressed as a liver phenotype.

If we mate a pure-breeding (that is, BB) black to a liver then all the progeny will be Bb and hence black. If we mate two of these together then we find that blacks and livers appear in the ratio of three blacks to every liver. However, if we look more closely at Figure 5 we find that the blacks are of two kinds BB or Bb and there is one BB to every two Bb. Thus rather than a 3:1 ratio we actually have a 1:2:1 ratio occurring.

In the illustration used in Figure 5 we term the original pure breeding strains the P or parental generation and their offspring the first filial or F_1 generation. Mating two F_1 individuals gives the F_2 generation and so forth.

There are several other ways that these particular two alleles can be combined and this is shown in Table 1. The six different types of matings will lead to six different kinds of progeny ratios but these figures will only apply to large numbers. If we mate two black dogs and get a small number of black progeny it does not mean that the parents are free of the liver gene, one may be Bb and the other BB or both may be Bb. However the more progeny that are born the greater the chances of confirming that both are not Bb. In contrast the appearance of even a single liver dog in a mating between two blacks will show that both parents are Bb in genotype. This is discussed in greater detail under test mating (see page 355).

It should be noted at this stage that the above explanation assumes that the B/b series is

Table 1

Mating results using the B series of coat colour genes

Parents (sex not important to colour results)			*% of progeny in each type** BB (Black)	Bb (Black)	bb (Liver)
BB Black	×	BB Black	100	—	—
BB Black	×	Bb Black	50	50	—
BB Black	×	bb Liver	—	100	—
Bb Black	×	Bb Black	25	50	25
Bb Black	×	bb Liver	—	50	50
bb Liver	×	bb Liver	—	—	100

*These percentages apply only over large numbers and not necessarily in any specific litter.

not affected by genes at other loci. As we shall see later (see page 9) this may not be a valid assumption in some breeds.

Gene Action—Incomplete Dominance

Sometimes an allele may act in such a way that when present with a different allele of the same series an intermediate type of phenotype exists. When there is complete dominance the homozygous dominant (for example, BB) and the heterozygous dominant (say, Bb) are phenotypically indistinguishable. When incomplete dominance exists then all three genotypes are identifiable because each has a distinct phenotype.

This can be illustrated by the agouti series affecting colour in a breed like the Rough Collie. The two alleles we are interested in are termed a^y and a^t. The former leads to sable coloration and the latter to bicolour or black-and-tan. Other genes lead to white colour so that these sable or black-and-tan colours may be present with white but for simplicity we can ignore that here.

With two alleles we have three genotypes $a^y a^y$, $a^y a^t$ and $a^t a^t$. The first two will be sable and the last one black-and-tan but the $a^y a^y$ type of sable is called a clear sable whereas the $a^y a^t$ type is called a shaded sable because black hairs will be interspersed through the coat.

In a dominant situation we can only accurately assess genotype by breeding performance (and sometimes by pedigree data) but with incomplete dominance we can identify each genotype from the visible phenotype. The predictions from breeding operations are thus easier to make but they will follow the example shown in Table 1 if one substitutes a^y for B and a^t for b. Then BB will correspond to $a^y a^y$ or clear sable, Bb to $a^y a^t$ or shaded sable and bb to $a^t a^t$ or black-and-tan.

When two or more alleles exist at a particular locus it is possible for an allele to be dominant to one and recessive to a third. This is more fully explained in the chapter on colour.

Gene Action—Epistasis

The two previous sections dealt with interaction between genes at the same locus. Sometimes genes at different loci interact and the situation is then one of epistasis. This means that the visible or phenotypic expression of the genotype at locus 1 will depend not only on that locus but also on the genotype at another locus 2.

To illustrate this let us use colour in Dobermanns. Although the breed has several genes controlling colour it is basically determined by the B/b series we have already examined. This leads to black or liver (red) Dobermanns. However there is another gene at a different locus known as the D or dilution series. This has two alleles: D which does not cause dilution of colour and which is fully dominant to d which causes dilution of colour.

We thus have three possible genotypes of the B/b series and three of the D/d series which means that if the two series segregate independently as they do there are three times three, or nine different genotypes. These nine are shown in Table 2.

We can see from Table 2 that for a dog to be black it must carry not only at least one B allele for black but also at least one D allele for non-dilution. There are thus four possible black genotypes. Similarly to be red or liver the Dobermann must carry not only bb which gives rise to red but also at least one D allele to allow that red colour to be expressed.

When the dilution allele d is present in duplicate (dd) then black is changed to blue and

Table 2

Colour in Dobermanns. Epistatic effects showing how only four colours result from nine different genotypes

Colour seen (Phenotype)	Possible genetic make up (Genotype)			
Black	BBDD	BbDD	BBDd	BbDd
Red	bbDD	bbDd	—	—
Blue	BBdd	Bbdd	—	—
Fawn	bbdd	—	—	—

red is altered to fawn or Isabella. Only the fawn coloration can be identified genetically from the phenotype. In all other cases we can only estimate certain aspects of the genotype from what we can see. Epistatic effects, where one locus is altered by what occurs at another locus, makes this complicated for the breeder but once one is aware of the mode of inheritance as in this instance with Dobermanns one can make certain predictions.

The various matings that can occur in Dobermanns are shown in Table 3 together with the percentages of progeny that might be expected given large numbers of young. One particular mating involving the double heterozygotes (that is, BbDd) can give rise to every one of the nine possible genotypes. In some countries Isabella is regarded as a disqualifying colour. The logic for this is hard to understand since it is not a colour which is associated with any biological defect and as long as black, red and blue are accepted then Isabella is bound to occur at intervals. However, given some study of the data in Table 3 matings to avoid Isabella can be easily organised.

Gene Action—Sex Linkage

It has already been shown that males carry an XY type of sex chromosome structure while females are XX. Since males basically determine the sex of their offspring it follows that any genes that are carried on the Y chromosome will be passed from father to son but not to daughters. Similarly genes carried on the X chromosome cannot be passed from father to son but only to his daughters. In contrast females will pass an X chromosome to each son or daughter although not necessarily the same one.

In actual fact it is believed that the Y chromosome is more or less inert, having few if any genes carried on it. The X chromosome is likewise believed to carry few important genes but it does carry some. In man genes for colour blindness and haemophilia are carried on the X chromosome. In cats the genes which give rise to tortoiseshell coloration are X-borne. In dogs haemophilia is known to exist in several breeds and, as in man, it is carried on the X chromosome. As a result haemophilia is mainly seen in males and only rarely in females. This is discussed in detail later (see page 243) and here we need only examine the basic principle.

Thus far all sex-linked conditions are known to be recessive and Figure 6 illustrates the situation most likely to be met with. This is when a female carrying one allele for the particular condition is mated to a normal male. Half the daughters of such a mating are perfectly normal and the other half are 'carriers' like their dam. In contrast half the males

Table 3

Mating results from all combinations of the B and D coat colour series (as seen in Dobermanns)

| | | Per cent of progeny in each possible type | | | | | | | | |
| | | Black | | | | Red | | Blue | | Fawn |
Parental types		BBDD	BBDd	BbDD	BbDd	bbDD	bbDd	BBdd	Bbdd	bbdd
BBDD	× BBDD	100	—	—	—	—	—	—	—	—
	× BBDd	50	50	—	—	—	—	—	—	—
	× BbDD	50	—	50	—	—	—	—	—	—
	× BbDd	25	25	25	25	—	—	—	—	—
	× bbDD	—	—	100	—	—	—	—	—	—
	× bbDd	—	—	50	50	—	—	—	—	—
	× BBdd	—	100	—	—	—	—	—	—	—
	× Bbdd	—	50	—	50	—	—	—	—	—
	× bbdd	—	—	—	100	—	—	—	—	—
BBDd	× BBDd	25	50	—	—	—	—	25	—	—
	× BbDD	25	25	25	25	—	—	—	—	—
	× BbDd	12½	25	12½	25	—	—	12½	12½	—
	× bbDD	—	—	50	50	—	—	—	—	—
	× bbDd	—	—	25	50	—	—	—	25	—
	× BBdd	—	50	—	—	—	—	50	—	—
	× Bbdd	—	25	—	25	—	—	25	25	—
	× bbdd	—	—	—	50	—	—	—	50	—
BbDD	× BbDD	25	—	50	—	25	—	—	—	—
	× BbDd	12½	12½	25	25	12½	12½	—	—	—
	× bbDD	—	—	50	—	50	—	—	—	—
	× bbDd	—	—	25	25	25	25	—	—	—
	× BBdd	—	50	—	50	—	—	—	—	—
	× Bbdd	—	25	—	50	—	25	—	—	—
	× bbdd	—	—	—	50	—	50	—	—	—
BbDd	× BbDd	6¼	12½	12½	25	6¼	12½	6¼	12½	6¼
	× bbDD	—	—	25	25	25	25	—	—	—
	× bbDd	—	—	12½	25	12½	25	12½	—	12½
	× BBdd	—	25	—	25	—	—	25	25	—
	× Bbdd	—	12½	—	25	—	12½	12½	25	12½
	× bbdd	—	—	—	25	—	25	—	25	25
bbDD	× bbDD	—	—	—	—	100	—	—	—	—
	× bbDd	—	—	—	—	50	50	—	—	—
	× BBdd	—	—	—	100	—	—	—	—	—
	× Bbdd	—	50	—	—	—	50	—	—	—
	× bbdd	—	—	—	—	—	100	—	—	—
bbDd	× bbDd	—	—	—	—	25	50	—	—	25
	× BBdd	—	—	—	50	—	—	—	50	—
	× Bbdd	—	—	—	25	—	25	—	25	25
	× bbdd	—	—	—	—	—	50	—	—	50
BBdd	× BBdd	—	—	—	—	—	—	100	—	—
	× Bbdd	—	—	—	—	—	—	50	50	—
	× bbdd	—	—	—	—	—	—	—	100	—
Bbdd	× Bbdd	—	—	—	—	—	—	25	50	25
	× bbdd	—	—	—	—	—	—	—	50	50
bbdd	× bbdd	—	—	—	—	—	—	—	—	100

Note Percentages in each progeny cell refer to expected percentages over a large number of progeny. They may not apply in any particular litter.

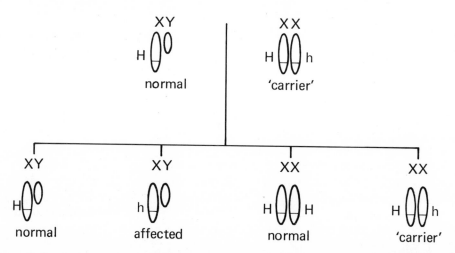

Figure 6 Sex linkage. Mode of transmission of a recessive trait (eg haemophilia A or B) when mating a normal male to an apparently normal but 'carrier' female. The cigar-like objects represent the sex chromosomes and H and h represent the normal and haemophilia alleles respectively.

are normal and the other half are affected. It is interesting that although the affected male carries only a single allele for the condition he will still exhibit it because the Y chromosome affords no counterbalance.

If we are dealing with a potentially lethal condition like haemophilia most affected males generally die in early life and thus the condition is not spread by males and will never appear in females. If, however, an affected male is kept alive (as is now possible with haemophilia) or if the condition is not lethal (as in colour blindness in man) then affected males can reproduce.

When affected males are mated to normal (non-carrier) females no affected progeny result but all the daughters will be carriers. However, if such an affected male is mated to a carrier female then affected males and females can occur as seen in Figure 7.

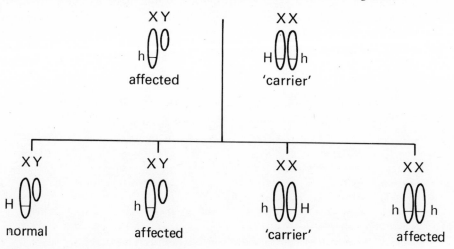

Figure 7 Sex linkage. Mode of transmission when mating an affected male to an apparently normal but 'carrier' female. Symbols are as shown in Figure 6.

Gene Action—Sex-limited Conditions

In sex-linked conditions the genes responsible must be carried on the sex chromosomes. In sex-limited conditions we have different results in each sex but the genes responsible are borne by the autosomes and are thus inherited equally by either sex but may be expressed more extremely in one sex.

Typical examples of a sex-limited character would be the expression of horns in some sheep breeds or pattern baldness in man. The illustration used in Table 4 relates to colour in Ayrshire cattle where the same genotype will result in different phenotypes according to whether the individual is a male or female.

Some conditions are sex limited because they cannot be expressed at all in one sex. For example milk yield is expressed only in females and cryptorchidism only in males but the genetic factors involved may be transmitted and carried by either sex. This makes genetic study harder and in some instances means that selection has to be based upon progeny performance rather than the individual itself because it cannot be demonstrated in the particular sex.

In a sense the secondary sexual characteristics—the greater size of males, their heavier heads and strength of forequarters—are sex-limited because the genes which control them are influenced by the sex of the bearer. For example the genes controlling head size are the same in each sex but because the male is XY and the female XX they have different hormone balances. It is the different hormones which cause the same genes to be expressed differently in each sex.

Sometimes characters are seen in both sexes but appear only very infrequently in one sex. Usually the term sex-controlled is applied to such traits. In man harelip and gout are sex-controlled in that they can appear in either sex but do so most frequently in males. In contrast spina bifida and hip dysplasia are human problems found most commonly in females. In this connection hip dysplasia in humans may be similar to that in dogs.

Gene Action—Incomplete Penetrance

In discussing dominant and recessive alleles it was assumed that whenever the dominant allele was present in a single dose then the animal concerned would exhibit this particular trait. Similarly the recessive allele had to be present in duplicate for the trait to be seen in the animal. In these instances we have what is called complete penetrance. This complete

Table 4

Sex limited expression (coat colour in Ayrshire Cattle)

Genotype	Male Phenotype*	Female Phenotype*
MM	Mahogany	Mahogany
Mm	Mahogany	Red
mm	Red	Red

* All animals will also show white markings but these are caused by other genes and need not be discussed here. They will not influence the expression of red or mahogany.

or 100% penetrance is the usual rule but there are occasional instances when a particular allele fails to reveal its presence in the phenotype. Usually this occurs at the heterozygote stage, that is in the Aa type of genotype.

Let us consider a trait where occasionally the Aa individual does not show the dominant phenotype but appears to be of the kind aa. Then we have a case of incomplete penetrance. If in 75% of such cases the Aa genotype was indistinguishable from the AA but in the remaining 25% of cases the Aa genotype appeared to be aa, then we have what is called 75% penetrance.

In dogs many cases of apparent incomplete penetrance are based on too few records to be reliable or are possibly polygenic traits rather than simple ones. However incomplete penetrance is a feasible explanation in some instances.

When incomplete penetrance is involved the breeder will have some difficulties because the breeding results will not appear to follow normal theory. Because of the different degrees of incomplete penetrance one cannot lay down any hard and fast rules. Breeders should bear in mind the existence of this phenomenon and if they are faced with unexpected results in progeny groups which cannot be explained by paucity of numbers then they should seek genetical advice.

Phenocopies

Breeders often assume that because something is congenital then it is under genetic control. This is not necessarily true. Congenital simply means present at birth and a trait can be present at birth and be genetic or not just as a trait may appear later in life and be genetic or not.

Accidents to the dam during pregnancy can result in developmental problems of the foetus which may be quite serious as far as the foetus is concerned but which will not affect the genetic make-up. Sometimes specific environmental effects may be strong enough to cause changes in the animal which resemble genetic conditions. When this occurs the individual is called a phenocopy.

Perhaps the most tragic example of phenocopies was the thalidomide case in humans. Thalidomide was a tranquilliser which, if taken by a woman at a certain stage of pregnancy, induced certain severe developmental changes in the foetus. Often these problems included shortened limbs or their total absence. It is known that there is a genetic condition in humans which is very rare but which can lead to shortened limbs (phocomelia) or their total absence (acheiropody). When thalidomide children began to appear in the 1960s it was first thought to be a genetic condition. Only when the numbers became too frequent did the workers involved seek other explanations and came up with the thalidomide explanation.

The situation can also work in reverse. The dog with soft ears for genetic reasons can have them erected by placing felt inside the ear during puppyhood. When erection occurs (and it does not always) the dog will appear normal in ear carriage. He will, however, only be a phenocopy since genetically he is soft-eared and will breed as such.

Variations in Chromosome Number

It was assumed earlier that all dogs carried 78 chromosomes in 39 pairs. In the vast majority of animals this is true but there are cases in some species and occasionally in dogs where variation in number occurs. Variation is usually an increase rather than a decrease and can involve an entire set of chromosomes (euploidy) or a single chromosome within a set (aneuploidy).

The best-known example of this sort of occurrence is possibly Down's syndrome in man. There are normally 23 pairs of chromosomes in man but occasionally an additional chromosome occurs in the pair designated 21. When three 21 chromosomes occur the child carrying them is affected by Down's syndrome. Such accidents occur at some stage of the gamete formation and, in the above case, are more likely in mothers around the age of 40 than in younger mothers.

It is probable that such chromosomal aberrations occur more frequently than is supposed but that usually the gamete either fails to be effective or else there is rapid reingestion of the embryo. The Down's Syndrome situation is one case where the aberration is not sufficiently serious in a genetic sense to cause early embryonic death. Problems of this kind in dogs have been observed but not very frequently because few scientists are looking for them.

A second type of chromosome duplication occurs in the case of sex chromosomes where an extra X is found in some females. These are then known as 'superfemales'. The terminology is more spectacular than the reality and I do not recommend male readers to begin searching for such human 'superfemales'!

The extra X chromosome can occur in males and cases are known in cats which give rise to tortoiseshell males. Normally such males are impossible because tortoiseshell results from an X chromosome carrying black and another bearing yellow. Since a male has only one X chromosome it can have only black or yellow. When male tortoiseshells have been located they have always been of the kind XXY and sterile. Sterility of animals with an odd chromosome is common and is typified by the mule which has 63 chromosomes having resulted from a cross between the horse with 64 chromosomes and the donkey with 62. All mules are sterile.

Sometimes an extra Y chromosome occurs. In humans males of the XYY type are believed to be excessively aggressive and among violent criminals more XYY types are found than in normal populations. It is not improbable that such types occur in dogs and that XYY males might have temperament traits which are undesirable.

Some Biochemical Aspects

When reviewing my book on the German Shepherd Dog (1976) it was the view of Burns (1977) that I had tended to be rather old-fashioned in my approach to basic genetics. That is a valid criticism true of the present volume but it is occasioned by a long experience of giving genetic lectures to practical breeders. They do tend, in my view, to be better able to understand genetics explained in terms of dominants and recessives than in terms of the more modern biochemical explanations. However Burns' point is a valid one and for the sense of completeness some brief explanation of biochemical aspects might be appropriate now that we have explained the action of genes in simple terms.

The analogy of a string of beads was used earlier to illustrate the concept of genes and chromosomes. It is not a correct one in the strict sense because genes are not isolated parts but integral portions of the chromosome. The information needed to determine the features we see in an individual are all contained in the structure of DNA which forms the gene. The DNA itself is made up of a sugar (deoxyribose), a molecule of phosphoric acid and a molecule of either a purine or a pyrimidine joined in a chemical unit called a nucleotide. The type of purine can be either adenine or guanine and the type of pyrimidine can be cytosine or thymine. These nucleotides of DNA will, according to the sequence of an arrangement in a molecule of DNA, determine the specific role of that sequence. The particular sequence in some way contains the information which will lead to the fitting together of a series of any number of some twenty amino acids which together form a protein. The particular message that a certain arrangement of DNA gives is transmitted by messenger riboneucleic acid (mRNA) and we know that genes act by controlling the specific chemical reactions in a series of biochemical reactions. They do this by acting upon enzymes (themselves proteins) which instigate a particular reaction but which do not form part of that reaction. The phenotypic differences we see in the animal are due to the effects of differences in the DNA. When a defect is attributed to a single gene effect it can be shown that at the biochemical level there is a change in a single protein molecule. There is likely to be a specific change in the base sequence of DNA. Thus instead of an order of AAA (three adenines) the order may become GAA when mutation changes one adenine to a guanine. This will then cause a different message to be transmitted. Genes which at the phenotypic level we call dominant are those where the correct message on only one chromosome is sufficient to make the biochemical reaction occur whereas a recessive trait needs both chromosomes to carry the message.

Good descriptions of these aspects with particular reference to the dog have been given by Patterson and Medway (1966) and by Patterson (1975). In the second of these references Patterson takes the example of sickle cell anaemia in man and shows how the complex and serious clinical picture of the disease can be traced back to the substitution of the amino acid valine for glutamic acid at a certain stage of the biochemical chain and this, in turn, can be traced to the substitution of adenine for thymine at a certain stage of mRNA.

Because the end product of a series of biochemical reactions will depend upon all of them occurring correctly it is possible to interfere with the chain at various stages and still have the same effect. Thus in haemophilia we can have a similar end product, namely failure of the blood to clot, for a variety of causes. Disruption of any of the various reactions in the chain will end up producing haemophilia but each stage has a different gene controlling it—some sex-linked, some autosomal.

When we look at the blood disease of cyclic neutropenia in the Rough Collie we are seeing the end product of some malfunction of the biochemical pathways which has prevented a normal blood pattern emerging. We also see the pleiotropic effect of a diluted colour—the so-called grey Collie syndrome. In fact this colour dilution occurs because the interference with the biochemical reaction affecting blood leukocytes also interferes with some biochemical reactions in pigment formation. There are two effects but there is probably only one primary function at the molecular level. At present we simply do not know the various biochemical mechanisms involved.

Biochemical genetics is a particular branch of the science outside my own experience as a population geneticist but it will clearly be invaluable in seeking to understand why and how certain things occur. The animal breeder is less interested in the biochemistry of the problem, however enlightening it may be, and more in the cruder mechanics of the mode of inheritance. If we know that a particular defect is due to a recessive allele appearing in duplicate we can plan breeding programmes accordingly and these ideas will not be enhanced by knowledge of the underlying biochemistry. The mathematics of genetic ratios will not be altered by the way we think about genes whether this be as DNA or as beads on a string. Dog breeders who wish to follow the subject much deeper would do well to read Patterson's papers referred to previously (see page 16) but those who are happy to deal with the subject at the Mendelian level can safely do so without any biochemical understanding.

Chapter 2

Polygenic Inheritance

The Concept of Continuous Variation

Thus far we have dealt with the genetics of what might be termed relatively simple characters. These are traits in which the genetic make-up of the dog is reasonably predictable from his own appearance or that of his progeny. They are characters controlled by one or two genes with fairly clear demarcations between the different genotypes in their phenotypic expression. As will be seen in the ensuing chapters there are many characters in dogs which fit this type of Mendelian inheritance but they are rarely those of greatest importance to the breeder. Colour may be crucial in some breeds and certain recessively controlled abnormalities may lead to economic loss but none of these kinds of things are as important as sound temperament or breed type, balance and construction. When we examine these important characters we do not find clear demarcation between animals. Dogs are not, for example, tall or short but exhibit a whole range of heights ranging from the substandard to those grossly in excess of the standard laid down. These fine divisions are not easily measured and it is certainly difficult to explain them in terms of the presence or absence of a specific gene.

In the early days of genetics the type of character which showed gradual variation from one extreme through to the other was thought to be the result of environmental influences. However it was also realised that tall animals tended to produce taller progeny than average and this was indicative of genetic influence. Eventually it emerged that such characters (by now called metric characters) were indeed under genetic control but they were under the influence of a relatively large number of genes each of which had a very small effect individually but which in unison could have very marked effects. Such genes are known as polygenes and characters controlled by them are known as polygenically inherited characters. Their study is the branch of genetics known as biometrical or population genetics or sometimes as quantitative genetics. It is this branch of the subject that is of greatest importance to the dog breeder.

To the casual observer it may seem difficult to understand any similarity between the Mendelian type of inheritance and the continuous variation exhibited by polygenic characters. To illustrate the similarity let us take the case of skin colour in humans. The genetics of human skin colour is much more complex than the example used here which has been simplified for purposes of explanation but the basic principle has not been altered.

In humans, skin colour is controlled by two pairs of genes which we will call A and B. There are two alleles at each locus, one being a 'plus' allele causing increased pigment (black) and the other leading to white. Thus the blackest pigment is the AABB type while the whitest is aabb. If a mating is made between these two types the result will be AaBb

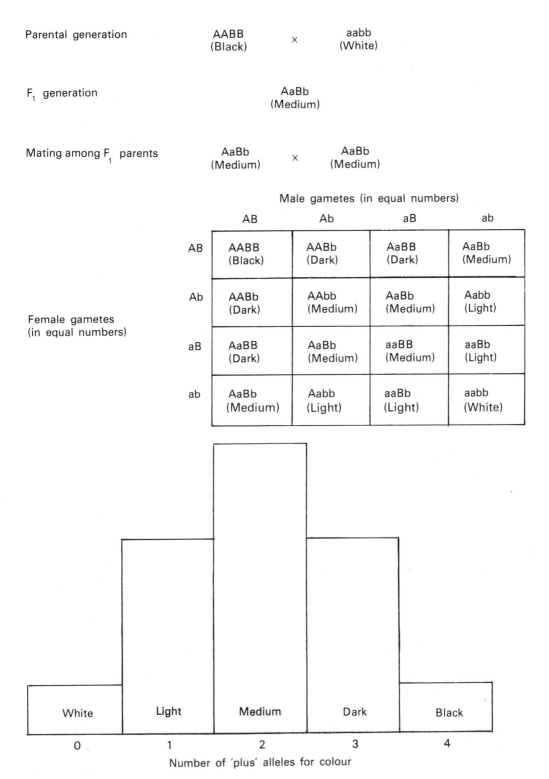

Parental generation   AABB   ×   aabb
                                  (Black)   (White)

F_1 generation   AaBb
                                   (Medium)

Mating among F_1 parents   AaBb   ×   AaBb
                                  (Medium)   (Medium)

Male gametes (in equal numbers)

	AB	Ab	aB	ab
AB	AABB (Black)	AABb (Dark)	AaBB (Dark)	AaBb (Medium)
Ab	AABb (Dark)	AAbb (Medium)	AaBb (Medium)	Aabb (Light)
aB	AaBB (Dark)	AaBb (Medium)	aaBB (Medium)	aaBb (Light)
ab	AaBb (Medium)	Aabb (Light)	aaBb (Light)	aabb (White)

Female gametes (in equal numbers)

White   Light   Medium   Dark   Black

0   1   2   3   4

Number of 'plus' alleles for colour

Figure 8   Segregation of two gene series affecting human skin colour (simplified version).

which brings about a medium pigmentation. If further mating is made among the AaBb types a whole series of different genotypes and phenotypes will result in the succeeding generation (the F_2 generation).

In every sixteen progeny there will be, for example, four 'Dark' pigmented persons and six 'Medium' pigmented types. The actual genotypes which give rise to any particular phenotype may differ considerably but they have one thing in common, namely the number of 'plus' alleles which are present. This is illustrated diagrammatically in the histogram at the foot of Figure 8. Thus 'Medium' colour will result when two 'plus' alleles are present and it is immaterial whether these are AA, BB or AB. Similarly 'Dark' pigment will occur when three 'plus' alleles are present and they can be AAB or ABB.

The illustration used is relatively simple involving only two gene pairs. If one was to take a situation involving three gene pairs but with the same type of 'plus' allele system then the number of phenotypes would increase but the same basic histogram pattern would result in which most individuals are situated around the mean and the numbers decline towards each extreme. The histogram resulting from three gene pairs is shown in Figure 9.

Increasing the number of gene pairs still more results in even further subdivision of the columns of the histogram with very fine divisions between each. If, in addition, one is able to show that environmental differences will make minor alterations to the phenotypic expression of specific genotypes then the histogram can gradually be smoothed off until it demonstrates the type of curve called a normal curve. This is shown superimposed in Figure 9 and it is this type of curve that is typical of the sort of polygenic characters in which the dog breeder is interested.

We can therefore conclude that polygenic traits are inherited in a very similar way to simple Mendelian traits but that they are controlled by a relatively larger number of minor genes (polygenes) such that the individual genotypes cannot easily be identified—if at all.

An actual population may not always show a perfect normal curve for a variety of reasons, mainly related to scarcity of observations and the fact that because man only measures to the nearest cm or kg or grade, the intervals between units will be more sharply defined than is true in reality. However to show that canine measurements do tend to

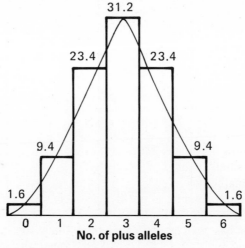

Figure 9   Histogram resulting from segregation of three gene pairs. The figures above the columns refer to the percentage of total animals in the appropriate group.

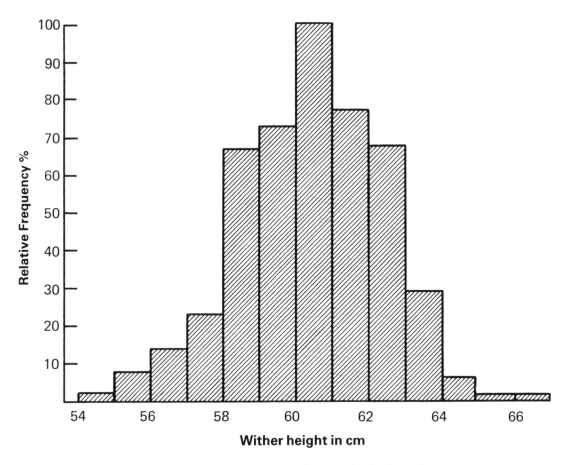

Figure 10   Wither heights in 469 German Shepherd females.

follow this kind of pattern Figure 10 shows the wither heights of 469 German Shepherd females as recorded in the SV Körbuch in 1927–28. I have calculated this sample from an early Körbuch because at that time little culling was made on height. Samples from recent Körbuchs show similar curves but show some truncation at each end—not because such under- and oversized animals do not exist but because they are not eligible for entry into the Körbuch.

The Normal Curve

Although we do not know how many genes are involved in the control of any particular polygenic trait we can safely assume that such traits do follow the patterns of a normal curve. There are some mathematical characteristics peculiar to all normal curves and these are essential to one's understanding of normal curves and therefore of polygenic traits. Assuming that the majority of readers will not be unduly enthusiastic at the prospect of mathematics an attempt has been made to keep these things to a minimum but the things one must understand are: means, standard error of the mean, variance, standard deviation and coefficient of variation.

In explaining these terms let us assume that we have a population of dogs which have been measured for some polygenic trait like wither height. The number of individuals (N) will each have a particular value (x) for wither height and the mean will simply be the total of all the heights divided by the number of dogs, that is $\Sigma x/N$ and will be designated $\bar{x}$.

The mean will be indicated by the highest point of the normal curve (see Figure 11) and there will be a spread either side of this mean. The extent of that spread is given by the variance (σ^2) which is measured by assessing the deviation of each individual from the mean, squaring this and dividing the whole by the number of individuals thus:

$$\sigma^2 = \frac{\Sigma(x - \bar{x})^2}{N - 1}$$

The more variable the character is the higher will be the variance and, as we shall see, this has important bearing upon the extent to which selection might be possible.

The standard deviation or SD is merely the square root of the variance. Thus the greater the variance the higher will be the SD and the more spread out along the base axis will the curve go. If the SD is low the curve will be a very narrow-based one with a very high central peak. The SD is useful in that with it we can assess certain things about the population. For example if we take one SD either side of the mean and draw a perpendicular line to meet the curve we can assume that 68% of the population will fall between these two lines. Similarly 95% of the population will fall within plus or minus two standard deviations of the mean whilst within three standard deviations of the mean almost the whole of the population is enclosed (99.7%). Even if we do not know the SD we can assume that the individual will have a 68% chance of being within one SD of the mean and a 95% chance of being within two.

If we take the population of German Shepherds used to compile Figure 10 we could calculate that the mean was 60.1 cm and the SD was 1.96 cm. We can therefore tell that 68% of bitches in that breed at that time were between 58.14 and 62.06 cm (that is to say, one SD either side of the mean) whilst almost the whole population was to be found between the wither heights of approximately 54 and 66 cm.

The coefficient of variation is obtained expressing the SD as a percentage of the mean. Thus $CV = (SD/\bar{x}) \times 100$. In the population just referred to this was 3.3%. The value of the CV is that it relates everything to percentage terms and thus enables comparison to be made between very different characters in terms of how variable they are.

The final statistic is the Standard Error (SE) of the mean which is obtained from the formula:

$$SE = \frac{SD}{\sqrt{N}}$$

The SE depends upon how many animals we have taken in our sample. The greater the number of animals we have the lower the SE is likely to be. Obviously, if we took five bitches at random and measured their wither height we would have a high chance of error if we assumed that this figure was typical of the breed. Another sample of five might give a totally different value. On the other hand a sample of 100 would be more reliable and it is probable that a second sample of 100 would yield almost identical results. For example in the sample of wither heights quoted the SE of the mean of 60.1 cm was a mere 0.09 cm. Thus we can be reasonably certain that the mean height of bitches at that time was somewhere between 60.01 and 60.19, a very narrow range indeed.

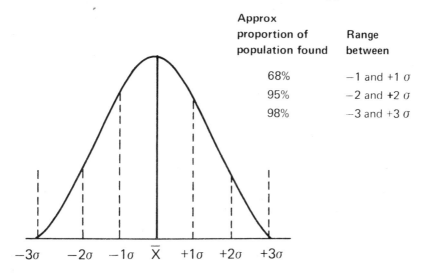

Figure 11   The Normal Curve. σ = Standard Deviation $\bar{x}$ = population mean.

Clearly the wither heights given refer only to the population extant at that time. There have been changes over the years and German Shepherd bitches in Germany now average only some 58 cm in height with a narrower spread about that mean. Clearly, too, we cannot make much use of normal curve statistics unless we record information from which they can be compiled. As will be seen in later discussion the statistics described are the basic material necessary for understanding the genetics of polygenic characters. We cannot tell how many genes we are dealing with but we can measure every trait in mathematical terms and with this data we can assess the degree to which any trait is genetically controlled and as a result the degree to which we, as breeders, might influence that trait in our breeding programmes.

The normal curve is shown in Figure 11 with the relevant statistics marked.

Partitioning the Phenotypic Variance

In the previous section we have discussed the idea of variation or variance. Although characters show considerable differences in the kind of variation they exhibit, all polygenically controlled traits will show some range and this is true whether it is wither height, adult body weight, shoulder angulation or simply overall excellence from a show ring point of view. However, what we see and measure is the phenotypic variance and this is not necessarily exclusively genetically produced. What we see is made up of a genetic component and an environmental component. The genetic component itself can be further subdivided into two sections called additive and non-additive and the non-additive section is further subdivisible into what are called dominance and epistatic component parts.

Using the term σ^2 to indicate variance we can add suffixes to denote the various component parts thus: phenotypic (P), genetic (G), environmental (E), additive (A), dominance deviations (D) and epistatic deviations (I). We therefore have:

$$\sigma_P^2 = \sigma_G^2 + \sigma_E^2$$
$$= \sigma_A^2 + \sigma_D^2 + \sigma_I^2 + \sigma_E^2$$

The relative importance of the different component parts will depend upon the type of character being studied and the population in which it is being studied. In simple traits the environmental component may be small enough to be ignored but in most complex characters there is always some environmental effect and even the genetic effect can vary considerably as to whether it is under additive or non-additive control.

The additive component is the portion of the variance of greatest interest to the breeder since it is the chief cause of resemblance between relatives and actually can be termed the breeding value. The non-additive part $(\sigma_D^2 + \sigma_I^2)$ is a difficult concept to discuss here but basically it is involved with genic interaction either at the same locus (σ_D^2) or between genes at different loci (σ_I^2). In other words, if the character depends upon the occurrence of specific combinations of genes at one or more loci then the non-additive component of variance will be relatively high. This means that if a character is largely under non-additive genetic control it will not respond well to selection. This arises from the fact that an animal can only pass on a sample of genes to its progeny and not specific combinations. An animal excelling in some trait which is largely non-additive in inheritance will be unable to produce its own excellence in its progeny because it cannot transmit the special combination of genes which led to its own excellence.

The extent to which a character is under genetic control is determined by the simple ratio σ_G^2/σ_P^2 but the fact that this may be high is of no help to the breeder unless the σ_A^2 component is high. This brings us to the concept of heritability or h^2 which indicates the proportion of the total variance we observe that is under additive genetic control and that is therefore available to the breeder in terms of potential progress through selection. The heritability of a character is given by:

$$h^2 = \frac{\sigma_A^2}{\sigma_P^2}$$

This may appear to be a rather difficult concept far removed from dog breeding but that is true only insofar as dog breeders do not bother to measure and record what is happening in their kennel or breed. In large animal breeding, as in laboratory mammals, a great deal of scientific work has been undertaken to show the heritabilities of numerous important traits and breeding programmes are designed to make use of such information.

Heritability values have been calculated for many of the traits important to farm livestock and also in laboratory species such as rats and mice. Strictly speaking, a heritability value is applicable only to the population from which it was assessed. However one can extrapolate to some degree and there are certain rules of thumb which appear to hold good for most animal species and which might logically be assumed to apply to dogs.

In the first place we can conclude that characters concerned with 'fitness' will be of low or negligible heritability. 'Fitness' characters include most of those relating to reproduction such as conception rate, litter size, survival ability and the like. The fact that heritabilities of such traits are low does not mean that they are not under genetic control. As breeders will be aware there are many differences between breeds in reproductive rates and these breed differences imply genetic control. But a low heritability means that the additive part of genetic control is low and hence the breeding value of an animal made difficult to assess. As we shall see when we discuss selection (Chapter 14) a low heritability indicates that selection for a trait is unlikely to yield any marked response. Certainly selection for increased litter size would have to be undertaken very intensively and for very many years before even an extra pup per litter could be added to the breed average.

On the other hand characters concerned with growth and development are likely to be of intermediate to high heritability. Swedish workers using German Shepherd data from the Swedish Army Dog Centre have assessed the heritability of 60-day weight in that breed as being about 45% in males and 34% in females. This would indicate that selection for an increase in weight at this age would be both effective and rapid assuming that breeders wished to do so. Similarly selection to reduce weight at this age would also be rapid. Since weight gain to one age is very much related to weight gain at another age, increases or decreases in 60-day weight will affect other age/weight relationships. In German Shepherds in the late 1920s males were about 64.4 cm in wither height and weighed 33.5 kg on average. By 1973 the average values were 63.5 cm and 37.2 kg indicating a slight decrease in average height and a substantial (about 11%) increase in weight over a period of about forty-five years. This is partly a result of improved nutritional methods but is also due to deliberate selection for a different type of Shepherd to that of the 1920s. It has only been possible because the characters involved (weight and height) were under reasonably high additive genetic control.

Although assessments of type are not known it is reasonable to assume that most are moderate to high in their heritability which would explain why man is able to alter the shape of his dogs with some degree of success. The cynic might question the wisdom of altering shape in the way that some breeds have done but there is no denial of the fact that it has been carried out effectively.

The genetics of canine behaviour has also been studied and such assessments as exist indicate rather low heritability values in the main but this is discussed in detail in Chapter 12.

The heritability concept may seem rather complex but it stems from the fact that relationships exist between parents and offspring and between brothers and sisters. The methods of assessment are based upon these relationships and consist either of examining the regressions between parents and offspring or the correlations between siblings. If a particular measurement is made on parents and their offspring then these data can be plotted on a graph and the slope of the line which fits the figures will give an indication of the heritability. Because of the greater use of males most heritability estimates are made either by the regression of offspring on their sire or by the correlation between paternal half sibs. The former regression line estimates half the heritability value whilst the latter correlation measures a quarter of the heritability.

Importance of the Environment

In the equation given on page 23 it was shown that the total variation which we could see or measure in a particular character depended essentially upon two things. Firstly the extent to which that character was under genetic control and secondly the importance of the environment.

There is a saying that 'half the pedigree goes in at the mouth' and this has considerable logic in the sense that whether or not a dog will live to exhibit true genetic potential will depend very much upon the environment to which it is exposed.

Environmental influences begin to act from the moment of conception and they can be shown to cover a great multitude of factors too extensive to list in detail. Some characters are much less influenced by the environment than others. Thus a white dog will not change his colour simply because his dam was badly fed during pregnancy or because the dog himself had rickets. On the other hand incorrect feeding of his dam or onset of rickets in the dog himself could well put paid to any genetic chance he might have had to develop into a strong, well-boned dog of show potential.

Most polygenically controlled characters will be influenced to a greater or lesser degree by environmental influences. These will not only comprise nutrition during the foetal, neo-natal and juvenile stages, which effects will be obvious to most experienced breeders, but they will include other influences less obvious to many. Disease, both clinical and sub-clinical, can adversely affect shape, type and survival itself and, as we shall see in Chapter 12, the type of socialisation to which a pup is exposed will have a lasting effect upon his behaviour patterns. Yet another aspect is climate and temperature. If exposed to certain hot climatic conditions dogs may exhibit certain traits (for example, skin problems or large scrotal sacs) that they might not have shown had they remained in a temperate climate.

All these environmental factors are external in that they are caused by factors external to the dog himself. There is also an internal environment which acts upon the animal and induces changes as a result. Age is the most obvious internal environment in that many traits appear only with increasing age. This includes not only desirable traits such as the change in coat colour from black to blue in Kerry Blue Terriers or the gradual erection of ears in erect eared breeds or the gradual darkening of eyes in all breeds but also undesirable traits like hip dysplasia and epilepsy or PRA, none of which conditions are obvious at birth but which occur at later stages of life. Some age effects have a fairly early time of onset such as eye colour or long coats while others like PRA in certain breeds or epilepsy may not manifest themselves until well into adult life.

Sex itself is both a genetic aspect and an environmental one in the sense that identical genes will have distinct expressions according to whether male or female hormones circulate in the blood. Some disease conditions may even be more prevalent in one sex than the other.

A final cause of variation which is environmental is that of error of definition or measurement. If we are measuring the heights of dogs any errors that we may make in our measurements will not actually affect the dogs themselves but they will affect the figures that we produce on the population. They will increase the σ_E^2 component of the total variance and will thus lead to a mathematical decline in the σ_A^2 component relative to the total variation. Errors of estimation will thus lead to reduced heritability values and this is true not only of physical measurements of height and weight but also of errors arising from classification of hips into the incorrect category of dysplasia.

Clearly any measures that reduce errors of estimation are to be welcomed. If a breed club is trying to assess physical standards in a breed then greater accuracy will result if age effects are eliminated by measuring all dogs at about the same age and if several measurements are taken on each trait and then the mean used.

Mathematical measurements have never been encouraged in most dog circles and certainly the fact that a man measures his dogs will not make him a better breeder. But until the traits that we are engaged in selecting for or against are fully documented we cannot hope to estimate either the success of our selection or decide which selection method is most appropriate. This is discussed more fully in Chapter 14.

Correlation

It is well accepted by experienced breeders that some characters seem to be related to others. This relationship or correlation may be positive or negative, large or small. If a

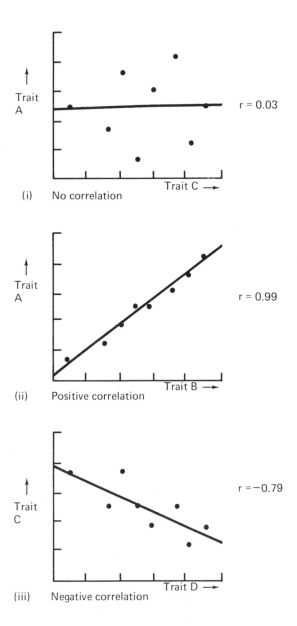

Figure 12 Correlations. The circles represent individual animals whose values for particular traits have been plotted on the appropriate graph. The thick line is the 'best fit' through the data.

relationship is negative (Figure 12iii) then improvement in one character leads to a decline in the other. If the correlation is positive (Figure 12ii) then improvement in one character leads to improvement in the other.

Dog breeders do not select simply for one character but are interested to a greater or lesser degree in a whole series of traits. Some understanding of the underlying correlations is essential if selection procedures are to give maximum success since it is no use selecting for some minor character if this will lead to rapid decline in a trait of major importance.

Although we know very little about correlations between traits it is logical to make certain assumptions. If, for example, we select for increased wither height then we will almost certainly get an increase in adult live-weight because the correlation between skeletal size and live-weight is positive. However certain other things might also result once such selection gets well under way. Increased skeletal size may lead to an increase in litter size (see page 43) and it may also lead to straighter hind angulation and to rather overbuilt rumps. If we undertake reverse selection and try to make a breed into a miniature or toy variety then our selection will be less effective because we may run into problems of dystocia (whelping troubles) and reduced prolificacy.

The reason for correlation may be twofold. One explanation is that the genes affecting the related traits are carried on the same chromosome and are thus linked. Linked genes will tend to be transmitted together and the chances of this occurring will be greater the closer the two genes are (see page 4). A more likely explanation when one is considering traits that are clearly controlled by polygenes, and where linkage in thus minimal, is pleiotropy. This is the ability of genes to have an effect upon two or more characters. This is almost certainly the case between skeletal size and liveweight which are controlled by several genes, some of which affect both traits in the same direction.

Pleiotropy has important connotations from a selection point of view but it must not be overemphasised. One has known, for example, Dobermann breeders who claim that the 'best' dogs in American lines seem to be related to the red colours. As will be seen colour inheritance is fairly simple in this breed (see Table 3 and page 88) and it is illogical to assume that a simple gene series can be linked so closely to the very many hundreds of genes that must be involved in producing the 'best' overall type. Such beliefs stem from a basic failure to document the situation and most probably if this were done on a big enough scale the facts would show the belief to be inaccurate. When a genuine link seems to exist between colour and some major trait it is usually found that the colour stems from some immediate and outstanding ancestor and all that has happened is that a good number of his or her stock have inherited the colour along with many of the outstanding physical traits. Such 'linkages' will be disrupted with time unless there is deliberate selection to retain both the colour and the 'type'.

Repeatability

Many characters in an animal can only be evaluated once. For example birth weight is only assessable at birth. We may take several weighings and use the average of these but we are still effectively making only one measurement. In contrast the speed with which a Greyhound covers a certain distance can be measured each time the dog runs and we can use these figures to get a better idea of the dog's racing ability.

In the same way we can measure characters like litter size each time a bitch has a litter. If bitches always had the same number of pups in each of their litters we could easily decide which were the most prolific and use these for breeding, discarding the others. Unfortunately bitches do not always have identically sized litters but by measuring several litters in a series of bitches we can assess how repeatable the trait 'litter size' is.

The repeatability (r) of any character measures the correlation between measurements of the same individual—in this case litter size. The extent to which a bitch will repeat her litter size depends upon the degree of genetic control of litter size plus some part of the environmental variation.

Hitherto we have considered environmental variance as a single factor but when we are considering the repetition of a character we can divide the environmental variance into two components. One of these is σ^2_{Eg} which is that part of the environmental variance general to all litters of the bitch (assuming we are looking at litter size). In contrast σ^2_{Es} is that part of the environmental variance which is peculiar or special to a particular litter.

Repeatability is thus a measure of the relationship between the special environmental variance on the one hand (σ^2_{Es}) and the genetic and general environmental variance on the other ($\sigma^2_G + \sigma^2_{Eg}$) and is thus expressed as:

$$r = \frac{\sigma^2_G + \sigma^2_{Eg}}{\sigma^2_P}$$

The repeatability thus measures the proportion of the variance due to permanent or non-localised differences between individuals. Repeatability will vary according to the character and species in which it is being measured but it has very important connotations in relation to selection.

In the first place repeatability sets an upper ceiling limit on the heritability in both the narrow (σ^2_A/σ^2_P) and broad senses (σ^2_G/σ^2_P). It is easier to assess than either of these two ratios and thus may be known when they are not.

In the second place knowledge of the repeatability tells us what gain in accuracy might be expected from multiple measurements of the same trait.

Suppose we measure a character like litter size by recording several litters from each bitch and taking the mean of her litters. What we are doing is reducing the amount of special environmental variance in the ratio of 1/n if n is the number of litters measured per bitch. The phenotypic variance of n measurements is reduced thus:

$$\sigma^2_{P(n)} = \sigma^2_G + \sigma^2_{Eg} + \tfrac{1}{n}\sigma^2_{Es}$$

This reduction in environmental variance represents a gain in accuracy. When the repeatability of a trait is high it will mean that special environmental variance is low and hence little is gained by waiting to make several measurements. In contrast, if repeatability is low it means that multiple measurements will increase the accuracy by which we can predict an individual's worth. Note that a character can be highly repeatable but have a low additive variance and hence a low heritability. This is likely to be true of litter size in the bitch which is very probably of low heritability yet with a high repeatability. This means that bitches with large (or small) litters will tend to keep producing large (or small) litters but that their progeny will not necessarily follow the same trend for large (or small) as their dams.

Data on repeatability measurements in dogs are rarely seen but the information in Figure 13 relates to litter size in Bernese Mountain Dogs. The raw data are taken from Kaiser (1971) and the calculations are made by myself. Essentially the material related to 70 bitches, each of which had three litters with total births being recorded. Individual

Raw Data

Litter size	1	2	3	4	5	6	7	8	9	10	11	12	13	14	15
Number of litters	5	7	13	10	18	29	34	31	16	18	16	7	3	2	1

Total pups produced	5	8	11	12	14	15	16	17	18	19	20	21	22
Number of bitches	1	1	2	2	3	2	6	1	4	3	7	3	4

Total pups produced	23	24	25	26	27	28	29	30	31	32	33	37	41
Number of bitches	4	4	4	5	3	2	2	1	1	1	2	1	1

Analysis of Variance

Total litters (n) 210   Total bitches (d) 70   Total pups 1514

Source of variation	df	Sum of squares	Mean square	Component
Between bitches	69	1008.11	14.61	$\sigma^2_w + k\sigma^2_D$
Within bitches	140	244.67	1.748	σ^2_w
Total	209	1252.78		

Between bitch component $= \dfrac{14.61 - 1.748}{3} = 4.287$

Within bitch component $= 1.748$

Repeatability $= \dfrac{4.287}{4.287 + 1.748} = 0.71$

Figure 13 Calculation of repeatability of litter size in Bernese Mountain Dogs—using data of Kaiser (1971).

bitches had litters ranging from 1 to 15 and total productivity in three litters ranged from 5 to 41 pups. Mean litter size for first, second and third litters was 7.36, 7.47 and 6.80 respectively. The overall repeatability of 0.71 is high but may not necessarily apply to other breeds although it possibly will to those breeds averaging similarly for litter size.

Threshold Characters

Thus far we have considered polygenic traits as though they all show continuous variation but this is not necessarily always the case. Some characters may be under polygenic control yet show only limited variation; perhaps only two categories may be seen. Whether a pup lives or dies may depend upon a very complex series of gene actions but the actual visible expression is either a live pup or a dead one.

At first sight such traits may seem to be caused by simple Mendelian arrangements (as with black or liver colours) rather than complex polygenic inheritance but we know from genetic studies that many such characters are very definitely under polygenic controls.

The clue to understanding such characters lies in the concept of a 'threshold' which in effect is a point at which the animal moves from one character to another expression of that character (for example it moves from being alive to dying when the underlying genetic arrangement reaches a certain point).

This phenomenon is illustrated by the classic example of polydactyly in guinea pigs. This was a study by Wright (1934) in which two strains of guinea pig were used, one having three toes and the other four toes. Only two visible expressions were seen and when crosses were made between the two strains all the progeny had three toes. When crosses were undertaken among these F_1 three-toed animals some four-toed progeny occurred but most were three-toed. Various other crosses were made (see Figure 14) and it was quite obvious that the character did not behave as a simple dominant/recessive.

Eventually Wright was able to determine that there were eight polydactylous genes involved and when an individual inherited five or more such genes it moved from being three-toed to four-toed. Although only one or other kind of animal was seen the underlying genetic arrangement followed normal curve patterns as shown in Figure 14. The original three-toed strain carried from 0 to 2 polydactylous genes whereas the four-toed

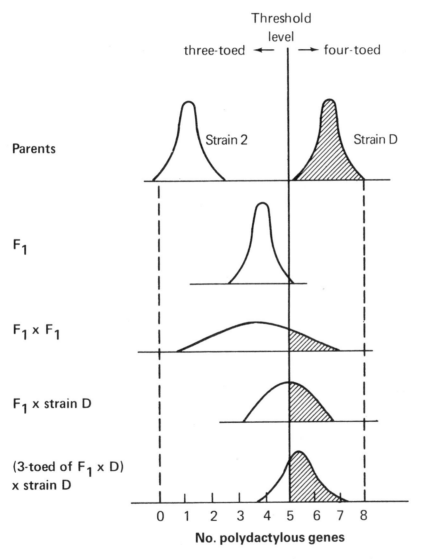

Figure 14 Example of a threshold character governing toe number in guinea pigs. Crosses of the paternal types gave only three-toed stock but these mated to other types gave differing proportions of three- and four-toed stock (from Strickberger 1968).

strain carried from 5 to 8. Crosses between the two threw up animals with from 2 to 4 polydactylous genes and thus only three-toed animals.

If we are dealing with a character controlled in this fashion the only way we can evaluate it is by obtaining some idea of the incidence of the different expressions in the population. If we know, for example, that 60% of the population exhibit one thing and the remaining 40% exhibit the other version then we can estimate where the threshold points occur relative to the mean of the population. The concept is a difficult one (see Falconer 1960) and is discussed again in Chapter 14 dealing with selection.

Chapter 3

The Inheritance of Reproductive Traits

Introduction

One could argue that the most important trait in any species is fertility. In the absolute sense this is beyond dispute since without the ability to reproduce a species is doomed. It is thus appropriate to begin the section on the genetics of particular characters in dogs with a chapter on what might loosely be termed reproductive traits. All breeders want their stock to be fertile because if they are not the line will die and any virtues it may have will die with it. On the other hand fertility to a dog breeder is not as crucial as it is to breeders of some other livestock.

In any kind of farm livestock the owner wants his animals to be mated as often as possible and for as long as possible. If a dairy cow is to maximise her potential milk production she must calve every 365 days and survive for several lactations. A similar situation is no less true of sheep, pigs, rabbits, mink, goats and the like and since many of these produce more than the single offspring generally given by a cow the question of prolificacy (number of young per litter) is also involved.

As litter producers, dogs come into the same kind of category as pigs or rabbits or mink but there is a fundamental difference of approach on the part of the breeder. In the pig, for example, the breeder wants the sow pregnant as soon as that is possible and as soon as the litter is weaned he wants her pregnant again. The dog breeder, on the other hand, may find it more expedient to exhibit his bitches during the first few years of life and not interrupt their show careers with pregnancies. Thereafter he may not be concerned to have a litter at each oestrus but be content with one litter per year. Finally, the end of the breeding life of a bitch does not coincide with her immediate disposal and she will continue to be an unprofitable, but welcome, pensioner until illness or senility brings about her end.

The difference in the intensity of breeding operations of commercial farmers and dog breeders stems largely from the fact that the latter are mainly concerned with a hobby whereas the farmer is running a business. Even in those cases where the dog breeder is making his living from dogs there is the added complication that dogs (at least some of them) will be part of the family and not simply there to be exploited for financial gain.

The above comments are not intended as criticism of farming or approval of dog breeding, merely to emphasise their differences on the important issue of fertility because this may have bearing upon the kind of breeding programmes that can be undertaken in dogs and not in farm livestock.

One does not, of course, need to mate bitches only once per year. Many German Shepherd breeders in the breed's homeland mate their bitches at each season and most Beagle colonies producing dogs for experimental purposes also breed at each season.

However, the fact that dog breeders do not generally exploit reproductive capacity to the full is one reason why we know so little about the genetic aspects of fertility of the dog. This chapter is an attempt to bring together some aspects of the subject using reproduction in the very loose sense of anything connected with fertility, the reproductive organs or longevity.

The Onset, Frequency and Duration of Oestrus

In some species the onset of oestrus for the first time (puberty) seems to depend upon body size whereas in others it is determined more by chronological age. In the sheep it is determined by a mixture of age and photoperiodicity (day length). In dogs age seems to be the most important factor with oestrus occurring anywhere between six months and a year of age. In a breeding kennel composed of Airedales, Foxhounds and mongrels Rowlands (1951) found that age at first oestrus was 13 ± 0.6 months in mongrels, 20 ± 0.9 months in Airedales and 16 ± 0.8 months in Foxhound/Airedale crosses. All these ages are greater than would be expected in show kennels but there is a dearth of data on this aspect. As a consequence the genetic nature is hardly understood but, in common with most reproductive traits, onset of oestrus is likely to be of complex inheritance with a low additive component (low h^2) and a large environmental influence.

Frequency of oestrus is only slightly better documented than age at onset. The ancestor of the dog, the wolf, will come into oestrus only once per year, usually in the spring. There is, however, a complication which stems from the social order known to exist in packs. Mech (1970) has shown that among those adult females which are low in the 'pecking' order as many as 40% lose all social initiative and this inhibits copulation. In times of population increase the proportion of such females increases within a pack and where tension exists between packs stress infertility is also induced in subordinate packs.

In his work with wolf/dog crosses Iljin (1941) reported that most F_1 and F_2 individuals resembled the wolf in that they came into oestrus once per year in winter. Among dog breeds the racing Greyhound is generally believed to be one which comes into oestrus once per year. Jochle and Paeske (1963) concluded that the long intervals between oestrus periods in racing Greyhounds were due to a simple recessive gene. They also found that long intervals and delayed puberty stemmed from British imports to Germany and that these aspects were associated with better racing performance. If that is true then it is not surprising that long dioestrus periods (intervals between oestrus) should occur in the racing Greyhound.

In a more recent study in Britain, based on some 200 racing Greyhounds in a Hertfordshire kennel, Prole (1973) found age at onset of oestrus was very similar to that in other breeds. He did, however, find that the dioestrus period was very variable. The mean length was 8.1 months which compared well with the figures of 7.8 months (Hancock and Rowlands 1949) and 7.2 months (Christie and Bell 1971) derived from other breeds. The range in Prole's data was from 3.3 to 13.6 months with a standard deviation of 2.1 months compared to Hancock and Rowlands (1949) figures of 5 to 11 months with a standard deviation of 1.6 months.

In domestic pet bitches Frost (1963) found that 67.6% of the total of 500 animals (half of which were mongrels) had dioestrus periods of 5 to 7 months. Only 3.2% of the total had periods which were usually less than 5 months.

In experimental dog breeding colonies (Beagles) several estimates are available for dioestrus periods. Andersen *et al* (1962) cite a figure of 220 ± 56 days while Strasser and Schumacher (1968) give a figure of 257 days for an American strain and 223 for a British strain. In the same year Smith and Reese published a value of 219 ± 4 with a range of 215 to 223 days. This was based on 121 bitches and 504 oestrus cycles. They calculated a repeatability of oestrus cycle length of 43% and a heritability of 38% which suggests that selection for cycle length would be effective. Age at first oestrus was 342 ± 16 days with a range of 216 to 696 days and a low heritability (8%). This appeared to be a very fertile colony since only 7.1% of matings failed to produce offspring.

The Basenji, originating in equatorial Africa, is a breed which frequently has long dioestrus periods and in its normal habitat was generally in oestrus only in the autumn. Fuller (1956) has shown that the breed can be stimulated by declining day length to give two oestrus cycles per year and Burns and Fraser (1966) state that in Britain this breed comes into oestrus twice yearly like other breeds. Scott *et al* (1959) showed that in their breeding group the first dioestrus interval in Basenjis was 12.5 ± 0.77 months and subsequent intervals averaged 11.87 ± 0.69 months. In contrast American Cockers in the same kennels had figures of 7.29 ± 1.91 and 6.45 ± 1.24 months. When crosses were made between these two breeds the F_1 animals had a first dioestrus interval of 8.74 ± 3.60 months and subsequent intervals of 7.50 ± 2.41 months. The greater variability of the crosses is thought to be due to gene segregation and Scott and his colleagues concluded that the annual breeding cycle was inherited as a simple recessive condition. This agrees with the view of Jochle and Paeske (1963) but appears to be an oversimplification and it is unlikely that dioestrus intervals are other than a character of moderate to low heritability with a high environmental component.

This is suggested by the photoperiodicity effects. Whitney (1971) claimed that most American bitches were in oestrus in April and fewest in December. Since this information was derived from birth dates of litters and many breeders deliberately avoid litters in autumn or winter the conclusion made by Whitney could be erroneous. Hancock and Rowlands (1949) found most oestrus periods in July while Prole's data on Greyhounds showed the greatest frequency of cycling occurred in February (17% of all bitches) with a general but irregular fall during the remainder of the year, only about 1% being in oestrus in November.

The issue is complicated by the fact that bitches can be induced to come into oestrus by the presence of other bitches which are already in heat. It is, however, likely that day length will affect cycling behaviour.

In respect of oestrus duration the normal period is held to be some 19–20 days based upon the time that the bitch first begins to discharge with ovulation beginning about day 16 (Whitney 1971). The bitch will usually 'stand' for the dog from day 11 to day 18. Kelley (1949) recommended mating on the first day of acceptance by the bitch and on alternate days thereafter. Hancock and Rowlands (1949) felt that maximum fertility resulted from mating during the first four days of oestrus with a second mating 48 hours later. Rowlands (1951) found a 32% benefit from double mating provided that the first service was not later than day four of the behavioural oestrus. In contrast Spreull (1949) advised against mating a second time if more than 48 hours had elapsed since this would cause some pups to be of younger age in physiological terms at birth.

There are obvious differences between bitches in both oestrus duration and dioestrus. Prole (1973) found that there was almost as much difference between dioestrus periods of the same bitch as there was between bitches. Somerfield (1955) reports on the case of a famous Boxer of hers which had not conceived to four matings but when mated on day 19 she always conceived. Doubtless many bitches have been designated as infertile because they were never given the opportunity to mate that late in oestrus.

Fertility

If we define fertility as the proportion of bitches which conceive to first service (mating) then data on the fertility of dogs are conspicuously absent. Rowlands' (1951) data on Airedales and mongrels found that 60% conceived to one service and 87% to two. Bradley (1975) suggests that in Beagle colonies 80–90% of bitches in oestrus should produce litters. If this is the case in practice then fertility in dogs is considerably higher than in most species. One cannot, of course, easily find reliable data. Many bitches may not conceive because they were mated at the wrong time—a failing of the owner not of the bitch. Others will not conceive because their nutritional status is impaired—again a failing of the owner. One cannot overemphasise the importance of nutrition in achieving a high level of fertility and as a general rule any kennel which finds that its fertility is declining would be well advised to check nutritional status before jumping to the conclusion that something is genetically wrong.

Bitches can, of course, be genuinely infertile and this can be due to genetic reasons but until they have been subjected to veterinary checks to ensure that their hormonal relationships are in order one cannot assume genetic causes. The same is no less true of dogs although in their case checks can more readily be made. Abnormalities of the sperm do occur in all species and are known to exist in dogs (Bane 1970). Abnormal spermatozoa may be due to genetic causes or to poor nutrition but the incidence of such problems is unknown. In a study of German Shepherd champions in Britain Willis (1976) showed that only 4 out of 194 had failed to sire a litter and one of these was deliberately destroyed unbred because of epilepsy. Three infertile dogs in 193 is about 1.5% but there is no way of knowing if this is typical of dogs in general or the breed in particular.

One must assume that infertility of a genetic nature exists in all breeds of dog and in both sexes but that the incidence is likely to be low and the mode of inheritance unknown. Specific cases when they come to light need genetic examination and subsequent publication.

Gestation Length

It is commonly believed that the gestation length in the dog is 63 days and most dog books accept this without question. Scientific studies show that this figure is probably rather high and that in any event there will be variation either side of the mean range.

A study of 4773 pregnancies among various breeds in Poland was undertaken by Krzyzanowski *et al* (1975) and mean values and ranges were produced for several breeds. These ranged from a mean of 63.5 days (56–71) in Boxers down to 61.4 days (54–72) in Pekingese. There seemed to be no real association between physical size and gestation length in that Dobermanns averaged 62.8 days whereas the similarly sized German Shepherd Dog averaged 61.7 days. This latter figure is very similar to the value of 61.98 days obtained by Willis (1978a) from GSDIL data. However, the GSDIL figures seemed to indicate that gestation length was influenced by parity increasing slightly with each pregnancy from the 61.7 days for first pregnancies through to 62.5 days for third or later parities.

Although reproductive characters are generally of low heritability it is known that in cattle the heritability of gestation length is of the order of 40% (see Preston and Willis 1970). This may hold good for the dog and if it does could result in specific sires which tend to give longer or shorter gestation periods than the average. This might have some bearing upon dystocia, stillbirths and birth weights but, as yet, no real evidence exists.

Litter Size (at Birth)

By comparison with some aspects of reproduction there is no shortage of information about litter size in dogs. One of the first studies was published as long ago as 1908 by Heape and there have been several papers at intervals since. Unfortunately not all the data are equally reliable. Many workers have gathered their basic material from registrations with kennel clubs and other such pedigree bodies and these frequently consist only of live pups rather than all births. Moreover the data rarely give information of dam age or parity which may well influence the number of pups born.

The best way of presentation seems to be to give the facts as they have been published by the various workers and then to comment on those facts. The data are presented in Table 5 and show not only litter size but also sex ratio. This latter aspect is discussed at a later stage (see page 49).

The data in Table 5 stem from several sources. Those breeds studied by Lyngset and Lyngset represent registrations with the Norwegian Kennel Club and those of Kaiser are Swiss figures. Heape's data are British and some of the Beagle data and the Cocker Spaniel figures of Little are from the USA. All the German Shepherd data stem from records in the SV Züchtbuchs except for those of Humphrey and Warner which were from their own Swiss-based kennel and the figures of Willis (1981) which are British figures collected by the German Shepherd Dog Improvement Foundation. In all cases the figures represent statistics collected from the years immediately prior to the date of publication with the exception of those figures of Whitney (1971) which were for GSD prior to 1927 and those of Willis (1977a) which were collated for this book and taken from the SV Züchtbuch of 1935. Data for several other breeds are given in the papers of Lyngset and Lyngset (1970) and Kaiser (1971) but have been omitted here because they were for breeds of local importance or were based upon few litters.

With the exception of the Beagle data and the papers of Little (1949), Kaiser (1971) and Willis (1981) which were based upon complete kennel records, or submissions directly from breeders to the investigator, the data are all drawn from registered litters and hence litters which were totally lost or destroyed may be excluded. The German Shepherd data from Germany did, prior to 1939, include full information in that all dogs born were recorded and losses noted for whatever cause. This did not, however, apply to litters from which no individual survived to be registered.

In theory the minimum litter size is one animal so that only maximum litter size is recorded in Table 5. In their paper on many breeds Lyngset and Lyngset (1970) recorded minimum size which in some instances was 2, 3, or 4 but this doubtless reflects paucity of litters. In breeds with a relatively high average (7 or 8 pups), litters of only one pup are rare and hence unlikely to be found unless a very large number of litters is recorded.

In all cases where a standard deviaton is given it is high relative to the breed mean. The

Table 5

Litter size and sex ratio in various breeds of dog

Breed	Number of litters	Number of pups	Mean litter size	SD*	Maximum size seen	Sex Ratio†	Author
Airedale	101	767	7.59	2.55	16	110	Lyngset and Lyngset 1970
	—	—	6.74	—	—	—	Heape 1908
Australian Terrier	31	154	4.97	1.88	8	130	Lyngset and Lyngset 1970
Appenzeller Sennenhund	135	1086	8.04	3.06	16	110	Kaiser 1971
Basenji	14	77	5.50	3.33	8	79	Lyngset and Lyngset 1970
Beagle	265	1606	6.06	2.27	—	—	Gaines and Van Vleck 1976
	297	1789	6.02	—	—	103	Strasser and Schumacher 1968
	235	1360	5.78	—	—	—	Marsboom *et al* 1971
	109	610	5.60	1.75	9	110	Lyngset and Lyngset 1970
	160	864	5.40	—	—	—	Jaeger and Kamphans 1968
	293	1492	5.09	—	—	—	Bielfelt *et al* 1971
	42	189	4.50	—	—	130	Strasser and Schumacher 1968
	418	2468	5.90	1.54	11	—	Willis 1988a
Bedlington Terrier	83	468	5.64	2.11	11	106	Lyngset and Lyngset 1970
Bernese Mountain Dog	995	6724	6.76	2.80	15	106	Kaiser 1971
Bloodhound	29	293	10.06	—	—	127	Heape 1908
Border Collie	—	—	5.7	—	—	85	Kelley 1949
Boston Terrier	29	105	3.62	1.28	7	114	Lyngset and Lyngset 1970
Boxer	110	753	6.85	2.14	12	108	Lyngset and Lyngset 1970
Briard	42	364	8.67	3.42	17	95	Willis 1978b
Bulldog	—	—	6.32	—	—	127	Heape 1908
	15	88	5.87	1.96	10	110	Lyngset and Lyngset 1970
Bull Terrier	—	—	6.34	—	—	114	Heape 1908
Cairn Terrier	35	126	3.60	1.48	7	121	Lyngset and Lyngset 1970
Chow Chow	31	143	4.61	1.59	9	110	Lyngset and Lyngset 1970
Cocker Spaniel	343	1935	5.64	1.89‡	14	107	Little 1949
	103	490	4.76	2.14	10	118	Lyngset and Lyngset 1970
Collie	109	866	7.94	2.28	13	105	Lyngset and Lyngset 1970
Dachshund (Long)	26	81	3.12	1.64	6	125	Lyngset and Lyngset 1970
(Smooth)	103	490	4.76	1.59	9	98	Lyngset and Lyngset 1970
(Wire)	93	420	4.51	1.60	10	107	Lyngset and Lyngset 1970
Dalmatian	43	251	5.84	1.65	9	126	Lyngset and Lyngset 1970
Dobermann	104	789	7.59	2.39	13	120	Lyngset and Lyngset 1970
Elkhound	102	612	6.00	2.30	13	102	Lyngset and Lyngset 1970
English Setter	106	662	6.25	2.15	11	104	Lyngset and Lyngset 1970
Entelbucher Mountain Dog	117	645	5.51	2.21	11	117	Kaiser 1971
Foxhound	339	2872	8.47	—	—	—	Potkay and Bacher 1977
Fox Terrier (Smooth)	105	435	4.14	1.60	8	135	Lyngset and Lyngset 1970
(Wire)	106	417	3.93	1.12	7	100	Lyngset and Lyngset 1970
French Bulldog	30	174	5.80	2.11	10	129	Lyngset and Lyngset 1970
German Shepherd	444	3447	7.76	2.90	16	112	Willis 1981
	113	899	7.96	2.78	15	101	Lyngset and Lyngset 1970
	104	794	7.63	—	—	98	Humphrey and Warner 1934
	3331	24291	7.29	2.61	17	107	Willis 1977a
	22281	159304	7.15	—	—	106	Winzenburger 1936

Breed	Number of litters	pups	Mean litter size	SD*	Maximum size seen	Sex Ratio†	Author
	7462	49650	6.65	2.31‡	15	106	Whitney 1971
German Pointer (Short)	103	781	7.58	2.57	15	108	Lyngset and Lyngset 1970
(Wire)	100	811	8.11	2.86	16	104	Lyngset and Lyngset 1970
(Long)	1129	8683	7.69	—	17	107	Kock 1984
Golden Retriever	43	349	8.12	1.18	14	107	Lyngset and Lyngset 1970
Gordon Setter	103	769	7.47	2.65	14	98	Lyngset and Lyngset 1970
Greyhound	43	292	6.79	2.63	13	130	Lyngset and Lyngset 1970
Griffon	27	107	3.96	1.88	8	123	Lyngset and Lyngset 1970
Irish Setter	78	559	7.17	1.81	15	118	Lyngset and Lyngset 1970
Kerry Blue Terrier	42	198	4.71	1.90	9	86	Lyngset and Lyngset 1970
King Charles	38	112	2.95	1.23	5	120	Lyngset and Lyngset 1970
Komondor	877	5858	6.67	—	15	105	Sierts-Roth 1958
Labrador Retriever	59	460	7.80	2.08	14	97	Lyngset and Lyngset 1970
Lakeland Terrier	47	157	3.34	1.09	6	104	Lyngset and Lyngset 1970
Mastiff	—	—	7.67	—	—	108	Heape 1908
Newfoundland	28	163	5.82	2.74	10	106	Lyngset and Lyngset 1970
Norwegian Buhund	44	224	5.09	0.70	9	104	Lyngset and Lyngset 1970
Papillon	34	87	2.56	1.16	5	78	Lyngset and Lyngset 1970
	57	138	2.42	0.73	4	126	Kaiser 1971
Pekingese	102	342	3.35	1.22	6	95	Lyngset and Lyngset 1970
Pointer (English)	112	752	6.71	2.33	12	114	Lyngset and Lyngset 1970
Pomeranian	108	220	2.04	0.31	5	98	Lyngset and Lyngset 1970
Poodle (Standard)	13	83	6.38	2.10	12	98	Kaiser 1971
(Miniature)	462	2236	4.84	1.62	8	110	Kaiser 1971
	132	564	4.27	1.42	8	98	Lyngset and Lyngset 1970
(Toy)	628	2444	3.89	1.44	8	110	Kaiser 1971
Rottweiler	82	618	7.53	2.60	12	117	Lyngset and Lyngset 1970
Samoyed	107	644	6.02	2.30	15	108	Lyngset and Lyngset 1970
St Bernard	43	365	8.49	3.11	15	93	Lyngset and Lyngset 1970
	397	3187	8.03	3.50	20	102	Kaiser 1971
Schnauzer (Giant)	61	360	5.90	1.97	12	108	Lyngset and Lyngset 1970
(Miniature)	103	482	4.68	1.83	9	103	Lyngset and Lyngset 1970
Scottish Terrier	44	167	3.80	1.49	6	96	Lyngset and Lyngset 1970
Shetland Sheepdog	90	365	4.06	1.24	7	125	Lyngset and Lyngset 1970
Shih Tzu	67	229	3.42	1.73	7	124	Lyngset and Lyngset 1970
Swiss Mountain Dog (Giant)	71	563	7.93	3.21	14	103	Kaiser 1971
Welsh Corgi (Pembroke)	23	127	5.52	1.20	8	95	Lyngset and Lyngset 1970
Welsh Terrier	26	104	4.00	0.98	6	100	Lyngset and Lyngset 1970
West Highland White	29	107	3.69	1.54	8	114	Lyngset and Lyngset 1970
Whippet	37	163	4.41	1.32	7	77	Lyngset and Lyngset 1970

* Standard deviation (see page 22).
† Males per 100 females.
‡ This statistic not given by author but calculated from his data.

coefficient of variation (see page 22) of litter size is generally in the range of 20–70% and if the reader attempts to calculate the range in any breed as being from three SDs below the mean to three SDs above the mean it will be found that in some breeds the lower figure is negative. This is clearly impossible but stems from the fact that most litter size data shows a curve that is not strictly normal but has a skew towards the right (higher end) of the scale. This is illustrated in Figure 15 using the data of Willis (1977a) for GSD litters taken from the GSDL.

Where the figures in Table 5 are based on a reasonably large number of litters or show very little variation one can accept them as giving a reasonable view of litter size in the breed. It is known that environmental factors will strongly influence litter size but with large numbers of litters it is reasonable to assume that these extraneous factors are randomly distributed and hence the figures suffice to quantify that breed in that country.

Attempts to examine some of the environmental factors which might influence litter size are not numerous. One such factor might be dam age or parity. We know from other species that litter size is affected by the age of the dam and it seems logical to assume that this may also be true of dogs. In Table 6 are shown the data from a colony in Germany using an English and an American strain of Beagles. The data are ranked by year of age of the dam and cover 71 dams of the English strain and 13 of the American. Conclusions on the American strain are difficult to make because of paucity of data but it does appear to be of poorer fertility than the English one. It does, however, seem that the English strain begins to show a marked decline in litter size once dams have passed four years of age and particularly after five where bitches are giving litters only 75% of the size of that achieved at the peak breeding age of three years.

Working with German Longhaired Pointers Kock (1984) showed that in 1129 litters there were significant negative regressions of litter size on age of both sire and dam.

The other way of looking at dam age is by parity and data exist for American Cockers, Briards and German Shepherds. These are shown in Table 7 and illustrate a gradual

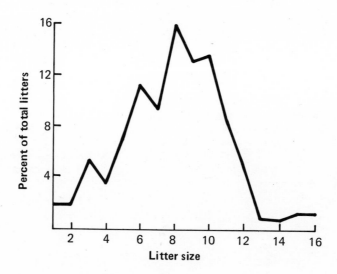

Figure 15   Distribution of litter size in German Shepherd Dogs (168 litters) (Willis 1978a).

Table 6

Effect of age of dam upon litter size in two strains of Beagle

Age of dam (years)	English strain			American strain		
		Mean size			Mean size	
	Litters	birth	weaning	Litters	birth	weaning
1	7	6.57	6.14	—	—	—
2	81	6.06	5.68	9	3.44	3.33
3	87	6.41	6.09	8	4.00	3.13
4	65	6.00	5.57	10	4.10	3.90
5	34	5.73	5.32	6	5.83	5.50
6–9	23	4.83	4.61	9	5.55	5.22
Overall	297	6.02	5.66	42	4.50	4.14

Source　Strasser and Schumacher 1968.

increase in the litter size of Cockers up to and including third parity. In the other two breeds figures are less indicative of trends.

Kamphans (1967) has suggested that in Beagle colonies bitches should be culled in their fifth year of age. In show kennels bitches would be culled on the basis of the quality they produced rather than the quantity and a breeder would hope to keep an outstanding producer in active litter production for as long as possible. This is particularly important when one bears in mind that the more litters a bitch produces the greater should be one's knowledge of her breeding ability and hence, in theory at least, her litters should be increasing in quality.

The effect of the male dog upon litter size has rarely been studied. Breeders frequently advertise their stud dogs as having sired such and such a big litter and thus imply that the litter size is a feature of the male. In actual fact one would imagine that any fertile dog would produce sufficient semen to fertilize a whole regiment of puppies and hence litter size is a question of how many ova are present. However, it is reasonable to imagine that as

Table 7

Effect of parity of the dam upon litter size

Parity	American Cockers		Briards		German Shepherd Dogs	
	Litters	Mean size	Litters	Mean size	Litters	Mean size
First	160	5.68	24	9.29	208	7.88
Second	85	5.69	8	9.38	105	7.62
Third	56	5.95	6	8.16	56	7.98
Fourth or more	42	5.00	4	4.25	75	7.48
Overall	343	5.64	42	8.67	444	7.76

Sources　American Cockers, Little 1949.　Briards, Willis 1978b.　German Shepherd Dogs, Willis 1981.

a dog ages his ability to produce sufficient viable sperm may decline. In his study of Hungarian Sheepdogs (Komondor) Sierts-Roth (1958) concluded that up to the age of eight years the age of sire had little effect upon litter size but that after this point there was a decline in litter size. He also observed that bitches had their largest litters at three years of age which corresponds to the German Shepherd data in Table 7 and may, perhaps, imply that this is likely to be true of most large breeds.

Lyngset (1973) has made an attempt to relate litter size to the sire by examining the mean litter size in 14 breeds with from 7 to 15 males per breed. The data are summarized in Table 8 and show that in 11 of the breeds no effect of sire on litter size could be observed but significant differences between sires did exist in Cockers, Airedales and Elkhounds. Whether this information is really meaningful would depend upon how effectively dam age had been randomised among sires. If dam age can affect litter size and if particular sires happened, by chance, to have mates that were above or below the average age then this could lead to sire differences being observed but which would effectively be spurious.

More recently Gaines and Van Vleck (1976) have sought to assess the influence of sire upon various reproductive traits using data from a Beagle colony. There were 265 bitches involved but only nine males of which three provided some 75% of all services. A least squares analysis of variance showed that litter size at birth and weaning was not influenced by sire but there were seasonal and year effects. They did find sire had an effect upon gestation length in that one sire had a significantly shorter period. The data are sparse due to the small number of sires involved and the authors suggest that studies with more paternal half sib groups are needed to determine the genetic effects of reproductive traits.

Any reader who has been studying the various tables on litter size will, by this stage,

Table 8

Effect of sire upon litter size

Breed	Overall			Lowest sire		Highest sire	
	Sires	Litters	Mean	Litters	Mean	Litters	Mean
Airedale*	12	209	6.58	20	4.50	26	7.88
Beagle	15	203	5.75	9	4.44	6	7.33
Boxer	7	81	6.90	9	6.11	16	7.50
Cocker Spaniel*	15	192	4.83	12	3.00	20	6.25
Dunker	11	195	7.32	28	6.36	19	8.16
Elkhound (grey)*	12	225	5.87	16	3.88	30	7.03
English Setter	11	170	6.04	26	5.23	8	7.25
Fox Terrier (Wire)	11	157	3.88	18	3.39	16	4.69
German Shepherd	11	210	7.50	16	5.94	26	8.31
Miniature Pinscher	11	147	3.41	6	2.67	15	4.13
Miniature Poodle	12	192	4.05	7	2.57	19	4.63
Pointer	7	78	7.35	21	6.76	8	8.00
Pomeranian	11	149	2.06	19	1.63	15	2.60
Samoyed	11	96	6.13	6	5.33	16	6.67

* Significant differences between sires existed for these breeds only.
Source Lyngset 1973.

have observed that the size of the breed seems to have some effect upon the size of the litter. In several species there is a suggestion that size of the dam is positively associated with litter size. The dog, more than any other species, provides an excellent opportunity to examine this because it shows a greater range in body weight than does any other. The 86 kg St Bernard is about 48 times as big as the 1.8 kg Chihuahua and there is a whole range of shapes and sizes within these two extremes.

A fairly extensive study has been undertaken by Kaiser (1971) using data from 47 breeds. He had dam and litter weights and sizes from about 145 litters in this group and more extensive data on 9 breeds all of which appear in Table 5 alongside the reference to Kaiser (1971). In these he examined the relationship between dam weight and litter weight and between wither height in the dam and litter size. Kaiser's paper is in German and rather long but the main conclusions that he drew in it and in an earlier study (Kaiser and Huber 1969) were as follows:

Litter size is directly proportional to wither height in that it increases with increasing height.
The litter maxima also showed a close positive relationship with increasing height.
The weight of a pup at birth was related to the weight of the dam producing it and to the mean weight of the breed to which it belonged.
The weight of the whole litter was in general about 12% of the weight of the dam, independent of individual pup weights. The range was generally very narrow, rarely varying outside of the extremes of 10–15% of the bitch weight.

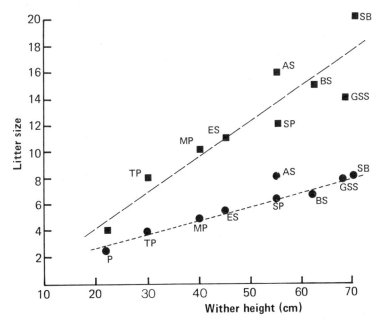

Figure 16 Regression of litter size on dam's wither height (Kaiser 1971).

AS	Appenzeller Mountain Dog	P	Papillon	—— ■	Maximum litter size
BS	Bernese Mountain Dog	SS	St Bernard	----- ●	Mean litter size
ES	Entelbucher Mountain Dog	SP	Standard Poodle		
GSS	Giant Swiss Mountain Dog	TP	Toy Poodle		
MP	Miniature Poodle				

Kaiser's graph showing the relationship between wither height and litter size is given in Figure 16 and shows the line for mean litter size and for maximum litter size. There is a closer fit to the mean line than to the maximum line as might be expected because large litters are rare and Kaiser's estimate of breed maxima may be underestimated. His data tended to show the Appenzeller Sennenhund as having a higher prolificacy than its wither height suggested.

Robinson (1973) has also looked at the relationship between dam size and litter size using mean litter sizes and breed weights derived from several sources. He, like Kaiser, showed that there was effectively a linear regression between dam weight and litter size with litter size (Y) being dependent upon dam weight (X) thus:

$$Y = 3.32 + 0.062 \, X \text{ where X is given in lb or}$$
$$Y = 3.32 + 0.136 \, X \text{ where X is given in kg.}$$

In his analysis Robinson eliminated the Mastiff, Newfoundland and St Bernard breeds because they do not fit the line (see Figure 17) being breeds with a lower mean litter size than their body weight would suggest. The correlation between litter size and dam weight is 0.83 which suggests that dam weight explains some 69% of the variance in litter size.

The problem with Robinson's data is that they do not take into account the actual weight of the individual bitches nor does he correct data for effects of age or parity or other environmental influences. The same criticism applies to Kaiser's data and the extent to which one can extrapolate from the results is limited.

A breeder is interested in the effects within his own breed and it does not help a Boxer breeder, for example, to know that larger breeds than his will have larger litters. He is interested in knowing whether litter size varies between different sized bitches within his breed.

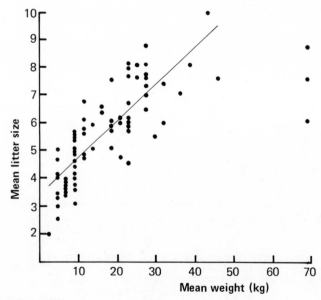

Figure 17   Regression of litter size on dam's body weight (Robinson 1973). (Three outliers to right excluded from regression.)

Variation in size within some breeds is quite marked as far as weight is concerned. The same is less true of height because most breeds have upper and/or lower limits for wither height. In the German Shepherd, for example, Willis (1976) has shown that bitches in 1973 had a mean height of 58.1 cm with a standard deviation of 1.06 cm. Males of that breed had values of 63.5 cm and 1.04 cm respectively. Insofar as weight was concerned males of the same height could vary by as much as 37% of the mean body weight of the breed. This is likely to be no less true of females and will apply to many breeds, though not to those in which weight limits are set.

The variation between breeds in litter size is not, of course, solely a function of body weight. Dogs vary also in shape and some of the achondroplastic breeds may be heavier than their litter size suggests. Similarly, dogs with a high wither height may be only as heavy as others which have a more thick-set appearance. Small-sized breeds are bound to have smaller litters in general because there is not sufficient room for a large litter to develop but the linear relationship observed by Robinson (1973) is unlikely to be the correct picture. It is more likely that there is a curvilinear relationship such that at the very heavy weights litter size tends to level out since such large breeds may have accumulated muscle without any extra endocrine activity.

The genetics of prolificacy have hardly been touched upon for the simple reason that data are hard to come by. If the dog behaves like other species then it is likely that litter size is of very low heritability (15% or less) with environmental factors such as those already discussed being responsible for a large part of the variation seen. However, non-additive genetic factors may be involved.

This would mean that specific breeds or bitches within breeds would be particularly prolific because they happened to have a combination of genes that was ideal for large litter size. If the repeatability of litter size is as high as 40–70%, as is likely, then such bitches will tend to keep on being prolific until age effects come into play. Similarly low prolificacy bitches will stay that way.

However, because a dog can only transmit a sample of its genes and not transmit specific combinations it does not follow that prolific bitches will have prolific daughters or bitches with low litter sizes have daughters equally lacking in prolificacy. In general there will be a regression towards the breed mean. As a result selection for litter size by breeding from those bitches whose mothers had large litters is unlikely to yield other than very slow progress towards increasing litter size in the breed.

On the other hand increasing the actual skeletal size of a breed might bring with it associated improvements in litter size. The extent to which that is possible in breeds with strictly defined limits of height and weight is not great.

Strains or lines within breeds will occur which are above or below the general average for the breed in litter size. This may be due, on occasion, to specific infertility genes but may also be a function of inbreeding. Anyone with a particularly prolific line would do well to cherish it, other qualities being equal, and those breeders with low prolificacy in their stock should think twice before persevering with them if equally good but more fertile stock exist.

Stillbirths and Litter Size at Weaning

Thus far litter size has been discussed in relation to what is actually born. Not all pups born are alive at birth and not all the living ones survive to be weaned or registered. From the biological point of view the survival rate is particularly important and this is no less true if one is seeking to examine selectional procedures in a species.

There is clearly a difference between the numbers born and those finally registered with the appropriate organisation. In German Shepherds in Britain Willis (1976) looked at 1665 registered litters sired by champions and found that the average size was 5.73. The modal value was 7 and the data were obviously skewed towards the lower end of the scale with a greater preponderance of litters in the 1–3 category than expected. If we accept litter size in this breed as being 7.76 (see Table 7) then we have 2.03 pups (26.2% of those born) not registered.

The extent to which this applies to other breeds is not known but clearly some losses must occur between birth and registration. Many will occur between 0 and 48 hours post-partum and one can generally accept all losses up to 48 hours as being non-viable and effectively stillborn. The following discussion assumes stillbirths to refer to pups dead at birth or dying prior to 48 hours.

The most extensive data on stillbirths stem from German Shepherds in their native country. Druckseis (1935) looked at data on 46,252 litters comprising 324,323 pups and

Table 9

Sex ratio and stillbirths in German Shepherd Dogs according to litter size. SV Züchtbuch 1935

Litter size	Litters	Total pups born	Sex ratio*	Stillbirths Male	Stillbirths Female	Stillbirths as % of total births	% of litters with 1 or more stillbirth
1	49†	49	188	—	—	—	—
2	104	208	108	9	7	4.33	8.65
3	143	429	100	21	7	6.53	15.38
4	193	772	106	27	13	3.89	11.92
5	309	1545	112	39	27	4.27	13.92
6	437	2622	112	62	26	3.36	11.67
7	460	3220	102	64	43	3.32	12.17
8	497	3976	107	109	52	4.05	14.89
9	465	4185	110	87	34	2.89	13.55
10	339	3390	104	77	46	3.63	16.22
11	203	2233	106	63	35	4.39	20.20
12	80	960	113	21	27	5.00	22.50
13	35	455	114	22	19	9.01	34.29
14	11	154	79	7	1	5.19	45.45
15	4	60	100	2	0	3.33	50.00
16–17	2	33	175	1	0	3.03	50.00
Total	3331	24291	107	611	337	3.83	14.26

* Males per 100 females.
† Any litter of 1 in which a stillbirth occurred would not be registered. The same is true of any litter in which all pups were born dead or died early in life. Only litters with at least one survivor are registered.
Source Willis 1977a.

obtained a stillbirth rate of 2.3%. His information came from the SV which recorded all pups born but his figure of 2.3% stillbirths undoubtedly relates only to actual deaths at birth and not those dying soon afterwards. Examination of SV Züchtbuch data from 1935 (Willis 1977a) shows the stillbirth rate quoted to be low, albeit higher than that given by Druckseis. The figures are shown in Table 9.

The overall stillbirth rate is 3.83%, equivalent to 0.28 pups per litter with very little difference between litters of different sizes until one is in the region of 10 pups. For litters of size 11 to 17 the stillbirth rate is 5.08%. An interesting feature is that the percentage of litters with at least one stillborn pup is fairly constant (12–15%) until a size of 10 pups is reached. From this point onwards the number of litters with stillbirths as a proportion of total litters increases rapidly. Numbers are small but the finding is probably significant. It might well be more so if all litters in which no survivors existed were known. Such litters would not, of course, be published in the Züchtbuch.

A tendency for increasing litter size to be associated with greater loss is not confined to German Shepherds. Hancock and Rowlands (1949) suggested that a possible cause of greater losses in autumn/winter litters stemmed from this. In Beagles Andersen *et al* (1962) found that dams whelping more than six pups had the lowest pup survival rate. In his study of nine breeds Kaiser (1971) found litters with stillbirths occurred more frequently in bitches having 10 or more pups than in those with 1–3 pups. This was very obvious in St Bernard bitches where more than half the pups of large litters were born dead. Kaiser felt this to be a reflection of the abnormal nature of large breeds since higher mortality was also a feature of miniature breeds.

Kaiser also observed that larger litters tended to be born with a shorter gestation length and hence at an earlier physiological age. This could account for more deaths in the first 48 hours.

Druckseis (1935) found stillbirths lowest in the litter sizes from 7 to 10. In his Airedale/mongrel/Foxhound stock Rowlands (1951) found 4.6% of 711 pups were still-born and that 27.9% more died during the first week of life and a further 6.1% by eight weeks. He found that mongrels had fewer losses than purebreds and isolated one Airedale with a tendency to sire pups of lower viability than another sire although both had similar viability in their stock out of mongrel bitches.

Other data on stillbirths are shown in Table 10. The limited number of breeds involved does not permit extrapolation to provide general theories but it is obvious that losses can be high in some breeds. There is evidence from some breeds that losses increase with parity. This is certainly true of stillbirths but less obvious in respect of other losses (Table 11).

Losses subsequent to birth are difficult to assess because breeders may actually destroy viable pups for aesthetic reasons or because they do not wish to rear more than a certain number. The SV Züchtbuchs, a useful guide in many instances, are valueless on this occasion because the organisation insists upon rearing only six whelps per bitch unless a foster mother is employed.

In their study of American Foxhounds Potkay and Bacher (1977) found that 17.4% died prior to weaning (6–7 weeks) and a further 4.0% prior to 30 weeks of age. Most losses (55.6%) were in the first week of life. They give detailed figures for losses by week and cause with the highest single factor being pneumonia. Congenital abnormalities accounted for only 4.7% of the actual losses and this low level corresponds to GSDIF information (Willis 1978a).

Table 10

Stillbirth rates in various breeds

Breed	Pups born	Stillbirths as % of all births	Other losses* %	Source
Appenzeller Sennenhund	1086	7.37	—	Kaiser 1971
Beagle (Belgium)	1360	13.67	8.38	Marsboom *et al* 1971
Beagle (American strain)	189	6.35	1.58	Strasser and Schumacher 1968
Beagle (English strain)	1789	4.75	1.34	Strasser and Schumacher 1968
Bernese Mountain Dog	6724	12.07	—	Kaiser 1971
Briard	364	5.49	11.26†	Willis 1978b
Cocker (American)	1927	4.83	—	Little 1949
Entelbucher Mountain Dog	645	4.50	—	Kaiser 1971
Foxhound (American)	2872	7.73	9.67	Potkay and Bacher 1977
German Longhaired Pointer	8683	17.86‡	—	Kock 1984
German Shepherd	3447	10.62	7.19	Willis 1981
Papillon	138	4.34	—	Kaiser 1971
Poodle (Miniature)	2236	1.83	—	Kaiser 1971
Poodle (Toy)	2444	2.95	—	Kaiser 1971
St Bernard	3187	17.89	—	Kaiser 1971
Swiss Mountain Dog	563	13.14	—	Kaiser 1971

* To weaning (between six and eight weeks), includes culling.
† 7.96 of this 11.26% represents pups culled deliberately to reduce litter size or because litter was not up to standard.
‡ All losses to weaning.

Table 11

Stillbirths and other losses, by parity of dam, in Briards and German Shepherd Dogs

Parity	Briard			German Shepherd Dog		
	Litters	% Stillborn*	% other losses*	Litters	% Stillborn*	% other losses*
First	24	4.48	3.59	208	8.60	6.44
Second	8	8.00	12.00	105	8.50	7.88
Third	6	4.08	48.98	56	14.77	7.16
Fourth	4	11.76	—	75	16.22	5.52
Total	42	5.49	11.26†	444	10.62	7.19

* As percentage of total pups born (364 Briards, 3447 German Shepherd Dogs).
† Of total of 41 pups lost from forty-eight hours to weaning 29 were actually culled as deliberate policy. If these are excluded losses are 3.30% in this period.
Source   Willis 1978a, 1981.

A study made on Pointers by Wilsman and Van Sickle (1973) reviewed losses in various reports and concluded that in 11 surveys made mainly in breeding colonies mortality approached 30% while in three other surveys it was 20% or less. Causes of high mortality were recorded as malnutrition, cardiopulmonary failure and problems of inadequate thermoregulation. Their own data were based upon 80 pups from ten litters, all sired by the same dog and thus were of limited scope. Nevertheless they identified three kinds of growth pattern among new born pups which were associated with different chances of survival. These were:

1 Pups which gained weight from the start;
2 Pups which did not lose more than 10% of body weight in the first two days of life and then gained weight;
3 Pups which lost more than 10% of birth weight.

The conclusion was that categories 1 and 2 had favourable chances of survival but that category 3 was associated with very high losses unless therapy was invoked. Wilsman and Van Sickle suggested that frequent weighing of pups was a good guide to survival and enabled the breeder to seek veterinary advice, if necessary, with more facts at his disposal. The importance of weight changes were emphasised by Gaines and Van Vleck (1976) in their more extensive study of Beagles covering 1451 pups. They found that heavier pups at birth were more likely to survive than smaller pups. The simple correlations between birth weight and mortality in any of the first six weeks averaging around -0.42. In addition they found that older dams had slightly smaller pups (and hence more potential losses) than did younger dams. Large litters also had adverse survival chances: an extra pup in a litter increasing mortality rate in the first week by 3.48% and by 3.43% at six weeks. Despite being smaller, females had a lower mortality than males. Heritability values for birth weight, mortality at one week and mortality at six weeks were 10.6, 9.5 and 8.2% respectively.

This particular Cornell study did indicate sire effects on birth weight and mortality rates. They found, for example, that the difference between two of their sires was as high as 16.7% in mortality at one week of age.

Sex Ratio

The explanation of how sexes are determined has already been given (see page 5) and two tables (Tables 5, 9) have shown the sex ratio obtained in various breeds expressed as males per 100 females.

Burns and Fraser (1966) suggest that the sex ratio is higher in large-sized breeds rather than small-sized breeds but this is not borne out by the more extensive data given in Table 5. There is a considerable range from 77 through to 135 males per 100 females with most breeds showing an excess of males. However, when one examines those figures based on more than 1000 animals the ratios are always in favour of the male and rarely exceed 110:100.

Sierts-Roth (1958) found that sex ratio was unaffected by parental age in Komondors but Little (1949), working with American Cockers, observed a ratio of 114 in first litters compared with 101 for subsequent litters. He refers to further data which make this difference significant.

Whitney (1971) produces data to show that the sex ratio in the colder months

(October–March) was 143 whereas in the rest of the year it was 116 and since his figures were based on 1440 pups it might be meaningful. All were reared on an outdoor system in Whitney's kennels. However, breeds were different and the relevance of the finding is limited. Using only one breed (American Cockers), but taking the same division of the year as did Whitney, identical ratios of 106 for each half-year were obtained by Little (1949).

Winzenburger (1936) claimed that in German Shepherds the sex ratio decreased with increasing litter size. The data in Table 9 on the same breed suggest that the difference is not really marked, there being a ratio of 108 for litters of 1–9 and 106 for litters of 10–17. Whitney (1971) looked at litters of 14 or more from several breeds and in 23 litters ranging from 14–23 pups he obtained a sex ratio of 142:100.

An interesting observation was made by Little (1949) in his American Cockers in that he found a sex ratio of 113 from dams that were black in colour compared with only 99 for red dams. There were 1031 pups in the first group and 898 in the second but though significant the explanation of the finding is unknown.

A higher sex ratio must occur at conception than will be apparent in live births so that sex ratio data must specifically include all pups born if they are meaningful. This is clear from the data in Table 9 where the sex ratio of stillbirths is 180 compared with an overall rate of 107 and a live birth rate of 105 in German Shepherds. Little (1949) also observed more male deaths in American Cockers where sex ratio of stillbirths was 140 versus 107 overall. In the breeds studied by Kaiser (1971) a higher sex ratio in stillbirths than in total births was observed and there are no conflicting papers.

Heape (1908) and Whitney (1971) have suggested that the male embryo (or predominantly male litters) are carried longer than females. This is certainly true of species bearing single young and is usually associated with greater problems at parturition. It could be that the greater gestation period in males could contribute to more deaths among them but this needs to be confirmed.

Numerous suggestions have been put forward in various species, including man, as to how the sex ratio might be manipulated. Many Russian scientists have worked on the subject in different species but thus far no convincing technique for doing so has been achieved. Were it to be possible it would have considerable benefit to livestock breeding, quite aside from any human uses. Certain animals do exist with abnormal sex ratios. This is well known in cattle and probably exists among dogs also. Because a female has few progeny little can be done to check it in that sex but in males such animals siring abnormally high or low ratios may be identified and exploited provided that breed organisations seek to collect the necessary information.

Whelping Trouble (Dystocia)

The word dystocia is a Greek term meaning literally 'difficult birth' and in most species difficulties at parturition occur from time to time. In some species like the cow dystocia can be met with in as many as 25% of births with serious dystocia in up to 5% of cases. In that species problems can be caused by the size of the calf relative to the dam and thus breed of sire, sex of calf, gestation length and many other factors can be involved, quite apart from any malpresentation of the calf at birth.

In dogs dystocia is not a common problem although it may be more prevalent in some breeds rather than others. In order to seek to understand dystocia one has to be aware of what is normal in the bitch since a knowledge of the normal is necessary before the abnormal can be recognised. Freak (1948) has defined normal parturition as being 'the delivery by the bitch of full-term, healthy puppies without outside assistance of any sort'. Many breeders will attempt to be present at whelping and may give some measure of assistance without this being absolutely necessary but that does not really mean that the whelping is no longer normal.

The first stage of labour in the bitch is begun when the cervix dilates. This is outwardly demonstrated by restlessness and lack of appetite in the bitch which attempts to seek seclusion or prepare a nest. Usually this may last from 6 to 12 hours. The second stage of the process is the expulsion of the pups which is brought about by hormonal balances involving oestrogen, progesterone and oxytocin. Each pup is covered by the amnion at the point of delivery and the bitch will remove this and sever the umbilical cord. The licking process not only cleans the pups but also stimulates circulation and respiration. The third stage of labour involves the expulsion of the foetal membranes which usually occurs within 15 minutes of the expulsion of each pup. In general it takes about 30 minutes between pups but the interval may be shorter than this or considerably longer and still constitute a normal birth. From the breeder's point of view it is necessary to identify the correct time so that assistance can be given if needed.

A full description of normality in the whelping process is given by Freak (1948) and Smith (1965). The issue here is to examine dystocia problems and discuss the possible genetic implications. Bennett (1974) has reviewed the subject comprehensively as regards the nature of dystocia and lists a whole series of potential causes. A summary of these causes derived from Bennett's paper is shown in Figure 18.

Essentially problems can be divided into maternal or foetal ones and, within these, broad areas can be categorised as being environmental or genetic in origin. In this connection genetic is used in the very loose sense of genetic predisposition rather than the result of specific genes.

It is most unlikely that specific genes exist which cause dystocia. What does happen is that specific genetic combinations lead to particular foetal or maternal conditions which lead to dystocia. Thus an abnormally large pup will bring about dystocia and the size of the pup will be under genetic control and hence the dystocia will have genetic overtones.

Dystocia can occur in any breed for any of the conditions shown in Figure 18 but the main genetical interest lies in whether or not specific breeds or particular animals within breeds are prone to dystocia problems.

Freak (1962) records 222 cases of dystocia seen over a 15 year period in a London veterinary practice. In view of the number of whelpings likely during that period of time it suggests that dystocia is a relatively minor problem in dogs. However Freak does cite some data from a Scottish Terrier kennel involving 47 whelpings from 23 bitches over a four year period. Only 19 whelpings (13 bitches) were normal according to her 1948 definition. In this kennel gestation period ranged from 58–63 days with 51 days in the case of a dead and aborted litter.

The data which Freak (1962) produced on dystocia suggest beyond any doubt that Scottish Terriers have more dystocia problems than might be expected. Of the 222 cases no fewer than 121 were in Scotties compared with only 6 cases in Miniature and Toy Poodles despite comparable numbers of those breeds in the area covered.

The Scottish Terrier is, of course, an achondroplastic breed where the pelvic diameter is greater in the horizontal plane rather than the vertical. The major cause of problems

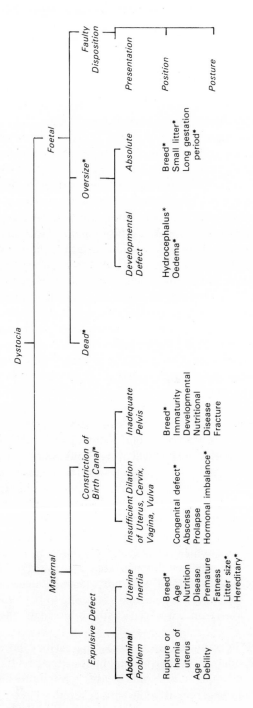

Figure 18   The causes of canine dystocia (adapted from Bennett 1974); items marked *could have a genetic base.

seemed to be relative oversize in the pups, that is, they were large relative to the pelvis of the dam. The difficulty lay not with all the pups in a litter but with individual pups which brought about the problem for the litter as a whole.

In other breeds of an achondroplastic type one might logically expect similar problems. Freak (1948) suggests that the Sealyham Terrier, Yorkshire Terrier, Corgi and King Charles Spaniel were all prone to producing individual pups which were oversize relative to pelvic structure and thus caused dystocia. Dachshunds, another achondroplastic breed, appear to suffer from primary inertia followed by general peritonitis (Freak 1948). In contrast many Cocker Spaniels fail to develop early maternal instincts due to nervousness (Freak 1948). According to Sweeney (1972) dystocia is rare in Greyhounds but Freak (1948) suggests that arrested foetal development and death of embryos at all stages can cause problems.

One would expect troubles to be fairly frequent in breeds which have been deliberately selected to have large heads, for example Bulldogs. In German Shepherds data on 254 litters (Willis 1978a) showed that caesarian section was needed in eleven cases (4.3%) with one other bitch haemorrhaging during whelping. Dystocia would seem to be a minor problem in that breed although normality of whelping seemed to be very variable in ranging from 5 to 24 hours. However, in bitches of third or later parity caesarian section was necessary in one in eight whelpings. According to Apgar (1940) leg length in the dam was often a problem causing bitches in giant breeds to have difficulties postpartum in adapting to the role of mother.

For most breeds dystocia is likely to be a fairly rare thing but it might be that bitches with the problem on one occasion are most likely to repeat it. Whether they will transmit this to their daughters is debatable, although if the difficulty is a result of physical shape of the dam the likelihood is higher that she will have daughters with similar problems. Breeds with structural aspects which encourage dystocia have problems that can only be alleviated by genetic means but for the others most dystocia will be avoided by attention to physical fitness and welfare of the bitch.

Absence of Testes (Anorchia and Monorchia)

Congenital anorchia is the total absence of testes and monorchia is the absence of one testicle. Dog breeders generally refer to males with only one descended testicle as being monorchids and those with none descended as cryptorchids. In this connection breeders are using faulty definitions. A dog which has undescended testicles is a cryptorchid and may be unilateral (one descended) or bilateral (neither descended) whereas the true monorchid only actually has one testicle in the body which may or may not be descended.

It is possible that some cryptorchids in dogs are actually suffering from anorchia or monorchia which has not been diagnosed because no surgical attempt has been made to locate the missing testes. However, it is probable that anorchia and monorchia are rare in dogs. Monorchia does exist and has been located in German Shepherd Dogs in Germany but it is probably rare enough in this breed and in most others to be considered unimportant.

Both conditions are known in man (see Warkany 1971a for a review) and there is some evidence that prenatal destruction of the testes occurs. It is known (Kreipe 1967) that thalidomide can induce anorchia in man and this suggests that the problem is one of arrested development from some cause or other rather than the result of specific genes as such.

Undescended Testicles (Cryptorchidism)

Incidence

The failure of testicles to descend into the scrotal sac is a development defect in that at some stage of the process leading to formation and correct location of the testes something has gone wrong. As Young (1971) has pointed out various problems could result in the same main effect. Thus too large a testicle, too tight an inguinal ring, too short, a peritoneal fold or a defective gubernaculum testes could all result in a dog that is a cryptorchid. Indeed it would be illogical to suppose that all cases of cryptorchidism are caused by the same thing which may help to explain the difficulty of determining any genetic implication.

In rats Manning (1950) was able to induce cryptorchidism by using biotin deficient diets. In the same species it was induced by vitamin A deficiencies (Wilson and Warkany 1948) while delayed migration of the testes to the scrotum could be brought about by folic acid deficiency (Monie *et al* 1957) or by various drugs known to cause malformations (teratogens).

Most dog breeders would be aware of dietary deficiencies so that it does not follow that nutritional explanations will apply as in rats though the possibility cannot be excluded. However nutritional deficiencies can only be rectified by nutritional means and this section will deal only with possible genetic explanations.

Cryptorchidism is known to exist in many species and to be of greater importance in some than in the dog. It seems appropriate to examine some of the data relating to other species since they may help to provide clues as to the situation in dogs.

In man about 0.3% of males are cryptorchids (Ward and Hunter 1960) while Warkany (1971a) suggests that about 20% are bilateral with 50% showing retention of the right testicle and 30% the left.

A survey of 6455 animals attending American or Canadian veterinary college clinics (Priester *et al* 1970) revealed 874 cases of cryptorchidism. The incidence was 3.2, 1.8, 0.7, 0.4 and 0.05% in pigs, horses, cats, dogs and cattle respectively. These workers considered cryptorchidism to be the most common equine defect and one of the three most common in pigs. The comparative rarity in cattle bears out other views (see Willis 1976) while the higher incidence in pigs is well established (McPhee and Buckley 1943; Johnston *et al* 1958; Sittmann and Woodhouse 1977). In sheep the condition is not uncommon and in one Russian breed Glembockii (1941) found that 15% of rams were affected, 90% of them bilaterally. The review data of Brandsch (1964) support this view. Goats, also, can have serious troubles as was shown in Angoras in Texas by Lush *et al* (1930) and Warwick (1961).

Hodgman (1963) reported cryptorchidism in numerous dog breeds but his contention that certain breeds were more badly affected mirrored breed popularity rather than having any true statistical significance. According to Koch (1935) the condition was commonest in dwarf breeds and in those with short skulls. The Boxer seems to be particularly prone. In a study of 57 Bavarian litters Hartl (1938) found that 23.2% of 168 males were affected. In a later analysis of this breed in Germany Ludwig (1968) found an incidence of 4% in 1951 rising to 9% by 1965. In a study of the same breed in Barbados Willis and Cuke (1978) obtained information on 84 litters with 128 males actually examined for testicular state. There were 65.6% normal, 16.4% unilateral and 18.0% bilateral cryptorchids suggesting a major problem in such a small population.

In German Shepherds in their homeland Brandsch (1964) examined data on 5213 litters comprising 11,944 males of which 3.9% were found to be cryptorchids. Of these 7.6% were bilateral. In reports published in the SV Zeitung Willis (1976) tabulated data for 1642 cryptorchids of which 6.1% were bilaterally affected. He showed a marked decline in reported cases but did not attribute this to any progress at reducing the incidence considering it to be a reflection of failure to identify or report affected animals.

In German Pointer breeds Kock (1984) found that the incidence ranged from 0.92% in the Large Munsterlander (545 dogs) through to 2.03% in the German Short-haired Pointer (641 dogs). The period of the study covered 1975–80 and certainly the overall incidence was very low.

In a Beagle colony in which 379 males were examined by autopsy Marsboom *et al* (1971) observed 6 cryptorchids (1.58%) of which two were bilaterally affected. More recently Pendergrass and Hayes (1975) presented data on 1266 cryptorchids observed over the period 1964–74 in an American clinical survey. They listed 24 breeds with 10 or more cases and Poodles (Miniature and Toy) had 259 cases whilst German Shepherds had 116. These figures tended to reflect breed popularity and statistical tests showed that there was a below average risk of cryptorchids in Beagles and Labrador Retrievers while an above average risk existed for Chihuahuas, Pomeranians, Poodles (all three types), Miniature Schnauzers, Shetland Sheepdogs, Siberian Huskies and Yorkshire Terriers. Of these nine groupings only the Standard Poodle and Husky can be considered large dogs and the implication that miniature or toy breeds have a greater risk of cryptorchidism agrees with the views of Koch (1935) and the findings of Priester *et al* (1970).

Burns and Fraser (1966) suggest that the higher incidence of the condition in dwarf and short-skulled breeds may be due to the same abnormal growth factors which bring about the dwarf size and brachycephalic head structure. This is a logical viewpoint insofar as it accepts that because dogs have different development patterns of growth they may have some differences in the development of testes.

Genetics

The genetics of cryptorchidism has been more widely studied in species other than the dog. Some theories have been formulated for the genetics of cryptorchidism in sheep (Glembockii 1941, Claxton and Yeates 1972) and in the pig (McPhee and Buckley 1943) with the prevalent view being that it is a simple sex-limited autosomal recessive. In Angora goats Lush *et al* (1930) believed that the unilateral condition was genetic in origin in most cases. They concluded that at least two pairs of autosomal recessive genes were involved. This is the view held by Sittmann and Woodhouse (1977) after reanalysing the data from various papers concerned with pigs. However these latter workers considered that this explanation was relevant only to the Chester White and Large White breeds and that a multifactorial explanation was more feasible for the Lacombe. In cattle Wheat (1961) held that a dominant gene was involved with some variable penetrance but his data are too sparse to exclude the possibility of a recessive trait.

In the canine field Pullig (1953b) considered the character to be a sex-limited recessive but her data comprised only two males and cannot be more than speculative. The same is true of the identical conclusion arrived at by Huber and Schmid (1959) from pedigree data of five unilaterally affected St Bernards.

Most early workers (Koch 1935, Bayer 1936, Hartl 1938) take the view that the condition is recessive but that does not necessarily mean a simple recessive. In his book Whitney (1971) states that the condition is definitely not a simple autosomal recessive. Most veterinary textbooks take the view that canine cryptorchidism is genetically transmitted but offer no evidence. The BVA (1954, 1955) produced reports which claimed the condition was a simple autosomal recessive but not one iota of evidence was presented to support this view. Willis (1963) felt that a single gene theory was untenable in the German Shepherd and thought a two gene theory more likely. Young (1971) was also sceptical of a simple recessive unless incomplete penetrance or other modifying factors are involved.

If one accepts a simple autosomal recessive theory for the unilateral cryptorchid then some other explanation is necessary to account for the bilateral cases. They may be unrelated but this seems to be unlikely. In their sheep paper Claxton and Yeates (1972) found that a recessive or dominant explanation was possible but that in either case there was some incomplete penetrance. It is not improbable that in the dog there is some form of incomplete penetrance so that animals of similar genotype will exhibit differing pheno-types. Cryptorchids certainly vary in the extent to which the testicle has descended. In a study of 43 unilateral and 4 bilateral cryptorchids Badinand *et al* (1972) found that seven had testes in the abdomen, one was inguinal-abdominal, 26 were inguinal and six just above the scrotum while three were indeterminate in position. In 27 cases the ectopic testicle was the right one.

Cryptorchidism runs in families with some animals being more serious in terms of producing the defect than others. This is generally accepted by most workers. Brandsch (1964) looked at several lines in the German Shepherd breed with from 17 to 2021 males

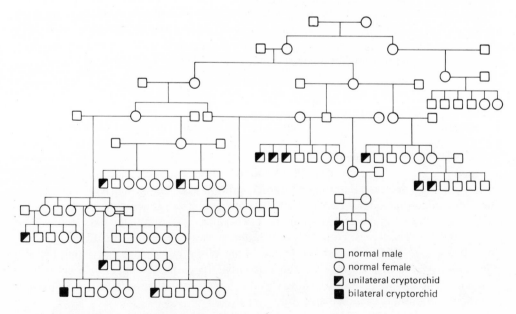

normal male
normal female
unilateral cryptorchid
bilateral cryptorchid

Figure 19   Pedigree of cryptorchidism in German Shepherd Dogs stemming from mating of Arras v Badeholz and Anita v Piastendamm (Brandsch 1964).

examined. The incidence of cryptorchidism ranged from 0 through to 9% of males seen. In another group of data incidence figures ranged from 3.3 to 13.0%. A typical pattern from Brandsch's data is shown in Figure 19.

Brandsch considered that litters with cryptorchids had an abnormally high sex ratio and that this might be due to the cryptorchid gene(s) acting lethally in females. In German Shepherds he found a sex ratio of 125 males per hundred females in litters containing cryptorchids compared with 102 overall. Using Hartl's Boxer data he obtained ratios of 156 and 102 for these same two categories. Koroveckaja (1938) considered an excessive number of males to be a feature of cryptorchid litters while Johnston *et al* (1958) contended that the failure to find cryptorchids in 21 litters of pigs from known 'carrier' parents could be due to the sterility of homozygous females. However, since this period Sittmann (1976) has reanalysed the data of Brandsch and Hartl and his conclusions negate the supposition of Brandsch.

The paper by Sittmann (1976) concluded that cryptorchidism in the German Boxer was caused by a simple autosomal recessive gene but did not exclude the possibility of a polygenic model with threshold points. The question of whether a dog was unilaterally or bilaterally affected was held to be caused by modifier genes or by environmental factors. Thus litter size itself was a factor in that the proportion of bilaterals was increased as litter size increased.

The Boxer data of Willis and Cuke (1978) do not support Sittmann's theory in that examination of litters from parents known to have produced the condition (that is, 'carrier' parents) gives too high a proportion of cryptorchids. The figures are shown in Table 12.

Perhaps the best evidence for the genetic basis of cryptorchidism comes from the Angora goat herds described by Lush *et al* (1930). During the period 1917 to 1959 selection for and against cryptorchidism was undertaken using different intensities of selection. The work was summarised by Warwick (1961) and the data in Table 13 show the main findings.

Table 12

Incidence of cryptorchids in Boxer litters from parents known to produce the condition

Litter size*	Litters	Progeny		
		Normal	Unilateral	Bilateral
1	16	4	4	8
2	10	13	6	1
3	6	8	4	6
4	3	5	3	4
5	2	7	2	1
6	1	4	2	0
Totals	38	41	21	20

*Refers only to males born and examined for cryptorchidism. All females, stillborn males and males not examined are excluded.
Source Willis and Cuke 1978.

Table 13

Effect of selection for and against cryptorchidism in two herds of Angora goats

Period	Selection system*	Total males born	Cryptorchids	
			Number	%
Herd number One				
1917–36	Mild	1168	79	6.76
1937–48	Moderate	798	23	2.88
1949–59	Rigid/Very rigid	227	1	0.44
Herd number Two†				
1921–23	Slight/Negative	257	17	6.61
1924–30	Negative	375	114	30.40
1931–34	Negative/Slight	55	28	50.91
1935–46	Slight	341	44	12.90
1947–59	Moderate/Rigid	856	7	0.82

* For explanation of selection system see text.
† In this herd selection was for the defect at certain periods. In Herd One selection was always against the defect.
Source   Warwick 1961.

The different kinds of selection procedure used were:

Negative   Deliberate use of cryptorchid sires;
Slight   Avoidance of cryptorchids in general but not totally;
Mild   Deliberate avoidance of cryptorchid sires;
Moderate   Using only entire sires and culling every sire or dam producing a cryptorchid;
Rigid   As moderate but culling also progeny of known 'carriers';
Very rigid   As rigid but also culling other close relatives of known 'carriers'.

The incidence of cryptorchid males in Herd one declined sharply as selection pressure against them was increased. In the second herd the use of defective males led to a rapid increase in their number and the selection against them brought about a rapid decline and almost complete elimination.

The goat data show conclusively that a genetic trait is involved since otherwise different intensities of selection would not have affected the incidence so markedly. The trait may be different in its mode of inheritance in dogs but it is reasonable to suppose that a genetic basis exists for the majority of cases. It is interesting to note that the exact nature of the genetics was never solved in the Angora goat herds but selection nevertheless worked to reduce the problem to negligible proportions.

In man cryptorchidism is frequently associated with inguinal hernia, hypospadia, hypogonadism and intersexuality (Warkany 1971a). It is also known that chromosomal anomalies can be associated with cryptorchid cases. Such conditions as Down's syndrome, where there is an extra chromosome at a specific pair, appear to have cryptorchid problems in many cases (Rosinsky 1942) and this is also true of other anomalies of the sex chromosomes. Karotypes such as XXXXY and others seem to have cryptorchidism as a frequent feature (see Warkany 1971a).

Such matters have rarely been examined in canine situations but it is known that excess chromosomes can occur and may, in some cases, account for cryptorchids. However, karotypes of this kind are not likely to be the causal factor behind most cryptorchids because the incidence of abnormal chromosome number is not as high as the incidence of cryptorchids. Nevertheless certain defects do seem to be excessively associated with cryptorchidism and some of these have been discussed by Pendergrass and Hayes (1975).

These workers found that hip dysplasia and other bone defects seemed to be associated with cryptorchidism in that non-entire dogs had a higher than normal expectation of such defects. This was true even in breeds not generally troubled by conditions such as hip dysplasia. A high relationship with umbilical hernia was noted and may have been due to a common mechanism. Testicular tumours were found in 39 of the cryptorchid animals with Sertoli cell tumours and seminomas accounting for over 97% of the tumours, only one case of interstitial cell tumour being observed. The authors concluded that the chance of testicular tumours was 10.9 times more likely in cryptorchid dogs than in entire animals. The data from clinic and hospital surveys is not the most satisfactory and it could be that some of the associations observed are artifacts rather than true relationships. Nevertheless the indications are sufficiently disturbing to justify some action against cryptorchidism.

Action to Take

There are some who argue that since cryptorchidism is not lethal no particular attention need be paid to it (Fitch-Daglish 1959) while Burns and Fraser (1966) seem to advocate a policy of inaction because nothing is known with certainty about the mode of inheritance. In some breeds there have been successful sires which were unilateral cryptorchids and their advocates often seem indifferent to the problem. Thus Somerfield (1955) argued that the famous Boxer Mazelaines Texas Ranger, a unilateral cryptorchid, produced fewer cryptorchids than his entire colleagues with no increase in the second generation. She does not, however, give any data to substantiate her opinion. In Bull Terriers a similar non-entire male, Ormandy Souperlative Bar Sinister produced, according to Oppenheimer (1969) about 2% affected males. He was undoubtedly a useful sire but personal conversation with Oppenheimer suggests that Bar Sinister was not a typical unilateral cryptorchid in that his testes did descend and retract at intervals.

In many countries cryptorchid males are ineligible for showing and in some breeds the progeny of such dogs cannot be registered. This is true, for example, of the German Shepherd Dog in Germany where the breed club (SV) publishes the names of all cryptorchids located and thus bans their use. In Britain the BVA published two reports (1954 and 1955) on the subject claiming, without evidence, that the trouble was a simple recessive condition and as a consequence the Kennel Club banned cryptorchids from exhibition. In 1969, still without having done any investigational work, the KC lifted the ban. They even adopted a Pontius Pilate approach by stating that it was a veterinary matter with which judges should not concern themselves. Since an MRCVS is not needed for anyone to count up to two and since it is breeders and not veterinarians who produce such dogs it seems inane for the KC to avoid its responsibilities in this way.

Cryptorchidism is a defect in a dog since it is a deviation from the normal state. The bilateral cryptorchid is of minimal concern because such dogs are sterile and hence are genetically dead whether or not one exhibits them. Unilateral cryptorchids are fertile but the popular belief that they are as fertile as normal dogs does not seem to be borne out by the available scientific data. In a study of 43 unilateral cryptorchids Badinand *et al* (1972) found that libido in such dogs was generally poorer than normal dogs with 33% of cryptorchids having sub-normal libido. These workers also found that sperm volume was lower in cryptorchids and that concentration, motility and percentage of live sperm was generally lower than in entire males. They concluded that unilateral cryptorchids had lower fertility than did normal males in about 69% of cases. The number of normal males used was low but if Badinand and his co-workers are correct in their conclusions one would be wise to select against such a condition as cryptorchidism. If to this one adds the greater risk of tumours in undescended testes and takes into account the previously mentioned views of Koroveckaja and Brandsch about related female fertility then one would be wise to place cryptorchidism high on the list of traits to be selected against.

The impaired fertility of cryptorchids was demonstrated by Kawakami *et al* (1984) who examined 29 affected mongrels (1.2% of a population of 2356 animals seen). Of the 29 cases 21 were inguinal and only 8 abdominal but most had reduced libido. Of 19 checked for ejaculatory function 8 did not seem to produce any ejaculate. In the main semen volume (7.2 ml) and total sperm number (1.2×10^8 per ejaculate) were low.

In practical terms the first stage must be to isolate the incidence data in each breed because without this one has no idea of the extent of the problem. If this incidence is appreciably high then culling of all 'carriers', in the sense of discarding all animals which produce an affected animal, is difficult. If, for example, 9% of Boxers are cryptorchids and the condition was due to a simple recessive allele then about 42% of Boxers would be 'carriers'. Clearly any attempt to cull 42% of the breed would be suicidal. If the condition is not as simple in its mode of inheritance we cannot assess which dogs 'carry' it because all animals may have greater or lesser predisposition towards it. In German Shepherds, for example, a very high proportion of major sires have caused cryptorchids in the sense that such dogs have appeared among their progeny. To cull such sires would mean that most of the best producers would disappear.

Action such as was taken in the Texas goat herd is feasible only up to the mild state, that is, not using affected dogs. To this can be added some culling of animals which produce several such dogs. In time this might lead to a slow decline of incidence but the urgent need for a genetic study of the subject is obvious.

Intersexuality (Hermaphroditism)

From time to time animals are born in which the sex is not readily determinable. A true hermaphrodite in the Greek mythology sense from which the term is coined would be of a dual nature being both male and female simultaneously. In reality hermaphrodites or intersexes are individuals whose genital organs have some of the characteristics of each sex.

A 'true' hermaphrodite is one which has gonadal tissue of both sexes and may be of three kinds. In a bilateral form ovotestes are present on both sides. In a unilateral form there is an ovotestes on one side and either ovarian or testicular tissue on the other. In the lateral form ovarian tissue exists on one side of the body and testicular tissue on the other.

The 'male pseudohermaphrodite' has testicular tissue and male genital organs with some female characteristics while the 'female pseudohermaphrodite' has ovarian gonadal tissue and genital organs with some male characteristics.

The condition of intersexuality is supposed to be rare in dogs and has been reviewed by Hare (1976) who examined 48 cases and a further 52 known to be drug induced. His cases came from published literature which he reviewed as well as dogs examined by his group in Ontario.

Doubtless the occurrence of intersexuality would be a matter of concern to a dog breeder but mainly the cases appear to be problems of development rather than the result of genetic factors. In some cases the animals do not have XX or XY sex chromosomes but can have XX in some cells and XXY in others or a mixture of XX and XY cells.

Several breeds have had cases reported but the only evidence for any genetic cause of XX male pseudohermaphroditism is that of Hare *et al* (1974) in Cocker Spaniels. Three dogs were affected and the authors considered the appearance consistent with a theory of a simple recessive gene. They suggested that when homozygous in a female the action of the XX chromosome was modified and caused some male genitalia to appear.

Hare (1976) points out that all known cases of XX male pseudohermaphroditism in dogs have been in Cockers. He further draws attention to the fact that if drug-induced cases are excluded one third of all canine hermaphroditism cases have been in Cockers. This is an interesting thought but has limited practical value since even in Cocker Spaniels such occurrences are rare. Stewart *et al* (1972) did find three cases of intersexuality in a Pug kennel in Missouri, all three cases having a common male ancestor and appearing to be male but having XX chromosomes in the one pup examined. Hare (1976) dismisses this as a drug induced case but the authors of the paper make no mention of drugs thus throwing some doubt upon some of Hare's conclusions.

Longevity

In many ways longevity is only very loosely classified as a reproductive trait but it fits in here better than anywhere else. Cynics might argue that longevity is immaterial in that once a dog's breeding life is ended it might as well be destroyed. Few reputable breeders will begrudge a pensioner space in their kennel so we need not dwell on the views of cynics.

In a practical sense longevity is important in a working dog because the longer the dog can stay active the longer the period of time over which the costs of training can be spread. This assumes, of course, that a longer life is related to a longer period of full activity and not merely a longer period of old age.

Dogs die when some vital organ fails to function as it should, excluding, of course, deaths from external influences like disease or accident. It is logical to assume that some of the controls which govern the workings of vital organs are genetic though few geneticists would deny that environment plays an important part in determining the length of life of a dog. Which particular environmental aspects are most important is difficult to say but there is no doubt that avoidance of disease (either via genetic resistance or man-induced medicines), correct nutrition, physical exercise and similar features would all be important.

Outside of man, zoo inmates and horses, domestic pets are one of the few categories of animal which get the chance to live out their lives. One might therefore have imagined that the dog, one of man's commonest pets, would be a subject of study for ageing with the interests not only of the dog but also of man involved. In fact there are few reliable studies on dogs and even these suffer from a paucity of data. According to Hubbard (1948) medium-sized and small breeds live longer than large ones and outbred and mongrel dogs longer than inbred ones. These may be true statements but Hubbard presents no reliable data to substantiate them so it might be as well to begin by examining such data as do exist regarding body size and longevity.

Sacher (1959) has tried to relate the life spans of animals with body and brain proportions and Stephen (1954) also tried to relate brain and body weights in dogs. Fox (1964) looked at brain and body weights and concluded that brain weight was about 0.8–1.0% of body weight regardless of age. This was true of four breeds but not of a fifth. In a study of four breeds of widely differing body weight Comfort (1960) found that his data seemed to fit reasonably well with Sacher's data albeit with different equations being concocted. There is little point in giving Comfort's equation because life span can only be calculated knowing body weight and the weight of the brain, which latter is somewhat difficult to obtain for any individual dog without drastically shortening the life span one is seeking to estimate. The findings do, however, seem to indicate greater life span of small breeds (Pekingese) relative to large ones (Irish Wolfhounds and Mastiffs). Whether the large breeds die earlier because of hormonal inadequacies or complications, such as are known with gigantism in man, one cannot say.

A problem with trying to calculate how long a dog will live on average is deciding where to start recording. If we count every pup born then a considerable number may be dead at birth or very early in life and will thus bring down the overall average very considerably.

In German Shepherds, for example, almost 12% may be dead by 48 hours and 17% by 8 weeks (Willis 1978a). Similarly, Comfort (1956) in his study of one Irish Wolfhound kennel found that 25% of males and 11% of females were dead by one month of age. Since Comfort's data did not include stillbirths these percentages must be minimal ones for the kennel concerned. In a study of Rough Collies in the USA Ford (1971) showed that 23% were dead at birth and a further 10% died before three months of age.

It can be argued that one is interested in the length of life of dogs reaching maturity rather than the absolute mean age for all dogs born. In this connection Willis (1976) has looked at the age at death of British champions in the German Shepherd breed. He had the length of life of 85 males and 58 females (about 33% of all deceased champions) and found the mean age at death to be 114 months in males and 121 months in females. Only 47% of the males and 64% of the females passed the ten year mark (120 months) despite the care likely to be given to such valuable breeding animals. Of course, it can be argued that an active breeding life is itself conducive to early death and there is work in rodents to suggest that this is the case.

Comfort's data in his 1956 paper covered an Irish Wolfhound kennel from 1927–45 (as regards birth dates) and he had exact life span for 103 of the 189 recorded animals with life span to the nearest year for a further 51. In his later paper (Comfort 1960) he added some data from another kennel together with breeder records on 158 Pekingese, 45 Cockers and 23 Mastiffs. There are various potential flaws in the data which would not get past most modern statisticians but if we concentrate more on the results than the dubious data which gave rise to them we find that at any age more Pekingese and Cockers survived than did Mastiffs and Irish Wolfhounds. Taking the two breeds with most individuals represented and ignoring all deaths prior to one year we find that 80% of Pekingese survived to 5 years compared with 60% of Wolfhounds. By ten years the figures were 62% and 8% respectively and while no Wolfhounds survived beyond the fourteenth year no less than 36% of Pekes did, although all these died in that year.

The suggestion is that the practical views of Hubbard (1948) which began this section appear to be borne out by such data as exist but that facts are limited in the extreme and would seem to be something that breed clubs could do well to compile.

Chapter 4

Coat Colour Inheritance

The Importance of Coat Colour

The type of colour pattern which develops in a particular species depends upon the nature of the species. Some animals have developed colorations which are mainly aimed at camouflage so that the individual blends with its background. This will make it less obvious to predators and/or to would-be prey. In other species the pattern has become of an aposematic or warning kind which discourages would-be attackers. A third kind of colour may be used for display and may be important in mating behaviour. Then again, coat colour may be aposematic at some stage and change with temperature to some other colour as in the case of certain northern mammals.

Large species like the elephant which have no prey and no predators other than man have developed dull colours because there has been no other evolutionary need. The dog is a descendant of the wolf which was either swift enough to outrun its enemies or strong enough, in the pack sense, to fight them off. The wolf thus had few evolutionary stimuli to produce varied colour patterns and as a consequence wolves are grey or occasionally black or white. With the domestication of the dog man has been able to bring to light hidden colours that would have been disadvantageous in nature and thus provide a more varied range of colours than is seen in most wild species.

All pedigree breeds of dog have certain colours laid down in the breed Standard as being acceptable. In some breeds the range is very wide, in others very limited. In most breeds specific colours are unacceptable or disqualifying. Generally such undesirable colours are selected against because they are aesthetically disliked rather than because they are associated with some particular biological defect. One might rightly select against a colour that is associated with blindness or deafness, or even against a colour which is unsuitable for specific kinds of work (for example, white guard dogs) but the wisdom of disqualifying a colour for no other reason than that it is disliked is open to question. Sometimes the colour under dispute may have been so categorised because it was, in the early days of the breed, associated with 'blood' from other breeds. Sometimes it is selected against because of a believed association with physical degeneration (such as white in German Shepherd Dogs). Usually such beliefs are without foundation.

However, it is not the purpose of this book to tell breeders which colours they should or should not produce. If a particular group of breeders wants to select against a colour for aesthetic reasons then they are perfectly entitled to make their breeding life harder than it inevitably will be. That is their choice. The purpose of this and the following chapter is to try to explain how each colour is produced in order that breeders can best obtain their objectives, however logical or illogical those objectives may be.

The Chemistry of Colour

Dogs, like most mammals, have a coat of hair. Frequently this is made up of two distinct types; an undercoat or underhair and an outercoat or overhair. In some breeds only one of these remains, in others both. Generally the underhair is made up of short downy hairs which are wavy or crimped. In contrast the outerhair is of various types and lengths with the long straight thick guard-hairs or monotrichs being the most important.

The various kinds of hair and coat types are dealt with in detail elsewhere (see page 114) but some mention is necessary here because it is the coat hair which carries the colour pigments. Each hair has a central core or medulla in which there are one or more rows of cells alternating with air spaces. Around the medulla is a solid cortex and around that a thin cuticle. The relative size of cortex and medulla will depend upon the type of hair and the species or breed which bears it. The coat colour will depend upon the pigments in the medulla and cortex of the hair so that in studying the genetic factors affecting coat colour we are really studying those influencing pigment granules.

In a study of coat colour in mice Russell (1946) found that there were seven different ways in which hair pigment granules could be altered and hence various colour combinations be observed. All colours were, he felt, dependent upon the relative changes of particular attributes. The seven aspects he isolated were:

1   Granule colour;
2   Granule shape (long oval, oval, round, irregular);
3   Number of granules per medullary cell;
4   Number of granules per unit of cortex;
5   Clumping of granules into loose or dense arrangements;
6   Granule size;
7   Tendency to distal arrangements within medullary cells.

Similar studies have not been undertaken in dogs but it seems logical to assume that colour changes in the species may well involve similar aspects.

In most mammals the pigmentary colours are very limited in chemical terms. Usually they are only haemoglobin and melanins. There are two forms of melanin: eumelanin (brown or black) and phaeomelanin (yellow or reddish). Coat colour depends upon the presence or absence of these types in the medullar cells or the cortex and the various arrangements of them as propounded above.

Clearly little would be served by a long treatise into the biochemistry of melanins and anyone wishing further insight is referred to Searle (1968). What is important is to understand that melanins are not formed at a specific time but at different stages of foetal and post-natal life depending upon the particular type. Some kinds are formed at a fairly early stage so that the animal has the final adult colour from birth, other colours are still being formed at birth and may not reach their final form until the animal is fully grown.

This lengthy process of colour formation does not make for easy assessment of colour in dogs. The breeder who registers his stock at weaning or earlier may, in all honesty, make errors in the colours allotted to each. Even experienced breeders can make very serious errors in colour nomenclature and the matter is further complicated by the fact that breeders in one breed may refer to a colour by one name and those in another may refer to the same colour by a different name.

Various workers have attempted to study colour in dogs, the most notable sources of reference being Iljin (1932), Little (1957), Burns and Fraser (1966) and Whitney (1971). Several of these, notably Iljin and Whitney, have worked with crosses and Little was concerned with data collected from breeders.

The problem that one is faced with in trying to give a global coverage to canine colour is the unenviable one of paucity of data. To come to definite conclusions about colour one must have sufficient data to work on and such data need to be accurate. A second difficulty is the need to assess colour in one breed from results in another breed or cross. One can sympathise with the desire for any theory that fits each breed but it does not necessarily follow that inheritance of a colour in one breed is the same as that in another.

The remainder of this chapter is concerned with the various genes affecting coat colour in dogs and the specific problems of particular breeds are dealt with in the following chapter. In examining the various genes, several of which are multiallelic, it must be remembered that the same genes may produce different colour shades in different breeds because the colour we see is going to be affected by coat length as well as by genetic make-up. Long hair will reflect light differently to short hair and hence can alter the visible colour.

The Agouti or A Series

This is perhaps the most complex of all canine colour series. It is named after a South American rodent which shows the pattern of this locus very clearly. In a genuine agouti we have pigment changes within the individual hair with the colour changing in bands according to whether the pigment is phaeomelanin or eumelanin. Changes in different alleles will lead to extension of the phaeomelanin or its loss but there is further complication by the fact that colours will vary from the dorsal (back) to the ventral (belly) parts of the dog and, in certain breeds, final colour is not achieved until adulthood.

According to Burns and Fraser (1966) the alleles in the agouti series are:

A   dominant black;
a^y dominant yellow (golden sable);
a^g agouti (wolf grey);
a^s saddle marking (black or liver saddle with extensive tan markings on head and
　　 legs);
a^t bicolour (black or liver saddle extending over most of the body with tan markings
　　 on feet and eyebrows).

Little (1957) uses A^s in place of A and a^w in place of a^g. He further does not accept the occurrence of a^s and lumps both it and a^t into the category a^t.

Little argues that there are plenty of genes in the dog which would account for the different amounts of tan on the a^s and a^t dogs without having to explain them by separate alleles. I have attempted to show that they are in fact distinct by means of German Shepherd data (Willis 1976).

Where we can agree is that all agouti series alleles are darker at birth than in adulthood (a gradual lightening occurring with time) and that they give darker dorsal colours than they give at the extremities and underbelly.

In breeds like the Rough Collie the $a^y a^y$ genotype and the $a^y a^t$ genotype give rise to different phenotypes since the latter has dark hairs among the sable. In other breeds they may be indistinguishable. Some breeders of Pekingese call sables brindle but this is erroneous nomenclature.

The depth of tan pigment may vary considerably and range from a very pale tan bordering on cream through to a rich dark liver colour.

There seems little doubt that genuine bicolours (a^ta^t) are recessive since in German Shepherds they give rise only to this colour unless white or non-agouti black is present. Little (1957) gives data on matings involving bicoloured Airedales, Dachshunds and Fox Terriers and in each breed only bicolours resulted in the progeny.

The B Series

This series was first described by Little in 1914 and is the one series on which every worker seems to be in accord. There are two alleles:

B   Black;
b   Chocolate, tan, liver or red.

Strictly speaking the terminology is misleading since a BB or Bb dog will not necessarily be black. The colour will depend upon what other series are present but the BB/Bb formula means that black pigment can be formed. In contrast dogs of the type bb cannot form black pigment and thus will not have black noses. The terms chocolate, tan, liver or red are used because a great deal seems to depend upon the breed one is talking about as to what a bb animal is called.

The allele B is dominant to b and appears to be fully so with no exceptions of importance. It thus acts exactly as was shown in Table 1 (see page 8).

The fact that bb animals cannot produce black pigment is important as far as breed standards are concerned because bb dogs will have liver noses rather than black ones. It is thus pointless asking for black noses in liver-coloured dogs. To my knowledge all breeds which permit this coat colour allow brown noses. They usually also permit lighter eyes since it is probable that the bb combination affects eye pigment as well as that of the coat.

There is reason to believe that modifying polygenes exist which act to modify the shades of liver or brown and also red coats. Robinson (1982) terms these rufus polygenes. Such genes are carried by black dogs but do not express themselves in the black coat. In brown/liver/red dogs these polygenes act to darken (plus polygenes) or lighten (minus polygenes) the basic colour. Breeders cannot identify the polygenes but can select for darker or lighter shades of brown/liver/red with some degree of success.

The Albino or C Series

Various workers have contributed to this series and according to Burns and Fraser (1966) there are five alleles. Little (1957) disputes the presence of one of these and uses alternative nomenclature for two others. He also questions the action of one. The series based on the different views is:

C   Colour factor which allows melanin to be formed;
c^{ch} Chinchilla (Burns and Fraser use c^r);
c^d White coat with black nose and dark eyes;
c^b Cornaz coat with blue eyes;
c   Albinism with pink eyes and nose (Little uses c^a)

The order of dominance in the series is in the descending order given but may not be complete in all cases.

The C allele is needed to allow full expression of colour and many breeds are actually CC. However the absence of C does not mean that a white animal automatically occurs, certainly $c^{ch}c^{ch}$ will not necessarily be white. Much will depend upon what other colours are present because it seems that c^{ch} has more effect upon tan pigment than it has upon black.

In many breeds it is possible that CC, Cc^{ch} and $c^{ch}c^{ch}$ will give rise to increasingly paler tans as one moves from the CC stage down. In breeds which are already carrying genes at other loci which give rise to yellow/tan, as opposed to black, it is possible that the $c^{ch}c^{ch}$ combination can bring about white coloration.

In combination with a^g the $c^{ch}c^{ch}$ structure causes a colour pattern very similar to that seen in the Chinchilla, hence Little's use of this nomenclature.

Little (1957) doubts the existence of c^d and claims that a white coat coupled with a black nose can occur when $c^{ch}c^{ch}$ is present with ee or a^y combinations. The fact that most whites with black noses have yellowish markings, if they have markings at all, supports Little's view and in my own experience I have known of white German Shepherds which from their progeny were a^ya^y.

The c^b allele gives rise to a pale greyish (cornaz) coat with blue eyes and stems from work by Pearson and Usher (1929) using Pekingese and Pomeranians. The allele is likely to be rare and not seen in many breeds.

Complete albinism cc is fairly rare in dogs and likely to remain so. According to Burns and Fraser (1966) the cc combination would give blue eyes but true albinism means that there is a total lack of melanin so that the hair is white and the eyes pink. Any blue-eyed white must contain melanins in the eye and cannot thus be a true albino.

The Dilution or D Series

As with the B/b situation this series seems to be one in which general agreement exists. It was named by Little and Jones (1919) and consists of two alleles:

D   Intense pigmentation;
d   Dilution of pigment.

This series differs from the others in that it does not cause any colour per se. What it does is to act upon other loci in an epistatic fashion to cause different expression. If D is present either singly or in duplicate, then a dog will have the colour of its coat determined by other loci. If dd is present then coat colour will be diluted. The degree of dilution will depend upon modifying factors.

The dilution effect will vary according to whether black or tan pigment is involved. The effect on the B/b series is illustrated in Table 3 (see page 11) and in Plate 4.

The problem with the dd combination is that it is not the only allelic combination causing dilution. The $c^{ch}c^{ch}$ type has been discussed already and there is another series G which also affects pigment intensity (see page 69).

It does, however, seem that the D/d series acts like a simple Mendelian one.

The Extension or E Series

This series was first named by Little (1914) and in his book (Little 1957) he gives four alleles. These are:

E   Superextension with dark mask;

E   Extension without black mask;
e^{br} Brindle or partial extension;
e   Restriction.

The term extension and restriction relate to dark pigment rather than tan. E^m and E permit black pigment to be formed in the coat, assuming that black pigment is carried by the animal and the difference between the two is that E^m causes a black mask while E does not permit black in the mask. Both will permit black noses and dark eyes.

The brindle allele e^{br} acts so as to permit black pigment to form in layers through tan pigment to give a tiger striped effect obvious in brindle Boxers, Bull Terriers and Great Danes.

The restriction allele e does not permit black pigment to be formed so that even if the dog carries genes for black the animal will not show black except in the nose and dark eyes.

E^m is dominant to E and e such that $E^m E^m$, $E^m E$ and $E^m e$ will all be phenotypically the same. In like manner E is dominant to e such that EE and Ee will appear identical in appearance. The brindle allele e^{br} is also dominant to e so that $e^{br} e^{br}$ and $e^{br} e$ will seem the same but when e^{br} is present with either E^m or E it will cause a brindle effect in the tan areas. Thus $E^m e^{br}$ will have a black mask and be brindle in the tan regions whereas Ee^{br} and $e^{br} e^{br}$ may be identical in having brindle markings without a black mask.

The extension series is, of course, affected by white genes (see, for example, the S locus page 71). When white genes are present the tan/black colours may be totally masked and as a result the genetic make-up of white dogs is difficult to assess.

In a similar way the extension series interacts with the agouti series in various ways. Together these two series can cause several interesting colour variants which deserve mention.

Assuming that no white genes are present (that is, the dogs are SS or S–) then any animal with at least one A allele coupled with E^m or E, together or separately, will be black if B is carried or liver if bb is carried. In such cases the black (or liver) markings will be uniform throughout the coat and as a consequence AE^m may not be distinguishable from AE except by pedigree or breeding records.

The allele A coupled with e^{br} will also produce black since the A allele acts to conceal the e^{br} allele. This is certainly true in AA animals and probably true in Aa^y animals although in some cases $e^{br} e^{br}$ with Aa^y may cause a faint marking through the coat.

When $a^y a^y$ is present with E^m the dog will be red-yellow or sable with a black mask. When present with E the dog will be sable without a black mask. When present with at least one e^{br} allele the red-yellow areas will be marked with dark brindle stripes. If $E^m e^{br}$ is carried the mask will be black but if Ee^{br} is carried the mask will also be brindle marked.

With any combination of a^s and a^t the E^m allele will allow black-and-tan pigment to form but the mask will be black. The E allele will allow black-and-tan to form but will have a tan-colour mask. With e^{br} the a^s and a^t alleles will give black-and-tan but with brindle markings in the tan.

The effect of e is concealed by E^m, E or e^{br} because all three are dominant to it. However in a homozygous state ee acts upon the agouti series in various ways. With a^s or a^t alleles in any kind of combination the ee structure will cause all black pigment to disappear except in the nose and the dog will be tan marked but with a different shade of tan in those areas that would normally be tan marked in black-and-tans.

Coupled with AA or Aa^y, Aa^s or Aa^t the ee factor will also cause black pigment to disappear but in this case it will lead to a clear uniform red-yellow pigment throughout the animal. Thus we can have two different kinds of red or yellow dog. One kind stems from A–ee while the other kind is $a^y a^y EE$. Fawn Boxers are examples of $a^y a^y EE$ reds while yellow Labradors are AAee animals.

The relationship between a^y and e is uncertain. Strictly it ought to lead to further red coloration. Little (1957) suggests that ee plus a^y or $a^y a^y$ plus e may cause early death but his data are tenuous. In the German Shepherd which has a^y and e alleles the most likely consequence is fading colours. The combination of a^g with ee is likely to give very pale grey sables. It could be that the grey sable in German Shepherds is a^g–E^m or a^g–E and that so-called golden sables are a^g coupled with ee rather than a^y animals. The faded gold dogs without a black tail tip are always carrying a^s or a^t or both with ee and cannot produce genuine sables unless mated with sables.

The effect of extension series alleles and the c^{ch} allele needs to be clarified but it is possible that ee and $c^{ch} c^{ch}$ could cause such dilution of colour as to give white or yellowish white dogs.

The Greying or G Series

This series is another one due to Little (1957) and is made up of two alleles G which causes progressive greying of the coat and which is dominant to g which does not cause greying.

The greying referred to is not the gradual greying of age but rather a progressive change in black coats until they become a blue or grey blue shade. Most breeds are actually gg and thus unaffected by this gene but several breeds such as Bedlingtons, Kerry Blues and Old English Sheepdogs do seem to carry G.

In breeds in which G and g exist all three genotypes GG, Gg and gg will be black at birth but the first two kinds will gradually become bluish in shade while the gg animals will remain black if the rest of the dog's genotype permits this. In many breeds where this type of blue shade is required the breed has become homozygous GG but in others like the Kerry Blue both alleles exist and can thus lead to occasional black dogs which stay black (gg) and represent some degree of economic loss although they can, of course, still be bred from successfully.

Since dd also gives rise to blue some doubt may exist as to the causal factor of blue in a breed. However, it seems that dd animals are slatish-blue at birth while GG or Gg dogs are black.

The Merling or M Series

The allele for merle M is dominant to the non-merle m. This series was described by Mitchell (1935) who pointed out the association of various defects with the MM genotype. Since that time Sorsby and Davey (1954) have studied the factor in Dachshunds, Collies and Shelties while Hackman (1953) has done so in Dachshunds and Little (1957) in various breeds. Most breeds are mm in genotype but the M allele exists in the various breeds of British sheepdog as well as Great Danes and Dachshunds.

Dogs which are mm will carry colours determined by their other loci but dogs which are Mm will have the pigment in certain areas reduced so as to leave flecks and patches of intense pigment.

The effect of the M allele seems to be greater on black than tan pigment such that in sable

Collies (a^ya^t or a^ya^y) the Mm form may not show very marked effect but simply give golden patches. As a result such dogs may not even be identified as merles even though they genetically are. In contrast a^sa^t or a^sa^s or, more commonly, a^ta^t dogs will be affected by the Mm combination and appear as blotchy grey and black. The gene may also affect the amount of white so that in breeds like Collies which carry white alleles ($s^ts^ps^w$) the blue-merle will be very obvious. In breeds like the Dachshund the effect is one of dappling and they are called dapples in that breed. In Great Danes the Harlequin variety is caused by Mm but Burns and Fraser (1966) suggest that genuine merles are EeMm or $Ee^{br}Mm$ while Harlequins are EEMm. Certainly the M allele has most effect on black pigment and thus makes a genuine black marked Harlequin difficult to obtain.

According to Sorsby and Davey (1954) the Mm combination can act upon the eye with the effect of producing wall eye (heterochromia iridis) which is seen in some merles.

Although Mm gives rise to difficult colours to control, in that regularity (much prized in many breeds) is not achieved, there is no evidence of any associated defects other than some deafness. Alas in the homozygous state MM that is not true.

In breeds which carry white spotting genes of the S locus MM dogs will be white or almost white in coat colour and according to Mitchell (1935) they may have deafness, blindness and structurally defective eyes. This is dealt with in more detail elsewhere (see page 228) but suggests that the M allele is a dangerous one to be operating with. Certainly Mm × Mm matings must be discouraged because they will result in about 25% MM animals. But it is by no means certain that Mm stock are totally free from problems and the FCI have recently (1976) suggested an exhibition ban on Mm animals.

In breeds which do not carry white and where Mm gives a dapple effect the MM form can vary from a dapple with some white markings through to an almost white dog with very limited dapple patches. The defects associated with Collies are also found in Dachshunds (Dausch *et al* 1977, Reetz *et al* 1977).

There is some suggestion that more than one merle gene exists. This was suggested by Schaible and Brumbaugh (1976) and discussed by Robinson (1982). More recently Sponenberg (1985) has produced data on the subject. It is considered that the harlequin colour of the Great Dane is caused by this second merle gene rather than the traditional one. The symbol M^h has been suggested for this version and it appears that the M^hm heterozygote produces whitish areas whereas the Mm heterozygote produces bluish areas. Sponenberg's data were suggestive of M^h being lethal in the homozygous state and lethal to about half the heterozygotes when combined with MM genotypes.

Sponenberg (1984) has also looked at merling in the Australian Shepherd dog (an American breed despite its name). A homozygous bitch produced 64 merle and 2 non-merle offspring which continued not to give rise to merles. The evidence was suggestive of the merle allele being due to a transposable DNA element. Later Sponenberg and Lamoreux (1985) were of the view that an autosomal mutation of the merle gene had given rise to what they called Tweed. They consider the Tweed merle pattern had a greater range of intensity in the dilute patches which were also larger than the patches on non-Tweed merles. They proposed the symbol Tw for this version.

The P Series

Little (1957) hypothesises that there is a dominant allele P which affects the depth of pigment and a recessive allele p which reduces black and brown pigment but does not affect tan or yellow. The evidence for such a series is not conclusive and accordingly it has been omitted from the breed descriptions in the following chapter.

The Spotting or S Series

One of the first scientists to study white markings in dogs was Warren (1927) in Greyhounds who found that white tended to be recessive to solid colour. He proposed a three allele series which Little (1957) has extended to a four allelic series and which is held to be a satisfactory explanation of white markings at this locus.

The four alleles are:

S   Self colour or totally pigmented surface;
s^i Irish spotting involving a few definite areas of white;
s^p Piebald spotting;
s^w Extreme-white piebald.

This series is accepted by Burns and Fraser (1966) although they suggest that s^i should be termed s'. In the ensuing discussion Little's terminology is used but before this some general ground rules need to be laid.

As long ago as 1914 Allen showed that as white markings were found they tended to appear in specific places in a kind of orderly fashion. This was true not only of dogs but also various other mammals. This certainly seems to be the case because dogs with only small amounts of white will have it on the toes, chest, belly, muzzle or tail tip. As white markings become more extensive they will be found further up the forelegs, the hind feet and around the neck. As more white is found the patches appear on the body and seem less regular but still follow some kind of pattern. Allen called these patches or areas in which pigment persists 'centres of pigmentation' and he argued that pigmentation of each one was inherited separately. If he is right then colour inheritance is even more complex than it may already seem in this book.

Burns and Fraser (1966) argue that the most important centres of pigmentation in the dog are on the ears and head and around the eyes such that these will be the last areas to become white. The next most important areas are at the root of the tail followed by patches on the ribs and finally by areas on the loin and lower part of the neck.

The colour of the patches seems to affect their size with black patches being larger than liver which in turn will be larger than red or yellow patches. Anyone seeking to establish all white breeds by selection in the S series must bear that in mind. This is borne out by Little's work in Cockers (see page 73).

In dealing with the S series it has to borne in mind that there are complicating factors caused by various minor genes called modifiers. Their number and effect is uncertain and likely to remain so but they can be basically described as plus or minus modifiers. Plus modifiers will lead to more colour and minus modifiers will lead to more white. These modifiers act on each of the four alleles of the S series and thus can lead to some degree of overlap between one genotype and another.

Most breeds which do not allow white markings are SS but from time to time white markings do appear and in accordance with the earlier discussion these generally are on the toes, chest, tail tip or muzzle. Frequently these marks are present at birth and are lost during early infancy but sometimes they may persist, particularly in black dogs. Little (1957) in a study of 2353 dogs from seven breeds in which white was not desired found that

11.3% were mismarked in the sense of having white. Such effects are not due to other s alleles but to minus modifiers of the S allele.

The dominance of S over the other three alleles depends upon the breed and the modifiers present. Usually it is dominant to s^i but in combination with s^P or s^w (that is, Ss^P or Ss^w) white markings may appear.

Irish spotting (s^i) is so named by Doncaster (1906) who first observed it in wild rats which were of Irish origin. It has a definite pattern causing white streaks or spots in one or other of the following places viz, muzzle, forehead, chest, belly, feet, tail tip. These are areas already known to be the first at which white will appear but in Irish spotting selective breeding has usually led to an increase in minus modifiers so that the effect is to give a very clear format. This is best seen in Basenjis which vary from very little white through to a clearly defined collar and white feet. All are due to s^{i}s^i but in the dogs with little white there are plus modifiers while those with much white have minus modifiers.

Clearly s^{i}s^i with plus modifiers may appear very like SS with minus modifiers and hence the latter is termed pseudo-Irish spotting. Generally, unless Irish spotting is known in a breed SS is the form but if S and s^i exist some overlap and hence difficulty of identification is inevitable.

Little (1957) reports on 68 matings involving various combinations of s^i and s^P and produced evidence to support the belief that s^i is dominant to s^P with s^i s^i matings to s^{i}s^P and s^{P}s^P dogs giving only Irish spotting.

Many breeds carry s^i (see Chapter 5) with Basenjis, Collies and Boxers being typical examples.

The piebald allele s^P causes very variable amounts of white to be formed. The most typical breed to show this is the Beagle (see Plates 5a and 5b)). Most Beagles are s^{P}s^P although S and s^w exist. Because of the combinations of plus and minus modifiers with s^{P}s^P a whole range of white markings can occur from almost no white through to almost no colour. Little (1957) studied various breeds for the proportion of white in their coat and the data are shown in Table 14.

These four distributions in Table 14 show up the different effects of s alleles and the pigment effect. The Boxer situation shows a distribution typical of S, s^i and s^w alleles. At the top of the table (1–10% white) we are concerned with Irish spotting and some modifiers of S whilst at the foot we have s^w s^w animals. In the intervening grades are the effects of minus modifiers of s^i and plus modifiers of s^w.

In contrast the American Cocker Spaniel has Irish spotting discouraged and hence has either S or s^P or s^w in various combinations. This is clearly shown along with the fact that white alleles have greater effect upon red rather than black pigment. The Beagle pattern, on the other hand, is showing s^{P}s^P and Ss^P effects with plus or minus modifiers but either has very few s^w alleles or none at all.

Generally s^P will act as dominant to s^w but much will depend upon the modifiers present as to the exact appearance of s^{P}s^w dogs. With many plus modifiers they may seem to be more like s^{P}s^P and with minus modifiers will show much more white.

The extreme-white piebald allele s^w is seen in those breeds which are white in colour. Generally these are s^{w}s^w and as a result all other colours are hidden. However, if plus modifiers are present some colours may occur and they will generally be seen on the ears and face around the eyes. This is seen very clearly in Sealyhams which are white s^{w}s^w but which, with plus genes have coloured areas in these regions. According to Little (1957) about 60% of Sealyhams have 1–10% of their body surface coloured whereas Samoyeds

Table 14

Proportions of dogs with different amounts of pigment (non white) in the coat

| | *Percentage of animals in each breed* | | | |
| | *American Cocker Spaniel* | | | |
Amount of pigment %	*Black*	*Red*	*Beagle*	*Boxer*
100 (self)	—	—	—	18.30
90–99	21.04	1.85	55.90	73.70
80–89	16.88	2.31	19.60	1.35
70–79	14.00	2.77	8.30	0.00
60–69	11.68	2.54	5.40	0.06
50–59	10.65	4.85	3.20	0.06
40–49	7.01	4.62	2.80	0.06
30–39	7.54	7.87	1.40	0.18
20–29	4.15	12.90	1.30	0.12
10–19	4.15	26.60	1.40	0.18
0– 9	2.86	33.60	0.70	5.73
Total dogs seen	385	432	816	1780

Source Little 1957.

have only 9% in this category. Little's data are not extensive but if they are representative would indicate selectional differences in these breeds in America with Samoyed breeders being insistent upon pure white and Sealyham breeders tolerating or even encouraging some coloured patches on the head.

The s^w allele ought to be recessive to all others but the issue is complicated by minus modifiers in SS breeds. The main difficulty with $s^w s^w$ breeds is identification of other alleles but unless crossing is to be done the paucity of data is academic rather than of practical importance.

The Ticking or T Series

In some breeds of dog the white areas are not pure white but have small coloured spots which is termed ticking. This appears to be caused by a dominant allele T which has a recessive allele t causing no ticking effect.

Most breeds are tt but in several gundog breeds ticking does occur and in the Dalmatian it is the most pronounced. The colour of the ticking will depend upon the basic colour of the breed on which white is imposed. In dogs which have white markings and carry TT or Tt the ticking effect will be seen but in dogs which carry TT or Tt but do not carry white alleles of the S series then the effect of ticking will be hidden.

Ticking is not necessarily present at birth and Little (1957) has suggested that ticking can interact with a^t even when the dog is Aa^t. This is suggested because in some dogs known to carry A the ticking in the extremities (those areas normally tan in an $a^t a^t$ dog) in tan. However, since the proof that these dogs were Aa^t and not AA is absent one cannot necessarily accept the theory.

Yet another locus, the R series, has been suggested by some authors (for example, Burns and Fraser 1966). This is held to carry two alleles R causing roaning and r causing no such effect with R dominant to r. Roaning is held to be a mixture of coloured hairs in the white regions and thus it differs from ticking in that ticking is caused by definite coloured areas.

Little (1957) is sceptical about this theory because it is clearly difficult to distinguish between a small coloured spot and a few pigmented hairs in a white area.

Some objections to the dominant effect of T have been put forward by Whitney (1971) who found it recessive in English Pointers and Burns and Fraser (1966) report a mating of two clear white Pointers which gave ticked pups. This does not, however, help any acceptance of a dominant roan gene and until further evidence is forthcoming it may be wisest to assume that ticking and roaning are just two versions of the same thing. That is the assumption made in the next chapter when discussing individual breeds.

Hypopigmentation

The loss of pigment from a specific area of normally pigmented skin is known to occur in man and has been studied on a few occasions in the dog. In man the condition, called vitiligo, is known to occur as an inherited condition that is dominant with variable penetrance (Lerner 1959) and it is also known to be associated with certain other diseases.

Three cases of vitiligo in German Shepherd Dogs in India were reported by Sen and Ansari (1972) with pigmental loss being mainly in the area of the mouth, nose and eyelids. Similar problems have been reported in the Chow Chow (Engstrom 1966) and Dobermann (Muller and Kirk 1976) and more recently in the Tervueren (Mahaffey *et al* 1978). In all cases the pigment loss was around the nose and mouth and in the Chow Chow case affected the tongue and buccal cavity.

It is known that certain chemicals, such as tyrosine, can rectify some cases of vitiligo and since tyrosine is involved in melanin production this is not necessarily surprising. This does not exclude a genetic basis for the problem and in the Tervueren cases it was found by Mahaffey and her co-workers that 20 of the 35 dogs had pedigree relationships. This is not in itself evidence of a genetic trait since the Tervueren population in the USA is very narrowly based following importations in the 1950s. Nevertheless no nutritional or other environmental explanation was forthcoming and it is probable that in a narrowly based pedigree population some recessive trait might emerge. No sex-linked or sex-limited influence was isolated but the mode of inheritance was unclear as to whether it was dominant, recessive or polygenic. The authors did point out that loss of pigment on the lower lip close to the maxillary canine teeth was to be excluded from the main syndrome being a feature of many breeds and resulting from pressure of the teeth on the skin surface rather than due to any metabolic defect.

Chapter 5

Coat Colour Genes in Specific Breeds

Introduction

The previous chapter was intended to describe the various genes which affect coat colour in dogs. This chapter seeks to define which alleles of specific genes exist in the particular breeds.

All breeds will have genes from the various series that were described in Chapter 4 but in many instances the breed may have only one allele of that gene and thus every individual in the breed will be homozygous for that particular allele. Clearly in such cases the breeder will not have to consider that gene in his breeding programme. His concern will be for those genes where his breed has alternative alleles present since only in this case can he hope to affect colour in one way or another.

The problem in most breeds is that detailed records of coat colour have not been available for analysis and the theories which are put forward here represent probable ones and may be subject to change as more information becomes available. This is particularly true of certain rare colours—rare because they are undesirable—which may not be documented and hence their existence is unknown to all but a few.

In the remainder of this chapter breeds are dealt with in alphabetical order without regard to whether they are in specific groups—Working, Toys, Hounds and so on. Since the number of breeds in the world is legion only those of numerical importance in several of the major dog breeding countries are considered. The absence of a breed from this list may reflect absence of data more than lack of importance.

Explanations given in this chapter are the best available but in some instances will be incomplete or even erroneous because of paucity of data. Readers with alternative evidence are invited to contact the author with, if possible, photographic evidence so as to enable updating to be made.

Afghan Hound

This is a complex breed in colour terms because there is a large number of acceptable colours and the long coat of the breed does not aid diagnosis. Added to that breeders use terms like brindle or grizzled to describe dogs which are possibly not genuine brindle animals.

The breed is almost certainly homozygous for the alleles B, g, m and t and is possibly homozygous for D and S.

Some blues are known suggesting that dd can be met with but most Afghans are DD and very few likely to be Dd. White markings can occur but these are likely to be modifiers of the S allele rather than caused by other members of the S series.

Solid blacks in the breed confirm the presence of A and E and several alleles of these two series are present. Possibly these are A, a^y and a^t together with E^m, E and e.

Reds and fawns are common in the breed and it is possible that two kinds exist. Many are carriers of the combination ee which leads to fading of the black markings and an overall red/fawn colour. However some Afghans are born dark sable and have a lot of dark brown or black markings along the spine. These frequently get much lighter with age and may become clear reds. This is typical of the a^ya^y or a^ya^t combinations. Certainly if they have black masks then this is more likely than ee. Those with black masks will carry E^m at least once. Rufus polygenes are also implicated.

Cream Afghans are possibly caused by the combination of $a^ya^yc^{ch}c^{ch}$ or $a^ya^tc^{ch}c^{ch}$ or even $eec^{ch}c^{ch}$. The latter kind is likely to be almost white and certainly lighter than the two other sorts.

Silver may be caused by A in combination with dd but it is more probably caused by $a^ya^tc^{ch}c^{ch}$.

Brindles are possibly not caused by e^{br} since that allele is perhaps not in the breed. Most so-called brindles are variations of sables (that is, they carry a^y).

Airedale Terrier

A fairly simple breed in colour terms since all dogs are homozygous for B, C, D, E, g, m, S and t. There is only likely to be any heterozygosity at the agouti locus where the breed has the alleles a^s and a^t.

Little (1957) does not accept this but Whitney (1971) does and it would explain the variable degrees of tan in the breed. Dogs of a^sa^s type would be more tan-marked than would those which were a^ta^t. Dogs of the type a^sa^t would be like a^sa^s or intermediate, possibly the latter. The shrinkage of black with time supports the Whitney view.

According to Little (1957) piebald spotting (s^p) occurred in the breed in America during the 1920s. One can assume such things to be rare enough to be ignored. Small white markings on extremities will occur from time to time and usually disappear. These are only modifiers of the S allele.

Basenji

This breed is largely homozygous for most loci and all carry B, C, E, g, m, s^i and t. The s^is^i condition of Irish spotting leads to the characteristic white front and collar. Individuals may vary in the amount of white because of plus and minus modifiers. The only locus at which variation exists in the A locus where the breed can have a^ya^y, a^ya^t or a^ta^t. Most animals are the first type and the last named kind are rare. Little (1957) records the existence of creams which he attributes to the d allele but most Basenjis are DD.

Basset Hound

Any recognised hound colour is acceptable in this breed. The homozygous alleles are C, D, g and M. It is probable also that B is carried in duplicate in most animals. The same is true of E but Little (1957) suggests that e may exist in some animals. Ticking is known and would be caused by the presence of T either singly or in duplicate but most Bassets are tt.

Little (1957) believes that c^{ch} is present and accounts for the depth of tan pigment but equally one could account for this by Iljin's Int series (see page 90).

The major genes determining colour in the breed are the A and S series. Dogs can carry a^y or a^t in various combinations and also S or s^p. Irish-type spotting may occur and if so indicates the presence of s^i.

Tricolours will be $a^t a^t s^p s^p$ plus all the other genes that are common to all members of the breed. Black-and-tans will be $a^t a^t SS$ and tans $a^y a^t$ or $a^y a^y$ with SS. Tan-and-white piebalds will be $a^y a^y$ or $a^y a^t$ with $s^p s^p$.

Beagle

This breed is homozygous for g and m and probably also for C and D. Little (1957) considers that c^{ch} is present to account for variations in the intensity of tan but it is possible that this stems from Int alleles (see page 90).

Livers can occur suggesting that b exists but most Beagles will be BB and very few Bb. Ticking occurs due to TT or Tt but in the remaining animals the combination will be tt.

Most animals carry a^s but in those with more extended black markings a^t may be present either as $a^t a^t$ or with a^s. According to Little (1957) black animals have been reported which implies that A is or was present in the breed. However this could be a result of breeders' errors since animals with small amounts of tan may be recorded as black.

White markings in the breed are mostly caused by $s^p s^p$ but in more extreme forms of white may be caused by $s^p s^w$ or even $s^w s^w$. The presence of modifiers of the S series makes it a difficult one to assess and it could be that s^i also exists in the breed. When no white is seen animals must be S– or SS.

Of the extension series E is present and in some cases ee can also occur and lead to an all-tan animal with all the black faded.

Bearded Collie

This breed has only recently begun to achieve importance and little has been studied as regards colour. The breed is probably homozygous for C, m and t.

Most dogs are $s^i s^i$ and carry a white collar but self-colours (S) and extreme whites ($s^w s^w$) can occur.

At the B locus both B and b exist with the latter being a cause of the sand-and-white colours which have liver noses. Blues (dd) can occur but most dogs are DD or Dd. Greying, due to the G allele, is common but many dogs remain black and are obviously gg. At the A and E loci the situation is unclear. Black masks (E^m) can be present or absent (EE) and dogs can carry A but it is not certain whether fawns are caused by a^y or by e. In view of the origins of the breed it is most likely to be a^y than e but proof is not available.

Bedlington Terrier

The breed is honozygous for the alleles D, G, m and t and possibly S. White markings can occur and if sizeable may be due to s^i but are more probably modifiers of the S allele. The breed may also be EE but Little (1957) suggests that the e allele exists. At the A locus there exists A or a^t and at other loci alternatives are B/b and C/c^{ch}.

Acceptable colours in the breed are blue, liver and sandy with or without tan points. In all cases animals are born darker. Blues are black at birth and lighten by about six months of age; sandy pups are born liver and lighten by a similar age. This fading of colour is caused by the presence of GG and the light pigment in the breed is a result of deliberate selection of pale colours.

The various colours are of the formulae given below:

Blues are AABBCCEE together with the DDGGmmSStt of all members of the breed. An A allele could be a^t, a B changed to b and an E to e without altering the basic effect.

Livers are AAbbCCEE and again an A or E could be changed to a^t or e without visible effect.

Sandy dogs are AAbbc^{ch}c^{ch}EE and again an A could be a^t and an E changed to e without phenotypic effect.

All three colours are altered to have tan points if the AA or Aa^t combination becomes a^{t}a^t and if a C allele is changed to c^{ch} in blues or livers then these will become paler. Some sandy animals are very pale and appear almost cream. This may be a result of ee combining with c^{ch}c^{ch} to cause an almost white effect.

Belgian Shepherd Dog

This breed is seen in four basic varieties: Groenendael which is long-coated and black, Tervueren which is long-coated and red, Laekenois which is wire-coated and red and Malinois which is short-coated and red. The actual length/type of coat will tend to alter the expression of colour and it is known that variations of the main colour types do exist. Thus grey and black-and-tan Tervuerens have been seen.

Colour data has been produced by Burnez and Burnez (1972) and Burnez *et al* (1972) and by Robinson (1987 in press). It does appear that the Tervueren is of the dominant sable colour (a^y) and the data suggest that the Groenendael black is dominant to sable and thus A. Hirschfeld (1933) is cited by Winge (1950) as having produced ten black-and-tans from a Groenendael/black-and-tan Doberman which might imply a recessive black but Robinson holds the view that some 'recessive' black Belgian Shepherds are actually black-and-tans (a^{t}a^t). Robinson also maintains that the 'grey' Tervueren is caused by the c^{ch} allele though he describes it simply as ch. It is likely that Laekenois/Malinois colours are identical in genetic terms to those of the Tervueren but altered in their expression by differential coat type.

Bernese Mountain Dog

This breed is likely to be homozygous for C, D, E, g, m and t. Most dogs carry s^{i}s^i but solid colours (S) and extreme whites (s^w) can occur. At the A locus A and a^t exist and possibly a^y also causing so-called russet-brown dogs which may, if they have liver noses, be bb but otherwise carry B.

Bloodhound

This old breed is generally homozygous for g, m, S and t but Whitney (1971) does speak of a white hound from black-and-tan parents. This would suggest that s^p or s^w was present in the breed but it is not likely to be common. Occasional white toes or chest spots in pups will be due to modifiers of the S allele.

Liver and blue are infrequent suggesting that b and d are rare alleles in the breed and most animals will be BBDD in genotype.

Variations in the depth of tan occur and Little (1957) claims this is caused by c^{ch} but I would prefer the Int series of Iljin as the explanation. Most members of the breed will be CC.

The main locus at which variation occurs is thus the agouti one and it is possible that three alleles of this series exist namely a^y, a^s and a^t.

Black-and-tan hounds will be $a^s a^s$ or $a^s a^t$ or $a^t a^t$ with the amount of tan decreasing as one moves from the first named to the last.

Red-and-tan hounds will be $a^y a^s$ or $a^y a^t$ and the so-called tawny hounds will be $a^y a^y$.

Border Terrier

This breed is probably homozygous for B, D, m, S and t and may be homozygous for C also. However the c^{ch} allele may be present and cause paling of colour or it may be a result of Int alleles.

The acceptable colours in the breed are red-wheaten, grizzle and blue-and-tan.

It seems certain that a^y is present in the breed along with a^s and possibly a^t. E and e are also likely and G and g.

Blue-and-tans are likely to be caused by the same genetic arrangement as in Bedlingtons, that is, $a^t a^t EEGG$. If any a^t allele is replaced by a^s then tan areas will be more extensive. The G allele may be homozygous or carried along with g without affecting the visible colour.

Wheaten is a less understood colour and in this breed it could be caused by $a^y a^y EE$ along with gg. An alternative would be $a^y a^y ee$ and this may be the better explanation.

Grizzle is an unclear term and may refer to a brindle caused by combinations of a^s and a^t with Ee^{br} or $e^{br} e^{br}$. Grizzle could be no more than a few lighter hairs in the dark areas as is seen in the Welsh Terrier (see page 101) and not due to e^{br} but to modifiers.

Borzoi (Russian Wolfhound)

The Borzoi is homozygous for the following alleles: B, D, g, m and t.

White is a predominant colour in the breed suggesting that the extreme white piebald allele s^w is common but less extreme white also exists suggesting that s^p is present and even solid coloured types which would be S. The s^i allele may be present but is likely to be rare.

Solid colours will carry A but the more common alleles of the series are likely to be a^y and a^t. The latter will lead to the formation of tricolours when present with alleles of the S series other than S itself.

Although the term brindle is sometimes used in this breed it is doubtful if e^{br} exists. Most Borzois are EE although some may carry ee or Ee. The so-called brindle is probably some aspect of a^y with or without a^t.

Markings vary from red through orange to fawn or lemon and these are probably variations of $a^y a^y$ coupled with paling factors of the Int series or by the presence of c^{ch}. This latter allele is present in the breed along with C.

Boston Terrier

A breed that is homozygous for one allele at most loci. It is known to be BBCCDDe^{br}e^{br}ggmmtt and thus only shows variation at the S and A loci.

The white pattern of the breed is characteristic of the s^i allele and most animals are probably s^{i}s^i with minus modifiers but some may be s^{i}s^p or even s^{i}s^w. Both latter types would be likely to exhibit more white. The fact that all-white animals are known, though disqualified, suggests that the s^{w}s^w type of genotype exists.

Most animals are a^{y}a^y but the fact that black coats are known implies that A is also present, either as AA or more probably as Aa^y. This is not, however, certain and it could represent selection for darkening modifiers of the basic brindle pattern in the breed.

All animals are e^{br}e^{br} but because breeders have selected for darker and darker coats some variations of this pattern have occurred. In some animals the lighter bands of the brindle have become reduced or almost indistinguishable and breeders refer to this as 'seal brindle'. It could be that the so-called black is merely an extension of this selective procedure.

Boxer

In some respects the Boxer is an easy breed to understand since it has only two acceptable colours—brindle and red/fawn. However it is by no means certain whether the fawn coloration is caused by ee or by a^{y}a^y. Little (1957) gives some data to suggest that the cause of red/fawn in this breed is a^{y}a^y and if this is so the crossing of fawn Boxers and yellow Labradors (ee) should give rise to black pups of the formula Aa^{y}Ee yet according to Cattanach (1978) fawns have occurred in such crosses thus casting doubt on Little's theory.

Until Cattanach or others publish their findings we must treat the colour inheritance of this breed with some caution. However we can probably conclude that this breed is BBCCDDggmmtt and that alternative alleles exist at the E and S loci with probably a^{y}a^y present at the A locus. If, however, fawn is caused by ee then the A locus will be AA.

Brindles are caused by e^{br} either in duplicate or in single dose. Brindles of the e^{br}e^{br} type will only produce brindle offspring but it is likely that most brindles are Ee^{br} or E^{m}e^{br}. The presence of E^m will give rise to a black mask white E will not do so. Two fawns cannot give rise to brindles but because the brindle allele may occasionally give only very faint brindle markings some can be mistaken for fawns and this could account for alleged fawn × fawn matings producing brindles.

A dog with no white markings is probably carrying at least one S allele and even those which are S? may have small white markings on the chest or forehead because of modifying genes. Those dogs with white markings on the feet, legs, chest, throat and muzzle and around the neck are probably s^{i}s^i or s^{i}s^w.

Because s^w exists in the breed many all-white or almost all-white pups will occur (s^{w}s^w) from time to time. According to Cattanach (1978) there is some doubt as to whether or not the s^i allele really is in the breed. He argues that most dogs will give rise to mismarked whites which is unlikely if s^{i}s^i is the main genetic combination. However the Irish spotting allele is a difficult one. Boxer breeders have, for years, been selecting for flashily marked dogs and it could be that they have been seeking minus modifiers which account for the flashy markings as much as do the s^i alleles. Perhaps the s^i allele is not totally dominant over s^w and that the 'best marked' Boxers are actually a combination of the two alleles, thus ensuring that whites will occur from such stock.

Breeders with excessive white problems would be well advised to use at least one mate that is SS in genotype if these can be isolated but if they insist upon flashy markings they must learn to live with a proportion of mismarked and unsaleable stock.

Briard

A French breed of sheepdog basically found as black or fawn. The colour inheritance of the breed has only recently been examined (Willis 1978b). It is clearly homozygous for B, g, m, S and t.

At the C locus C exists and possibly also c^{ch} while at the A locus there is A (accounting for black) and a^t which can give rise to bicolours, unacceptable in some countries but not prohibited in the USA. Fawns are either caused by a^y or by E and some doubt exists. The presence of blacks, fawns and bicolours in matings of two blacks is evidence that all three colours cannot be from the same series. Some blacks have white hairs along the back and the cause is not known. White markings on chest, toes and so on are small and obviously modifiers of the S allele but this would not be true of white hairs through the coat. So-called grey dogs do occur and this may be the result of dd combinations.

Bulldog (English)

This breed allows a much wider range of colour patterns than does the previously discussed Boxer but in many ways colour genes are similar. The breed is homozygous for B, D, g, m and possibly t though Little (1957) suggests that the ticking factor T may be present in some specimens. At the E locus the alleles present are E^m, E and e^{br} as in Boxers. The major difference between Boxers and Bulldogs is that the latter have all four alleles of the S series S, s^i, s^p and s^w while at the A locus the Bulldog has A, a^y and a^t.

Because whites are not frowned upon in Bulldogs as they are in Boxers animals can vary from solid colours devoid of white through all combinations down to all-white.

Outside of white the main colours met with are shades of fawn and brindle. Most Bulldogs are CC and thus fully pigmented unless carrying white alleles but c^{ch} may be present to account for paler tans. Black (A) and black-and-tan (a^{t}a^t) occur in Bulldogs but not in Boxers although black is generally frowned upon and the A allele likely to be rare as a consequence. The same is true of black-and-tan but since this is a recessive allele it may linger on longer than A.

Bullmastiff

A breed identical in colour genetics to the Boxer with the exception of the S locus where it carries only the S allele. Breeders of Bullmastiffs should thus check with the details given for Boxers.

Although originating from Bulldog–Mastiff crosses the Bullmastiff has been selected to have no white markings and hence all s^i, s^p and s^w alleles have been lost or are at such a low frequency as to be unimportant. White markings as spots on the extremities and chest can occur but are minus modifiers of the S allele. They will usually disappear but if breeders were to deliberately mate such animals together white-marked dogs could increase and markings persist.

Bull Terrier

According to Burns and Fraser (1966) the coat colour inheritance of this breed is unclear but Little (1957) seems to find difficulty only in respect of fawn markings. We can say that the breed is homozygous for B, C, D, g, m and t. At one time blues were known suggesting that d existed but it is now either lost or very rare indeed. At the E locus the alleles present are E and e^{br} while at the A locus there is A, a^y and a^t. At the S locus all the alleles except s^P are present (that is, S, s^i and s^w).

Essentially Bull Terriers can be classed as white or coloured but the main difference lies at the S locus. Any coloured dog must be SS, Ss^i or Ss^w and in each case would show no white markings. If he is $s^i s^i$ then Irish spotting will be seen on chest, legs, feet, head or collar while if $s^w s^w$ the dog will be white.

Some whites do have a patch over the eye or ear but these are only plus modifiers of the s^w allele, a feature seen also in Sealyhams. The Brindle dog is Ee^{br} or $e^{br}e^{br}$ while red fawns are $a^y a^y$ with EE. Black-and-tans carry $a^t a^t$ and solid blacks at least one A. White markings will occur in all cases if the necessary allele of the spotting series is present.

At one time great controversy raged in this breed over what were called colour-bred whites, that is to say, whites born of coloured parents or ancestry. Breeders were afraid that, used in white lines, such dogs would cause parti-colours to appear. In fact the s^P allele is not present so only all-white or Irish spotting is possible and whites from coloured ancestry are no risk whatsoever. Briggs (1940) published a paper showing that colour-bred whites did not cause the problems breeders erroneously imagined but, until 1950, breeders of white Bull Terriers had maintained a pledge not to use coloured dogs. This is perhaps an ideal illustration of how a lack of knowledge of genetic principles acted as a barrier to breed improvement. Much of the genetics of colour in the breed was set out by Briggs and Kaliss in 1942 yet lay unheeded by most breeders.

Cairn Terrier

A complex breed for colour because the long coat does not aid descriptions and the breed can change gradually in colour as dogs age.

The breed is homozygous for B, D, m, S and t and though mostly CC some animals carry c^{ch}. Most dogs are gg but Little (1957) believes that the G allele exists in the breed. If so this could lead to a gradual greying of black pigment.

At the extension locus Little (1957) believes that E^m, E and e^{br} are present. The breed requires a dark mask suggesting the E is unlikely to be common. Most animals are brindle with a whole series of lighter shades among the hairs due either to c^{ch} or to Int series alleles. Many animals carry CC.

The A alleles present are a^y and a^t, the latter causing darker poins while the former is likely to be present in duplicate in wheatens which are $a^y a^y E^m E^m$ or perhaps $a^y a^y$ with EE or $E^m E$.

Chesapeake Bay Retriever

This American 'water' breed is of fairly simple genetic constitution as far as coat colour is concerned. It is very probably homozygous at all loci with a formula AAbbCCDDEEggmmSStt and thus brings about an all-brown coloration. There are, however, several shades of brown ranging from dark tan through to what is termed 'dead-grass' or 'straw' shades. This variation in shade is either a consequence of c^{ch} alleles or Int alleles.

White markings are considered to be blemishes but may occur as modifiers of the S allele.

Chihuahua

Although this breed has long and short-haired varieties the colour genetics are identical and complex. The complexity arises from the fact that aside from homozygosity at g, m and t every allele of the other series is present in the breed, though obviously not in individual dogs. We thus have A/a^y/a^s/A^t, B/b, C/c^{ch}, D/d, E^m/E/e^{br}/e, S/s^i/s^p/s^w.

As far as white markings are concerned these will follow the established pattern described earlier (see page 71). Blue dilutes (dd) are rare as are livers (bb). Tans or fawns can be caused by ee or various combinations of a^{y}a^y.

Chow Chow

Although the long hair can confuse some of the shades in this breed it is basically red, black or blue in colour with each of these colours existing also in paler shades.

The breed is homozygous for B, g, m, S and t so that essentially it is a black breed as opposed to a liver (bb) one. White markings when they occur are modifiers of the S allele.

Most dogs are AA and hence solid-coloured and though shaded sables (a^{y}a^t) and black with tan extremities (a^{t}a^t) are known they are rare and selected against.

Reds are either a^{y}a^y or ee, blacks are AA and blues carry dd as opposed to DD or Dd. Pale colours stem from c^{ch} or Int alleles which, in unison with a^{y}a^y or ee cause cream.

Clumber Spaniel

This breed has a fairly simple genetic make-up for coat colour with all members being AABBDDeeggmm. Most are tt but since ticking can occur some may be Tt or even TT. Most markings are restricted to the head which means that the type of white in the breed is the extreme spotting type s^w and most animals will be homozygous for this allele. Some dogs with more extensive markings may carry s^p but it is doubtful if this allele is common.

Because the breed carries ee black markings in the coat are not present but the BB composition leads to black noses. The colour of the markings is lemon or orange with the former being favoured. This suggests that either the Int series is involved and by acting together with ee causes variation of shade or, more probably the c^{ch} allele is present along with C in the breed. Possibly orange dogs are CC and others are Cc^{ch} or even c^{ch}c^{ch} although this latter combination may lead to almost pure white.

Cocker Spaniel (English and American)

Although very different in appearance these two types of Cocker have common descent and carry more or less the same genetic structure for coat colour. The Cocker in one or other of its types has been the subject of more coat-colour studies than most with papers by Barrows and Phillips (1915), Phillips (1938) and Little (1949) amongst others.

The Cocker is homozygous only for g and m but all English and most American Cockers are DD with a few of the latter breed being Dd and, very occasionally blues (dd) do occur.

At other loci the alleles carried are $A/a^y/a^s/a^t$, B/b, C/c^{ch}, E/e, $S/s^p/s^w$ and T/t.

Essentially Cockers can be divided into solid or self-coloured animals (into which category can be put bicolours) and the parti-colours which carry white spots or patches.

Solid coloured dogs all carry A and S and generally T in single or double dose. Solid blacks also carry E and B in single or double dose. If A is replaced by $a^t a^t$ then the dog will be bicolour. If B is replaced by bb then the dog will be liver but with a black nose. The difference between AA and Aa^t animals is not phenotypically obvious in the majority of cases but sometimes the latter type may show a reddish tinge in the coat at those areas where brown would be seen in $a^t a^t$ dogs that is, on the feet and parts of the head.

Reds and Golds are usually carrying A, B and S in single doses but carry ee instead of EE or Ee. Such reds will vary in shade from dark red through to gold according to whether CC, Cc^{ch} or $c^{ch}c^{ch}$ is present. Because B is present such animals will have black noses. Blacks which are Ee can, when mated together give rise to reds but reds of type ee cannot produce blacks since the ee combination causes fading of the black pigment.

However Phillips (1938) recorded the existence of a^y in the breed and if $a^y a^y$ is present in place of A– but with EE or Ee such animals will be red. If a red of type AAee is mated to a red of type $a^y a^y EE$ then the progeny will be $Aa^y Ee$ and be black. According to Little (1957) such blacks have been produced and generally have a clear deep colour. Occasionally they have a reddish sheen. Since $a^y a^y$ reds are rare one can often suppose that reds giving rise to blacks indicate mismatings but one is better to check before condemning the breeder or the bitch concerned.

If bb is present in place of BB or Bb but with ee then such dogs will be red or gold but will carry liver noses.

All these solid-coloured dogs can have white spots occurring which are regarded as mismarkings by the Standard. Generally such spots are modifiers of the S allele and frequently they would be lost in early life, but not always.

In relation to mismarkings some difference may exist between reds and blacks. According to Little (1957) who analysed the data on 1842 blacks and 1058 reds from red × black matings only 25% of reds were mismarked compared with 33% of blacks. As Little points out, white hairs can easily be missed in the paler reds so this difference may be spurious. However, 48% of mismarked reds had a forehead spot compared with only 0.32% of mismarked blacks. The cause of this is unknown.

Turning to parti-coloured Cockers the main difference between these and solid-coloured dogs is that the former carry $s^p s^p$ in place of SS or Ss^p. Colour patterns will be exactly like those of solid colours but with white patches being present. Because of these white patches the ticking factor (TT or Tt) will become obvious in the white areas whereas it was not apparent in solid-coloured dogs. Breeders term these ticked dogs roans but the roan gene R is not confirmed (see page 74). Although blue roans are known in the breed they do not generally carry dd but are really black-and-white dogs with black ticking in the white areas. This is an example of misuse of the term 'blue'.

Little provides some evidence that black parti-colours carry less white than do red parti-colours. In his book (1957) he gives data on 385 blacks and 432 reds and shows that the amount of colour was less in the blacks. He used a simple scale of 1 to 10 with increasing number indicating increased amount of white. The average grade of blacks was 3.93 while the average grade of reds was 8.11. Little claims that progeny (red or black) from black

April _____ ,1998

To Whom it May Concern,

I Rose Illiano am selling this:

1972 Dhrysler Satellite Sebring
Serial Number RP23M2C193757

"As Is", with no warranty as to emission testing or condition of the vehicle.

_____   _____
Purchaser Signature   Date

_____   _____
Witness Signature   Date

Tail curl

willie Pg 108

Herman _____ × Oklahoma Dawn
all carried their tails over their backs like
the elephant. ____ tail act _____
carriage allowing it to be carried forward
over the back.

22 lower teeth
20 upper teeth

Cochrane Pg 84

A-5-t+
(what color would an
At At b b

mothers have more colour than the progeny (red or black) from red mothers. The former graded 4.85 on average while the latter were 7.15 but this is misleading because the red dams produced more red progeny and hence more white. If blacks from red or black dams are compared and reds from red or black dams then the differences are less obvious and probably do not reach significance.

It is dangerous to read too much into colours when trying to evaluate non-colour aspects but the red v black Cocker has long been debated and some interesting aspects have been noted (see page 50).

Collie (Rough or Smooth)

Because of the variation in coat length different phenotypic effects may occur in these two varieties of Collie but essentially they are identical for colour of the coat. Homozygosity exists for the alleles B, C, g and t and possibly also for E.

As the agouti locus it is possible that only a^y and a^t exist so that the breed can be clear sable ($a^y a^y$), shaded sable ($a^y a^t$) or bicolour ($a^t a^t$). However all Collies carry white markings (S is absent from the breed) so that all the above types carry white and the bicolours actually become tricolours (black/white/tan).

The white alleles carried are s^i and s^w but it could be that s^p also exists. However, s^p would give a less uniform pattern than s^i and since Collies carry very clearly defined white areas on legs, collar and face it is most likely that s^i is the causal factor rather than s^p. Since all-whites or almost all-whites do occur s^w must be present and when homozygous for this all colours will be inhibited. Such dogs would be selected against because all-white is against the Standard.

The Collie colour is complicated by the fact that it carries M and m. The merling series is not carried in many breeds (most are mm) and brings with it problems. In the homozygous state MM dogs are all-white, usually deaf and frequently have defective eyesight. This is dealt with in greater detail elsewhere (see page 70) so need not be enlarged upon here other than to point out to breeders that all merles must be Mm and that if one crosses two merles a quarter of the offspring are likely to be MM.

In heterozygous state the M allele is not always obvious. In $a^y a^y$ dogs the Mm condition may not appear any different phenotypically to mm. In $a^y a^t$ animals Mm may show some of the merle pattern at birth and less thereafter. In $a^t a^t$ dogs Mm will be seen as a blue merle and sometimes will exhibit wall eye (see page 70).

According to Little (1957) the breed is mainly DD but some animals are Dd and hence dd can occur at intervals. According to Little dd would act upon sables to give a duller, flatter and lighter colour. In $a^t a^t$ dogs it would give rise to a pale blue or grey colour.

Another kind of so-called grey is seen in the Collie and has been reported on by Ford (1969) and Lund *et al* (1970) among others. This is a colour dilution associated with canine cyclic neutropenia (see page 241). Ford (1969) presents data on 39 litters in which silver grey appears and the data are summarized in Table 15.

Ford does not clearly explain if the blues she had were blue merles or caused by dd and I have assumed the former. The silver grey pups all died by the age of 12 months except for two which died soon afterwards so this colour can be accepted as a lethal. Lethality is discussed in detail elsewhere (see page 241) but it is important here to deal with the colour aspect. Ford's data show that the silver grey appears in the expected ratios that would ensure if it was caused by a simple autosomal recessive but this does not necessarily mean

Table 15

Parental and progeny colours of litters of Rough Collies in which grey pups appeared

Parental colours	Litters	Progeny colours				% Greys dead at 7 days
		Sable	Tricolour	White	Grey	
Sable × Sable	29	135	4	3	64	76.6
Sable × Tricolour	5	24	3	—	14	57.1
Tricolour × Tricolour	3	9	7	—	6	—
Sable × Blue Merle	2	9	—	—	8	62.5
Overall	39	177	14	3	92	67.4

Source Ford 1969.

that it is a colour allele as such. What is inherited as a simple autosomal recessive is the gene for cyclic neutropenia and this condition influences colour in a pleiotropic fashion in that the biochemical effect upon the blood has also been instrumental in causing some kind of interference with melanin formation. As a consequence dogs which inherit two neutropenia alleles have their colour modified. Sable dogs will become anything from a light beige to a silver grey (see Lund *et al* 1970). In contrast tricolours will lose their black colour—which fades to a deep grey—and the brown markings on the mask and eyebrows will become white, or as near white as to render identification difficult (Lund *et al* 1970 and Plate 18). White markings are not affected by this condition but coat texture is finer and may be wavier. Identification is possible very early in life (see Plate 19).

Ford (1969) estimated that 32% of American Collies carried the cyclic neutropenia allele but in view of its lethal nature the frequency of the allele will now have declined somewhat, although it may still be fairly high.

Dachshund (all Varieties)

The three coat-types complicate matters slightly in this breed but essentially they all carry similar alleles. Homozygosity exists for D, g, S and t.

If white markings occur they are modifiers of the S allele and usually will be lost in early life. At the E locus most dogs are EE but according to Burns and Fraser (1966) brindle (e^{br}) is known but rare. It may be that e also exists but this is not proven. Most dogs are CC but c^{ch} may occur and cause lightening of colour as might Int alleles. In essence this breed is colour determined by alleles of the A, B and M loci.

In black-nosed varieties there are three kinds $a^y a^y BB$ giving clear red, $a^y a^t BB$ giving dark red-sable and $a^t a^t BB$ giving black-and-tan. If one of the B alleles is changed for b then no phenotypic effect will be apparent. If BB becomes bb then the second series of colours will occur all of which will be brown-nosed. These will be $a^y a^y bb$ giving clear red, $a^y a^t bb$ giving clear but perhaps darker red and $a^t a^t bb$ which will be liver-and-tan.

As with the Collie the merle series exists in this breed with similar effects but breeders of Dachshunds refer to it as dappled. In the mm normal form coat colour will be determined by other loci but in the Mm form dogs will be dappled. In black animals Mm leads to a bluish-grey tinge, in liver animals to a beige and in deep red dogs it causes lighter red. In a^ya^y or a^ya^t animals the dappling effect is most apparent at birth and may disappear by adulthood. In a^ta^tMm animals the dappling will continue.

Dapple to dapple can lead to MM animals in 25% of cases and as with Collies this is white in colour although according to Little (1957) the white area is never as large as in Collies. Wall eye can occur as well as eye defects and also deafness (Reetz *et al* 1977) (see page 275).

Dalmatian

An interesting colour breed, the Dalmatian has a fairly simple genetic structure for colour being $CCDDggs^ws^wTT$. The characteristic pattern of white coat with spots distributed evenly over the body is caused by the joint action of s^ws^w and TT. Pups are born white or near white (indicative of s^ws^w) and then develop dominant ticking.

The fact that the colour pattern is spread over the body suggests that the breed is AA but Little (1957) records that tan spots on the face and legs are known which would indicate a^ta^t make-up.

Spots are either black or liver. Those with black spots are BB or Bb and those with liver are bb so liver spots will act as recessive to black as explained on page 66.

Most dogs are EE but some animals can have yellowish orange or lemon spots which might indicate ee is present.

Dandie Dinmont

Basically a simple colour structure with dogs being BBCCDDEEGGmmSStt and showing variation only at the agouti locus where a^ya^y, a^ya^t or a^ta^t can occur.

The colours in the breed are basically 'pepper' or 'mustard'. Pups are all born darker in shade than they finally become because the breed is GG and this leads to gradual greying. Those dogs with a^ta^t are black-and-tan becoming 'peppers' while those with a^ya^t or a^ya^y are dark sable and become 'mustard'. The a^ya^t type of 'mustard' will be the darker of the two.

'Peppers' without tan feet and such, may be Aa^t but the existence of the A allele is uncertain.

Deerhound

The breed has a complex colour make-up because it is basically brindle and the brindle allele is variable in expression. The breed is homozygous for B, D, g, m, S and t. Some dogs may carry s^i but they are rare. At the A locus A and a^y are present, at the C locus C and c^{ch} and at the E locus all four alleles E^m, E, e^{br} and e are present.

Generally E^m and E are rare and most dogs are $e^{br}e^{br}$ or ee. The darkest brindles will carry $a^ya^ye^{br}e^{br}CC$ and if one C allele is changed to c^{ch} a lighter colour will occur. If $c^{ch}c^{ch}$ is present the dog will be even lighter.

Reds and wheatens can occur and these would be a^ya^yee with either CC, Cc^{ch} or $c^{ch}c^{ch}$ according to shade with these getting lighter as one moves away from CC.

Blues may occur indicating dd is present. According to Wilson (1953) all-whites can occur which suggests that s^w may be present in some lines.

Dobermann

This breed is homozygous for a^t, C, E, g, m, S and t. Colour is thus determined by the B/b and D/d combinations and this was shown in detail in Table 3 (see page 11).

Different shades of brown or liver can occur and according to Little (1957) this is due to c^{ch}. I tend to prefer an explanation involving more modifiers and think Int alleles may exist. Some German lines have been selected to have very dark masks which are no longer tan but exhibit muddy splotches. This is not due to E^m but probably represents selection for darker and darker masks caused by modifiers similar to those giving white spots in the S locus.

Some Dobermanns can have white markings on the chest or feet which do not usually persist. These are caused by S modifiers. Rare all-whites are due to $s^w s^w$.

Elkhound

All Elkhounds are grey dogs and they are born black with grey hairs scattered in them. This is caused by the a^g allele and the breed is of colour formula $a^g a^g B B c^{ch} c^{ch} D D E^m E^m g g m m S S t t$. There have been cases of liver-coloured dogs in the USA and in Scandinavia which would be due to bb in place of BB.

The characteristic lightish bands in the coat are caused by c^{ch} and occasional white spots by S modifiers.

English Setter

This breed is homozygous for C, D, g, m and usually B but liver types (bb) are known. Ticking is caused by TT or Tt and is absent in tt dogs. The white coat is generally $s^p s^p$ but sometimes $s^w s^w$ animals occur which will show markings only on head and tail regions.

Dogs which carry A and E together and either heterozygously or homozygously will be black and white. Those which carry $a^t a^t$ with E will be tricoloured and those which are A with ee will have orange or lemon markings as will dogs which are $a^t a^t ee$ and the two types cannot be identified in physical appearance. In all these cases ticking (TT or Tt) or non-ticking (tt) can occur.

Field Spaniel

This breed is homozygous for D, g and m and carries similar genes for colour to the Cocker namely A/a^t B/b C/c^{ch} E/e $S/s^i/s^p/s^w$ and T/t. Most dogs are black but other colours are permitted and encouraged, especially in America. For details see Cocker Spaniel (see page 83).

Foxhound (English or American)

A breed that is more or less identical to the Beagle in coat colour (see page 77). The breed is homozygous for B, D, g and m and most dogs are CC with a few carrying c^{ch}. White markings are usually due to s^p but s^i and s^w individuals are known. In the American variety solid tan (ee) is known as are black-and-tans with no white ($a^t a^t$) and in both cases S is carried.

Fox Terrier (Smooth-haired or Wire-haired)

Coat length may alter colour appearance but both varieties carry identical colour genes. The breed is homozygous for B, C, D, g and m. Little (1957) records a line of liver-and-tans suggesting that bb was present but this allele is likely to be very rare.

The basic colour pattern is caused by a^s and a^t in various of the three alternatives with the white markings being due to s^p and s^w in various combinations. The greater the white areas the more s^w is involved. Ticking (TT or Tt) also occurs, especially in the Smooth variety but most dogs are tt.

At the E locus most dogs are EE but tan-and-white dogs are known. These could be caused by ee or alternatively by a^y. It is unclear which factor causes the colour. It is, of course, possible that $a^s a^s$ dogs could appear tan-and-white if the white markings are located in the normally black areas and thus hide that colour.

The so-called Hound marked animals are $a^s a^t$ or $a^t a^t$ with $s^p s^p$.

French Bulldog

Colour in this breed is similar to that of the English Bulldog (see page 81). French Bulldogs are homozygous for B, C, D, g, m and usually t although ticking (TT or Tt) does occur in some individuals. As with the English Bulldog all four alleles of the S series (S/s^i/s^p/s^w) exist but at the agouti locus only a^y. Most animals are brindle $e^{br}e^{br}$ but the e allele exists and in the ee state leads to fawns.

The white markings in the breed are irregular which is a sign of s^p and dogs with extreme white are s^w. The s^i allele is less certain because the symmetry usually associated with this allele is rare in the breed. Large spots on the chest which persist could be modifiers of S or s^i.

German Shepherd Dog

This breed has a complex colour inheritance as might be expected when many colours are generally permissible. The colour genetics of the breed have been described in detail elsewhere (Willis 1976) and more recently by Carver (1984). This constitutes only a summary.

The breed is homozygous for g, m and t. Most dogs are BB but some must be Bb because browns are known and are bb with liver noses and light eyes. Most animals are also DD but Dd types do occur because blues (dd) are known although, like livers, disqualified in most countries.

The main colour patterns are formed by the agouti series with a^s and a^t causing the black and tan colorations. Although Little (1957) denies the existence of a^s Willis (1976) put forward data on 4327 dogs which clearly showed distinction between the a^s and a^t alleles. Sable dogs occur and can be many shades ranging from grey through to golden. Most workers assume greys to be a^g but the distinction between grey and golden sables is not always clear although Carver's data (1984) suggest that a^y and a^g (he uses a^w) exist in that order of dominance. Certainly there is no doubt that sables of any type are dominant to black and tans and that to produce sable pups at least one parent must be sable (or grey). Most breeders use the term sable to identify either a golden or a grey dog.

At the extension locus E^m, E and e are known. The first two will allow black pigment to form but only E^m will produce a black mask. Dogs carrying ee will have the black pigment fade such that they will appear rather like golden sables as adults. They are, however, free of sable genes and can be distinguished from true sables by their red tipped tails in lieu of black. Carver (1984) clearly shows that E and e act in accordance with accepted theory. Brindle (e^{br}) was known in the breed and may be seen very rarely but is indeed a rarity in modern animals.

Most dogs are CC or Cc^{ch} but those with $c^{ch}c^{ch}$ may show bright tan pigment. In combination with ee the $c^{ch}c^{ch}$ type will be yellowish white. Little argued that this only occurred in conjunction with a^y but Carver (1984) rejects both theories. He favours the production of white as being a simple recessive. At the S locus most Shepherds are SS but extreme white spotting s^w may exist but Carver does not favour this and certainly his data, drawn from breeder records, suggest a simple recessive trait. He labels this w^h and considers it recessive to Non-white Wh. More information on whites seems called for.

Different shades of tan occur through the Int series. These lead to so-called colour paling which is aesthetically unpleasant but which is not associated with any physiological degeneration as many suppose.

According to Iljin the order of dominance of the Int allele is from cream to fawn through to tan, i.e. the lightest colours being the most dominant. Carver tends to support this with data drawn from US kennels seeking to produce black and cream animals.

All-blacks do exist in this breed but are clearly not caused by A as in most other breeds. If black were dominant then all blacks would have at least one black parent. Willis (1976) showed this to be untrue when only 55 in 115 blacks had at least one black parent. He proposed a two gene theory but more detailed analyses from Carver (1984) confirm the recessive nature of black in this breed and he puts it firmly into the agouti series as a. However most blacks tend not to be pure black but to carry some tan or greyish leg markings and there may be some modification of the $a^t a^t$ genotype.

Little (1957) refers to recessive black in the breed but did not follow it up while Burns and Fraser (1966) cite a case of a Border Collie showing that black is not necessarily in the same allelic series as sable/bicolour. Whitney (1971) also tries to explain away blacks of this kind but Carver's (1984) data which covered 564 blacks is clear evidence of the recessive nature of the colour.

Golden Retriever

The breed has the colour formula AABBDDggmmSStt and is thus a solid-coloured animal with a black nose. Various shades of golden colour occur in the breed and are due to variation at the C and E loci with C/C^{ch} and E/e alleles being present. The darkest colours will be CCEE and the very palest $c^{ch}c^{ch}$ee. The Int series may be involved.

White markings can occur on chest and extremities due to modifiers of the S locus and although Little (1957) has recorded s^i in the breed it must be very rare.

Gordon Setter

Only one basic colour is acceptable in this breed which is black with rich chestnut tan points. Most members of the breed will be of colour formula $a^t a^t$BBCCDDEEggmmSStt. A lighter-coloured tan may occur if c^{ch} replaces C or if Int series alleles are present. Little (1957) refers to all red animals which would be due to the replacement of EE with ee but since such animals are unacceptable the variety will not be established. White once existed in the breed but nowadays the white spots that can occur on chest and feet are modifiers of the S allele.

Great Dane

The breed is homozygous for B, C, g and t. At other loci the alternatives are A/a^y D/d E^m/E/e^{br}/e, M/m and S/s^p/s^w.

The breed can be split into two varieties, solid-coloured and Harlequin. Solid-coloured dogs can be black, fawn, brindle or blue and these will be dealt with first.

Blacks carry A–, D–, mmS– and either E^m or E or combinations of these. Fawns are, according to Little (1957), caused by a^{y}a^y and if they are black masked they will be E^m and if not EE. They will also carry D–mmS–. Burns and Fraser (1966) consider that the allele e may also exist in the breed and Little (1957) does not reject that possibility. In that event some fawns may be A–D–eemmS–.

Brindle dogs will occur when e^{br} is present in single or double dose. In black dogs this brindling may be hidden but in fawns it will be apparent. The mask of brindles will be black if E^{m}e^{br} is carried but will be brindled if Ee^{br} or e^{br}e^{br} is carried.

Blues will occur when D– is changed to dd. The best coloured blues will be diluted blacks, that is, A–ddmmS– with E^m or E combinations. Dilutes in fawn shades will be a duller shade and hence less favoured.

Harlequin Great Danes are very striking animals but very difficult to breed because the Standard insists upon irregular markings. According to Little, Harlequins all carry Mm and s^{p}s^p with AA. This causes an irregular distribution of black or grey patches on a white background. Ideally the breeder wants irregular but also causes greyish colour and Harlequin breeders thus are seeking something that is almost mutually exclusive. As a result many mismarkings are likely in Harlequin litters. If they bred for mms^{p}s^p they would get the required colour of spot but not the irregularity and the markings would be too extensive. The gene for merle can be present without white markings as in AAMmSS animals but if present with s^{w}s^w the white areas will be too extensive and hence s^w is likely to be a rare allele.

Sponenberg's (1985) work suggests that the M^h version of merle is present and may be the cause of Harlequin dogs rather than the M version though both may well exist in the breed.

Greyhound

This is a breed in which colour is considered to be immaterial and hence a wide range of possibilities exist. The first major work on the breed came from Warren (1927) and it is believed to be homozygous for B, g, m and t and at other loci alternatives are A/a^y, C/c^{ch}, D/d, E/e^{br}/e and S/s^i/s^p/s^w.

Two types of fawn-red occur caused by either ee or a^{y}a^y. Reds will be a^{y}a^y E– and fawns A–ee. Crossing the two could thus give rise to blacks of the type Aa^{y}Ee as well as reds and fawns.

Brindles will occur with e^{br} and various blues and other dilutes will stem from dd alleles. The effects of dd will depend upon what other alleles are present for the phenotypic appearance.

When white markings are absent S is present either singly or in duplicate. Other white markings will depend upon the various combinations of s^i, s^p and s^w as was discussed previously.

Depth of tan pigment will depend upon c^{ch} but also upon Int series alleles.

Griffon Bruxellois

A relatively simple breed for colour. The favoured colour is reddish with a dark mask and most animals would be of the formula $a^y a^y BBCCDDE^m E^m ggmmSStt$. If the black mask is absent EE is present but in the wire-coated dog this is not obvious. According to Little (1934) a^t also exists in the breed and in the form $a^t a^t$ will give bicoloured animals.

Identical colour forms occur in the smooth-haired Griffon or Brabançon.

Irish Setter

A breed that is expected to be a rich golden chestnut colour and as such has a simple genetic composition for colour. Most dogs will be AABBCCDDeeggmmSStt.

Marchlewski (1930a) reported black specimens and Little (1957) cites one case in 1197 pups of the breed. Such dogs would be EE or, more probably Ee, and represent mutations of the e allele. Burns and Fraser (1966) state that black-and-tans and shaded sables are known in the breed which would suggest that A has mutated to a^t or a^y respectively. White spots are not uncommon and represent modifiers of the S allele. Some Red-and-White Setters are known and these are caused by the presence of $s^p s^p$.

Irish Terrier

Another relatively simple colour breed. Animals are basically $a^y a^y BBCCDDEE$-ggmmSStt with pups being born darker and fading as they get older. Variations in shade are probably due to c^{ch} and white markings when they occur are modifiers of the S allele.

Irish Water Spaniel

Yet another Irish breed of relatively easy genetic structure for coat colour. Dogs are a rich puce liver and this is due to the following colour form: AAbbCCDDEEggmmSStt. Again c^{ch} may be present to give some variation in shade. Because the breed is bb noses are liver. Some bicolours ($a^t a^t$) are known in this breed but are rare.

Irish Wolfhound

The breed is homozygous a^y, B, D, g, m, S and t. Most dogs are brindle e^{br} with some wheatens due to ee. At the C locus most are CC but c^{ch} is likely and causes variation in shade as will Int alleles. White spots will be due to S modifiers but Little (1957) reports occasional white dogs. These could be $c^d c^d$ if bearing black noses but are more likely to be variations of faded yellow and be $c^{ch} c^{ch} ee$ as in most white German Shepherds. Such whites would show dirty yellow markings in some areas.

Keeshond

This breed is homozygous for B, D, E, g, m, S and t. Since pups are born very dark in colour with scattered grey hairs and then change to a wolf-grey or ash-grey the possible explanation is that they are all $a^g a^g$ like the Elkhound. They would also be CC but c^{ch} may exist and cause banding of lighter areas.

Orange sables are known, sometimes called tawny and this might suggest that $a^y a^y$ is present. However it could be that a^g and a^y are the same and that variation of shade from grey to golden is due to modifiers. This would tie in with German Shepherd colours.

The explanation for the spectacles of Keeshonden is unclear but doubtless represents selection of modifier genes.

Kerry Blue Terrier

Another relatively simple colour breed of Irish origin. It is, however, misnamed in colour terms since the so-called Blue is not due to BBdd but to greying caused by the G allele. The breed is basically AABBCCDDEEmmSStt with either GG, Gg or gg. All pups are born black and those carrying GG or Gg will become blue ranging from a very deep slate colour through to a light silvery form. Those dogs which are gg will stay black and thus be unacceptable for the standard. The shades of blue may stem from the fact that GG gives a different form to Gg. If the Gg type is favoured then gg animals are bound to occur. Although not really suitable for exhibition they can be bred from and mated to GG dogs will give 100% Gg whereas Gg animals mated together will give about 25% blacks.

White spotting in the breed is due to S modifiers.

King Charles Spaniel (all Types)

This breed is seen in various forms which have common origin but are distinguished by size or colour. The King Charles is a black-and-tan breed and likely to be of formula $a^t a^t$ BBCCDDEEggmmSStt with white hairs on the chest stemming from S modifiers.

The Tricolour is essentially the same but bears white markings caused by $s^i s^i$ or perhaps $s^i s^p$ in place of SS.

The Ruby version is a rich chestnut red and represents a change from the King Charles in that EE is replaced by ee and AA for $a^t a^t$. White markings can result from S modifiers and are unacceptable when on the feet but tolerated on the breast or head. Intensity of colour is most sought after suggesting modifiers.

Blenheims are versions of the Ruby with $s^i s^i$ in place of SS and the 'spot' of red chestnut colour on the forehead represents deliberate selection for modifiers of the s^i allele.

Cavalier King Charles Spaniels can be any of the above colour combinations although usually chestnut and white.

Labrador Retriever

There is ample evidence that the yellow colour in this breed is due to the ee combination rather than $a^y a^y$ because matings to a sable Collie ($a^y a^t$) produced blacks (Burns and Fraser 1966). If the yellow Labrador were $a^y a^y$ this would be impossible.

The breed is thus AACCDDggmmSStt in all cases and shows alternative alleles only at the B and E loci. The alternatives are B or b and E or e. Dogs carrying at least one B and one E will be black with black noses (BBEE, BbEE, BBEe, BbEe). Yellows will occur when there are two e alleles present so that BBee or Bbee will be yellow with black noses. A variation known as chocolate or liver appears and this is due to bb. All chocolate dogs will be bbEE or bbEe and, because black is diluted by the bb combination, these dogs will always have a pale nose and lips. Any dog which is bbee will be yellow but will have a pale nose and lips so that yellows carrying two chocolate genes can be identified in this case.

White spots are due to S modifiers and it is not impossible that c^{ch} exists in the breed leading to variation in the intensity of yellow. Breeders wishing to check the details of the main colours should consult a comprehensive paper by Templeton *et al* (1977) which shows all the necessary facts.

Lakeland Terrier

Very similar to the Airedale in colour form the breed is probably homozygous for B, C, E, g, m, S and t. At the agouti locus a^s and a^t exist with more tan being found on $a^s a^s$ types. At the D locus D and d may exist because blues are known but the definition is not clear and they may be caused by other factors. Reds are known suggesting that ee can occur in place of EE and since the tan is required to be pale to distinguish the breed from Welsh Terriers this could mean c^{ch} or Int alleles are involved.

Maltese

The colour in this breed is stipulated as white but the exact nature of that white in genetic terms is unclear. It is likely to be $s^w s^w$ because cream spots are found and this is less common in those whites formed by dilutions caused by $eec^{ch}c^{ch}$. Black noses are required and found suggesting that B rather than b is present. The probable genetic make up is $AABBc^{ch}c^{ch}DDeeggmms^w s^w tt$.

Mastiff

Colours in this breed are brindle and various shades of fawn from dark through to apricot or silver. Colour genes will be similar to the Bullmastiff (see page 81) except at the C locus. In general the breed is $a^y a^y BBDDggmmSStt$ with variation at the C locus (C or c^{ch}) and the E ($E^m E$ or e^{br}). Brindles carry e^{br} in single or double dose while fawns are E^m or E depending upon whether or not a black mask is present. Variations of the fawn colour will depend upon the combination of C and c^{ch} with the c^{ch} allele causing silver fawns. The Int series may also be involved, white markings probably are modifiers of the S allele with all-whites unknown.

Newfoundland

The breed accepts three colours: black, liver and Landseer (black-and-white). The breed is likely to be homozygous for A C and E as well as g and m. Blacks would be AAB–CCD–EEggmmS– and could carry TT, Tt or tt without the version being obvious. Browns or livers would carry bb and rufus polygenes (not obvious in blacks) could lead to variable shades of brown/liver. The Landseer version differs from the black in carrying $s^p s^p$

instead of S–. This means that two blacks can produce Landseers but two Landseers cannot give rise to blacks. It is quite feasible when using brown carrying and Landseer lines to produce bbs^{p}s^p dogs which would be brown and white (an unacceptable colour). Little (1957) records black and tan animals suggesting that a^{t}a^t exists but such dogs are likely to be infrequently seen. This same author also reports blues sometimes called greys and it is likely that these are dd in place of DD or Dd. These, too, could be mixed with s^{p}s^p to give grey-and-white (unacceptable) and the combination of bb and dd is not impossible to achieve which would be a sandy-colour.

Whitney (1971) reports ticking so that T exists in the breed. It is not visible in blacks but frequently seen in Landseers, particularly those in Britain. The so-called ECT Landseer is generally freer of ticking through selection against it and the avoidance of blacks (which could bring in the ticking allele).

Norwich Terrier

The basic colour of this breed is red but black-and-tans do occur. The former will be a^{y}a^y or a^{y}a^t with BBCCDDEEggmmSStt and the latter will be a^{t}a^t with the other colour genes.

Old English Sheepdog

This breed is AABBCCDDEEtt and carries variation at the G, M and S loci. Unlike other Collies black has been preferred to fawn so a^y and a^t have been lost. The blue nature of many dogs is very probably due to GG because pups are nearly black at birth. Gg and gg (non-blue) will also occur.

Merles exist as in other sheepdog breeds with similar results being caused by Mm and non merles are mm. The white markings in the breed are very clear suggesting that they are s^{i}s^i or may be Ss^p. Non-spotted types SS do occur but are less common.

Papillon

A breed that can be of several colours, mainly shades of red or fawn with or without white markings and also black-and-white. It is likely to be similar to the King Charles Spaniel in many respects. The breed is likely to be homozygous for B, D, g, m and t. Reds and fawns are either a^y– or ee with A and E also existing in the breed. At the S locus S and s^w exist along with s^p and s^i in various combinations.

Pekingese

A complex colour breed because of various shades and long hair. It is likely to be homozygous only for B, g, m and t. At other loci alternatives are A/a^y/a^t, C/c^{ch}/c^b/c, D/d, E^m/E/e and S/s^i/s^p/s^w. Parti-colours carry various combinations of the S series depending upon the degree of white.

Most sables or reds are a^{y}a^y but A (black) and a^{t}a^t (black-and-tan) have been seen. Blues caused by dd are known but rare and most dogs will be DD. The c^b and c alleles are rare (see page 66 for explanation) with most dogs carrying CC or Cc^{ch} or c^{ch}a^{ch} and causing various dilutions in the latter case. Reds of type ee may occur and with c^{ch}c^{ch} could give rise to creams or whites.

Pointer

This breed is one that has been studied for a long time, Little publishing a paper on Pointer colour in 1914. It is homozygous for C, D, g, m and usually A. Because S is absent the breed is white marked and usually this is due to s^p or s^w or combinations of the two. Irish spotting (s^i) may be absent. Ticking (TT or Tt) exists as does its absence (tt). At the E locus E and e exist and at the B locus B and b.

The basic colour will be determined by the B/E alleles carried and the white by s^p or s^w. Blacks will be BBEE, BbEE, BBEe or BbEe but will appear similar phenotypically. Livers will be bbEE or bbEe. Lemon markings will occur with BBee or Bbee and dogs that are bbee will be orange. Black noses will occur with all these types except for those which carry bb. Lemon and orange coat colours may be difficult or impossible to separate visually.

Pointer (German Shorthaired) (German Wirehaired)

This is a brown breed caused by bb. Its basic colour make-up is AAbbCCDDEEggmm and to this it may be solid-coloured (S) or carry various white patches (s^p or s^w). Ticking may occur due to TT or Tt but will not be obvious in SS animals or those carrying one S allele. The wirehaired version is identical to the short but the coat type (wire) enhances the effect of ticking.

Pomeranian

Another breed with a long coat and a wide range of colours causing difficulty in genetic identification. It is held to be homozygous for E, g, m and t and is possibly also SS.

Black masks (E^m) can occur but since the preference is for a clear colour that allele is rare. Similarly white markings and parti-colours once existed but also are rare suggesting that any allele like s^p or s^w has a low frequency. Blues due to dd are known but also rare and most dogs are DD.

The basic colour pattern is thus determined by the A and B loci with intensity of colour determined by the C and Int loci.

Black-and-tans ($a^t a^t$) are known but rare and most dogs are solid coloured (AA or Aa^y) or sable ($a^y a^y$). With BB or Bb these colours are likely to be rich and dark, for example the so-called wolf sable is $a^y a^y BB$. In contrast with the bb series colours are clearer and brighter. Orange is probably bb with $a^y a^y$. With CC full expression is possible but with c^{ch} or even c^d pale creams and whites can occur.

Poodle (all Varieties)

One of the most complex of breeds to identify genetically whichever type one is looking at. Geneticists are not helped by the motley assortment of terms used by breeders. Probably the breed is homozygous for m, S and t and carries at least two alleles at every other locus. It thus has A/a^t, B/b, C/c^{ch}, D/d, E/e and G/g.

Colour will depend in part upon which of the B series is present or which of the E series. Dilution may occur due to d or to the G series or to c^{ch}, particularly in combination with ee.

Some likely colour formulae are:

Intense black   A–   B–   C–   D–   E–   gg

Greyish blue	A–	B–	C–	D–	E–	G
Maltese blue	A–	B–	C–	dd–	E–	gg
Silver	A–	B–	C–	dd–	E–	G
Light red	A–	B–	C–	D–	ee–	gg
Silvery red	A–	B–	C–	D–	ee–	GG

All these types will also carry mmSStt and will have black noses. If c^{ch} replaces one or both C alleles then dilution will occur and in the case of those carrying ee could lead to cream and white dogs.

Liver	A–	bb	C–	D–	E–	gg
Silvery brown	A–	bb	C–	dd	E–	GG
Silver beige	A–	bb	C–	D–	ee	gg
Dull cream	A–	bb	C–	dd	ee	gg

All these dogs will also carry mmSStt and have brown noses.

Apricots can be born apricot or black. The latter are carrying G and it is misleading to give the two varieties the same colour description. Some apricots are born apricot and become cream which further complicates matters. Some genetic consultancy work in this breed to draw up a uniform colour code description is long overdue.

Pug

The breed is homozygous for B, D, E^m, g, m, S and t. Blacks are AA or Aa^y and carry at least one C. Apricot fawns are a^{y}a^y with C. Silver fawns are similar to apricot fawns but have c^{ch} or Int alleles causing dilution. White spots if they occur are modifiers of S and blues may result from dd but most dogs will be DD.

Pyrenean Mountain Dog

Essentially a white breed and as such colour genetics are uncertain. It is likely to be homozygous for B, c^{ch}, D, g, m, s^w and t. At the A and E loci the situation is not clear. However since whites can carry lemon, biscuit or light tan markings it is probable that they are a^{y}a^{y}EE rather than AAee.

Rottweiler

This breed is required to be black with well-defined mahogany markings on the legs and muzzle. It is a^{t}a^{t}BBCCDDEEggmmSStt and white markings when they occur are due to S modifiers.

St Bernard

Basically a white-and-red or red-and-white breed according to which colour predominates. So-called brindles are unlikely to be due to e^{br} but to a^y.

Homozygosity exists for a^y, B, C, D, g, m and possibly t though some ticked animals (TT or Tt) are known. At the E locus E^m (black mask) and E (no black mask) exist while at the S locus there are s^i, s^p and s^w. The most usual white pattern is s^{i}s^i or s^{i}s^p but extreme white s^{p}s^w or even s^{w}s^w may occur.

Shades of red are likely to be due to Int series or perhaps c^{ch}.

Saluki

This breed is homozygous B, D, g, m and usually t though ticking (TT or Tt) is known. At the agouti locus A, a^y and a^t exist and the so-called grizzles are a^ya^t. Reds are a^ya^y or can be ee. Black masks occur with E^m and fading of various shades with c^{ch} or Int alleles with other dogs being CC.

All of the S alleles exist causing any combination from solid colour through to extreme piebald (s^ws^w). However piebalds are rare and most white-marked dogs are a form of s^i suggesting that white is likely to be a combination of ee and $c^{ch}c^{ch}$.

Samoyed

This breed is white or white with biscuit and/or cream markings. This suggests that it is of formula $a^ya^yBBc^{ch}c^{ch}EEggmms^ws^wtt$. It is however feasible that it could be AAee in place of a^ya^yEE. It may also be that C exists in place of c^{ch} in some dogs.

Schipperke

Essentially a jet black breed but other varieties of colour (chocolates, fawns, reds and blues are known). The breed is homozygous for g, m, S and t. Blacks are AABBCCDDEE with one A, B, D or E being replaced by a^y, b or d respectively without phenotypic effect. Chocolates carry bb and blues dd. Fawns may be a^ya^yEE or AAee.

Schnauzer (Giant, Standard or Miniature)

All three varieties are homozygous for B, D, g, m, S and t. Solid blacks are A combined with E while black-and-tans are a^ta^tE-. The tan markings can vary in shade suggesting that some dogs are CC while others are Cc^{ch} or even $c^{ch}c^{ch}$. Giant Schnauzers are all thought to be the last named but it is possible that Int alleles are involved.

The so-called 'pepper and salt' colour which is common in the Giant variety is unclear. Little (1957) considers it to be either brindle (e^{br}) or due to a^g coupled with c^{ch} in Giants but in the two other varieties he seems to accept the latter version. Since all three varieties have a common origin it is probable that the same explanation will apply to all.

Scottish Terrier

The most fashionable colour in this breed is black with brindle, grey and wheaten also occurring. In the main Scotties are homozygous for B, D, g, m, S and t. Little (1920) records the case of a piebald specimen (caused by s^p) but the allele is likely to be so rare as to be ignored. The same is true of a liver version (bb) also recorded by Little (1957).

Brindle dogs are generally a^ya^y with $e^{br}e^{br}$ and the shade will vary from reds to greys according to which C alleles are present. In CC animals colours will be darkest and $c^{ch}c^{ch}$ dogs will be lightest with Cc^{ch} intermediate but it is also possible that Int alleles could add further to the variation.

Blacks could be a very dark brindle caused by modifying factors or they could be due to

A replacing a^y. In that event blacks could be $AAe^{br}e^{br}$ or $Aa^ye^{br}e^{br}$ and in the former case would breed true.

The Wheaten version (once termed Roseneath Terrier) is lightish cream or yellow and represents $c^{ch}c^{ch}$ or possibly c^dc^d (see page 66).

Sealyham

This is a white breed with or without markings which can be biscuit, lemon, tan or black but which are usually confined to the head and flanks.

This type of marking is typical of s^ws^w animals and most of the breed are this type though some may carry s^ps^w. As might be expected with white dogs the genetics of their markings is unclear. The breed is probably homozygous for B, C, D, g, m and t and is possibly a^ya^yEE or may be a^ya^yee. Sometimes a^y may be changed to a^t enabling black marking to show up.

Shetland Sheepdog

This is similar to the Collie and likely to have very similar colour genetics although some colours may be less popular than in Collies. The genes likely to exist in the breed are: BBCCEEggtt with alternatives existing at the other four loci namely: a^y/a^t D/D M/m $s^p/s^w/s^i$.

For explanations see Collie page 85.

Skye Terrier

Another complex breed since it carries the G allele the brindle allele (e^{br}) and is long coated. The genes likely to be homozygous in the breed are B, D, G, m, S and t. Little (1957) does record bb animals but this is likely to be rare in a breed seeking dark noses.

At the agouti locus a^y and a^t can exist, at the C locus C and c^{ch} and at the E locus e^{be}, e and possibly E^m. Int alleles may exist and cause variation in shade.

Springer Spaniel (English)

This breed is homozygous for C, D, g and m. All dogs carry white in various combinations of s^p and s^w and may be ticked (TT or Tt) or not (tt). The remaining colours depend upon the A, B and E loci.

The most common S allele in the breed is s^p with most dogs being s^ps^p and the following colour formulae assume s^ps^p being present. If s^ps^w or s^ws^w is present then the colour descriptions may be more difficult to identify because more white exists on the dog.

Black piebalds are A–B–E–. Tricolours are a^ta^t B–E–. Liver piebalds are A–bbEE and will have brown noses. Liver tricolours are a^ta^tbbEE and will have brown noses. Red piebalds can be either A–B–ee or a^ta^tB–ee and be difficult to separate. Lemon piebalds will be A–bbee or a^ta^tbbee and have brown noses but be indistinguishable one from the other.

Springer Spaniel (Welsh)

This and the previous breed have been placed out of strict alphabetical order to illustrate the differences in their colour despite their common origins. The Welsh version allows only rich red and white coloration and is liver nosed. It is probable that the breed is AAbbCCDDeeggmms^{P}s^P and carries TT or Tt (ticked) or tt (unticked).

Staffordshire Bull Terrier

A progenitor of the Bull Terrier this old breed has similar genetic make-up for colour being homozygous for B, C, D, g, m and t.

At the S locus it carries S, s^i and s^w as in the Bull Terrier but also s^P causing piebald. At the extension locus E and e^{br} are present and possibly e also. At the agouti locus A, a^y and a^t will exist. Since black-and-tan is disliked a^{t}a^t is likely to be rare. Liver (bb) may have existed and might still occur but as it is unacceptable is unlikely to have a high frequency in the breed.

Sussex Spaniel

A simple breed in colour terms since the recognised coat colour is rich golden liver with variations in shade being frowned upon. The breed is thus likely to be AAbbCCDDEEggmmSStt. White markings will be modifiers of the S allele and quickly lost.

Tibetan Terrier

Despite its name this breed is a herding dog and thus is more complex in colour than most terriers. The only colour not accepted is chocolate or liver (bb) which is surprising because it exists in Tibet and is in no way detrimental to the dog. The only homozygous series is likely to be mm but T giving ticking may not be present and in any event is likely to be rare with most dogs being tt.

Solid blacks exist which will be A?B?C?D?S? with any minor white markings being S modifiers. Fawns and golds are complex and may be of several kinds. The a^{y}a^y type is likely but also ee fawns. Since there are dogs known as smokes which may be blue dilutes (B?dd) it follows that fawns of the type bbdd exist and will have pink noses. However any dog carrying bb will have a pink nose regardless of its final colour. At the S locus there is Irish spotting (s^i) as well as parti-colour (s^P) and all-white (s^{w}s^w). However some whites may be eec^{ch}c^{ch} and creams may carry c^{ch}c^{ch}. Black dogs which end up blue-grey exist, suggesting that G is present but most dogs will be gg in genotype. In view of the limited bloodlines in this breed it seems desirable to introduce liver as an acceptable colour to thus expand possible lines and broaden the base of the breed. In the extension series E is present and possibly E^m but e^{br} is unlikely.

Vizsla (Hungarian Pointer)

This breed accepts a yellow sedge-like shade of colour and it is possible that its colour genetics are similar to the Chesapeake Bay Retriever (see page 82).

Welsh Corgi (Cardigan and Pembroke)

Both breeds are probably homozygous for B, C, D, g, m and t. In the Pembroke dogs are either solid-coloured (S) or carry Irish spotting (s^i) whereas in the Cardigan the s^P allele also exists causing more extensive white markings.

The Pembroke is probably EE whereas the Cardigan can be EE, Ee^{br} or e^{br}e^{br} and in the two latter instances carry brindle markings. At the A locus a^{y}a^y, a^{y}a^t and a^{t}a^t exist in both breeds giving various shades of sable or tri-colours. Little (1957) considers that the Cardigan may carry A and thus could give rise to black-and-white dogs. However an a^{t}a^t dog could appear black-and-white if the tan markings happened to coincide with the white areas and hence were hidden.

Welsh Terrier

This breed is either black-and-tan or black-grizzle-and-tan. The tan areas are extensive and the breed is possibly homozygous at all loci being: a^{s}a^{s}BBCCDDEEggmmSStt. White markings on feet and chest will be due to S modifiers.

West Highland White Terrier

A breed that is actually the Roseneath version of the Scottish Terrier and is possibly of genetic formula a^{y}a^{y}BBc^{ch}c^{ch}DDEEggmmSStt with the only doubt existing about c^{ch} in that it may be that c^d is carried.

Whippet

Like the Greyhound, colour is immaterial and hence many versions exist with homo-zygosity likely only for B, g, m and t alleles.

At other loci A/a^y, C/c^{ch}, D/d, E/e^{br}/e and S/s^i/s^p/s^w exist. The various combinations possible thus resemble Greyhounds to which the reader is referred (see page 91).

Yorkshire Terrier

A breed in which puppies are born very dark and then change to a steel-blue and tan. It is likely to have the colour formula a^{s}a^{s}BBCCDDEEGGmmSStt. The allele a^t may exist causing a greater extension of the saddle marking and the allele c^{ch} may exist and cause shading of the tan region to lighter versions but this is unlikely to be encouraged.

The breeds listed here do not embrace all possible breeds and readers are referred to Robinson (1982) for a more comprehensive treatment of some breeds as well as to assess differences of opinion. For those interested in the mathematical aspects of colour predictions there is a useful paper by Ladd and Robinson (1983) using the Dobermann as an example.

It must be realised that any geneticist can only describe that which he has seen or had reported either personally or in the literature. Many breeders may have seen colour variants in their breeds which are rare and which have not been discussed here or by Robinson (1982). Explanations could well be found but these variations need to be reported. To this end the author would welcome comments from breeders on colour variations not seen here but which have cropped up in litters. Colour photographs would be helpful.

Chapter 6

Inheritance of Structural Traits and Aspects of the Skin and Coat

Introduction

Any breeder of show stock is interested in the basic shape and structure of his dogs as well as their character and mental attributes. His breeding objectives are mainly directed to altering (improving) the basic structural aspects by selective breeding. He is, rightly or wrongly, seeking to alter relatively minor points—a bit more length here, a bit more curve there—within the same overall pattern. To this extent he is interested in the underlying skeletal structure of the dog although in many instances it would be true to say that he is altering muscle shape or affecting fat deposition or skin folding rather than the actual bony structure.

Structural peculiarities are usually avoided although the definition of what is peculiar or abnormal depends very largely on the breed under discussion. The brachycephalic head structure of the Bull-breeds would be a decided abnormality in any others as would be the achondroplastic legs of the Dachshund or the naturally docked tail of some Pembroke Corgis. One cannot therefore talk about structural or skeletal abnormalities in the global sense across breeds since many of these very abnormalities are the norm in certain breeds. We can only deal with the variations in general terms and refer to them as abnormalities in specific instances where they represent deviations from the norm in that breed.

Unfortunately data on the relatively minor differences in form between members of the same breed are rare or non-existent. With the exception of colour, minor changes within a breed and the mode of inheritance of them are very much a matter of conjecture and breed lore rather than the result of any scientific study. Studies that have been undertaken on skeletal differences have been largely confined to crosses between breeds which are thus of academic interest to most breeders. Much of this work has been reviewed by Burns and Fraser (1966) and will not be dealt with extensively here. This chapter is concerned with basic structure. Structural deformities and hip dysplasia are dealt with in detail in Chapters 7 and 8.

Skull and Head Shape

Comparison between the dog and the wolf
Some of the earliest works on wolf versus dog comparisons were made over a century ago (Giebel 1859) and claim great differences but later work from various authors reviewed by Iljin (1941) shows that most of these differences were quantitative rather than qualitative with the obvious exception of brachycephalic breeds.

We are thus concerned with differences of degree rather than obvious absolute differences. One such area of discussion has been the orbital angle, that is, the angle formed by a line drawn orbitally through the upper and lower marginal edges of the eye and the horizontal plane drawn through the upper margins of the *ossa frontalia*. According Studer (1901) the angle in wolves is from 40 to 45° while in dogs it is much higher. This was confirmed by Bockelmann (1920) who found the orbital angle in wolves to be 41–42° and in dogs to be 47–48° and even up to 56°. Iljin (1941) supported this thesis putting the limits of variation in wolves at 39.5 to 46.5° while in German Shepherd Dogs it was 49–55°.

Length of skull in wolves was found to be larger than that in dogs (see Iljin 1941) but in this instance considerable overlap occurred. Iljin, in a review of nineteenth century work concludes that several differences occur between wolves and dogs but that many of these may be environmental in origin in that they are the result of nutritional changes as much as a consequence of selection. Iljin reported on various crosses made between wolves and German Shepherd Dogs and found that most F_1 and F_2 crosses seemed to take after the dog rather than the wolf in a variety of skull characteristics. Some of the differences were considered genetic in origin and Iljin attempts to associate them with a two gene series. This is not likely to be valid. Most differences that are genetic are certain to be polygenic in their mode of control. He did conclude that greater breadth of the upper jaw was likely to be dominant to the smaller one, albeit under polygenic control.

Comparison between breeds of dog
Possibly the most comprehensive study of breed crossing was that undertaken by Stockard *et al* (1941). They crossed several breeds to produce F_1 animals and then several F_2 and backcrosses. In most instances crosses tended to be intermediate, suggesting polygenic inheritance while a single backcross of an F_1 to either of the parental breeds tended to resemble that breed quite markedly. The exception occurred when one parental breed was the Bulldog or French Bulldog. It seemed that short-faced (brachycephalic) types tended to be more dominant although simple inheritance was ruled out. There was more variability in skull types than in most other characters and this was very apparent with crosses involving a Bull-breed. Since the length of upper and lower jaw appeared to be inherited differently many cases of under- and overshot jaws occurred.

The large skull size and pronounced parietal crest of the Basset Hound seemed to be recessive (not simply) to the small flatter-topped skull of the Dachshund.

The consequences of crossing breeds seem to be variable but, except with Bull-breeds are probably quickly incorporated into some degree of uniformity. Most Kennel Clubs would demand about four top crosses before accepting any breed as being 'pure' and it is likely that by this stage variability will be minimal if selection has been practised.

Selection within a breed
Marchlewski (1930b) suggested that the narrow Greyhound-like head of some Pointers appeared dominant to the more correct type of Pointer head but it is clearly not a simple dominant. My own experience with German Shepherd Dogs suggests that in lines which have been selected for fine heads their subsequent correction is not easy. One particularly important German-bred sire Klodo v d Eremitenklause (born 1959 died 1970) was known to have a rather fine muzzle and this was seen in many of his full sibs and his parents. It was also very obvious in direct descendants for some generations, albeit not in all.

It is not improbable that breeders, in any breed, seeking to fine down the head structure will run into problems, especially in respect of overshot and undershot jaws. The German Shepherd Dog line mentioned above had a goodly share of overshot jaws and with this some measure of missing teeth (see page 108).

Selecting for strong broad heads—much desired in males—may bring with it problems of rather doggy bitches. It is apparently very difficult in some breeds to establish strength of head in males and at the same time femininity in bitch head structure. It may also be likely that selection for massive head structure brings with it such things as lippy mouths. Stockard and his colleagues (1941) noted that an overgrowth of skin was common in giant breeds as if selection for size of the frame and the skin to cover it had not gone hand-in-hand. Again, personal experience in German Shepherds suggests that many very masculine animals often have lippy heads and are frequently 'throaty' but the genetics of this is unknown.

The Rough Collie has the reputation of having had its head shape altered very markedly over the years. This was well demonstrated by Vanderlip (1986) using Collie skulls of 1886, 1910, 1929, 1953, 1967 and 1982. Although only samples were used and these might not have been typical the overall effect was quite marked. The 1886 skull was shorter and broader with large rounded zygomatic processes (leading to fuller cheeks and a broader head). From then on the skulls showed lengthening and narrowing so that increasingly they resembled Borzoi skulls which were used as comparative items. The illustrations of Borzoi skulls showed little change between 1904 and 1980. Vanderlip argues that the skull changes in the Rough Collie have not affected eye space or brain space which may well be true but does not prove that no change in actual eye size has occurred. The article is a good illustration of the genetic consequences of selection on skeletal aspects and excessive emphasis upon one aspect of the dog, in this case the head. Rough Collie breeders would do well to not only read this article but seek to reverse the trend started 100 years ago if that is still feasible.

One of the few studies looking at conformational aspects is that of Verryn and Geerthsen (1987) looking at a population of 201 GSD in South Africa. They looked at various measurements and assessed the heritability and standard errors of 20 items. The most highly heritable was chest width ($81 \pm 15\%$) and the least heritable leg circumference ($8 - 11\%$). Such aspects as weight ($41 \pm 17\%$) and body stature ($54 \pm 17\%$) appeared to be quite highly heritable. The authors rightly concluded that various features considered important in the breed could be altered by selection quite quickly.

Leg Length

Breed crosses

Leg length is one of the most variable canine traits, ranging from dwarf breeds to giants. The most comprehensive work in crossing is that of Stockard *et al* (1941) who found that using short-legged breeds like Dachshunds and Basset Hounds with normal dogs like German Shepherds produced an intermediate leg length in the F_1. Mating of two F_1 animals led to segregation of long, intermediate and short but this does not necessarily suggest a simple mode of inheritance.

There is an added complication in that leg length genes may be influenced by bone type. Slender but hard bones (Saluki) had a tendency to be dominant to Basset-type bone, Bulldog bone was dominant to Hound bone and Pekingese bone dominant to Saluki bone.

It is suggested by Burns and Fraser (1966) that light bone is denser and harder than heavy bone but it may also be more brittle and they cite as confirmatory evidence the high fracture rate among the fine, light-boned Greyhound. In crosses between bone types the extreme types (light or heavy) tend to dominate intermediate types. However achondroplastic (short-legged) factors seem to affect heavy bone more then fine bone so that short-legged dogs will have more chance of having straight legs if they are light-boned than if they are heavy boned.

Whitney (1971) reports on crosses between a Fox Terrier and a Boston Terrier with a Dachshund. In both cases leg length was intermediate. He subsequently crossed Basset Hounds and Bloodhounds and found variable leg length but none as short as the Basset Hound. A backcross gave no clear segregation as had been seen by Stockard. Whitney also cites the case of a three-quarters length leg in Hounds where he claims a single dominant gene is involved which is dominant to normal length of leg.

Within a breed

Within any breed less variability exists than across breeds. One is generally dealing with a polygenic trait in that selection for greater length will gradually bring about an increase or vice versa. It may be more difficult in achondroplastic breeds to increase leg length. Breeds like the Dachshund are achondroplastic in that they have a different type of growth of the long bones of the leg. In a normal breed the bone gradually increases in length and width until what are called the epiphyseal rings at each end of the bone, just below the head and foot, are completely ossified. In an anchondroplastic dog the epiphyseal ring is very quickly ossified and fused but the bone then continues to increase in diameter. This results in a short but thick bone.

In most breeds of dog there are minimum and maximum heights so that selection is aimed at producing dogs within this range rather than extending it. Dogs at the extremes are correctively mated to dogs of more correct size or discarded altogether. What does occur in some breeds is the excessive shortening of the legs in an otherwise correct body structure. In some cases it seems to have become fashionable and sought after which has the result of splitting the breed into camps—those seeking shorter legs and those seeking the original correct length.

Any discussion of length of leg and bone structure cannot be undertaken without some mention of nutrition. In the research work undertaken by Stockard *et al* (1941) dogs were fed in controlled situations but in breeding kennels there is considerable variation. Bone quality and leg length as well as other aspects of shape can be markedly affected by nutrition and exercise. Rickets, which ought to be a rare disease in any breed, can affect bone structure and lead to some deformation of the leg. High levels of feeding early in life (up to three or four months of age) will influence not only body weight but also bone structure and perhaps even alter such things as length of back and leg. It is known that high levels of feeding will not aid hip dysplasia (see Chapter 8) and, according to Burns and Fraser (1966), moderate feeding will tend to thicken the long bones and coarsen the skull when it is followed by a period of high nutrition.

Sheng and Huggins (1971) have studied the chemical growth of Beagles showing a rapid increase in total fat from birth to one and a half months of age and a relatively constant percentage thereafter. They found that chemical maturity occurred differently in time for different substances: being three months for total body water, four months for protein, two months for calcium and birth for sodium and chlorine. It would be useful to see scientific studies on the effect of growth and nutrition upon body shape but this has not been done although De Pugh (1956) and Weiss (1966) have discussed it.

Sommer (1931), in a somewhat contentious paper in which rather unjustified conclusions are drawn, considered that long bone and skeletal growth generally were more or less complete by nine months of age. This emphasises the potential importance of nutrition in early life upon the animal.

The breeder has the complication to face that what he sees in his dogs or those of others is a combination of nutrition and genetics with the same apparent result being arrived at by different means. Until heritability studies are made on particular traits like leg length and body shape he will have to work as he does now on using those animals which most closely approach the ideal *and* which seem to be transmitting this.

Ear Carriage and Size

Ear carriage is considered important in most breeds of dog. Even those in which cropping is permitted will have an interest in the set of those ears upon the head although size is obviously not important because of cropping.

Iljin (1937) suggested that in terms of carriage there were three genes or alleles of one series. He termed these:

H^a Semi-erect or tipped ears as in Collies;
H   Lop ears as in hounds;
h   Erect ears.

According to Iljin H^a was completely dominant to H while H was only partially dominant to h. He suggests a separate gene for the type of ear seen in Borzois and another gene for dropped ears which is recessive to erect in certain breeds. As Burns and Fraser (1966) have pointed out ear carriage will depend upon ear size and texture so that Iljin's explanation is oversimplified.

Kelley (1949) states that in his Border Collies fully erect ears bred true and thus represented a simple recessive with dogs carrying both alleles for erect ears in order to have them. This is certainly not the case in German Shepherds where the erect ear is dominant or partially dominant to the dropped or 'soft' ear. This was the view of Humphrey and Warner (1934) and is borne out by practical observation but it is by no means a simple condition. There is considerable range among dogs in respect of speed of erection, all Shepherds being born with soft drop ears. Some sires seem to produce very rapid erection, even as early as eight weeks, while others linger on to six months or more. Carriage is not always uniform with some dogs having one erect and one soft when they reach adulthood —this type of carriage is common during the erection stage. Other dogs have their ears erect but show lack of muscle tone so that the ear tends to 'wave' in motion, especially at the tip. Stockard *et al* (1941) felt that in German Shepherds the erect ear was due to several factors and that carriage was, in some instances, independent of size. They thus have a Boston Terrier × Dachshund with the large ears of the latter breed carried erect. Hauck (1949) also found no relationship between ear size and degree of erection.

Marchlewski (1930a) found the small size of German Shepherd ears to be dominant to the larger ear size of Pointers but the small triangular shape of English Pointer ears was dominant to the larger ears of German Pointers. This does not seem to agree with Whitney (1971) who crossed many long-eared and short-eared dogs. According to him the F_1 stock were never intermediate and no F_2 ever had ears as long as the longest eared original parent. It does however seem that lop ears are dominant to erect ones in most instances when breed crosses are involved.

Foot Shape

This is an area of study that appears to have been neglected, surprising in view of the importance of feet to both the show and working dog. Humphrey and Warner (1934) reported the short compact foot to be dominant or partially dominant to the open-toed long foot. This seemed to be the view of Marchlewski (1930a) in Pointers but is not confirmed by Kelley (1949) in Border Collies.

The inheritance of webbed feet is not known.

Dew Claws

Dew claws represent a fifth toe in dogs which is, through some evolutionary process no longer really needed. Most show dogs will have the hind dew claws removed as they interfere with movement but certain breeds, such as Pyrenean Mountain Dogs and Briards, should possess hind claws and these should be double. The wisdom of this is questionable although Whitney (1971) argues that dew claws might be useful in swimming breeds. Poodle breeders remove dew claws from both legs—front and back—but the majority of breeds are left with front dew claws intact.

The mode of inheritance of front dew claws is unknown but there seems to be general agreement about the inheritance of single hind dew claws. Whitney (1971) considered that the hind dew claw was dominant to its non-appearance. This is the situation in German Shepherds where many dogs are born without dew claws and, when mated together, continue to produce none. It also appears to be the case in the Braque (Falaschini 1941) based upon crosses between Pointers and Braques. This also agrees with data presented by Grundmann (1954).

The situation appears to be different in the Collie and in Border Collies. In the latter breed Kelley (cited by Burns and Fraser 1966) claimed that parents without dew claws could produce offspring with these appendages. This suggests a recessive trait. Earlier work by Keeler and Trimble (1938), also working with Collies but in their case crossed with Dalmatians, was inconclusive. They found that in dogs which carried one gene for dew claws and ought to have had them only 47% did show dew claws. In crosses between heterozygous stock when 75% dew claws were expected only 58.3% did have them. This suggests some form of incomplete penetrance.

Insofar as double dew claws are concerned Stockard *et al* (1941) considered that they were recessive to single dew claws. However it was the view of Grundmann (1954) that double and single dew claws were both autosomal dominants but independent. Some families of dogs could carry both genes. In view of the desirability of double dew claws in certain breed standards it would seem that compilation of data from a breed like the Briard could rapidly solve the genetic situation.

Tails

According to Leinhart (1932) the naturally docked tail in Breton Spaniels was due to multiple genetic factors but was not associated with any lethal problems. Burns and Fraser

(1966) suggest that the popular theory is that the short tail is dominant or incompletely dominant to normal tail length but that in a homozygous form is lethal. If this is true it means that all naturally docked pups are Tt (where T is the tail-less allele) and that TT pups die while tt dogs are normal as regards tail length.

Not all 'docked' breeds are born naturally docked. Some Old English Sheepdogs have tails, others only stubs but all are docked artificially if born with a tail. Mating naturally docked dogs ought to result in 25% mortality if the views on the lethal nature of the TT combination are correct.

Pullig (1953a, 1957) claimed that tail-lessness in Cocker Spaniels was inherited as a simple recessive but that two independent types existed one being totally tail-less (anury) and the other a short stub tail (brachyury). Selection would suggest a relatively easy pathway exists to produce stub tailed or tail-less Cockers—unless a lethal situation also exists. Anury in two Cairn terriers in America has been reported by Hall *et al* (1987) who suggested a genetic aetiology.

Screw tails as seen in Bulldogs and French Bulldogs was thought by Stockard *et al* (1941) to be long or short according to a dominant (long) gene but that this was independent to the actual screw tail which was dominant to the straight tail. Whitney (1971) does not agree with this view and considers that the issue is much more complex with considerable variation in tail type even among inbred strains.

Sailer (1954) considered five tail abnormalities to be inherited. Of these he considered stumpy tail to be caused by an autosomal dominant gene with incomplete penetrance. This is supported by Curtis *et al* (1964) who reported a stub tail (in Beagles) which had the same mode of inheritance. Selection for it had led to fewer caudal vertebrae and when inbreeding was undertaken spina bifida was produced.

Whitney (1971) lists various crosses among breeds with different tail lengths and carriages. An interesting one was the German Shepherd/Elkhound cross which gave pups all carrying their tails curled over their back like the Elkhound. Some bad tail carriage in breeds like the German Shepherd is caused by a high set on of the tail allowing it to be carried forward over the back. Others have excessively long tails which seem more a hindrance than a help in movement. The extra length is certainly genetic and due to conscious selection for it but the mode of inheritance is unknown.

Long-tailed dogs with a sideways bend or curl near the tip are considered by Whitney (1971) to be possibly due to bending in embryo. My own view is that some genetic factor is involved because specific lines of German Shepherd seem to throw this problem at intervals. However the mode of inheritance is conjecture.

Mouths, Jaws and Teeth

The correct dentition of any dog, regardless of breed should comprise 42 teeth, 20 on the upper and 22 on the lower jaw. On each jaw there should be six incisors, two canines, eight premolars but only four molars on the upper and six on the lower jaw (see Figure 20).

The degree of attention paid to teeth seems to vary with the breed. In those of German origin breeders, especially in their homeland, often have an almost fanatical approach to teeth and dogs with two or three missing will be discarded regardless of other virtues. This seems to be an excessive approach and, in small populations of dogs where physical and mental excellence is at a premium, could result in limiting progress for other more important traits. One the other hand one cannot condone the approach of some breeders of British or British-based breeds who seem indifferent to whether the dog does or does not possess teeth. One German Shepherd breeder who could not be called a tooth fanatic expressed her horror to me on judging Dalmatians and finding missing teeth in abundance and apparent indifference among exhibitors.

Breeders and judges should, in my view, pay attention to teeth and penalise excessive loss but we know insufficient about the mode of inheritance of teeth number to be dogmatic.

In their breeding work with German Shepherds, Humphrey and Warner (1934) found that when mating animals with complete dentition some 44% of the progeny (88 in 202) had missing teeth (at least one). When two dogs with missing teeth were mated together they found 55% of the progeny (21 in 38) had complete dentition. Their data do not specify which teeth or the numbers per animal that were missing but almost certainly it would be premolars that were involved. The data are certainly not indicative of any simple mode of inheritance and do not conform to the view of Skrentny (1964) that missing teeth were an autosomal recessive in Dobermanns.

In some cases teeth are not apparent but are not actually missing from the head since a cut in the gum will often show the unerupted tooth to be present. This emphasises the dangers of being fanatical about teeth.

In breeds with brachycephalic heads or with dwarf size it is likely that dentition will frequently be imperfect. It is not uncommon in Bulldogs and Boxers where there has been selection for a broad head to find extra incisors. Thus Aitchison (1963) found that 28 out of 71 Bulldogs seen had seven incisors in the upper jaw. This author looked at Bulldog skulls at the British Museum and found them to be longer and narrower than contemporary Bulldogs. (The Museum skulls dated to pre-1936.) In a later study Aitchison (1964) checked other breeds and found the incidence of seven upper incisors to be as shown in Table 16. Boxer breeders were said, in some cases, to favour dogs with seven incisors as they had wider muzzles but Burns and Fraser (1966) viewed this with alarm, claiming that teeth anomalies were often accompanied by abnormal calcification of the bones. I would concur with them.

In German Shepherds I have examined many hundreds of dogs and never come across seven incisors though I have heard of two cases. An extra premolar is more common but the incidence is not known. Some data on mating policy within German Shepherds with

Table 16

Incidence of seven incisors (upper jaw) in various breeds

Breed	*Dogs seen*	*% dogs with 7 incisors*
Bulldog	71	39.4
Boxer	140	26
Bullmastiff	36	8
Pug	101	4
Pekingese	74	1.3
Mastiff	23	—

Source Aitchison 1963, 1964.

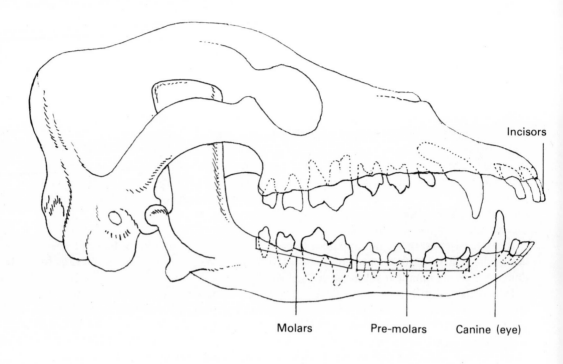

Incisors

Molars   Pre-molars   Canine (eye)

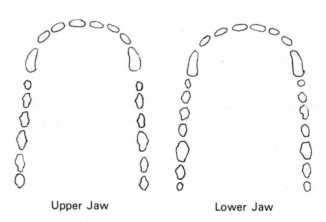

Upper Jaw   Lower Jaw

$$\frac{\text{Upper Jaw} \quad I6 \quad C2 \quad PM8 \quad M4 = 20}{\text{Lower Jaw} \quad I6 \quad C2 \quad PM8 \quad M6 = 22} = 42$$

Figure 20   The dentition of the dog *(above and opposite)*.

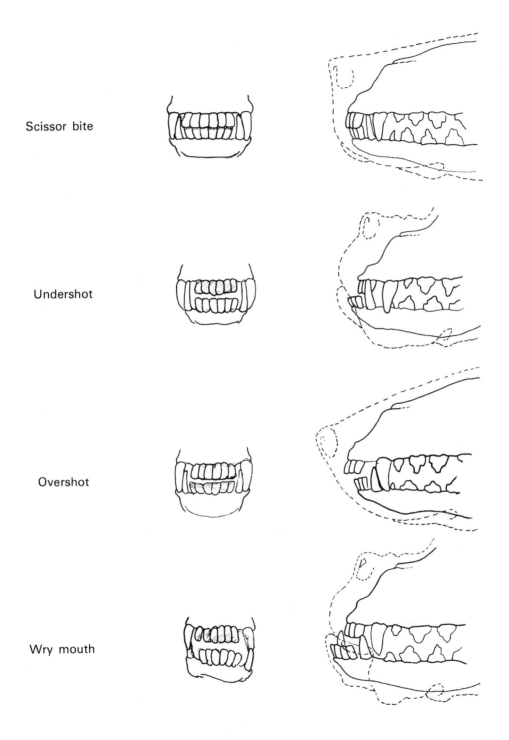

Scissor bite

Undershot

Overshot

Wry mouth

Table 17

Mating Policy (104 litters) in respect of missing teeth in German Shepherd Dogs

		Teeth missing in the dam				
		0	1	2	3	Total
Teeth	0	85*	10	2	1	98
missing	1	0	1	0	0	1
in sire	2	2	0	0	0	2
	3	2	0	0	0	2
	Total	89	11	2	1	103

*Includes one litter where sire had an extra tooth.
Source   Willis 1978a.

regard to teeth is shown in Table 17. As yet the results of such obvious attempts to select for a full complement of teeth by tending to concentrate on full-mouthed animals (especially sires) is not known.

Some genetic studies have been undertaken in humans on the heritability of tooth dimensions. Alvesalo and Tigerstedt (1974) have reviewed the subject and produced some data to suggest very high h^2 values for most teeth, albeit based upon twin analyses which tend to inflate the values. Their own data showed a value in excess of 50% in most cases with the highest values applying to, among others, the first premolars. Whether similar situations occur in dogs is unknown but it is interesting that in German Shepherds first premolars are the most frequently missing teeth.

In her study of dental anomalies among German Pointer breeds Kock (1984) found that the incidence ranged from 6.65% in the Weimaraner (331 dogs) to 33.3% in the Brittany Spaniel (18 dogs). In those breeds with over 1000 dogs examined incidence figures were 16.63% for the German Wire-haired Pointer (8192 dogs), 9.55% in the Munsterlander (2732) and 8.24% in the German Long-haired Pointer (1955). In this last named breed heritability of tooth anomalies was 2.1%–2.8% i.e. not significantly different from zero. She recommended that missing P 1s should no longer be a criterion for culling from breeding.

Hitchin and Morris (1966) have reported cases of incisors being united by enamel. This was reported in inbred Lakeland Terriers and breeding data suggested that the problem was genetic in origin though not simple. It appeared that the same genes controlled the effect in both jaws.

When one looks at jaw structure and the bite (way in which the incisors meet) the picture is no clearer than for teeth number. Although some breeds have an undershot jaw (lower incisors coming in front of the upper) and others have an even bite (incisors meet) the most common type of bite is a scissor bite (see Figure 20). Since this demands that the back of the upper incisors is in contact with the front of the lower incisors it is very easy to see how faulty bites of the overshot nature can occur. It takes only a small variation in jaw length or tooth arrangement for the teeth not to meet and the mouth to be faulty.

Philips (1945) described a case of overshot jaws in Cocker Spaniels and concluded that it was a simple recessive but with some irregular manifestations which is as useful as saying that it was of unknown mode of inheritance. However Kelley (cited by Burns and Fraser

1966) suggests a recessive type cause of lower jaw shortening in Border Collies and personal experience in German Shepherds suggests that overshot bites in this breed are recessive. However this does not mean simple recessive inheritance nor does it imply a shortened lower jaw.

Selecting for longer heads will undoubtedly not aid the bite development and may also adversely affect dentition. An overshot jaw in Long-Haired Dachshunds was reported by Grüneberg and Lea (1940) and attributed to a recessive gene. In this case the teeth of the affected dogs were smaller than normal and in addition to some shortening of the lower jaw some increase of the upper was noted. It is not likely that this relates to more usual overshot jaw cases but was a specific problem.

In crosses between German Shepherds (scissor bite) and Boxers (undershot) Ritter (1937) found intermediate jaw structures in the progeny but none were undershot. Backcrossing the F_1 to the Boxer gave above 50% undershot jaws suggesting a type of recessive.

Data collection on teeth is something that many breed societies could readily undertake and judges would do a service to breeds if they commented upon missing teeth in reports being specific as to numbers. Alas, personal experience suggests that many judges and breeders do not know what correct dentition is, still less select for it.

Body Size and Weight

Body size is certainly a polygenic character in any breed and, as in other species, it is something controlled not only by genes but also by the environment. What we do not really know, and it is a serious omission, is the degree to which heredity plays its part. In most other species growth rate and body size are moderate to highly heritable traits. In beef cattle, for example, rate of gain post weaning and final live weight after testing for a period of time or to a fixed weight will be from 40 to 60% heritable (see Preston and Willis 1970). In dogs we have few if any estimates.

The dog is rather different to farm livestock, in which there is constant selection for increased weight deposition, since most breeders ostensibly aim to keep their breed within fixed limits. This does not mean that changes have not occurred. For example, Willis (1976) examined the wither heights and weights of German Shepherds taken from the German Körbuch in 1927–8 and again in 1973. He showed that in males, for example, the mean height had changed from 64.4 cm (SD 1.85) to 63.5 cm (SD 1.04) whereas body weight (as adults) had altered from 33.5 to 37.2 kg in the same period. There was, however, very considerable variation in weight at any given height. In 1973 males with an average height of 63 cm ranged from 29 to 43 kg in weight. This does not mean that genetic variation was high since this could be more a reflection of environmental changes than genetic differences, especially in respect of height where males outside the extremes of 59 and 66 cm would be rarely bred from. Unfortunately the data from the Körbuch represent selected animals and thus do not provide any basis for genetic studies on heritability.

In a study made on the same breed using Swedish Army data Reuterwall and Ryman (1973) examined the 60-day weights of 488 males and 438 females from 168 litters sired by 29 different sires and out of 103 different dams. They found a heritability of 44% among males and 35% among females. These are high enough to suggest considerable variation in this population and also that selection for an increase or decrease in 60-day weight would be effective. A more extensive study using 2404 GSDs but from the same Swedish Army source (Hedhammar *et al* 1979) confirmed the heritability of 60-day weight in this breed to be $42 \pm 8\%$.

Since body weight at any age is likely to show good relationship with weight at another it suggests that the heritability of adult weight in this breed is likely to be moderate to high. Extrapolation to other large-sized breeds suggests this may also be true but there is no evidence to prove this statement.

Any breeder seeking to modify size within his dogs must seek to breed from those animals at the extremes of the range in the direction in which he is seeking to go. Initially success in increased or decreased body size will result. It is likely that in the long term selection in an upwards direction will be better than in a downwards one since decreased skeletal size will also bring with it decreased body weight and there is some evidence (see Chapter 3) that body weight and litter size are linearly related. As a breed becomes smaller it will produce smaller litters and thus selection differentials (see page 298) will decrease making further progress harder. The wisdom of selecting for reduced body size is open to question. Toy breeds may make better child substitutes than Working dogs but they will have inherent problems associated with their size which may make them less efficient dogs. On the other hand giant breeds are not free of problems, particularly in respect of growth, and it is probably true to say that increases in skeletal size not only bring inevitable increases in body size but also alter conformation. Even within a breed it is likely that increasing wither height will bring with it straighter hind angulation, overbuilt rumps and more difficulty in seeking right angled shoulders where these are desired. This is a view based upon observation rather than data so must be interpreted with care but it is my personal view that man is best seeking to produce the medium-sized to moderately large dog rather than moving to extremes outside of this range.

Coat Type

There are numerous coat types found in dog breeds with many gradations between the more obvious forms. This is sufficient to suggest that simple Mendelian inheritance is unlikely, at least when we consider breeds in total. However, in specific breeds distinct coat types do exist and in most instances the observed mode of inheritance tends to be relatively simple.

Scott and Fuller (1951) suggest that several genes affect the texture and colour of the coat and those affecting colour have already been discussed. In considering coat type it must be obvious to any thinking breeder that no simple explanation is likely to cover the numerous components of the coat. These include not only the more obvious one of length but involve such aspects as wave or curl, coarseness, density (that is, hairs per unit of skin area) and medullation (the presence or absence of the central core of the hair).

In a study of five wild and fourteen domestic breeds of dog Brunsch (1956) concluded that domestic dog coats have been changed by selection. This would seem to be almost inevitable in view of the numerous other changes that man has wrought upon the dog. In some breeds hair has become wool-like, a feature mentioned by Lochte (1963) in a study of breeds like the Kuvasz, Komondor, Puli and Pyrenean sheepdog. In a study of Poodles Miessner (1964) considered that coat formation was similar to that in the Karakul sheep, albeit later in onset in the Poodle.

As Crawford and Loomis (1978) have pointed out there is a dearth of documented information upon the inheritance of coat types which is not helped by some rules that seem to be applied in various breeds. Thus some breeds have long- and short-coated types maintained as separate entities while in others both types are acceptable in the same register. Sometimes long-coated varieties are considered to be undesirable and either eliminated or sold on a pet basis with little or no use of such dogs as breeding stock. These anomalies do not help genetic understanding but it does seem that certain basic rules hold good in most instances. These are that short coats are generally dominant to long coats and recessive to wire coats. This is demonstrated, at least circumstantially, in the German Shepherd Dog which at its beginning had all three coat types but from which the wire coat has been totally lost—only really feasible if wire coat was dominant to the other two types.

That long coat in German Shepherds is recessive to short is demonstrated by the data in Table 18. This is based upon GSDIF records and covers all litters in which both parents were short-coated but known to produce long-coated progeny. In the 64 litters cited there were six in which no long coats appeared but the overall ratio of 3.47 short to one long is in agreement with Mendelian ratios for a simple autosomal recessive. Because of the undesirable feature of long coats no matings between two such types were recorded by the GSDIF and only five litters were noted between long coats and short-coated 'carriers'. In these latter cases the data agreed with the expected 50% of each type.

Willis (1978a) has estimated that the current incidence of long-coated dogs in German Shepherds in Britain is about 12% which suggests that about half of the apparently normal-coated stock carry a long coat recessive allele.

Table 18

Results of mating together normal-coated German Shepherds known to carry a long-coated recessive allele

| Litter size* | Litters | Pups born | |
		Normal-coated	*Long-coated*
1	1	1	—
2	1	1	1
3	3	5	4
4	7	21	7
5	7	27	8
6	9	40	14
7	3	17	4
8	11	66	22
9	8	56	16
10	7	56	14
11	5	46	9
12	1	9	3
13	1	12	1
Total	64	357	103

*Pups in which coat type not identified excluded (this covers all those dying early in life as coat type is only identifiable by 6 to 8 weeks of age).
Source Willis 1978a.

Table 19

Inheritance of coat type in St Bernards

Mating type*	Litters	Progeny checked		Expected†	
		Short	Long	Short	Long
Short × Short	33	142	38	135	45
Short × Long	118	282	308	295	295
Long × Long	55	—	337	—	337

*After excluding all matings involving known homozygous short-coated stock. All short-coated stock which were listed as parents were known to be or presumed to be carriers of the long-coated allele.
† Expected and observed figures are in agreement with Mendelian ratios.
Source   Crawford and Loomis 1978.

In the St Bernard both types of coat are acceptable although the long variety is favoured. Crawford and Loomis (1978) have shown that the mode of inheritance is identical to that in German Shepherds and a summary of their findings is given in Table 19. It is interesting that they cite breeders as believing that interbreeding of the two coat types is essential to maintain size, type and soundness. Such beliefs are without proof and apparently without logic.

It is probable that the situation in St Bernards and German Shepherds is identical with that in other breeds like the Basset Hound (Willis 1977a) and Dobermann. Whitney (1971) presents several breeding results in which long- and short-coated breeds were mated together and in all cases short coat acted as a dominant to long. He claims that in his extensive experience he never knew of two long-coated dogs producing short-coated progeny but cites one case of mating long-coated F_1 stock produced from Rough/Old English Sheepdog combinations. These F_1 stock produced some short-coated offspring suggesting that the two long-coat types may have been due to different genes.

In crosses involving tail feathering Whitney (1971) considered the presence of feathering to be dominant to its absence. Whether a long coat is straight or wavy does not seem to alter the basic genetic rules but the curly type of coat seen in Poodles is thought to be somewhat different (Burns and Fraser 1966) and may be dominant to both short and long varieties.

In Griffon Bruxellois, Little (1934) found wire coat was a simple dominant to smooth and this is confirmed by Whitney in various breeds.

Coat density—hairs per unit surface area—is more complex and most studies on it are subjective. Whitney (1971) considered the dense coat of the Elkhound acted as a dominant to the sparser coat of the Foxhound but this may not be a hard and fast rule. Density can be influenced by climatic conditions and any breeder will know that dogs kept in kennels will have a more luxurious and thicker coat than their housed mates. Colour itself may affect this in that some coat colours seem to produce better (denser?) coats than others. It is generally held that pigmented areas on parti-coloured coats grow longer than the neighbouring white hairs and black hairs grow longer than red but these rules may hold only within a breed and not across breeds.

Undercoat inheritance is not understood. In long-coated German Shepherds the undercoat is frequently absent (hence the selection against the type) and it seems that inheritance of undercoat is in some way linked to outer coat type.

Whitney (1971) refers to a puppy coat type which he calls ripple. It was noted in numerous Bloodhounds at birth but disappeared by about one week after birth. It would seem to be a skin rather than a coat characteristic and, according to Whitney, was inherited as a simple autosomal recessive. Cocker Spaniels as well as Bloodhounds seem to carry this factor.

Whorls in the Coat

A whorl occurs in a coat when the hair lies in the contrary direction to the general hair stream. This gives the impression of a circle of rough hair rather as if the coat has been brushed in the wrong direction at that point. In some breeds they are known as 'cowlicks' and the descriptive term is accurate enough in that it often appears that the animal has been licked.

Whorls are known in a variety of species, particularly in cattle and swine. In the dog they were first recorded by Pullig (1950) in Cocker Spaniels and they are known to exist in breeds like the Boxer and Dobermann in which they are currently thought to be a problem. Many Swine Breed Associations in the USA would penalise a pig with whorls (Nordby 1932) and this seems to be the policy adopted by some canine breed groups. In Britain the Dobermann groups have stated 'cowlicks' to be a disqualifying fault which seems a premature and illogical step. If, as seems likely, the condition is inherited then the logical first stage is to attempt to understand the mode of inheritance so that it can be bred out. Simply banning the defect from the show ring will neither prevent affected dogs being used nor will it enable the production of genetic data to be compiled and it will very probably encourage breeders to 'doctor' the coats.

According to Pullig (1950) whorls in her dogs appeared mainly in the flanks and shoulders though she reports other breeders as observing them on the head and neck. Similar regions are affected in Boxers and Dobermanns and these were the regions affected in swine according to Nordby (1932), although he also implicated the region of the tailhead.

Apparently the type of coat affects the expression of the whorl in that Pullig observed them more readily in red Cockers than in black ones. This may be a feature of coat texture differences or it may indicate descent from an original red line. Pullig observed that whorls

Table 20

Transmission of hair whorls in Cocker Spaniels

		Progeny*	
Type of mating	Litters	Normal	Whorls
Normal × Normal	5	20	7
Normal × Whorled	4	9	7

* One pup not observed is excluded.
Source   Pullig 1950.

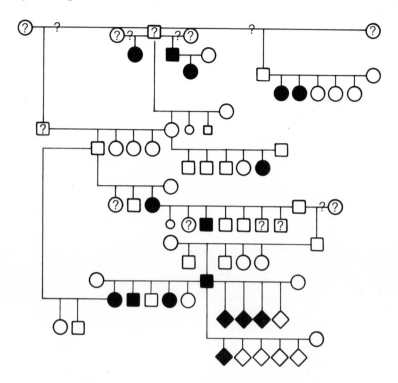

Figure 21   Pedigree of hair whorls (solid symbols) in Cocker Spaniels (Pullig 1950).
◇ Unknown sex   ? not examined   □○ stillborn

were generally, though not always, located in similar regions on progeny and parents but this was not obvious in swine data (Craft 1930, Nordby 1932).

In swine Craft (1930) and Nordby (1932) postulated a two gene series in which whorling acted as a dominant feature. This suggests that both genes are necessary to produce whorling and thus, although dominant it is possible for smooth-coated stock to give rise to offspring with whorls.

Pullig's data in the Cocker Spaniel do not confirm this view. Her breeding results tabulated above (Table 20) suggest an autosomal recessive condition which is confirmed by the pedigree chart (Figure 21). She suggests a relationship with red colour but as explained previously this may be fortuitous. However it is interesting that in the Dobermann red dogs are believed to be more subject to cowlicks than black ones.

The situation is in need of further study in affected breeds with the collection of litter data cataloguing both incidence and the location of whorls. That the condition is genetic seems to be beyond doubt.

The ridge in Rhodesian Ridgebacks is a form of whorl in that it represents a contrarywise slope of the hair. It is presumably an inherited recessive. It does seem that this ridge is associated with other genetic factors relating to cyst formation (see page 141).

Chapter 7

Inheritance of Specific Skeletal and Structural Defects

Achondroplasia and Chondrodystrophy

As has been explained previously an achondroplastic is an animal in which the long bones cease growing relatively early in life as regards their length but continue to grow in diameter. The animal thus results as a short-legged dwarf.

The condition is known in a variety of species including man and in most instances it has been shown to be caused by a simple autosomal recessive.

Achondroplasia was reported in Miniature Poodles by Gardner (1959) and by Amlof (1961) while a similar short-legged mutant was reported by Whitney (1971) in the Cocker Spaniel. The Miniature Poodle cases were attributed to a simple autosomal recessive but insufficient data existed to categorise the Cocker Spaniel case or another Cocker reported by Beachley and Graham in 1973.

It is probable that dwarf dogs of this kind appear in most breeds at intervals but are rarely reported and quickly eliminated. This is understandable but is to be regretted since more would be gained by reporting them to a central authority. If, as seems likely, the condition is a simple recessive and rare in most breeds then there is little need of any organised testing programme or eradication scheme since the affected stock can be disposed of and the parents bred from with relative impunity if the gene has a low frequency in the breed. Inbreeding of carrier stock or repeat matings of litters where achondroplastics occurred would not be recommended but overall the risk to a breed would be minimal.

The same is less true of a situation developing in the Alaskan Malamute in America where an achondroplastic type of dwarfism has been known for some time. Since 1970 various publications have arisen from North America on this subject and the breed club in that area is organising testing programmes to identify carrier dogs.

In the Alaskan Malamute the condition is very obvious with the affected dogs developing a typical stunted appearance and a frontal limb assembly not unlike that of the Basset Hound (Smart and Fletch 1971). There is enlargement of the carpal joints, turning out of the feet and a bowing of the radius and ulna bones. In a detailed clinical-pathological report Fletch *et al* (1973) consider that the correct terminology is chondrodysplasia because there is a marked increase in the number of hypertrophied chondrocytes. These are cartilage cells found in the bone. This same term was, in fact, used by Beachley and Graham (1973) for their Cocker Spaniel case.

Returning to the Miniature Poodle cases noted earlier it does appear from a review by Riser *et al* (1980) that dwarfism has been reported sporadically in this breed in several countries. Riser's group studied 13 affected animals and concluded that the condition resembled one in man known as pseudoachondroplastic dysplasia. The epiphyseal areas of the long bones had patchy density and bones were shortened and deformed. Dogs grew much slower than normal litter mates and because of hind limb defects often lay on their sternums causing rib deformities. Riser's group suggest an autosomal recessive inheritance but give no statistical proof. The paper is, however, an excellent source of radiographic material.

Chondrodysplasia in the Alaskan Malamute has been widely documented in the scientific literature (Smart and Fletch 1971; Subden *et al* 1972; Fletch *et al* 1973, 1975; Sande *et al* 1974) and the genetics is well established as being a simple autosomal recessive which has been designated dan. There are thus three types of dog: the normal +/+, the carrier +/dan and the chondrodysplastic dan/dan.

Affected animals appear to have no impairment of their lifespan in that a Toronto colony had some aged 5 years or more. There is also no increase in litter mortality (Subden *et al* 1972) but there is some, as yet, unconfirmed suggestion by Fletch *et al* (1975) that a poor fertility record may exist due to some sperm defect. A more interesting development has been the association of this condition with a form of anaemia. This was first reported by Pinkerton and Fletch (1972) and more fully discussed by Pinkerton *et al* (1974) and Fletch *et al* (1975).

The anaemia seems to be characterised by a decreased survival of red blood cells (erythrocytes) but can be identified from other anaemias by a characteristic red cell index. It resembles a certain condition found in man and the Alaskan Malamute dwarfs can thus play a part as a model for human investigations. Obviously the dan allele has a pleiotropic affect in that it influences not only bone growth but red blood cell development.

It is important to appreciate that the chondrodysplastic cases can have variable expression and that although dwarf in size because of their short legs they cannot be considered as miniatures since they have normal body development (see Plates 6a and 6b).

Pituitary Dwarfism

The pituitary gland is situated on the lower part of the brain and is possibly the most important endocrine gland in the body. From the anterior lobe of this gland come several hormones, one of which is growth hormone or somatotrophin. This particular hormone is known to stimulate growth of all body cells, in particular those concerned with bone and muscular tissue. The amount of somatotrophin produced varied with different animals but those which produce more per unit of body size will tend to grow faster and terminate at a larger mature size. Growth will usually cease when the amount of hormone produced per unit of weight is only sufficient to allow replacement of damaged cells rather than the production of new ones. Generally when we are selecting animals to grow faster we are really selecting for a higher production of somatotrophin per unit of body size. An excess of growth hormone in a young animal will lead to the production of long limbs and giant stature. Any lack of hormone will lead to dwarfism. However, unlike achondroplasia or chondrodystrophy the pituitary dwarf will have normal body proportions although small in stature.

Dwarfism of the pituitary kind is not unknown in a variety of species and possibly exists in many dog breeds although most reports have related to German Shepherd Dogs. Over a period of some twenty years or more the scientific literature has noted pituitary dwarfs in this breed (Moch and Haase 1953; Baker 1955; Jensen 1959; Alexander 1963; Krook 1969; Muller and Jones 1973) all of which have been basically normal in proportions but of dwarf size. In some of the cases a cystic condition of the pituitary was noted but not in all.

Until recently the possible genetic origin of such dwarfs was not documented but Danish workers have thrown new light on this aspect. The work was undertaken at the Royal Veterinary and Agricultural University in Copenhagen and though based on relatively small numbers of dwarf animals has tended to confirm the mode of inheritance as being a simple autosomal recessive. Genetic aspects have been dealt with by Andresen *et al* (1974) and Andresen and Willeberg (1976a) while another paper (Willeberg *et al* 1975) has dealt with the hormone picture in some detail.

In most animals there are growth promoting hormone-like substances known as somatomedins which can be isolated from plasma and which are stimulated by growth hormones from the anterior pituitary gland. It seems from Danish work that somatomedin activity in dwarf animals is much reduced compared to normal dogs. Thus Willeberg *et al* (1975) found levels in four control dogs to be about 0.50 units of somatomedin activity whereas in dwarfs the values were around 0.10 units. Assays made in relatives of dwarfs showed values between these two levels.

German Shepherd dwarfs have been reported fairly frequently in breed literature in Australia since 1972 which was the time when importations were again permitted in this breed after a 44-year gap. The sudden splurge of dwarfs—almost entirely from imported British and German lines—caused much anxiety in Australia and it would seem from descriptions of the cases that they are identical with those in Denmark. Nicholas (1978) has analysed data on eight dwarfs born in the Sydney region and reached the same conclusion as the Danish workers regarded the mode of inheritance as well as implicating one of the same ancestors (Vello zd Sieben Faulen). Nicholas criticised the statistical techniques used by Andresen and his colleagues and reanalysed their data but reached more or less the same conclusion. He does, however, include some stillbirths as being presumptive dwarfs for which little justification can be made. GSDIF data shows that there are appreciable stillbirth levels in this breed and it is illogical to consider them all as potential dwarfs. It is claimed (Andresen *et al* 1974; Andresen and Willeberg 1976a) that the relative fitness of these dwarfs is lower than non-dwarf litter mates but this is by no means certain. Two cases have been reported to the GSDIF (Willis 1978a), one in a litter born in 1963 and the other in 1971. The latter was still alive at the time of writing and is shown in Plate 7. Both British cases trace back to the same dog who is also implicated as an ancestor in one of the British dogs known to have sired dwarfs in Australia. Since then more have been seen.

Ancestral data relating to Danish cases is shown in Figure 22 and the British cases in Figure 23. No assays were undertaken on the British dogs but they were typical of pituitary dwarfs elsewhere. The animals pictured in Plate 7 had one season and thereafter no reproductive activity but had normal behaviour patterns. A case from British stock in Malaya and two cases in Britain in the 1940s suggest that ancestors implicated in dwarfism go back further than those named by Andresen and Willeberg (1976a).

The condition would appear to be limited in incidence and no major cause for concern. Dwarf pups will be normal at birth but will be recognisable from about eight weeks onwards and can be readily culled. There is little point in test matings since the incidence of the dwarf gene is low and test mating would be costly and have to be with known carriers. However reporting of dwarfs to a central agency such as the GSDIF seems sensible and will enable those who wish to avoid dwarf stock to ignore known carriers as potential mates.

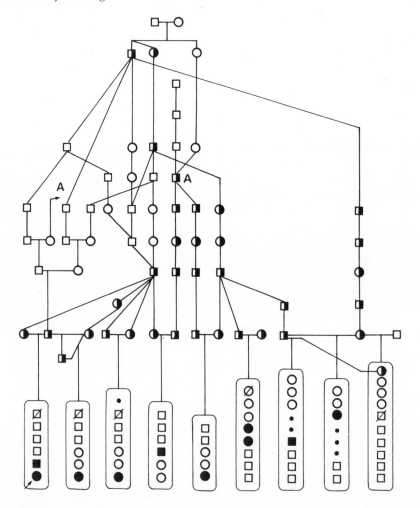

Figure 22 Pedigree showing descent of the pituitary dwarf gene in German Shepherd Dogs (Andresen 1978).

☐ ●| affected   ◧ ◑| carriers   • stillborn   ☒ died early

Dwarfism of an identical kind has been reported in Karelian Bear Dogs by the same Danish group (Andresen and Willeberg 1976b). Nine dwarfs were observed in six litters born in the period 1968–75 and although post mortems were not made the physical size and form was akin to the GSD cases (Plate 8). The data fit an autosomal recessive situation and Andresen and Willeberg (1976b) postulated that it may be an identical gene to that seen in German Shepherds. They make this comment on the grounds that crossing between the two breeds was undertaken in the mid 1940s (Ingeberg 1960) and the dwarf gene in German Shepherds is known to trace back at least to this peiod of time and possibly earlier. A diagrammatic representation of the Karelian Bear Dog pedigrees is shown in Figure 24.

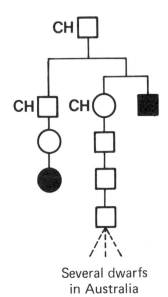

Several dwarfs
in Australia

Figure 23   Pedigree showing line of descent of the pituitary dwarf allele from a British Champion male German Shepherd Dog (Willis 1978a).

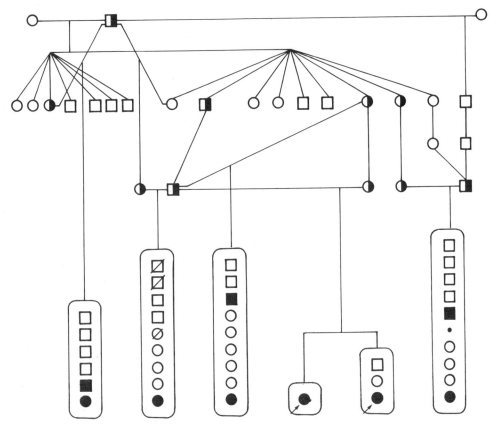

Figure 24   Pedigree of dwarfs (solid symbols) in Karelian Bear Dogs (Andresen and Willeberg 1976b).
◰ ⬓ died undiagnosed   •   stillborn

Elbow Dysplasia

The term elbow dysplasia is a descriptive and somewhat popularised term applied to a development of the elbow joint. In the normal dog there is a piece of bone called the anconeal process which is united to the rear part of the ulna bone. The anconeal process is completely enclosed in the joint capsule but can be seen on X-ray when the elbow is semi-flexed and viewed laterally. In some dogs this process becomes completely or partially detached and then acts rather like a foreign body within the joint itself leading to pain and lameness and later arthritis. It can occur in one or both elbows and in either sex.

Clinical signs are usually seen in dogs aged four to six months and involve intermittent lameness over a period of some weeks. It can best be seen at speed when the animal may elbow out and throw a foot out when reaching forward. Handling the elbow will usually cause pain and radiography should isolate the problem.

The condition was first reported by Stiern (1956) who termed it 'ectopic sesamoid' after a similar condition in man but this is a misnomer as the sesamoid bone is not involved. Cawley and Archibald (1959) coined the phrase un-united anconeal process after examining several affected German Shepherds. The term elbow dysplasia was a later introduction and is preferable in that the condition can occur when the anconeal process is actually united to the ulna or there is osteoarthritis (Carlsson and Severin 1961).

A variety of breeds in various countries is affected. In the USA it has been noted in several large breeds—St Bernards, Newfoundlands, Great Danes, Irish Wolfhounds, Bloodhounds, Labradors and Basset Hounds—but most commonly in German Shepherds (Corley *et al* 1963, Corley and Carlsson 1965). In Britain Hodgman (1963) reported similar findings and in Austria Pobisch *et al* (1972) confirmed the high involvement of German Shepherds while adding several other breeds to the list, not all of them large ones. In a recent study Grøndalen (1976) found forelimb lameness in 15 breeds of dog aged from 5 to 9 months. He found un-united anconeal process or un-united or fragmented coronoid process was the causal factor and that both gave osteoarthritis. He also suggested that the

Table 21

Incidence of elbow dysplasia in various kinds of mating

Sire × Dam	Normal × Normal	Normal* × Normal	Normal* × Dysplastic	Dysplastic × Normal	Dysplastic × Dysplastic
Total progeny	17	27	22	49	72
Number normal	17	25	16	28	32
Number with ununited anconeal process	—	—	—	6	13
Number arthritic	—	—	3	3	11
Number unknown†	—	2	3	12	16

* Greyhound, all others German Shepherd Dogs.
† Includes all animals which died prior to 90 days of age by which time ossification of anconeal process is incomplete.
Source   Corley *et al* 1968.

problem was twice as common in males as females, a feature confirmed by Hayes *et al* (1979).

Familial patterns were seen in German Shepherds by Cawley and Archibald (1959) suggesting a possible hereditary mode of inheritance which was supported by later work from Vaughan (1962) in Britain. In contrast Stewart (1972) examined pedigrees of 38 affected German Shepherds and claimed that they were of different lines although she did suggest that inbreeding increased the incidence of the problem. Australian workers (Bradney 1967, CAVA 1967) have accepted the problem as being a genetic one but the main evidence stems from the USA. This concerned breeding work undertaken by Corley *et al* (1968) involving German Shepherds and, in one instance, German Shepherds crossed with Greyhounds.

The results of American work are shown in Table 21 and illustrate a 30% incidence in the breeding colony (33 cases in 109 progeny). The workers concluded that the disease is genetic in origin and that it is caused by three dominant genes.

Recessive inheritance can be ruled out because dysplastic × dysplastic mating gave 24 dysplastic and 32 normal progeny whereas in a recessive situation all would have been dysplastic. Similarly a single dominant gene is ruled out because 24:32 does not approach a 3:1 ratio. The same is true of a situation involving two dominant genes but the three dominant gene theory involves ratios almost identical to those obtained. This suggests that elbow dysplasia will occur in animals which carry the three genes in at least a single dose.

However, as Corley *et al* (1968) point out, the data are sparse and the theory is a tentative one. It does nevertheless seem that we are dealing with a polygenic trait which is dominant rather than recessive. Breed incidence is unknown but it could clearly spread rapidly. Stewart (1972) was of the opinion that it was increasing in German Shepherds in Britain and as Corley *et al* (1968) observed it in some cases only on examination of the dead animal by dissection it may be more prevalent than hitherto imagined.

A survey using veterinary hospital data from 14 North American universities (Hayes *et al* 1979) confirms the high risk nature of large breeds, notably the St Bernard and GSD, but also the Basset Hound. However the evidence did not favour the genetic mode of inheritance put forward by Corley and his colleagues. Hayes and his group did suggest that elbow and hip dysplasia might be related in that animals with both conditions were in excess of those expected. The validity of this finding is questionable. Both conditions are features of rapidly growing breeds and all that may be being observed is a predisposition of such breeds to both defects rather than indications that they are pleiotropic effects of the same genetic structure. There are too many flaws in hospital data of this kind to allow unequivocal acceptance of the published findings.

A useful study indicating possible genetic features in elbow joint problems has been published by Klingeborn (1986) for the Bernese Mountain Dog in Sweden. Lesions studied were varied but mostly involved fragmentation and/or fissure of the coronoid process. Five sires mated to from 8 to 12 bitches were assessed and the incidence of elbow joint lesions serious enough to warrant surgery ranged from 4.1 to 43.8% for the five sires. Dams which had themselves undergone surgery showed a higher incidence of problems among their progeny. A radiographic study of the breed was instigated and in the first 105 dogs seen 53.3% showed joint lesions of the elbow.

Other kinds of elbow luxation occur which are not related to the anconeal or coronoid processes but which may be genetic in origin. Thus Campbell (1969) reported that in a survey of non-fracture injuries to the elbow some 17% were due to congenital luxations, principally in small breeds such as the Pekingese, Shetland Sheepdog and Yorkshire Terrier. In these cases and in a later report (Campbell 1971) there was a variable degree of deformity ranging from mild subluxation of the radius head to severe bowing of the leg and an inability to extend the elbow when bearing weight. Grøndalen (1973) reported three Afghan Hound littermates with elbow deformities caused by incongruity of the joint surfaces of radius, ulna and humerus. Bingel and Riser (1977) reported cases in Miniature Poodles and a crossbred Terrier. In these cases there was deformity of the anconeal process and coronoid process. A deformity of the antibrachial bone in 20 Basset Hounds aged from 10 weeks to 9 years was reported by Grull and Henschel (1973) with similar results to elbow dysplasia though it may not be identical.

Bingel and Riser (1977) have postulated on the embryological development of the luxation problem and suggest that it may be inherited. Their reasoning is based upon a high incidence of bilateral involvement, more than one animal per litter affected in some cases, the embryonic stage at which development failure occurred was genetically controlled and in some instances other anomalies existed. Breeding data seem called for to confirm this and the question of whether all the differing types of elbow problem are symptoms of a single major defect must also be examined.

Recent papers dealing with the aetiology and treatment of elbow problems are those of Milton *et al* (1979), Grøndalen (1979abc), Robins (1980), Denny (1980) and Denny and Gibbs (1980b). In addition to the conditions dealt with above some mention is made of osteochondritis dissecans and arthritic complications. These are useful articles for the veterinary profession but add little to genetic knowledge.

Premature Closure of the Distal Ulnar Physis

The ulna is one of the two bones forming the foreleg—the other is the radius—and the distal physis or epiphysis is the end of the bone furthest from the body. It appears that in this condition the distal end of the bone closes earlier than normal thus preventing the correct fitting together of the ulna and carpal bones. This in turn causes the ulna to become bowed and the radius, which is fixed to the ulna, becomes misplaced at the elbow. It thus causes elbow dysplasia or subluxation although not through the same aetiology as in elbow dysplasia described earlier (see page 124).

Clinical signs are lameness that can persist over a few days or for several months. Affected dogs swing their elbows out and are in pain when the elbow is extended. Diagnosis is generally confirmed by radiography (Hanlon 1962, Riser 1964, Clayton-Jones and Vaughan 1970a, O'Brien *et al* 1971, Skaggs *et al* 1973, Carrig *et al* 1975). Erosion of the articular cartilages can occur and boney growth may occur on non-weightbearing surfaces.

It seems that premature growth of the ulnar physis can be caused most frequently by trauma. It can also be caused by radiation (Clayton-Jones and Vaughan 1970a) and by nutritional imbalances (Carrig *et al* 1975). However genetic causes also exist.

Lau (1977) has described this condition in 23 Skye Terrier pups born to two different bitches by four different sires. Twenty of the dogs were clinically lame and 15 were examined by X-ray. Various breedings were available from different types of parental stock. In one involving two normal parents there were two affected pups in nine born. In a mating between affected parents all six offspring that lived (three died) were affected. In a third mating between an affected bitch and a known producing (carrier) male there were seven affected offspring in eight born while in a father-daughter mating all five offspring were affected. In this last mating the bitch concerned was affected and the author concluded that the sire was assumed to be homozygous for the condition though he was not checked by X-ray.

Lau concluded that in this instance he was dealing with a simple autosomal recessive condition with complete penetrance. Thus AA and Aa animals would be normal but aa stock would be suffering from premature closure of the ulnar physis. Differential ages of closure may be a reflection of environmental differences but it seems that the earlier the closure occurs the greater will be the secondary changes in the elbow region.

A similar condition has been described in Basset Hounds by Rasmussen and Reimann (1977). They had six pups born to an affected sire but normal dam. Clinical signs occurred after three and a half months and they concluded that the decreased growth of the ulna may have been inherited. This condition and that in the Skye Terrier may not be identical but may be related.

Yet another problem of the ulna and radius has been described by Carrig and Seawright (1969) in Australian Dobermanns. This was a cystic bone condition at the distal end of the radius and/or ulna in young pups aged 5–7 months. The litter concerned had three affected pups in five survivors from eight born. It was inbred 2:3 on a certain male which was itself 6.25% inbred. The authors tentatively put forward a simple recessive theory but it cannot be proven at this stage.

Subluxation of the Carpus

The carpus is the name given to the knee bones in the foreleg of the dog and an interesting case of subluxation of this particular part of the leg was described by Pick *et al* (1967). Cases occurred in a colony of dogs maintained by the University of North Carolina for studies in haemophilia.

The breed of dog was not given in the paper but Pick (1978) has stated that it was originally Irish Setter to which Standard Poodle 'blood' was added to give the black coloration and to correct fertility problems.

The limb deformity was limited to the carporadial joints and always occurred in both legs. It was not obvious at birth but by about three weeks of age there was a sideways displacement of the legs so that the dog ended up walking on its knees. All tests that were undertaken showed the bone structure to be normal apart from the obvious dislocation.

The condition appeared to be a sex-linked condition carried on the X chromosome. Only males were affected when their parents were 'carrier' dams and normal sires. When affected males were bred to 'carrier' dams then both sexes could be affected. Some of the data given by Pick *et al* (1967) are shown in Table 22. No animals were affected by both carpal subluxation and haemophilia which is most unusual in view of the number of dogs involved. The authors suggest that the two defects may be alleles of the same gene which, as they admit, is difficult to accept in view of the extreme difference. It may be that carpal subluxation is a pleiotropic symptom of haemophilia which in some way prevents haemophilia occurring but this is really no more acceptable than the view that they are both alleles of the same gene. In man carpal dislocation is dominant (Ellsworth 1927) but that was not associated with haemophilia nor was any sex-linked theory put forward. The importance of this problem is fortunately academic since haemophiliac pups will be destroyed in breeding kennels as would carpal subluxation cases and thus far no other cases seem to have been reported outside of this colony.

Table 22

Association between carpal subluxation and haemophilia A in a colony of dogs

Mating type			Male progeny*				Female progeny*			
			Carpal X^sY	Haem X^hY	Normal XY	Total	Carpal X^sX^s	Haem X^hX^h	Carrier† XX	Total
Sire	×	Dam								
XY (Normal)		X^hX^s (Double carrier)	9	10	0	19	0	0	8	8
X^hY (Haem)		X^hX^s (Double carrier)	8	11	0	19	0	7	9	16
X^sY (Carpal defect)		X^hX^s (Double carrier)	3	2	0	5	3	0	0	3
X^hY (Haem)		X^hX^h (Haem)	0	5	0	5	0	1	0	1
Total observed			20	28	0	48	3	8	17	28
Total expected			21.5	26.5	0	—	1.5	9	17.5	—

* Progeny not known or unchecked are excluded.
† These are either XX^s XX^h or X^sX^h depending upon the particular cross.
Source   Pick *et al* 1967.

Patellar Luxation

The patella is the kneecap and in dogs it can be luxated or dislocated causing lameness. It can be intermittent or recurrent and is characterised by a dog that is normal one minute and carries its hind limb the next. No pain is felt and the dog will usually tolerate palpation of the limb but lameness is obvious if the dog is asked to use the limb. In most cases the dislocation is medial (that is turning inwards towards the centre) and in only a few instances is lateral (turning outwards). This is shown by a survey of 169 dogs reported by Endres (1977) in which 143 had medial luxation, 21 lateral and 5 had both.

The patella can be manipulated into place but will usually be dislocated again and in this case will lead to persistent lameness and abnormal movement. It seems that the primary aetiology is due to a shallowness or total absence of the trochlea (femoral groove). This causes the patella to slip sideways to be temporarily or permanently dislocated.

Priester (1972) has studied the sex, size and breed incidence of this problem in a population of 69,245 patients at an animal clinic of which 542 had patellar luxation. There appeared to be 1.5 times more problems in females than males and small breeds (under 9kg adult weight) had some 12 times greater chance of the problem than large dogs with very little differential risk among medium, large or giant breeds. The relative risks for various breeds are shown in Table 23. These clearly show the high relative risk of small breeds which confirms earlier reports from Britain (Hodgman 1963, Knight 1963). The high relative risk among Poodles of the Miniature or Toy varieties is supported by Endres (1977) whose sample of 169 cases in Germany included over 50% from these two varieties.

Table 23

Relative risk for patellar luxation by sex, size and breed

Risk category	Cases seen†	Relative risk
Sex		
Female	341	1.6*
Male	201	1.0
Adult weight		
Small (up to 9 kg)	400	6.6*
Medium (9.1–18.1 kg)	31	0.7
Large (18.2–36.2 kg)	45	0.5*
Giant (36.3 kg or more)	3	0.5
Not specified	63	1.0
Breed		
Pomeranian	37	8.1*
Yorkshire Terrier	18	7.6*
Chihuahua	43	5.1*
Poodle (Miniature and Toy)	243	4.2*
Boston Terrier	23	2.1*
Pekingese	11	1.8
Poodle (Standard)	15	1.8
Fox Terrier	10	1.4
All breeds	542	1.0
Cocker Spaniel	13	0.6
Beagle	5	0.2*
Dachshund	6	0.2*
Collie	3	0.2*
Labrador Retriever	3	0.2*
Boxer	1	0.1
German Shepherd Dog	0	0.0

*Relative risk differs significantly from R = 1. Values above 1 are above average risk and below 1 are less than average risk.
†Only breeds with sufficient cases seen or expected (relative to total number) are included. Sufficient = 20.
Source   Priester 1972.

Knight suggests that the abnormality is a consequence of dwarfing. Kodituwakku (1962) considers that the defect is due to a simple autosomal recessive whereas the view of Loeffler and Meyer (1961) and Loeffler (1964) is in favour of a polygenic mode of inheritance. Several reports (AHT 1965, CAVA 1967) consider this to be an inherited condition as did Hodgman (1963) but no reliable genetic evidence exists. It seems most probable that a simple genetic explanation does not exist and that the mode of inheritance, if any, is likely to be polygenic.

Although small breeds are mostly at risk Hodgman (1963) did list 43 breeds in which the condition was known while Priester (1972) lists 34 and suggests that other non-recognised breeds also had the problem. It does not follow that the genetics will be identical in each case.

Calvé-Perthes Disease (Legg-Perthes Disease)

This disease is a relatively common problem in small breeds of dog and a similar condition occurs in children. It is a very similar disease to hip dysplasia (see Chapter 8) and in many of the earlier reports there is some confusion between the two. Both involve some necrosis of the hip joint. However, whereas in hip dysplasia the essential problem stems from a shallow acetabulum, in Calvé-Perthes disease the main area of necrosis is the femoral head. There is enlargement of the femoral neck, loss of minerals and some degree of collapse of the bony support of the head. If the process is halted then the femoral head may be flattened and degenerative joint disease may result. It is at this stage that confusion between the two diseases often occurs. Generally, though not inevitably, hip dysplasia is bilateral with both hips similarly affected whereas in 90% of cases Calvé-Perthes disease is unilateral. The sequence of events which occur once necrosis of the femoral head has ccurred was reported by Lee (1970) but the original cause of the necrosis is uncertain.

It does appear that hip dysplasia is a feature of large breeds while Calvé-Perthes disease is generally confined to small breeds. Most early authors who lump the two together (for example Wamberg 1961, 1963) would appear to be in error and the view of Burns and Fraser (1966) that the two are manifestations of the same genetic abnormality would seem to be outdated.

Having said this, the genetics of Calve-Perthes disease is not at all clear. In humans Wynne-Davies and Gormley (1978) could detect no genetic involvement though they did show an association with parity and parental age as well as underdevelopment in the child. The most recent attempt to examine the genetics of the disease in the dog was undertaken by Pidduck and Webbon (1978) using four cases in a Toy Poodle kennels. They concluded that the condition was caused by a simple autosomal recessive gene but, as the authors point out, the view can only be regarded as tentative in view of the limited number of cases and the absence of test matings. The difficulties of diagnosis do not aid genetic studies but it is clear that miniature breeds, where this is likely to occur, need to begin collection of data for genetic studies to be made if the disease is to be controlled.

More recently Wallin (1986) has undertaken a study in the West Highland White Terrier in Sweden. Over the period 1976–82 he showed a frequency of 4% of animals affected by this disease. In a study of 39 litters which contained 144 animals there were 51 affected dogs, more or less equally divided by the sexes. The data were indicative of a simple autosomal recessive but further breeding tests were being undertaken.

Intertarsal and Tarso-metatarsal Subluxation

The hock is made up of the hock joint and the hock proper. The hock joint is the tarsus and it is a complex system. At the proximal end it is a ginglymus or hinge joint formed by the distal end of the tibia and the tibial tarsal bone or talus. The remaining tarsal bones have only limited movement between them and form an arthrodial type joint. This is a flat joint allowing slight gliding movement between the opposing surfaces or facets. These tarsal bones at their distal surface form a joint with the metatarsals of the hock proper.

Luxation or subluxation of the hock can involve the intertarsal joints, the tibio-tarsal joint or the tarso-metatarsal joints. The first mention of intertarsal luxation seems to have been by Lawson (1961) and this has been followed by further communications from Meutstege (1971) and Clayton-Jones (1974). Luxation of the tibio-tarsal joint was reported by Pettit (1974) and more recently Campbell *et al* (1976) have reported on intertarsal and tarso-metatarsal subluxation, although this last kind of subluxation was reported as far back as 1954 by Arwedsson.

Severe trauma can be a cause of luxation of this joint (see Holt 1974) but in the comprehensive study by Campbell *et al* (1976) 44 cases of intertarsal luxation were examined at Glasgow Veterinary School and in 75% of cases trauma was absent or minimal. A high proportion of cases were Shetland Sheepdogs (22 in 44) and Collies or Collie crosses (10 in 44). The incidence of Shetland Sheepdogs and Collies in the population seen at the clinic was 2.7 and 6.7% respectively, suggesting that there was an obvious predisposition in these two sheepdog types.

Of the 44 cases 11 had been the subject of severe trauma (for example road accident) whereas a further nine had received minor trauma (landing badly on jumping). However the remaining 24 cases had no obvious trauma to account for the injury. All but two of the Shetland Sheepdogs were in the non or minimal trauma categories. This very obvious predisposition among Shetland Sheepdogs was also noted by Clayton-Jones (1974) and suggests some genetic basis.

In respect of tarso-metatarsal subluxation the Glasgow data related to only eight dogs and although three were Collies no real conclusions can be drawn. In both conditions age was advanced being 3–10 years in the case of tarso-metatarsal subluxation and averaging 7.8 years in respect of intertarsal subluxation. Both sexes were affected and a preponderance of males may reflect the general population situation. Shetland Sheepdogs had a specific age incidence spread of 6–9 years making genetic studies difficult to undertake but it would seem worthwhile doing so. Until more data are forthcoming no genetic theories can be postulated.

Invertebral Disc Protrusion or Disc Disease

Invertebral disc protrusion is another term for what man generally refers to as 'slipped disc'. As in man, it is not uncommon in dogs although some doubts exist over certain descriptions in the literature. The symptoms, diagnosis and treatment of disc disease have been described in detail by Vaughan (1958a, b, c, d) and it could well be that certain other conditions described in the literature are merely extensions of an original disc problem. Thus Glenney (1956) describes some 85 cases of spinal osteo-arthritis or spondylitis deformans which may have occurred from disc protrusion. The same is true of a condition in Boxers where there was stiffening of the vertebral column (Zimmer and Stahli 1960).

An excellent paper by Hoerlein (1979) looks at the problems of disc disease in man and the dog in a comparative sense. Although grossly similar in spinal formation man has only about 33 vertebrae compared with about 50 in the dog. Generally dogs have 7 cervical, 13 thoracic, 7 lumbar and 3 saccral vertebrae with the rest being coccygeal and varying widely in number as well as being removed in docked breeds. Disc disease, especially in the thoraco-lumbar area is much more serious in the dog than in man and Hoerlein provides good diagrammatic explanations for this.

Hansen (1952) has suggested that disc protrusion is likely to be most frequently found in achondroplastic or chondrodystrophic breeds and he singled out Dachshunds, French Bulldogs and Pekingese which are achondroplastic, brachycephalic and achondroplastic and brachycephalic respectively. This seems to be supported by Vaughan in his series of 1958 papers since he cites 67 cases of which 34 were Dachshunds and 10 Pekingese. However Vaughan also had nine cases in Cocker Spaniels and he considered that Spaniels (Cockers and Springers?) were susceptible to slipped disc problems. Hansen (1964) tends to confirm the susceptibility of Cockers by considering American Cockers to have an above average degree of risk. Glenney (1956) also found a high number of cases in American Cockers (29 cases in 85) as well as Dachshunds (13) and Boxers (16) which suggests that he was dealing with the same problem. However Glenney points out that no cases were seen in Beagles, the most numerically popular breed at that time in the USA where he was working. More recently, Goggin *et al* (1970) have examined the breed incidence risk in America and considered that Dachshunds were at greatest risk with Pekingese, Beagles and Cockers being less so in that order. Russell and Griffiths (1968) looked at 110 cases of disc protrusion and found that 24 were mongrels but among the rest there were 31 Beagles, 20 Dachshunds and 17 Cockers. An extensive study by Priester (1976) shows a measurably high incidence of disc disease in the Dachshund of about 24% which was a rate some 12.6 times greater than for all other breeds combined. Data on sites of disc lesions are provided by Hoerlein (1979).

It therefore seems that disc protrusion is a particular problem in certain breeds and that they are not necessarily of the achondroplastic or brachycephalic type. There appear to be some differences between breeds in the region of the spinal column that is affected. Thus disc protrusion in Dachshunds is mainly in the thoraco-lumbar region while in Spaniels it tends to be cervical but cases can occur in either or both sites (see Goggin *et al* 1970).

There does seem to be some sex-related factor involved since Goggin and his colleagues found a difference in age at onset between the sexes, generally being earlier in females. However they also found some differences between sites in respect of age of onset which varied by both breed and sex. In general, cervical problems had a later age at onset than did thoraco-lumbar disc protrusion.

In a study of 324 Boxers in Switzerland some 92.4% were found by Muhlebach and Freudiger (1973) to have spondylosis to some degree. They found that it could occur at any age from nine months onwards and at any point in the thoraco-lumbar region but most frequently in the 12/13 thoracic vertebrae.

The fact that different breeds seem to be more at risk than others seems to indicate genetic involvement and Muhlebach and Freudiger were convinced that there was some genetic influence in their Boxer data. However the mode of inheritance is unknown and unlikely to be simple. Whether the condition is due to selectional problems in breed standards is unclear but it is certainly not correct to condemn all achondroplastic breeds since the Basset Hound is one that does not seem to suffer from the problem. It is also clear that individuals in susceptible breeds like Cockers and Dachshunds do remain free from the problem but until data are collected on an organised basis the way to ensure proliferation of such clear dogs will remain a matter for conjecture.

Hemivertebra

This condition arises due to abnormal development of the spinal vertebrae causing them to be wedge-shaped. It has been recorded in a variety of breeds in North America (Olsson 1965, Grenn and Lindo 1969, Hoerlein 1971), Continental Europe (Loeffler 1964, Morgan 1968, Schieffer 1968) and Britain (Wright and Palmer 1969, Done *et al* 1975).

According to Morgan (1968) the condition does not usually give rise to any obvious clinical symptoms but in some cases a series of problems can occur. These vary from hind leg weakness or spinal curvature to pain in the spinal regions. Several of these symptoms are discussed in detail by Done *et al* (1975) who also give details of the vertebrae affected. These are almost always thoracic and generally in the 7th–9th region.

Breed incidence seems to centre mainly around small brachycephalic types with screw tails. Hence the Bulldog, Boston Terrier and French Bulldog appear to be frequently implicated. Others include the Pug but breeds like the Pekingese, Yorkshire Terrier and West Highland White have been involved (see Done *et al* 1975). It has been suggested by Carlsson (1961) that hemivertebrae are so common in screw-tailed breeds as to be considered a breed characteristic rather than an abnormality. Whether this is true or not it would seem to be a dangerous hypothesis since Drew (1974) has commented upon a possible relationship between developmental anomalies of the spine and neonatal mortality in Bulldogs.

According to Done *et al* (1975) familial relationships suggest a possible genetic basis to the disease. These workers cite the case of a Yorkshire Terrier which had the condition and whose grand-dam and great-grand-dam had clinical signs suggestive of hemivertebra. Similarly the dam of three Bulldog pups affected by the condition was herself known to have hemivertebra.

The condition seems to be congenital—present at birth—but may only be seen on X-ray. A genetic basis may exist but it may, in fact, be a complex trait caused by deliberate selection for a shortened body. Woods *et al* (1978) have reported four cases of an oesophageal deviation in Bulldogs and they concluded that an anatomical shortening of the thorax may have led to a 'redundant oesophagus'. Hemivertebrae in these dogs helped to support this theory.

Hemivertebra and oesophageal deviation may be symptoms of the dog breeders' 'success' in altering the shape of some brachycephalic breeds to the point at which their deformity is becoming a distinct disadvantage. This would suggest that a polygenic mode of inheritance is more likely than any simple explanation.

Other Malformations of the Spinal Vertebrae

Various authors have been concerned with spinal cord compression arising from abnormality of the vertebrae or their articulations (see reviews by Trotter *et al* 1976; Mason 1978). Generally this is in the cervical region.

The main clinical symptoms tend to be ataxia of the pelvic limbs which is rather difficult to distinguish from the normal poor coordination of a rapidly growing dog. Usually, however, the symptoms are progressive and the dog begins to move with a swaying or wobbling hind end rather like the Wobbler Syndrome in horses. According to Trotter and his colleagues the symptoms were less obvious in a dog moving at speed but a change of pace could result in complete collapse of the hind limbs. Radiography of the spinal column in the cervical region usually revealed abnormal relationships between adjacent vertebra and in the later stages there is marked degenerative change. Usually the sixth or seventh vertebrae are the main ones affected. Neurological examination will distinguish this disease from others such as spinal cord myelitis and invertebral disc protrusion and their uncoordinated limb movement and spastic type gait is not typical of skeletal faults but very typical of spinal cord compression.

The condition was described by Trotter *et al* (1976) in 40 Great Danes and 17 Dobermanns. Mason (1978) reports that small numbers of cases have been seen in the Rhodesian Ridgeback, Basset Hound, Old English Sheepdog, Weimaraner and German Shepherd but agrees that Great Danes and Dobermanns are the predominantly affected ones. The exact aetiology is uncertain but Wright *et al* (1973) have postulated that the relatively long neck and heavy head coupled with rapid growth lead to vertebrae becoming misshapen. The role of nutrition is important (Hedhammar *et al* 1974) but there does seem to be a genetic component in that breeding from affected dogs seemed to increase the incidence (Selcer and Oliver 1975). Mason (1977) has examined the pedigrees of 60 Dobermanns in Australia and supports the view that there is a genetic basis for the disease, as yet uncertain. Early papers by Stockard (1936) and Innes and Saunders (1957) refer to hind limb paralysis in Great Danes and St Bernards which may be part of the same syndrome.

In contrast Palmer and Wallace (1967) report cases of paralysis in Basset Hounds in the period from birth to six months of age. Cervical vertebrae were deformed but only males were affected and a sex-linked or sex-limited explanation was not ruled out. The deformity was at the third cervical vertebra causing pressure on the spinal cord which led to paralysis. A pedigree of related dogs is shown in Figure 25.

Spondylosis deformans characterised by bony spurs of the spine, particularly in the lumbosacral region, were studied by Larsen and Selby (1981) using standard hip X-rays submitted to the OFA. The condition was certainly age related with most affected dogs being aged but there did appear to be some differential breed risk. The Boxer is alleged to be at particular risk and was in this study but 28% of the cases seen were in Irish Setters and this breed and the flat-coated Retriever were at greater risk than the Boxer. Higher than average risk was seen also in Bloodhounds and Rhodesian Ridgebacks. The genetic implications of this American study are uncertain.

Osteochondritis dissecans (Osteochondrosis)

The disease is essentially a problem affecting the formation of bone and cartilage in the epiphysis of young animals. This is the extremity (either end) of the long bones and the disease causes uneven bone/cartilage formation and wearing at these points. Articular cartilage and bone may be found lying free within or around the joint and this invariably causes lameness. The most common site seems to be at the proximal articular surface of the humerus (Craig and Riser 1965; Birkeland 1967; Clayton-Jones and Vaughan 1970b). Lesions have, however, been seen at other sites such as the condyles of the femur (Hickman 1964) and the distal end of the radius (Butler *et al* 1971).

The aetiology is uncertain. Carrig and Morgan (1974) have found that it can be caused by delayed ossification of one part of the humerus head relative to another and that this causes trauma in larger breeds. In contrast Palmer (1970) suggested that vitamin C, calcium and phosphorus were involved. Wood *et al* (1975) and Robins (1978) briefly reviewed the subject while treatment of the condition in the stifle and shoulder joints were described by Denny and Gibbs (1980a).

Bergsten and Nordin (1986) looked at insurance claims for this disease in Swedish breeds in 1979, 1981 and 1983 covering some 40% of the canine population in these years. From these figures the incidence of osteochondrosis was significantly greater than average in Rottweiler, St Bernard, Great Dane, Golden Retriever and Labrador Retriever breeds.

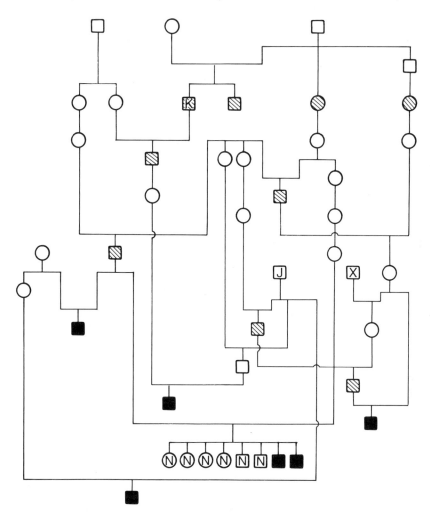

Figure 25 Cervical malformation in the Basset Hound (redrawn from Palmer and Wallace 1967). X, K and J are closely related ▨ champions ■ affected Ⓝ Ⓝ normal

Other breeds not common in Sweden such as Bernese Mountain Dogs and Newfoundlands are certainly troubled in Britain and the problem seems to exhibit breed predispositions. Whether there are genetic overtones is uncertain. In the GSD Lindstedt *et al* (1986) found a sex effect in that males were more prone to the condition than bitches but the overall incidence was not high. Only 31 cases were seen in 1458 dogs.

Panosteitis

Sometimes referred to as osteomyelitis or enostosis this is a disease affecting the long bones, particularly humerus, ulna, radius, femur and tibia. Symptoms are intermittent lameness in one or more limbs and radiographic examination will reveal density changes in the bones. It appears most commonly in the German Shepherd (Cotter *et al* 1968; Bohning *et al* 1970; Bone 1980) but is also known in the Pyrenean, Rottweiler, Basset Hound and others. In a study of 1458 GSD in Sweden Lindstedt *et al* (1986) found an incidence of about 4.5% and assessed the heritability at 13%. Excellent radiographic plates were produced by Bone (1980) which would help in diagnosis. In USA many breeders of GSD consider the condition to be a simple recessive and talk of the 'gene for panosteitis' but there is no evidence to support this belief. According to Foley *et al* (1979) and Lindstedt *et al* (1986) males are more prone to the problem than females.

Multiple Cartilaginous Exostoses

Bony growths on the long bones have been reported in the dog by Banks and Bridges (1956) and by Owen and Nielsen (1968). In some instances ribs as well as long bones of the legs were affected. A case in three out of five litter mates was reported by Gee and Doige (1970). The litter was a mongrel one and neither the sire nor dam was examined. In several cases the condition appeared to be progressive and there was a spastic-like gait. The genetic implications, if any, are unknown.

Ectromelia (Missing Limbs)

In many species, individuals can be born without limbs. In some instances, as in the thalidomide cases in man, this is a developmental defect caused by drugs or some similar agent during a crucial stage of foetal development. However, in rare cases, it can be genetic in origin and one such case has been reported by Ladrat *et al* (1969). They mated a bitch born without any forelegs to a normal male and produced four normal offspring. One of these was subsequently mated to its dam and produced three litters comprising 12 offspring, seven of which were born without forelimbs. In seven matings among progeny of the original bitch there were 23 pups of which 13 had ectromelia. The evidence seems fairly conclusive that this is a simple recessive autosomal genetic problem. It is, however, so rare as to present no difficulties to any breeder.

Short Spine (Baboon Dogs)

A condition in which the whole spinal column is shortened so as to lead to the baboon-like appearance of a high shoulder and very steeply sloping backline has been known in a Japanese breed called the Shiba-Inu (Suu 1956, Suu and Ueshima 1957, 1958, 1963, Ueshima 1961). It appears to be caused by early cartilaginous degeneration and ossification during foetal and immediate post-natal life. A similar condition was reported in a family of Greyhounds in South Africa (De Boom 1956) where it was thought to be caused by a simple recessive gene. Like the previous defect it is unlikely to cause problems to breeders and is thus largely of academic interest.

Temporomandibular Dysplasia

The temporomandibular joint is a hinged one between the mandible or jaw bone and the temporal bone of the skull. The hinged effect operates during opening and closing of the jaw but there is also an arthrodial or sliding effect with this joint when the jaw is moved from side to side during the grinding of food.

Subluxation or dysplasia of this joint has been noted in the Basset Hound (Robbins and Grandage 1977; Gibbs 1977) and the Irish Setter (Stewart *et al* 1975). More recently Hoppe and Svalastoga (1980) described various degrees of dysplasia in an American Cocker and five of its relatives. No clinical signs were noticed and similar defects in the formation of the joint was noticed in two unrelated American Cockers although in their case it was unilateral and not affecting both sides of the joint as in the previous six cases. Pedigree relationship might suggest a genetic cause but no mode of inheritance can be put forward.

Craniomandibular Osteopathy (CMO)

This condition is sometimes called lion jaw, westy jaw or scotty jaw. It is essentially a bone disorder involving the formation of excessive dense bone on the mandible. Very occasionally other areas such as the cranium, radius and ulna may also develop the same kind of problem but it primarily affects the mandible. It is most often seen at an age from 4 to 7 months with discomfort during chewing being observed. Palpation is often sufficient to identify the problem but X-ray will confirm CMO. The defect tends to be self-limiting and it usually responds to corticosteroid treatment. Boston and Cairn Terriers are known to show the problem as are Great Danes and Dobermanns and a case has been seen in a Labrador. However, as the popular names imply, it is most often observed in Scottish Terriers and West Highland White Terriers. Padgett and Mostovsky (1986) have reviewed the condition and also undertook a study involving 18 WHWT litters in each of which at least one CMO case was identified. The authors presented a pedigree chart involving 24 cases among 126 offspring and their data clearly indicated a simple autosomal recessive trait. Data on other breeds are not as clear but it is highly probable that a similar explanation holds good, especially in Scottish Terriers which are closely connected to WHWT.

Hernias

Hernias in the dog have been found to be mainly of three kinds: inguinal; umbilical; and diaphragmatic. An inguinal hernia occurs in the region of the groin, umbilical in the abdomen and diaphragmatic in the diaphragm. In all cases there is a protrusion of parts of the inner organs into a region where those parts are not supposed to be. Thus in diaphragmatic hernias there is a break in the diaphragm and a protrusion of abdominal viscera into the thorax. In umbilical hernias there is protrusion of abdominal viscera through the umbilical region into the exterior while in inguinal hernias there is protrusion of viscera through the inguinal ring.

Little information exists on the diaphragmatic hernia and it is possible that most are occasioned by injury rather than congenital. However Feldmann *et al* (1968) have reported cases of congenital hernias of this type in a cross between an American Foxhound and a Labrador. Out of 17 pups there were four affected animals all of which died early in life. The authors suggested a recessive mode of inheritance but the evidence for this is not satisfactory.

As regards the other two kinds of hernia some excellent descriptive statistics were provided by Hayes (1974) based on 1313 cases of umbilical and 705 inguinal hernias in a

Table 24

Relative risk of hernias in various animal species with proportions corrected by surgical intervention

Species	Rate per 1000 patients		Percent corrected by surgery	
	Umbilical	Inguinal	Umbilical	Inguinal
Pigs	38.84	69.92	92	96
Cattle	6.52	0.51	88	70
Horses	4.66	1.13	89	91
Dogs	2.35	0.54	41	52
Cats	1.66	0.20	55	80

Source   Hayes 1974.

clinical population of 323,961 cases reported by 12 American and Canadian veterinary college hospitals. Rates per 1000 patients of the two defects are shown for each species in Table 24 and the relative risks in certain canine breeds are shown in Table 25.

It can generally be concluded that with the exception of the pig there is a higher risk of umbilical than inguinal hernias in each species. Within breeds of dogs certain show an apparent predisposition to hernias of one or the other kind and in this instance umbilical do not necessarily outnumber inguinal. Sex distribution was about equal in the case of inguinal hernias in the dog but in the case of umbilical hernias there was, according to Hayes (1974), a much higher risk in females. This appears to be uniform throughout all breeds affected. In this respect Hayes is in disagreement with Phillips and Felton (1939)

Table 25

Relative risk of hernias in various breeds of dog

Breed	Umbilical		Inguinal	
	Cases	R	Cases	R
West Highland White	0	0	9	37.6*
Basenji	8	7.1*	4	18.7*
Cairn Terrier	2	1.6	5	16.4*
Basset Hound	2	0.5	8	9.4*
Pekingese	27	5.6*	12	9.3*
Airedale Terrier	8	7.9*	0	0
Weimaraner	7	3.7*	0	0
Pointer	13	2.5*	0	0
All breeds	382	1.0	88	1.0

* An R value thus marked is significantly different from the overall value of 1($P < 0.001$).
Source   Hayes 1974.

who reported no sex-limited effects in respect of umbilical hernia in the Bull Terrier, Cocker Spaniel and Collie.

Phillips and Felton (1939) suggested that in the breeds which they studied the condition was controlled in a polygenic fashion. This is an opinion shared by Angus and Young (1972). More recently Robinson (1977) has postulated that umbilical hernia is inherited as a polygenic threshold character which may involve a major gene whose expression is modified by the breed background in genetic terms. The case for Robinson's hypothesis is strengthened by Hayes' survey data showing a generally low incidence across breeds but with occasionally high values in certain breeds.

In Hayes' data most breeds showed a predisposition for one or other defect rather than for both. The exceptions were the Basenji and Pekingese and this may mean that no association between inguinal and umbilical hernias exists.

Ashdown (1963) has postulated that inguinal hernia arises from anatomical causes in that differences in sizes of the vaginal orifice will predispose certain breeds to the problem. This does not mean that a genetic explanation is unacceptable since the form of expression may well be via the effect on the vaginal orifice or inguinal ring.

In a highly inbred strain of Basenjis (from 62 to 86% inbred), Fox (1963) noted the occurrence of various forms of inguinal hernia and midline defects. A genetic explanation seemed likely and again a polygenic threshold situation may be involved.

There is a need to understand hernia genetics in the dog in view of the relatively low proportion of dogs where successful surgery is performed. This may mean that owners prefer not to bother correcting the defect or that correction is difficult. Studies in breeds with a particular predisposition to both problems (for example Pekingese) would seem to be desirable.

A final form of hernia is that involving the perineum, the region lying between the anus and the genital organs in the male. It is the view of Harvey (1977) that this type of hernia is mainly seen in old males, particularly Collies, and more frequent on the right than left side. There is no evidence that the condition is genetic. However a paper by Hayes *et al* (1978) based on 771 dogs with perineal hernia showed that male Boston Terriers, Collies, Boxers, Pekingese and mongrels had higher than expected risks for the lesion. The age effect was confirmed by these workers.

Hair and Skin Problems

General

According to Evans *et al* (1974) the average small-animal veterinary practitioner in Britain will treat some 27 dogs per week for skin disease. In a scathing review Bagnall (1977) has suggested that a high proportion return uncured for further empirical treatment. Many skin disorders are undoubtedly caused by external agents or may be the result of nutritional disorders and hence they will be cured by non-genetic means as and when the veterinary profession makes up its mind as to the causal factors involved. At present there is considerable dispute as to identification of many problems still less their cure and the situation is unlikely to be rectified very rapidly unless veterinarians learn to specialise and be accepted as such by their professional bodies.

At present several breeds are criticised by breeders as being prone to particular skin disorders but this does not necessarily imply a genetic basis. The fact that Cheyletiella infestations are recognisable in Boxers (Bagnall 1977) does not mean that this is something peculiar to the breed or that Boxers are in some way genetically predisposed to the problem.

It is not improbable to assume that certain animals, lines or breeds are predisposed to particular skin disorders but until there are research results available it would be unwise for breeders to assume that a genetic basis exists. Because a particular line seems prone to some disorder does not mean it has a genetic predisposition, it might just as easily be that the line is maintained in a specific climatic environment or subject to a particular nutritional regime which predisposes it to the problem. Coat type may, in itself, be a predisposing factor and since coat type is clearly under genetic control it can be inferred that the skin disorder is connected. But this, however, would be a rather sweeping conclusion.

Some glandular disorders can lead to skin conditions of an abnormal kind. Thus hyperadrenocorticalism is known in several breeds and according to some workers (see Kelly 1973) is not uncommon in Toy and Miniature Poodles and Dachshunds. The adrenal glands are abnormal and this leads to hair loss, particularly over the rear part of the body. There are other symptoms including a pot-bellied appearance but the skin/coat problem is a symptom of the adrenal problem not the cause. This particularl disorder may be a result of neoplasms but when it is not the aetiology may include some genetic component. Breeds with this kind of difficulty can only be identified and helped by breeder cooperation and genetic analyses which, as yet, have not been attempted.

Hairlessness

This problem occurs in several kinds of dog and has been studied by various workers (Kohn 1911; Anon 1917; Prinzhorn 1921; Gaspar 1930; Zulueta 1949). The general consensus view is that the condition is a dominant one such that crosses with normal dogs will tend to have hairlessness predominating. However, hairlessness can occur in some breeds and in a pattern that does not suggest any dominant mode of inheritance.

A form of partial hairlessness was described in the Whippet by Thomsett (1961) who considered it to be non-hereditary but offered only limited evidence in support of his view. Kral and Schwartzman (1964) describe a Cocker Spaniel with no ventral haircoat from birth while Selmanowitz *et al* (1970) reported on a case in Miniature Poodles where two males in a litter of five had extensive alopecia (see Plate 10). The alopecic regions seemed to be the same in the affected dogs and there was an absence of hair follicles, arrector pili muscles, sebaceous and sweat glands. There were also dental faults in affected dogs (Selmanowitz *et al* 1977a) but this may reflect the well-established incidence of such problems in this breed and be unrelated to the hair problem though conjunctivitis may have been. Some breeding work was undertaken by mating affected males to normal and unrelated bitches and no alopecia occurred in 37 offspring. Subsequently F_1 females were backcrossed with their abnormal fathers (Selmanowitz *et al* 1977a) and there were eight affected stock in 14 births. The condition was apparent early in life (Plate 10) and the breeding data rule out any dominant condition. The authors favour a sex-linked mode of inheritance or an autosomal one, preferring the former on the grounds that the original pair of affected animals were males and sex-linked hairlessness problems have been found in other species. In fact either theory is acceptable and the data are insufficient to enable one theory to be favoured above the other although the recessive nature of the condition is obvious.

Alopecia has been reported by various authors in isolated cases in several breeds.

Frequently these involved dilution colours as for example in a blue Italian Greyhound (Briggs and Botha, 1986). This case was in South Africa and the authors review several cases from the literature.

Follicular dysplasia
In 1972 Selmanowitz *et al* reported on a litter of mongrel pups (6) in which some members had an anomaly of the black hair regions. These showed bare patches, fractured hairs lacking proper sheen and periodic scaliness of the skin. The litter was the result of a brother/sister mating, both of which exhibited the same problem.

The transmission of the problem suggests an inherited condition and some experimental matings were made using the same pair (Selmanowitz *et al* 1977b). In two matings there were 15 pups of which all 12 black-and-white animals developed the problem while three white pups did not. It was suggested that the original pair were homozygous for the autosomal gene responsible but the data do not confirm this nor do they enable any theory as to dominance or recessivity. A similar problem was seen in Bearded Collies by Harper (1978) but in this instance both brown and black hair were affected, one pup of each colour being reported.

Dermoid cysts
This condition, sometimes called dermoid sinus, is found in the Rhodesian Ridgeback and occurs along the ridge, though not actually on it. The sinus is a kind of tube opening on the skin surface and running in towards the spine. Different types occur in respect of how deeply the sinus runs.

The problem was first described by Hare (1932) and the term dermoid sinus was coined by Steyn *et al* (1939). The possibility of a genetic involvement was put forward by Hare (1932) who provided some data but did not analyse them. Hofmeyr (1963) suggested that the condition was inherited because crosses with the Ridgeback often had the problem. This was taken to mean a dominant condition on the grounds that a recessive gene would not be carried by the other half of the cross but this is not necessarily true in the region where such crosses occurred. Lord *et al* (1957) had earlier postulated a more complex mode of inheritance, considering it to be related to the ridge and with most dogs of the breed carrying some genes for the problem. Stratton (1964) was also of the view that the mode of inheritance was complex.

Later Mann and Stratton (1966) reanalysed Hare's data and were of the opinion that it supported a simple autosomal recessive mode of inheritance. They also analysed data on 48 litters covering 376 recorded offspring from which 28 litters with 225 offspring provided evidence on dermoid sinus inheritance. The data (Table 26) did not fit a simple autosomal theory due to a shortage of affected offspring and the authors concluded that a problem of irregular penetrance was involved or that the accuracy of some of the data was in question. On this latter point it does seem that the dermoid sinus is not always easily recognised in young pups and hence errors among those culled early in life are not unlikely. It is possible that this condition is indeed a simple autosomal recessive with full penetrance but more data must be collected under careful supervision to confirm this.

The condition is believed to be peculiar to the Rhodesian Ridgeback but Burgisser and Hintermann (1961) have reported a very similar sinus on the heads of Boxers. Pedigree data suggested a genetic involvement but no mode of transmission was presented.

Table 26

Transmission of dermoid sinus in the Rhodesian Ridgeback

| Litter size | Litters* | Progeny | |
		Normal	Affected
2	1	2	0
4	1	3	1
5	1	4	1
6	2	9	3
7	4	25	3
8	9	62	10
9	3	19	8
10	5	44	6
11	1	3	8
14	1	12	2
Totals	28	183	42

*Only those litters in which parents were assumed to be Nn in
genotype (known to have produced dermoid sinus).
Source   Mann and Stratton 1966.

Ehlers-Danlos syndrome
A disease in which there is extreme fragility of the skin and peripheral blood vessels as well
as hyperextensibility and skin laxity is known in man as the Ehlers-Danlos syndrome. It has
been reported in the mink and is known to occur in dogs (Arlein 1947; Hegreberg and
Padgett 1967). Details of the symptoms have been given by a group of workers at
Washington State University (Hegreberg *et al* 1966, 1969) and seem to involve a reduction

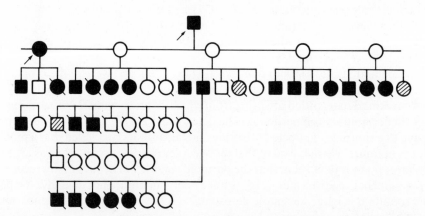

Figure 26 Pedigree showing the transmission of Ehlers-Danlos syndrome in Springer Spaniels.
Affected animals are shown by solid symbols, shaded symbols indicate unknown animals and slashed
symbols represent deceased stock. The arrows indicate the two animals which led to the formation of
the colony (Hegreberg *et al* 1969).

Table 27

Inheritance of Ehlers-Danlos syndrome in Springer Spaniels

		Offspring			
				Percent affected	
Type of mating	*Litters*	*Normal*	*Affected*	*Observed*	*Expected**
Normal × Affected	7	15	20	57.1	50
Affected × Affected	2	2	3	60.0	75

*Expected percentage assuming defect to be dominant and all affected parents are heterozygous.
Source   Hegreberg *et al* 1969.

of the tensile strength of the skin to about 1/27th of normal skin. This means that lacerations can be made very easily leaving large gaping wounds. Affected dogs develop numerous scars as a consequence in the regions of the head, neck, ears and back.

A breeding colony of Springer Spaniels was set up from an affected brother and sister. A pedigree is shown in Figure 26 and mating data in Table 27. The evidence seems to be conclusively in favour of an autosomal dominant with 100% penetrance. The mode of inheritance is thus identical with that in man and mink.

Chapter 8

Hip Dysplasia

Introduction

In recent years the canine press and related literature have probably given more publicity to dysplasia of the hip joint than to any other breeding subject. Despite this scrutiny there seems to be an almost inverse relationship between the amount of ink spilled and the understanding which dog breeders have of the subject. Many breeds in all countries of the world are affected by the condition but in numerous instances their breeders adopt an ostrich-like approach in the mistaken belief that by denying the existence of the problem it will somehow disappear.

Hip dysplasia is not the most important problem in dogs. There are many other defects which, though perhaps less widespread, are more serious in their effects upon the dog itself and in their potential for harm within a breed. Epilepsy or progressive retinal atrophy will frequently be more debilitating to the animal than hip dysplasia and such traits as nervousness or viciousness more harmful to the breed as a whole. However, these problems are generally accepted for what they are by breeders even though in many instances breeders pay only lip serice to their eradication. With hip dysplasia many breeders, including some who are considered to be leaders in their field, neither understand hip dysplasia nor, apparently, do anything about it. For this reason it seems appropriate to devote a whole chapter to reviewing the subject in detail.

The Condition (Definition and Diagnosis)

Hip dysplasia is not a new problem. It has been known in man since Roman times and it has been found not only in dogs but in the horse (Buer 1943), the cat (Henricson *et al* 1966) and beef cattle (Carnahan *et al* 1968; Weaver 1978). More recently it has been reported in a timber wolf (Douglass 1981) albeit in a captive environment. It was first reported in dogs by an American veterinarian (Schnelle 1935) but did not appear to attract much attention until the early 1950s when American breeders of German Shepherds began to be concerned by the problem. In this connection it is perhaps important to point out that much of the impetus for research into this problem has been occasioned by breeders of German Shepherds. This is by no means the only affected breed, nor is it even the worst affected but it is certainly the one on which most work has been undertaken. It will be apparent from the ensuing discussion that most of the information presented stems from the German Shepherd Dog. This is not a reflection of my own interest in that breed but occasioned by a dearth of information from other breeds.

The condition has been given various names over a period of time: subluxation, acetabular dysplasia, congenital hip luxation and congenital hip dysplasia. The term 'congenital' is a misnomer since that means 'present at birth' which is certainly not the case in the dog although it is the situation in man. The present nomenclature of hip dysplasia is simple and accurate and generally the one to be preferred.

The hip joint is a ball-and-socket arrangement with the head of the femur representing the ball and the acetabulum the socket. In a normal animal the femur fits tightly into a relatively deep socket with no looseness (see Plate 12). Abnormalities of the joint can occur for a variety of reasons and in varying degrees of severity. Hip dysplasia simply means a 'badly formed joint' and to this extent any variation from the normal can be defined as a case of dysplasia.

The basic problem is generally one of a rather shallow acetabulum causing the femur head to be loose. In terms of analogy one can imagine the normal hip as being like a cup into which one places a tennis ball. There will be a very close tight fit between the tennis ball and the lip of the cup. If one changes the cup for a saucer the tennis ball will roll around loosely upon it. These represent the two extremes within which a wide range of cases will occur as one varies the receptacle shape into which the ball fits.

In some cases the fit of the hip joint is so poor as to allow total dislocation of the femur head while in others the degree of dysplasia is so minor as to be obvious only to the trained observer. The poorer the fit the more likely one is to see secondary changes taking place and, in badly fitting cases, there will be friction between the contacting surfaces leading to a gradual wearing away of the bone surfaces. The femur head may become flattened and worn and the edges of the acetabulum may become chipped.

Malformation of the hip joint might reasonably be expected to lead to malfunction in the gait of the dog but this is by no means always the case. Clinical data based upon observation of an animal's gait can be misleading and even dangerous as a diagnostic tool. Breeds differ considerably in what type of movement they are expected to demonstrate. Movement considered ideal in one breed would be thought to be highly stilted in another, such that diagnosis by the unskilled is bound to be erroneous. In my own breed I have seen dogs which were so severely affected by hip dysplasia that they could not turn at right angles without falling over. In contrast I have seen known cases of hip dysplasia move apparently soundly in the show ring and win titles.

Some breeders hold the view that if the dog can move well enough to win in the ring then its hip status does not matter. This fails to appreciate that the degree of exertion required in the show ring is generally minimal. Moreover it also fails to take heed of the fact that certain dogs can develop compensatory structures around the hip joint which will enable a dysplastic hip to appear normal by external observation. Much also depends upon age. Some dogs with hip dysplasia will appear poor movers in early life, learn to compensate between the ages of 18 months and three years and be crippled at four.

There is ample evidence that poor hipped animals in youth are likely to exhibit arthritic conditions in later life. In a study of 86 GSD radiographically assessed in early life and restudied in later life Zedler *et al* (1978) showed no arthritic development in normals (15 dogs) but an 83.3% incidence in medium HD cases (18 dogs). Similar findings were reported by Niedermeyer (1984) in the same breed.

There are certain signs which may be useful guides to potential hip troubles. Dogs with stilted gaits or with croups which sway from side to side or which show signs of discomfort when rising or which avoid excessive exercise or dislike jumping may all be cases of hip dysplasia. But they may be demonstrating some other problem and it is an unwise breeder or veterinarian who makes his diagnosis on such things alone. A dog the author owned was a notorious bunny hopper in his puppyhood (often a sign of hip dysplasia) but passed the BVA hip scheme at 19 months.

Clinical signs may be used as a guide to potential hip trouble but they must be confirmed by X-ray. It cannot be overemphasised that diagnosis of hip dysplasia is dependent upon an X-ray being made of the hip joint. There was a time in the early 1960s when veterinarians in the USA and Britain gave the impression that only they were competent to diagnose the disease on X-ray. This was to be regretted since it does not require five years in veterinary school to be able to read X-ray plates nor are all veterinarians good at either taking suitable plates or reading them. This will be obvious to many practical breeders and it is confirmed by US Army work (Stunkard *et al* 1969) that local practitioners can act as good screeners but do not diagnose as reliably as trained radiographers. Having said this it should not be construed as meaning that I approve of the tendency among some breeders to undertake their own diagnoses of hip plates.

Fortunately most countries have realised the problems which occur with widespread diagnosis and in general they have adopted policies under which a trained individual or panel undertakes the diagnosis using plates submitted by local practitioners. Most errors seem to stem from incorrect positioning of the dog (Lawson 1963; Wright 1963; Stunkard *et al* 1969) and there is still need for veterinarians everywhere to perfect their techniques of X-raying so as to minimise the number of times a dog must be seen and to provide the diagnostic panel with clear plates and well-positioned subjects.

The usual position for placing the dog is to lie it on its back in a semi-sitting position so that the pelvis is flat rather than angled on the subsequent X-ray plate. The legs are then drawn back so that the animal is posed rather like a man standing. Since this can be rather painful, especially in a dysplastic dog it is usual for the dog to be anaesthetised. It is perhaps easier to correctly position the dog when it is unconscious but it is by no means essential and some veterinarians do not restrain the dog in this fashion but X-ray with the dog physically restrained. Breeders will have to accept the particular technique of their veterinarian and provided that well positioned plates result there should be no problem.

Bardens, an Indiana veterinarian, has pioneered a different method of X-ray known as the fulcrum system. This involves positioning the dog in the normal way and then placing a fulcrum (a jar, roll of cotton or such like) slightly below the stifle joints. The hock joints are then subjected to pressure so that the femoral head is luxated laterally if there is any joint laxity. Exponents of this system claim that it will identify dogs which would be declared normal under normal methods. Such dogs are termed luxoids and are claimed to be dysplastic by the time they reach three years of age. Details of these ideals have been published by Bardens and Hardwick (1968) and in popularised form by Anon (1971).

Some experts (Olsson and Schnelle 1973) have criticised the fulcrum technique as being geared towards the production of a high incidence of dysplasia on diagnosis. It seems to me that if one tries hard enough almost every hip can be made to appear dysplastic and no useful purpose can be served by setting so high a standard that few animals can reach it. It may be of academic interest as an exercise in veterinary skills but it is bad public relations in the canine breeder's eyes and will only confuse an already confused situation.

Hip dysplasia can be defined as a biomechanical problem but arriving at a comprehensive mechanistic description of hip dysplasia is a complex task. It has been attempted by Badoux and Hoogeveen (1976) who successfully explain the biomechanical consequences of the aberrant shape of the dysplastic acetabulum but who can give no real satisfactory explanation of the initial cause of the aberration itself. They conclude that the aetiology of hip dysplasia is involved with the complex constructional changes of the canine skeleton which are due to domestication.

In recent years attempts have been made to obtain early diagnosis of the problem. As will be seen later most hip dysplasia control schemes involve X-raying at not less than 12 months of age which is rather late for genetic selection purposes. Any method which will enable earlier diagnosis to be accurately made is to be welcomed.

One attempt at early diagnosis was the palpation technique pioneered by Bardens and Hardwick (1968). These workers believed that the pectineus muscle in the thigh was involved with hip dysplasia. They felt that the shallow acetabulum and femoral head changes seen in dysplastic cases were merely the result of a neuromuscular disease of the pectineus muscle. Bardens developed a technique for palpating hip joint laxity and the tension of the pectineus muscle in puppies at about eight to nine weeks of age.

According to Anon (1971) palpation by trained operators could be 100% effective in diagnosis of hip dysplasia at some two months of age although it was admitted that the technique was more an art than a science. Clearly if this were true early diagnosis by means of palpation would be a major step forward in hip dysplasia control since it would enable early culling of any affected stock and thus save considerably in the time, costs and heartbreak of hip dysplasia.

Unfortunately the evidence for palpation is not conclusive. Cornell workers (Lust and Kindlon 1960; Lust and Baker 1970) had shown that the pectineus muscle had a decreased rate of overall protein formulation and this might be a factor in hip dysplasia but there was a need for objective evaluation of the palpation technique and its comparison with X-ray methods.

The original paper by Bardens and Hardwick (1968) was very imprecise in terms of

Table 28

Comparison of palpation results with pelvic radiography for hip dysplasia

Source (palpation diagnosis at about 2 months of age)	Dogs	Radiographic diagnosis at 12–18 months of age		% correct
		Normal	*Dysplastic*	
Giardina and MacCarthy 1971				
Normal	27	25	2	92.6
Dysplastic	19	4	15	78.9
Lust *et al* 1973*				
Normal	35	17	18	48.6
Dysplastic	69	24	45	65.2
Wright and Mason 1977†				
Normal	28	25	3	89.3
Dysplastic	20	8	12	60.0

*Dogs reared on abnormally retarded growth rates excluded.
†These workers graded hips at both stages. Normal has been considered as a laxity score of less than 4 on palpation and less than 3 on X-ray while dysplastic was considered to be 4 or more and 3 or more respectively.

viable evidence but several papers have been produced since that time using early palpation and subsequent radiography of the stock when reaching 12 months of age or so (Table 28). The work has been undertaken in the USA and Australia using a variety of breeds. The American workers used German Shepherds, Golden Retrievers, Beagles and Alaskan Malamutes whereas the Australians used Labradors, Kelpies, German Shepherds, Boxers and two kinds of cross-bred dogs. All groups of workers used Bardens original technique but the Australian workers (Wright and Mason 1977) sought to introduce more objective measurements in what they termed the Laxity Distance Method.

If palpation were 100% accurate as was originally claimed then the diagnoses determined at 8–9 weeks of age would be confirmed by radiography at 12–18 months and correlations between the two would be 1.0. Any correlation less than unity represents some degree of error but this is acceptable if the percentage success rate is high.

Before discussing the results in more detail it is important to discuss two kinds of error that can occur. These are termed type 1 and type 2 errors. A type 1 error is going to occur when a pup is diagnosed by palpation as dysplastic when in reality it is not. Such a pup would presumably be destroyed on initial diagnosis and hence the original mistake cannot be rectified. A type 2 error will occur when a dog is diagnosed as normal in puppyhood and is subsequently found to be dysplastic. This type of error is costly in that a defective dog has been reared but it is possible to correct the error and dispose of the dog, albeit at a later date than might have been ideal. Errors, if they are of type 2, can be acceptable but errors of type 1 are serious if they are numerous. Breeders may, at this point, query how type 1 errors can be identified since the pup will be dead. This is true and in the application of a scheme no check would be possible, hence the crucial nature of early work.

The data of several groups of workers are shown in Table 28 and illustrate that considerable error exists between original palpation and subsequent radiographic diagnosis. The degree of error was greatest in the Cornell University work of Lust *et al* but if we pool all the data we find that of 90 animals graded normal on palpation 74.4% remained normal on X-ray (a type 2 error of 25.6% which is high). Of the 108 animals graded dysplastic on palpation only 66.7% remained so (a type 1 error of 33.3% which is even higher).

It can be argued that it is not strictly valid to pool data from three groups of workers but in practice palpation would have to be undertaken by large numbers of different veterinarians and errors, both types 1 and 2, would inevitably be high. Wright and Mason (1977) stress that they obtained a Spearman's rank correlation value of 0.49 between laxity distance and radiographic data on the worst hip and a similar correlation of 0.41 between laxity score and the worst hip on radiography. Both correlations were very highly significant but this is of less import than the fact that they indicate laxity score or laxity distance will explain only some 17–24% of the variation in radiographic result which is too low to be biologically very meaningful.

Wright and Mason (1977) did examine the cost of using laxity palpation results in a guide dog breeding programme and found that without a hip scheme it was about A$1036 per dog compared with an average of A$987 using some laxity system. This was, of course, dependent upon the incidence of hip dysplasia in the population (31.3% in their case) and the accuracy of palpation readings. They concluded that a palpation system would be economically feasible as long as the incidence of hip dysplasia was in excess of 15.2%.

In most countries the incidence of hip dysplasia in large and giant breeds is in excess of this figure but we have no evidence as to the accuracy of palpation on a global scale. One must thus conclude, as did the OFA (Anon 1973), that the palpation technique is, as yet, basically investigative rather than something which could be applied in breeding kennels.

Other attempts to seek early diagnosis of hip dysplasia have been similarly limited in value. Thrall *et al* (1977) looked at bone scanning which involved using 'bone seeking' radiopharmaceutical preparations to identify lesions altering the rate of osteogenesis in the various bones. Only seven animals were used but the workers had to conclude that the technique was less sensitive than pelvic radiography as a diagnostic tool.

This does not preclude the possibility that other techniques may be found more useful in the future but at present breeders will have to accept that radiography is the only reasonably accurate method of hip dysplasia identification.

The Genetics of Hip Dysplasia

One of the first attempts to assess the genetic components of hip dysplasia was that of Grounds *et al* (1955) in a pedigree study based on American data from German Shepherd Dogs. They traced the condition back to Dachs v Bern and concluded it was caused by a simple autosomal recessive. Since this dog was the sire of two of America's most widely used Shepherds it was probable that in the early 1950s every dog in America traced back to Dachs and thus the finding was largely irrelevant. However Henricson and Olsson (1959) also favoured a simple autosomal recessive with the proviso that some heterozygote animals ('carriers') showed up abnormally on X-ray.

In contrast Schalles (1956, 1958) postulated a dominant mode of inheritance with irregular manifestations. Schalles supported his view with data from 108 litters in which dysplastics occurred and in all but 8 cases at least one parent was dysplastic. Similar views regarding inheritance were held by Snavely (1959) and Abbott (1959) while Burns and Fraser (1966) also plump for a relatively simple explanation involving incomplete penetrance. Hein (1963) argued that the condition was a polygenic one and claimed support for her view from the fact that a wide range of hip structural defects occurred. A wide range of expression for a defect does not automatically imply a polygenic inheritance since gene segregation and the modifying influence of different environments could all lead to this feature.

However there is considerable evidence accumulating now to suggest very clearly that hip dysplasia is controlled by several genes and that it must be considered to be a polygenic character with visible expression being determined by a combination of genetic and environmental factors. This is very clearly shown in the data compiled in Table 29.

The data in Table 29 refer to various countries with differing standards as to what constitutes normality so that comparison over the various papers is difficult. Nevertheless it is apparent that dysplastic stock can occur in any kind of mating but that the better the parental status for hip structure the better, on average, will be their progeny. This is typical of a polygenic character in which there are genetic and environmental components involved.

It is generally accepted by most workers involved that hip dysplasia is a polygenic trait. It should therefore have a heritability (see page 24). Estimates of heritability of hip dysplasia are not numerous and any attempt to seek a median value or best estimate is complicated by the fact that different diagnostic systems exist throughout the world. It does not follow that an estimate made from American OFA data is necessarily relevant to British BVA/KC data. Similarly, estimates based upon German Shepherd Dogs—and thus far most published estimates have been in that breed—may not be applicable to other breeds.

Table 29

Incidence of normal progeny (non-hip dysplastic) in various types of mating

Normal × Normal		Normal × Dysplastic		Dysplastic × Dysplastic			
Number*	%†	Number	%	Number	%	Source	Country
32	81.2	56	41.1	31	12.9	Snavely 1959	USA
226	73.9	88	42.0	5	20.0	Bornfors et al 1964	Sweden
152	56.6	55	61.8	15	6.7	Riser et al 1964	USA
101	76.2	71	47.9	28	7.1	Kaman and Gossling 1967	USA
462	62.5	302	55.3	88	15.9	Henricson et al 1966	Sweden
545	68.1	187	47.6	—	—	Jenny-Gredig et al 1970	Switzerland
—	64.5	—	55.4	—	—	Henricson et al 1973‡	Sweden
—	64.0	—	54.0	—	37.0	Nicholas 1975‡	Australia
2106	76.2	298	66.8	—	—	Hedhammar 1976	Sweden
	28		38		44	Swenson 1986b	Sweden

*Total number of progeny examined.
†Percent normal according to the standards of the appropriate country.
‡Numbers not given but 3007 animals involved in total.
‡Labrador Retrievers, all others are German Shepherd Dogs.

One of the first estimates was made in Sweden by Henricson *et al* (1966) who put the heritability of hip dysplasia at between 42 and 60%. In a later paper using more animals (Henricson *et al* 1973) they revised this downwards to 20–30%. More recently Hedhammar (1976) using data on 2404 dogs from 401 litters arrived at a figure of 40 to 45% and later (Hedhammar *et al* 1979) set this as 44 ± 8% in Swedish Army dogs. Using 1458 GSD in Sweden Lindstedt *et al* (1986) gave an estimate of 30%.

Using American OFA data Jessen and Spurrel (1973) put the heritability at 0.25 ± 0.07. This figure is very similar to those obtained by Leighton *et al* (1977) using information on 1186 dogs born in 258 litters in the American Army Bio-Sensor programme. The army group analysed their data in two ways: one using only two categories (dysplastic or not dysplastic) and the other having nine grades ranging from Excellent hips (9) down to Grade IV dysplasia (1). Various heritability calculations were made but all oscillated around 20 to 24% with a standard error of some 8–10%.

The analyses undertaken by Leighton *et al* (1977) were fairly comprehensive and an interesting finding was that there was an interaction between sire and age. This meant that the age at which progeny developed hip dysplasia was not consistent across sires but was earlier in some than in others. This is strong evidence for a polygenic character. However this group were evaluating at 5, 8 and 11 months of age which is earlier than most schemes. Differences in age at onset might not be apparent if initial X-ray was at 12 or 24 months of age.

More recently the author has looked at the heritability of hip dysplasia in four breeds using the BVA/KC system of three categories (Normal/near normal/failure) and examined the same dogs using the total score system described later in this chapter. For the GSD,

Golden Retriever, Labrador Retriever and Rottweiler breeds the BVA/KC classes gave heritabilities of 25, 13, 22 and 25% respectively but for total scores these were increased to 40, 18, 28 and 39% respectively. The implication was quite clear that scoring was a more effective technique. Differences between breeds could be explained by differences in the inbreeding levels within the various breeds. The success of more rather than fewer classes for hip dysplasia was illustrated by Andersen *et al* (1988) using 2674 GSD sired by 82 sires in Denmark. Using a 7-category system the heritability for hip dysplasia was 35%. The 7-category system was about 1.5 times more effective than a 2-category system.

All these estimates were made on German Shepherd Dogs and are the best available. They suggest that between 25 and 40% of the variation seen in hip structure is due to additive genetic factors and the remaining 75–60% is caused by non-additive genetic factors or by environmental aspects.

German estimates have been made on 1782 Hovawarts and 1654 Boxers by Distl *et al* (1985). Using paternal half sib correlations they obtained estimates of 34 and 20% respectively. Krempl *et al* (1988) studied 1457 litters of Hovawarts and obtained heritabilities from 36 to 60% depending upon the corrections made.

Several dog breeders still refuse to accept these facts. Thus we have Appleton and Appleton (1977a) stating the 'many leading authorities, both scientists and laymen, feel that hip dysplasia is nutritional in cause rather than hereditary'. It is possibly true that the environmental component accounts for a greater proportion of the variability in hip dysplasia than does the genetic component but that does not mean that the genetic component can be ignored or that one can avoid hip dysplasia by nutritional means as Appleton and Appleton seem to suggest. The statement that many 'leading authorities' feel this to be true is misleading. No doubt many breeders feel it but I know of few scientists who do and of no geneticists.

If one was dealing with a non-genetic problem then certain environmental situations would lead to hip dysplasia and others would not. Moreover breeding from affected or non-affected animals would not lead to differential results. There is ample evidence that dogs with better hips will, on average, produce better hips regardless of the nutritional and environmental situation in which the progeny are kept. This is further emphasised by some Australian data on Labradors. This was presented by Nicholas (1975) and related to dogs which were born to parents which both had normal hips. Their pedigrees were extended to the grandparent generation to examine how many grandparents were also normal. As is

Table 30

**Grandparent status of progeny produced from
normal × normal matings in Labrador Retrievers**

Number of grandparents within normal limits	*% of grandprogeny within normal limits*
0	50
1	68
2	71
3	100

Source Nicholas 1975.

shown in Table 30 the better the grandparent status the higher the percentage of normal hips in the grandchildren. Nicholas' data suffer from small numbers and it does not follow that the percentage figures are accurate. Certainly one cannot guarantee that having both parents and three grandparents normal will lead to 100% normality in hip status. But the principle that the better the hips in the pedigree the better the hips in the descendants is clear.

Age and Sex

It is generally agreed that dogs are born with normal hips. In this respect dysplasia in the dog differs from that in man where it is present at birth. The effect of age is to increase the chance of hip breakdown such that, as they age, dogs will show increasing signs of hip dysplasia, assuming that they have inherited the tendency and are exposed to the environmental conditions which enhance it.

British workers are generally agreed that X-ray diagnosis is not possible under 12 months of age and this view is held by some European workers (Freudiger 1973). This does not mean that dogs will not show radiographic signs earlier than 12 months since in many instances they undoubtedly will. It does, however, mean that a 'normal' reading prior to 12 months must be confirmed after that age. Dogs which X-ray as defective prior to 12 months will be most likely to become worse with age, certainly they are unlikely to improve.

Some American veterinarians have held the view that 12 months is too early for accurate diagnosis. Larsen and Corley (1971) using OFA data showed that the dogs classified as normal had a higher mean age than those in which a repeat study was advised because of an inability to diagnose accurately. Lust *et al* (1973) concluded that the period from 3 to 8 months was crucial since initial diagnosis was frequently made in this period. Libbey *et al* (1970) felt that some 70% of dysplastic cases could be diagnosed by 12 months of age but that the disease developed slowly in many dogs and greater accuracy was obtained by X-raying later in life. This is confirmed by Townsend *et al* (1971) and by Jessen and Spurrell (1973) who estimated a 95% accuracy in dogs X-rayed at 24 months or more. Since the mid-1970s the OFA have increased their lower age limit to 24 months in the light of these findings.

The older the dog when diagnosed as normal the more reliable that diagnosis will be. An animal X-rayed normal at six years is a better prospect than one X-rayed normal at 12 months of age. However the breeder needs to make up his mind about breeding prospects as early as possible so that a compromise has to be arrived at between this and waiting for greater accuracy. The OFA have compromised at 24 months and the BVA/KC at 12 months.

There should be no upper limit although some schemes did place an upper age limit of six years. This stems from the fact that as a dog ages it will often exhibit signs of arthritis and other degenerative diseases which will complicate diagnosis. Clearly in such cases a verdict cannot be reached but in many cases where a dog is over six years of age and still has perfect hips I feel a certificate of normality cannot be refused.

The finding of Leighton *et al* (1977) that sires varied in the age at which progeny could be radiographically diagnosed for dysplasia is interesting but these workers X-rayed at 5, 8 and 11 months of age. It does not mean that with more acceptable limits of 12 months or 24 months there would be any differences of importance since by these ages most progeny with hip dysplasia would have demonstrated that fact.

In respect of sex it is known that in humans the female is at a much greater risk than the male (Warkany 1971a). In dogs both sexes are believed to be at equal risk (Priester and Mulvihill 1972; Leighton *et al* 1977). On the other hand Hedhammar *et al* (1979) considered that more females were affected than males (49 *v* 43% overall and 27 *v* 22% for serious cases). Under the old BVA/KC scheme more females were passed than males (60.3% of the first 305 BVA certificates in German Shepherds were females) despite more males being born. This may, however, reflect a tendency to X-ray more females or to retain more in the population of breeding stock.

Breed Incidence

In a British study based upon a survey made at veterinary surgeries Hodgman (1963) concluded that 44 breeds were affected by hip dysplasia. In terms of actual occurrence within a breed this was useful information but as incidence levels the data are meaningless, reflecting nothing more than the relative popularity and numerical strength of certain breeds. Studies in other countries have shown that a wide variety of breeds are affected and it would seem that only the racing Greyhound (Paatsama, 1963) is free of the condition though it has been found in show Greyhounds.

In the study referred to in the previous section Priester and Mulvihill (1972) found evidence of hip dysplasia in 40 breeds but they showed certain breeds to be more seriously affected in terms of incidence than others. This is illustrated in Table 31 for specific breeds and in Table 32 for adult weight category.

Table 31

Relative risk of hip dysplasia for certain breeds—American OFA data

Breed*	Adult Weight Category†	Cases Observed	R‡
St Bernard	Giant	144	9.9
Chesapeake Bay Retriever	Large	11	5.8
Golden Retriever	Large	65	5.0
Labrador Retriever	Large	153	4.3
German Shepherd Dog	Large	404	4.2
Samoyed	Large	16	4.0
English Setter	Large	32	2.4
All breeds	—	1193	1.0
Boxer	Large	14	0.6
Poodle (Miniature or Toy)	Small	21	0.2
Cocker Spaniel	Medium	3	0.1
Rough Collie	Large	3	0.1
Chihuahua	Small	1	0
Beagle	Medium	1	0

* Adjusted for location and sex.
† For definition see Table 32.
‡ Values above 1 indicate greater than average risk, below 1 a lower than average risk.
Source   Priester and Mulvihill 1972.

Table 32

Relative risk of hip dysplasia by adult weight category—American OFA data

Adult weight category	Weight range kg	Cases	R*
Giant	> 36.3	153	10.2
Large	18.2–36.2	803	3.6
Medium	9.1–18.1	17	0.2
Small	< 9.1	39	0.2
Not specified	—	181	1.0

*Values above 1 indicate greater than average risk and below 1 a less than average risk.
Source Priester and Mulvihill 1972.

This American study was undertaken at veterinary clinics which cannot necessarily be taken as representing unbiased samples of the canine population, however there does seem to be general acceptance of the fact that dysplasia is more readily found in large and giant breeds than in small and medium-sized ones.

Although this seems to be a general rule there are some exceptions to it in that breeds like Rough Collies and Afghan Hounds appear to be less at risk than other breeds of comparable size. The reasons for this are not clear but it has been suggested by various workers that growth rate may be involved. This is discussed at some length later (see page 157).

It is difficult to produce reliable data on the relative incidence rates of hip dysplasia within breeds. Certain breeds which are reputed to be 'badly affected' may be X-rayed more readily by breeders while other breeds with an alleged 'low incidence' may be rarely examined for hip dysplasia. Comparisons between countries are made difficult or misleading because standards for diagnosis of the disease are not uniform across national boundaries. In areas where eradication schemes are in operation there may well be a steady decrease in the incidence of the problem so that published figures very soon become dated and of limited use in comparative studies.

Data from OFA work in USA have been published by Corley (1978) covering over 46,000 animals. He showed that in 3810 GSD the incidence of mild, moderate and severe dysplasia was 11.8, 7.9 and 2.1% respectively. Corresponding figures for 4082 Labradors were 7.4, 6.1 and 1.2% while for 564 German Short-haired Pointers they were 4.6, 2.5 and 0.5%. Such data are valuable but relate to animals in different periods of time and thus cannot assist in assessing trends.

A refinement of breed incidence studies was published by Martin *et al* (1980) using Canadian data. Although they examined over 2000 dogs in total few breeds were numerically strong. In 402 GSDs the percentage of dysplasia was 46.8 while in 211 Labradors it was 37.4. Breeds with more than 100 dogs examined were (with number of dogs and % dysplasia) Siberian huskies (151, 5.3%), St Bernard (131, 73.3%), Golden Retriever (140, 55.7%), Old English Sheepdog (119, 47.1%), Great Dane (118, 16.1%) and Newfoundland (116, 63.8%). All of these named breeds had a significantly *greater* than average risk of hip dysplasia with the exception of the Husky and Great Dane where the risk was significantly *less* than average. Like the OFA study this one suffers from an inability to examine annual trends though some attempt was made to look at the period 1970–74 and that from 1975–78.

More recently Corley and Hogan (1985) published data on OFA hip readings for the period 1974–84. This covered 143,218 radiographs from 151 breeds of dog. Their paper tabulated results for 70 breeds each with over 100 submissions and time trends were also given showing a significant reduction in HD frequency in 27 breeds with only one breed (German Short-haired Pointer) showing a significant increase over time. Table 33 shows overall results for a few selected breeds listed in descending order of severity of dysplasia.

One problem frequently overlooked in the development of radiographic standards for

Table 33

Breed incidence for OFA data 1974–84

Breed	No. dogs Evaluated	Dysplastic	Normal	Borderline
		Percentage graded		
St Bernard	873	46.9	52.1	0.9
Newfoundland	2190	32.5	65.2	2.2
Bullmastiff	477	30.4	66.1	3.4
Bernese Mountain Dog	792	30.3	68.1	1.5
English Setter	1801	26.5	71.1	2.3
Gordon Setter	1310	24.2	74.3	1.4
Norwegian Elkhound	1128	23.9	74.3	1.6
Giant Schnauzer	1115	23.8	74.2	2.0
Golden Retriever	20804	23.1	74.6	2.3
Rottweiler	9272	23.1	74.8	2.2
Old English Sheepdog	5183	23.0	75.9	1.1
German Shepherd Dog	14458	20.7	77.2	2.0
Brittany Spaniel	3043	20.4	78.6	1.1
English Springer Spaniel	2080	20.1	78.5	1.4
Japanese Akita	2609	17.5	80.7	1.8
Irish Setter	4167	14.9	84.2	0.9
Labrador Retriever	17432	14.4	84.6	1.1
Alaskan Malamute	4149	13.8	85.4	0.8
Samoyed	4651	13.4	85.1	1.4
Weimaraner	1842	11.9	87.0	1.0
Rhodesian Ridgeback	1373	11.7	87.9	0.4
Vizsla	1768	10.1	89.1	0.7
Dobermann	2619	8.1	90.3	1.6
German Short-haired Pointer	1525	7.4	92.2	0.4
Afghan Hound	2778	5.3	94.5	0.2
Flat-coated Retriever	452	3.7	95.3	0.9
Siberian Husky	4982	2.7	96.8	0.4

Source   Corley and Hogan, 1985.
Breeds represented are just a selection from the original paper which covered 70 breeds.

hip joint is the variability between breeds. There is a tendency to assume that normality is a constant feature identical in all breeds. This is unlikely to be true. The canine species shows more variation within itself than any other species known to man. It has an enormous range of sizes and within these a variety of growth types. It seems logical to assume that normality in achondroplastic breeds cannot be synonymous with normality in others. Thus definitions of normality ought, by rights, to take account of breed type yet rarely appear to do so.

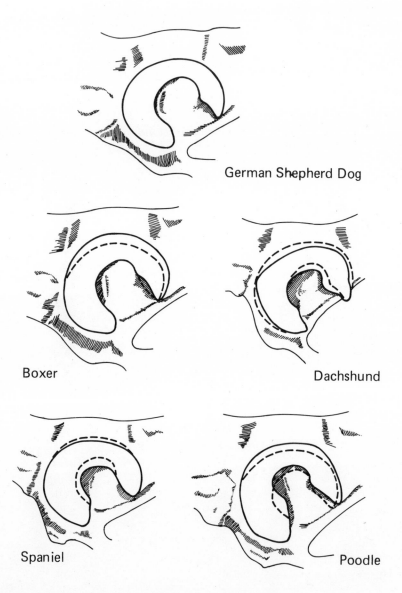

Figure 27   The acetabulum shape of various breeds of dog contrasted with that of the German Shepherd Dog (contour of lunar face of GSD shown in dotted line) (from Richter 1977).

One recent attempt to assess 'normality' in the hip joint assembly of various breeds has been undertaken in Germany by Richter (1977). She made dissectional studies on German Shepherds, Boxers, Cocker Spaniels, Miniature Poodles and the three coat varieties of Dachshund. The total number of dogs was only 95 (ranging from 16 to 22 per breed) and ages ranged over a wide area (from one to over ten years). However additional studies were made on 434 X-rays covering these five breeds and five other large breeds. Richter's thesis is too long to quote in any detail but she did observe basic differences in the type of pelves. In her view only the Dachshund had a typical configuration for the pelvis yet had the shallowest acetabulum of the five. This breed and the Cocker had looser hip joints than the other three without exhibiting pathological changes. Examples of the 'typical' acetabulum of each breed are shown in Figure 27 and of the femoral head in Figure 28.

One cannot take Richter's work as being standard because of the numbers involved but it certainly suggests the need for greater study of what constitutes normality. It is possible that only in the German Shepherd and Labrador Retriever is there a sufficient body of data world-wide to be precise about what constitutes normality in a breed. In the remaining breeds we may well be working with conjecture.

Growth Rate and Weight

The fact that large and giant breeds appear to be at greater risk for hip dysplasia suggests that some of the environmental features involved in the problem must be concerned with growth rate or weight.

One of the first group of workers to suggest this was the Philadelphia group of Riser and his co-workers. In a study of German Shepherd Dogs from the Swedish army kennels Riser *et al* (1964) suggested that there was a marked relationship between weight in those pups which subsequently became dysplastic than in those which did not (Table 34).

Statistical significance levels were not given but judging from graphical presentation in the original text it is unlikely that the difference between normal and dysplastic pups in

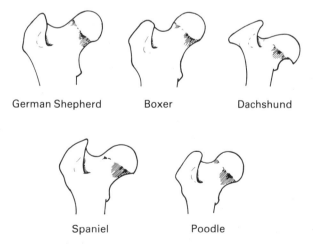

German Shepherd   Boxer   Dachshund

Spaniel   Poodle

Figure 28   The femoral head shape in various breeds of dog (from Richter 1977).

Table 34

Mean weights (kg) of German Shepherd Dogs at 60 days of age according to sex and subsequent hip structure

	Normal pups		Dysplastic pups	
Sex	*Number*	*Weight*	*Number*	*Weight*
Male	68	6.08	49	6.59
Female	54	5.60	51	6.29
Total	122	5.87	100	6.44

Source Riser *et al* 1964.

60-day weight were significant. In this connection the study by Hedhammar (1976) based on a larger sample of dogs (2404) showed that 60-day weight was not a factor influencing hip dysplasia. It is, however, interesting to note that the 60-day weights in the Table above are low by some British standards. Data from the GSDIF on 125 males and 94 females show unadjusted mean weights at 56 days of 6.94 and 6.74 kg respectively (Willis 1978a).

In a later study (Riser and Shirer 1967) 95 dogs were killed and their pelvic muscles dissected out. The group comprised 20 racing Greyhounds, 63 German Shepherds and 12 July Hounds (a type of Foxhound). These dogs were of varying ages and different sexes but were selected because hip dysplasia was effectively unknown in the Greyhounds and had an incidence of 50 and 100% in Shepherds and July Hounds respectively.

Using the weights of the dissected-out muscles an index of pelvic muscle mass was calculated as:

$$\text{Pelvic muscle mass index} = \frac{\text{Total weight of pelvic muscle}}{\text{Live weight of the dog}} \times 100$$

Statistical tests showed that this index was associated with hip dysplasia in that the lower the index figure the greater was the risk of dysplasia occurring. In view of this Riser and Shirer produced a table of critical points (Table 35) showing that at index levels above 10.89 dysplasia was rare whereas below 9.0 it was almost inevitable.

The authors concluded that the muscle mass index was an inherited rather than a developmental feature. Several of the Greyhounds studied had never been exercised or trained yet had index values averaging 13.67

There are obvious flaws in this particular study—different ages, variable backgrounds and so on—but there nevertheless seems to be some indication that a well-developed muscular structure in the pelvic region was a prerequisite for avoidance of hip dysplasia or a symptom of normality.

Lust *et al* (1972) showed that up to some 3 months of age the protein formation was similar in dogs which remained normal and those which subsequently became dysplastic. However, after 3 months of age the protein synthesis was decreased in those dogs which became dysplastic. This may be related to Riser's findings since protein is an integral part of muscle. Unfortunately it is not clear whether decreased protein synthesis is a causal factor of dysplasia or a manifestation brought about by that dysplasia.

That growth rate and body weight were definitely involved in hip dysplasia development

Table 35

Critical points on the pelvic muscles mass index scale

Index	Incidence of hip dysplasia*
14.20	All dogs have normal hips—disease unknown
12.17	All dogs have normal hips, some sibs affected
11.63	Probability of 94% that dogs of this index will have normal hips
10.89	Probability of 86% that hips will be normal
9.00	All dogs have some degree of dysplasia
8.00	All dogs badly dysplastic
5.60	All dogs dysplastic and luxated

*Comments refer to OFA standards on hips.
Source   Riser and Shirer 1967.

was demonstrated by Lust *et al* (1973). These Cornell workers took Labrador Retriever pups from parental breedings that were considered poor for hip structure. A total of 35 pups were reared in one of three ways:

A   Eight pups fed a high calorific (normal) type diet;
B   Eight pups fed a low calorific (70% of normal) diet;
C   Nineteen pups delivered by caesarian section, colostrum deprived and hand-fed.

All dogs in this experiment were monitored for hip dysplasia at intervals and by 12 months of age all the animals in groups A and B had developed hip dysplasia. In contrast only 3 out of 19 pups in group C had developed hip dysplasia by this age. The major differences between the three groups lay in their growth rates (see Figure 29) which were drastically reduced in the group C animals.

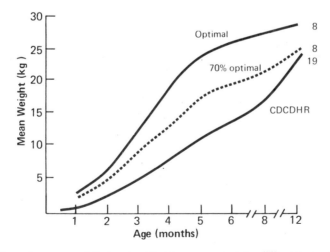

Figure 29   Growth curves of Labrador Retrievers reared in different ways (Lust *et al* 1973). Optimal: Normal nutritional regime (8 animals). 70% of normal nutritional regime (8 animals). CDCDHR: Caesarian delivered, colostrum deprived and hand reared (19 animals). See text for further explanation.

Although the numbers involved in this work were small it does suggest that rapid deposition of weight early in life is detrimental to hip structure. This is not unexpected in that dogs are born with incompletely ossified bones which gradually ossify during the first nine months or so of life. Excessive body weight when bones are still not ossified might logically be expected to harm the hip and Hedhammar *et al* (1974) have shown that over-nutrition, leading to maximal growth rate in Great Dane puppies not only predisposed them to hip dysplasia but also to a wide range of osseous abnormalities.

However, as Mason (1976) has pointed out, the Cornell work cited above does not give any comfort to those who merely advocate some restriction of growth. The pups in group B were fed only 70% of the optimal level yet all developed hip dysplasia. Those in group C were reared at an abnormally slow rate and it is impractical to suppose that breeders will resort to caesarian section and an abnormal rate of growth simply to avoid hip dysplasia. Although it was found by Lust and his colleagues that at 18 months the weights of all three groups were similar the effect of retardation upon conformation was not stated and that might well have been adversely affected.

In any event it must be realised that simply retarding growth as in group C did not eliminate hip dysplasia in any genetic sense. Animals in group C were genetically just as bad for hips as those in groups A and B as subsequent matings proved. The nutritional regime had merely disguised the inherent dysplasia problem which re-emerged in progeny once the nutritional system was discontinued.

In connection with nutrition Tvedten *et al* (1977) fed Beagle pups on different levels of protein and carbohydrate and found that 32% developed hip dysplasia with no evidence that the inclusion or exclusion of carbohydrate into an otherwise adequate diet affected hip dysplasia. Similarly, increasing the dietary protein to twice the normal level did not significantly alter hip dysplasia incidence.

More recently Lust *et al* (1978) have indicated that retarding growth rate can disguise the genetic background in hip dysplasia. They reared Labrador Retrievers from Normal × Normal, Normal × Dysplastic and Dysplastic matings. In each instance some pups were reared in the usual fashion for the breed while others were fed on a forcing system (above normal) or on a restricted system. Forcing was only used for progeny of the normal matings while restriction was used for the progeny of the other two groups. Numbers involved were too small to be very meaningful but it was found that, despite their genetic background, force-fed dogs exhibited hip dysplasia by about 18 weeks of age. In contrast, pups from Normal × Dysplastic matings were dysplastic by 17 weeks of age if fed normally but did not exhibit dysplasia by 17 months when restricted. From dysplastic matings most pups fed normally were dysplastic by 17 weeks but dysplasia did not occur until 35 weeks when restricted. Again the effects on conformation were not stated but it does suggest that hip dysplasia can be either reduced or its onset delayed by avoidance of the stress of rapid growth.

Exercise

Breeders vary considerably in their attitude to exercise in young stock. Some advocate minimal activity while others seem to be unconcerned about the degree of exercise. Many do advocate not allowing pups to stand on their hind legs or to jump and it seems not unreasonable to suppose that exercise might be involved in the aetiology of hip dysplasia.

Exercise on a hip that is already predisposed to hip dysplasia might well be regarded as detrimental but it might be argued that exercise would increase muscle tone and mitigate against the problem. In this connection Riser (1963) showed that confinement of puppies in small cages could prevent hip dysplasia development and at the same time improve the joint status of affected stock.

The Cornell workers (Lust *et al* 1973) have attempted to study exercise in 26 dogs bred from parents with poor dysplastic records. Half of the animals were reared from 5 to 20 weeks of age in wire cages then transferred to an enclosed unit. The remaining pups were kept in these enclosed units from 5 weeks of age and exercised 3 times per week for a month by allowing them to run out of doors. They were then trained to run on a treadmill for various periods of time. Both groups were fed the optimum diet to ensure normal growth rates for the breed.

Despite the different exercise regimes both groups of dogs developed hip dysplasia at a similar rate and by 12 months of age all 26 animals were dysplastic.

This particular experiment suggests that exercise did not affect dysplasia but the trial involved dogs from a poor dysplastic background. In dogs of more normal pedigree and with more normal methods of exercise the role of exercise is still unclear.

Hormones

Pierce *et al* (1965) claimed that imbalances in oestrogen metabolism were causal factors in the expression of hip dysplasia and in a later paper (Pierce and Bridges 1967) claimed that there was a distinct reduction in the capacity of dysplastic dogs to metabolise oestradiol-17B.

Finnish workers (Paatsama *et al* 1968) suggested that the administration of oestrogens to dogs caused degeneration of the epiphyseal cartilage. This degeneration involved cyst-like formation similar to Legg-Perthes disease. Similar cysts were found in the acetabulum and when parathyroid hormone was used there was marked destruction of the femoral head. Using oestrogens Gustafsson (1968) was able to produce hip dysplasia in Greyhound pups—a breed not known to suffer from hip dysplasia to any extent.

In contrast, a thesis by Kasstrom (1975) produced very conflicting evidence. He showed that the depression of cartilage cell growth caused by oestrogen was greater than the stimulating effect of growth hormone. When oestradiol was given to pregnant bitches it produced a long-term growth depression in their pups' hip joints. On the other hand Kasstrom found that German Shepherd females with a high hip dysplasia frequency had lower plasma levels of oestradiol than did Greyhound females in which dysplasia was not known. Furthermore German Shepherds with hip dysplasia had lower plasma oestradiol levels than did bitches of the same breed without hip dysplasia. The low level of oestradiol in dysplastic dogs seems to contradict the hypotheses that oestrogen is involved in hip dysplasia. Kasstrom concluded that individuals with dysplasia may have metabolised oestradiol after it had achieved its end of causing hip dysplasia but the explanation is very tenacious.

Hormones are, of course, produced naturally in all dogs and the normal functioning of the animal depends upon them. In themselves at normal levels hormones cannot be harmful but imbalances at certain stages of life may be. It is not inconceivable that hip dysplasia is encouraged by hormonal imbalances but at present the unequivocal evidence to support this view does not exist.

Other Factors Involved

Some dog breeders are only too eager to seek causal factors for hip dysplasia (and other genetic problems) by blaming some external features. Clearly, if one has severe hip dysplasia problems in one's kennels it is expedient to blame something other than one's breeding skill or lack of it.

Of course, not all breeders fall into this category. Some do put forward suggestions that they make in all honesty believing them to be valid. Thus we find Appleton and Appleton (1977a, b) putting the blame squarely on nutrition and claiming that hip dysplasia is now more prevalent because we no longer feed such balanced diets as we once did. They also suggest other factors like exercise and vitamin levels but offer no scientific data or experimental evidence of their own to support their case. The same is true of Roslin-Williams (1975) who suggested that certain kinds of distemper inoculations can induce hip dysplasia but provided no evidence other than her own opinion.

Some of the factors frequently implicated by breeders have been examined by Lust *et al* (1973). They found that the presence or absence of fever at teething time (12–16 weeks of age) showed no relationship to hip dysplasia. Similarly they found live vaccines for distemper or canine hepatitis to have no role as pathogens leading to hip dysplasia.

It is interesting to note that all 42 dogs used by Lust and his colleagues in the exercise/no exercise trial and the optimum/70% optimum caloric intake trial had a two fold excess for dietary calcium and vitamins C, D and E. All 42 dogs developed hip dysplasia suggesting that nutritional supplements did not have the therapeutic effects upon the disease which breeders frequently claim.

This last point is critical in view of the alleged findings of Belfield (1976) that hip dysplasia was a symptom of sub-clinical scurvy and that certain component parts of vitamin C would rectify this condition and prevent hip dysplasia. His paper was hailed as a major advance by many breeders eager to find a panacea solution to their ills but it has many serious drawbacks. It was undertaken without controls and the theory that vitamin C deficiency can affect joints, but only those of the hip, is too unsound to be acceptable. An effective rebuttal was made by Teare *et al* (1979).

It is sometimes believed that anaesthetics used in preparing the dog for radiography will adversely affect muscles and cause joint laxity. If this were true it could mean that dysplasia might be diagnosed when none really existed. A recent German study by Schnepf (1976) suggests that this is not the case. He examined 122 dogs radiographically with or without neuroleptic analgesics (anaesthetic). These were found to have no real effect upon the diagnosis of hip dysplasia and it can thus be concluded that while some joint laxity may occur with anaesthetics the overall effect is negligible.

Although the pectineus muscle has been implicated in hip dysplasia by many workers and one of the techniques used to relieve pain involves resectioning of this muscle there has been little reliable work on the subject. Ihemelandu *et al* (1983) working in California did suggest that in two month old German Shepherds which subsequently developed HD the pectineal muscles contained certain fibres that were significantly smaller than in dogs which were to prove normal. If this were a general finding with clear cut differentiation between the types it would be useful but the number of dogs used was small and the differences are not such as to lead, at present, to an alternative to radiographic diagnosis.

More interestingly the same school (Hauptman *et al* 1985) looked at the angle of femoral head and neck (angles of inclination and anteversion) in a series of GSD, Greyhounds and crosses between the two. They found no evidence supporting the view that hip angles related to hip dysplasia. Extension of this work may yet indicate that hind angulation is also unrelated to hip dysplasia. Many breeders, especially those not involved with the GSD, often put forward unproven views to the effect that HD is caused by well angulated hind limbs. The evidence is not available to support such views.

Schemes in Operation to Combat Hip Dysplasia

Probably the first nationally organised scheme to combat hip dysplasia was set up in the Swedish army kennels (Olsson 1958; Henricson and Olsson 1959). This particular scheme, like all subsequent ones, was based upon radiographic diagnosis. Originally X-rays were taken at under two years of age and plates were placed into one of six categories or grades. Grades O, B and I were considered to be normal and grades II, III and IV to be dysplastic. From 1959 the Swedish KC began to introduce regulations governing the breeding of German Shepherd Dogs in an effort to restrict the use of dogs below a certain standard as regards hip structure. Over the years the scheme was applied to other breeds and some modifications were made to it. Similar schemes have been operated in other Scandinavian countries, all based upon the original Swedish one.

In 1960 the then Alsatian League and Club of Great Britain (now the GSD League), after pressure from the author and others, also introduced an X-raying scheme. It suffered from being somewhat lax in its terms of reference in that no panel of veterinarians existed to ensure a uniform standard. Only 58 animals were certified as being normal and in 1965 the scheme was abandoned in favour of the BVA/KC scheme. This latter was much stricter, involving a panel of experienced veterinary radiographers and entailed three grades of dog. These were normal, breeder's letter (near normal) and fail. The scheme was applied to all breeds by the KC but with no regulations governing the use of dogs. Names of all dogs passing as normal were published in the KC *Gazette* and, more recently, those of breeder's letter dogs were also published.

In 1965 the Swiss KC introduced a national scheme, again begun in German Shepherds, using five grades: frei, I, II, III, and IV. The system was similar to that in Sweden with similar standards. The grades frei and I were originally held to be normal hips. Details have been given by Freudiger *et al* (1973a,b). Since 1965 various breed clubs have imposed restrictions on the use of dogs for breeding purposes. The GSD Club permitted only grades frei and I to be used, as do several other clubs, whereas others allow anything up to grade II. Details of the particular breed standards set for this are given by Freudiger *et al* (1973a).

In late 1966 the Orthopaedic Foundation for Animals (OFA) was set up as a private scheme in the USA and it receives moral support from the American KC and various breed clubs. It originally insisted that, as in the BVA/KC scheme, all dogs be at least 12 months of age but in 1974 increased this minimum age to 24 months. It had no maximum age limit like the BVA/KC scheme which would not certify dogs aged six years or more.

The German SV introduced an 'a' stamp system in January 1967 applicable to German Shepherds. This was rather lax in its early rules, accepting dogs from six months upwards and being liberal in what constituted normality. More recently the 'a' stamp has covered three categories of dog: no dysplasia, indicative of dysplasia and light dysplasia. Dogs which have no 'a' stamp have a limit placed upon their usage and this limit is lower than that for 'a' stamp animals. Dogs with severe hip dysplasia are named in the SV Zeitung and progeny from them will not be registered. In recent years dogs without an 'a' stamp could

Classification FCI	Description	Country				
		Finland	Germany	Holland	Sweden	Switzerland
1 (A)	No signs of hip dysplasia	Ei-dysplasiaa 'hyvat'	Kein Hinweis für HD	Negatief geheel gaaf (1)	Utmark	Frei
2 (A)		Ei-dysplasiaa		Negatief niet geheel gaaf (2)	UA	
1 (B)	Transitional	Rajatapaus	Ubergangsform (Verdächtig für HD)	Transitional (TC)		
2 (B)					I	I
1 (C)	Mild	I	Leichte HD	Licht positief (3)		
2 (C)						
1 (D)	Moderate	II	Mittlere HD	Positief (3½)	II	II
2 (D)				Positief (4)		
1 (E)	Severe	III	Schwere HD		III	III
2 (E)		IV		Positief optima forma (5)	IV	IV

Figure 30   The new FCI classification for hip dysplasia and the corresponding European standards previously used (after Brass *et al* 1978).

not obtain the VA award at the annual Sieger show. In East Germany dogs with severe and moderate hip dysplasia have been officially culled from breeding.

In the late 1960s a scheme was launched in Australia under the veterinary association's banner with tacit KC support. It was similar to the BVA/KC scheme in approach though not necessarily in standard. It received little support.

Various private schemes doubtless exist and some countries not mentioned here may have them. However all have the same basic system of using radiography and they differ in the type and number of grades used—if any—and the standard of severity.

The FCI has been trying to adopt an international and unified standard and it is generally accepted that the BVA/KC standard is much stricter than any in Europe. Many dogs which pass other schemes fail to obtain a BVA/KC certificate of normality and dogs which have failed this system have passed others. However, a severe system is not necessarily the most successful method of reducing hip dysplasia incidence.

The FCI commission on hip dysplasia has produced the format of a grading scheme to be applied in their area of authority (Brass *et al* 1978). The details are shown in Figure 30 along with the existing standards in five European countries.

A uniform system would be ideal assuming that such uniformity is achieved, but it is difficult to grade hips into categories in that one has to decide whether one particular flaw has to count more than some other flaw. It is undoubtedly true that schemes which are rather liberal in their standards will be well supported by breeders while those which are severe will find antagonism growing as breeders increasingly fail to achieve the high standards set. A further problem with schemes like the BVA/KC system is that because so few dogs actually pass, the breeder has little choice among stud dogs that have BVA/KC certificates. Many of these, while acceptable in hip standard, are defective in some other, more serious trait.

Although the BVA/KC scheme was criticised by breeders for its severity and by geneticists for its failure to grade (Willis 1977b) it made little attempt to modify matters other than to introduce a kennel scheme (BVA 1976). Since this was intended merely to rank dogs in merit order within a kennel but not to make comparisons between kennels it was doomed to failure.

The BVA's insistence upon a high standard of excellence may be justified in the long term but a high failure rate leads to low usage. In the period 1965 to 1976 the total number of dogs submitted was 4,291, an average of only 358 per year for all breeds. Moreover, since the objective was really to identify normal/near normal animals it was highly biased.

A major advance came in 1978 when the BVA and GSDIF (now GSD League) agreed a new trial scheme. This began in mid 1978, was extended to a few other breeds in the next two years and became the national scheme in December 1983 when the old scheme was abandoned. The new scheme involved assessing nine radiographic features of each hip on the scale 0 (ideal) to 6 (worst). A copy of the submission form is shown in Figure 31.

For the first time a geneticist (the author) saw all results and analyses could be fed back to breed clubs. The success of the scheme is shown by the fact that in 1987 over 10,000 animals were submitted, some 28 times as many as the previous annual submissions of the defunct scheme. Results for the most recently available data are shown in Table 36.

The scheme has been adopted in Australia (Prof R. S. Wyburn/Murdoch University) and New Zealand (NZVA) as well as by the GSD Council of Australia (R. B. Lavelle/Melbourne) all the data from which schemes reach the author for analysis. Heritability studies have been cited earlier and progeny test data appear later.

JOINT BVA/GSDL HIP DYSPLASIA SCHEME   K.C. Reg. No.....................................

To British Veterinary Association   Breed...

7, Mansfield Street,   Date Radiograph taken ....

LONDON W1M 0AT   Sex.................... Date Born.............................

K.C. Registered Name..

Name of Owner..Address..

Sire:	PGS	
	PGD	
Dam:	MGS	
	MGD	

I hereby declare that:
(a) the particulars above are correct and relate to the dog submitted for radiographic examination.
(b) the dog has not previously been scored under this scheme.
(c) I give permission for a copy of this completed certificate to be sent to the GSDL geneticist for evaluation and use.
(NB deletion of any of these items invalidates this application)

Owner's signature.. Date...........................
The veterinary surgeon should check with the registration certificate.
Name of Veterinary Surgeon submitting radiograph..

Address..

....

Signature of Veterinary Surgeon... Date...........................
PLEASE TYPE ALL INFORMATION (OR USE BLOCK CAPITALS)

FILM   **DEGREE OF TILT** [   ]   **SCORING UNIT** [   ]
QUALITY: Satisfactory; Too thin; Too dark; Extraneous marks.
POSITION: Satisfactory; Tilted laterally left/right; Femora not sufficiently extended; Femora not evenly extended.

HIP JOINT	RIGHT	LEFT	
Norberg Angle			
Subluxation			
Cranial Acetabular Edge			
Dorsal Acetabular Edge			
Cranial Effective Acetabular Rim			
Acetabular Fossa			
Caudal Acetabular Edge			
Femoral Head/Neck Exostosis			
Femoral Head Recontouring			Total Score
TOTALS			

I HEREBY CERTIFY that the above-named animal was examined under the rules of the BVA/GSDL Hip Dysplasia Scheme.
Signed... Date of Examination...
                                                   (Scheme Secretary)

Figure 31   Hip scoring form used in Britain since 1978.

Table 36   **Hip scoring results of British scheme (to October 1988)**

Breed	Number of dogs seen	Range of scores	Mean score
BREEDS WITH 1000 OR MORE SCORED (4)			
German Shepherd Dog	14169	0–106	17.02
Golden Retriever	6143	0–104	18.45
Labrador Retriever	4897	0–100	14.95
Rottweiler	4547	0–99	13.14
Sub-total	29756		
BREEDS WITH 100 OR MORE SCORED (28)			
Airedale Terrier	145	0–91	18.09
Bearded Collie	405	0–42	9.35
Bernese Mountain Dog	809	0–102	14.55
Border Collie/Working Sheepdog	949	0–89	11.72
Briard	139	0–98	20.28
Bullmastiff	148	0–88	24.02
Chow Chow	286	0–102	13.15
Clumber Spaniel	130	3–102	41.73
Dobermann	227	0–49	9.14
English Setter	326	0–95	20.49
English Springer Spaniel	131	0–62	11.07
Flat-coated Retriever	701	0–69	8.10
Gordon Setter	432	0–104	23.97
Irish Setter	132	0–76	15.91
Irish Water Spaniel	113	0–73	15.61
Japanese Akita	296	0–70	10.99
Newfoundland	572	0–106	32.54
Old English Sheepdog	374	0–100	19.52
Pyrenean Mountain Dog	109	0–84	13.14
Rhodesian Ridgeback	256	0–65	9.38
Rough Collie	221	0–89	12.70
St Bernard	100	0–64	20.65
Samoyed	227	0–76	12.68
Siberian Husky	434	0–30	4.81
Tibetan Terrier	116	2–79	18.61
Tervueren	235	0–82	8.27
Weimaraner	313	0–61	12.35
Welsh Springer Spaniel	242	0–104	15.57
Sub-total	8568		
BREEDS WITH 40 TO 99 SCORED (18)			
Anatolian Shepherd Dog	48	0–64	10.33
Boxer	92	0–65	16.48
Brittany	52	0–74	19.94
Cavalier King Charles Spaniel	76	4–91	16.86

Table 36 cont.

Breed	Number of dogs seen	Range of scores	Mean score
Chesapeake Bay Retriever	63	0–52	11.76
Elkhound	82	0–61	13.04
German Short-haired Pointer	48	0–25	7.61
German Wire-haired Pointer	58	0–53	9.57
Giant Schnauzer	69	0–66	14.20
Great Dane	88	0–71	10.65
Groenendael	49	0–42	10.06
Hungarian Puli	47	1–102	17.95
Italian Spinone	58	0–67	13.60
Large Munsterlander	84	0–88	18.35
Mastiff	59	0–59	17.23
Otterhound	56	4–102	43.62
Soft-Coated Wheaten Terrier	54	2–51	12.70
Swedish Vallhund	48	2–28	11.85
Sub-total	1131		
BREEDS WITH 10 TO 39 SCORED (21)			
Afghan Hound	10	2–29	11.40
Alaskan Malamute	29	2–66	17.55
Bouvier des Flandres	29	6–48	17.10
Cocker Spaniel	21	5–44	15.63
Curly-coated Retriever	37	1–23	8.36
Dalmatian	24	0–15	6.70
Field Spaniel	17	0–25	13.47
Irish Red/White Setter	18	3–30	8.23
Hovawart	33	0–79	9.45
Hungarian Vizsla	32	2–27	10.22
Irish Wolfhound	34	0–23	3.31
Keeshond	20	3–18	9.55
Leonberger	25	0–55	10.45
Maremma	39	2–83	14.11
Norwegian Buhund	18	2–42	11.94
Polish Lowland Sheepdog	20	8–26	15.99
Shetland Sheepdog	15	4–83	20.06
Smooth Collie	15	0–17	3.67
Staffordshire Bull Terrier	27	5–28	11.18
Standard Poodle	36	2–68	15.62
Tibetan Spaniel	20	2–20	10.65
Sub-total	520		
GRAND TOTAL	39975		

Breeds with fewer than 10 scored are excluded.
Some Australian/New Zealand results are included for certain breeds.

The Effectiveness of Control Schemes

Before discussing the effectiveness, if any, of control methods it is relevant to establish definitions of what the breeder is trying to achieve. Some appear to think that the objective is the total eradication of hip dysplasia while others appear indifferent to the problem.

Thus we see Loeb (1969), a well-known American breeder-importer of German Shepherds, claiming that hip dysplasia was not *the* evil but one of the evils and feeling that it was being highlighted by veterinarians for their own personal financial gain. Other breeders (Snavely 1960) felt that only about 10% of dogs were really affected by the disease. One breeder, also a medical practitioner (Rickards 1975), has gone so far as to claim that X-ray diagnosis was actually limiting progress and that it was nonsense to term a dog dysplastic if it could jump a five-bar-gate with ease. One has only to talk about hip dysplasia to a group of breeders to see that some do absolutely nothing about it while others are almost paranoid about eliminating it.

Dog breeders are aiming towards physical and mental perfection in their stock and use the breed standard as their guide to physical excellence. Anything which impairs the usefulness of the dog is detrimental to progress and there is no doubt that hip dysplasia will impair the usefulness of the dog. Henricson *et al* (1966) stated that 10% of Swedish army dogs had to be withdrawn from service because of dysplasia and I know of similar cases in British police forces. The harder a dog is required to work the more likely he is to require good hips. It is true that some dogs with hip dysplasia can lead normal enough lives but most of those with severe hip dysplasia will be affected by lameness to some degree at some stage of their life.

We must therefore conclude that action against hip dysplasia is desirable but we must also be sensible in our approach. The oft quoted claim that all dogs with hip dysplasia should be prevented from breeding would be fatal to most breeds if applied at the early stages of any hip scheme.

Methods of combating hip dysplasia must be aimed at a marked reduction of the disease with, at the same time, preservation of the virtues in the breed. Thus methods used by Henricson *et al* (1973) and Gustafsson (1975) in which German Shepherds were crossed with racing Greyhounds were interesting and effective in reducing hip dysplasia but are clearly academic in a pedigree breeding situation since they place hip dysplasia in premier position in the selection stakes.

We need to develop methods which will reduce hip dysplasia but which will be politically acceptable to breeders. As a first stage it is necessary to prove to breeders that reduction in the incidence of hip dysplasia—and in particular in the incidence of severe cases—is feasible by breeding methods.

One of the first claims to have achieved this was that of McClave (1957) in a Samoyed kennel. In a guard/blind leading Shepherd kennels run by Fidelco it was claimed (Riser and Miller 1966) that a decline in severe cases was achieved by the use of normal or near normal dogs while the subsequent use of only dogs with parents and grandparents free accelerated the progress. This particular kennel instituted the scheme because of a high incidence of unsuitable stock due to hip dysplasia.

In the American Bio-Sensor army dog programme Riser (1973) claimed that the incidence of dysplasia in the first 100 dogs seen was 40% dysplasia whereas the incidence in the sixth group of 100 dogs was only 20%. This army programme was instituted because of the difficulties of getting the right kind of temperament and hip structure from breeders.

Leighton *et al* (1977) writing on this same programme showed that, over the period 1969–75, the overall incidence of hip dysplasia was 27%. This compared with general estimates for the German Shepherd in America of 63.4% (Townsend 1973) and 80.3% (Jessen and Spurrell 1973) although in part this reflects a lower diagnostic age in the army data as well as the selection programme.

In Sweden Henricson *et al* (1973) reported disappointing results in the selection for good hips. This may appear very damaging in a country which has ostensibly been selecting rigorously against the problem and which involved X-raying 11,036 German Shepherds in the period 1959–69. However, closer examination of the Swedish system shows that while show stock and imports were rigorously checked little control existed over breeding stock and as a result minimal progress is not surprising. More encouraging results came from the Swedish army programme (Hedhammar *et al* 1979) where improved selection standards reduced hip dysplasia from 46% in the period 1965–73 to only 28% in 1975. At the same time severe dysplasia declined from 25 to 15%. In more recent years studies by Hedhammar (1986) and Swenson (1986b) have shown considerable progress from the Swedish scheme at reducing hip dysplasia and some of the figures for various breeds are shown in Table 37.

The Hovawart Breed Society began a scheme in 1965 whereby at least one parent in any mating had to be free of dysplasia. As a result medium and severe cases declined from 26% prior to 1965 to 15.6% over the period 1966–70. During the same period unaffected dogs increased from 39.6 to 53.7% (Müller and Saar 1972).

A study of the condition in Leonbergers was made by Schneider (1984) covering 856 animals in West Germany, 460 in the Netherlands and 143 in Switzerland. Frequency of dysplasia was 40, 45 and 30% in the three countries respectively which needs to be considered in the light of differential methods of assessment. Schneider considered the scheme in the Netherlands to be the most stringent and he emphasised the value of progeny testing.

In Switzerland where only dogs of category 0 and 1 for hips have been bred from in

Table 37

Progress in hip dysplasia reduction in Sweden for various breeds. (Percent in each category.)

Breed		*Normal*				*Grade 1*				*Grade 2–4*			
	Year	*76*	*80*	*84*	*85*	*76*	*80*	*84*	*85*	*76*	*80*	*84*	*85*
Bernese Mountain Dog		64	72	72	77	14	14	14	12	19	15	11	9
English Setter		59	76	71	88	12	6	14	6	29	18	14	6
German Shepherd Dog		66	74	78	79	16	13	11	11	19	13	11	10
Gordon Setter		62	94	93	96	23	6	7	4	15	0	0	0
Irish Setter		90	92	79	78	6	5	12	14	4	3	9	8
Labrador Retriever		75	78	83	85	11	10	10	8	14	12	8	7
Rottweiler		64	70	82	82	20	16	13	12	16	14	5	7
St Bernard		38	39	47	42	29	22	17	28	34	39	36	29

Source Hedhammar, 1986 Swenson, 1986b
Data rounded up to nearest whole number.

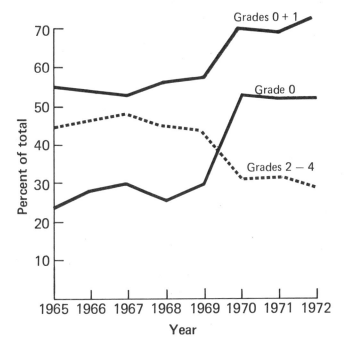

Figure 32   Incidence of different grades of hip dysplasia in German Shepherd Dogs in Switzerland (Freudiger *et al* 1973b).

German Shepherds since 1965 some progress has been reported by Freudiger *et al* (1973b). The data as shown in Figure 32 for the period 1965–72 and demonstrate a clear increase in dogs categorised 0 or grade 1 in this period. Most of the progress came after 1969 but this is not surprising. The generation interval in German Shepherds is about 48 months (Willis, 1976) so most progress will be relatively slow getting started.

In East Germany there has been a policy of excluding from breeding German Shepherds which were classed as having severe hip dysplasia or a moderate level of the condition. In a study covering the period from 1968 to 1975 during which time the regulations were in force Bohme *et al* (1978) showed that the proportion of normals increased from 55.7 to 87.6%. At the same time severe cases declined from 13.2 to 2.1%, moderate cases from 14.4 to 3.6% and mild cases from 16.7 to 6.7%. The authors concluded that the time had come to exclude even mildly affected dogs from breeding. Even if one allows for the fact that the standard of normality may not be equal to the high standard chosen in Britain the improvement obtained in a relatively short period is quite marked. It has been achieved by a gradual tightening of the standard of hip that was permitted in breeding stock and serves as an example of what might be achieved elsewhere by sensible control. Initially standards may have to be fairly lax to allow for the high incidence of dysplasia but with time, as the proportion of normals increases, standards can be tightened to accelerate genetic progress. The rate of progress was such as to suggest a high heritability for the condition.

In West Germany the SV has encouraged X-raying of GSD to such an extent that numbers examined by Prof. Brass (Hanover) have risen from 1498 in 1968 to 9510 in 1987. Animals granted the 'a' stamp normal have risen from 9.9% in 1968 to 48.4% in 1987 while in the same period medium HD cases have declined from 26.3 to 7.6%. Since 1975 the percentage of 'a' stamps has not altered much from the 90% mark but the proportion that were 'normals' has steadily risen. Full details are given by SV (1980a) and Brass (1988).

In Britain little or no progress was made for years. The critics of the BVA/KC scheme point to this as proof that the scheme was valueless but in reality failure to progress was a criticism of breeders rather than the scheme since no scheme can work if it is not used. Macan (1978) compiled a booklet of 124 Labrador Retrievers which had received either a BVA/KC certificate or breeder's letter and of these 59 (47.5%) were from parents which had either not been X-rayed or which had failed the scheme. However 36 (29%) had one parent with a certificate or letter and a further 29 (23.4%) had both parents so categorised. That 52.4% of Labradors gaining near normal or normal certification should be from at least one such parent indicated the success of the scheme at indicating possible useful parental stock.

The argument that selection for hips will reduce show quality is highly exaggerated and was ably refuted by Charlton (1976). She cited four Labrador kennels which had paid attention to hips. Between them they had produced 36 dogs with BVA/KC letters or certificates. Of these 9 were champions, 3 had won CCs and a further 4 had won RCC's, proof if any were needed that selection for hips is not an automatic indication of poorer quality of type.

The new scheme had obviously been instrumental in accelerating the numbers assessed and by categorising different degrees of failure has allowed breeders to distinguish between the total hip disaster and the near miss (previously both lumped together under failure). Progress by breeds is not readily demonstrated since the scheme only came into full operation in December 1983 but on individual kennel bases progress can be seen.

Progress is, of course only possible if breeders make positive efforts. The data in Table 38 from Australia show clearly that at the time Labrador breeders in NSW were making little effort to improve hips and it is not surprising that little progress should result. The success of the Swedish scheme is produced by mass selection on a fairly large scale and can

Table 38

Parental status of Labrador Retriever litters in New South Wales

Year	Number of parents within normal limits for hip dysplasia*		
	Both	One	Neither
1969	23.6	38.0	38.4
1970	21.8	32.5	45.7
1971	17.9	32.3	49.8
1972	17.4	33.6	49.0
1973 (5 months)	21.1	37.9	41.0
1974	14.7	34.5	50.8
1975 (3 months)	18.8	36.5	44.8

*Figures in body of table refer to percentage of litters in each year in the appropriate category.
Source   Allan and Nicholas 1975.

Table 39

Percentage of Normal × Normal matings (hips) in Sweden for selected breeds

Breed	*1976*	*1980*	*1984*	*1985*
		Year		
Bernese Mountain Dog	68.8	75.0	86.7	95.2
English Setter	0	10.2	25.0	31.6
German Shepherd Dog	45.4	46.5	69.9	82.8
Gordon Setter	37.5	75.0	78.6	85.7
Irish Setter	30.0	46.3	73.1	75.0
Labrador Retriever	60.5	65.3	80.0	91.4
Rottweiler	51.9	58.2	81.0	96.1
St Bernard	5.5	15.3	46.0	49.1

Source   Swenson (1986b)

be demonstrated by looking at the percentages of normal to normal matings in various breeds over a period of time. This is seen in Table 39.

The advantage for Swedish breeders is that high proportions of registered stock are hip assessed and thus mass selection will be both effective and speedy if the trait is quite highly heritable as seems to be the case. Swenson puts the figure at from 40 to 50% which is comparable with British figures for certain breeds.

In mass selection one is breeding from the 'best' animals but an animal's own performance is only a guide to his breeding value although the higher the heritability the higher the reliability. Nevertheless not all 'good' animals produce well and progeny testing (usually though not exclusively of sires) is an added guide being more reliable than performance testing though not as fast to obtain.

This is demonstrated in data from Jenny-Gredig *et al* (1970) concerning six German Shepherd sires, all free of hip dysplasia yet giving a wide range of results in terms of progeny grading normal. Similar findings have been produced by Hedhammar (1976) again with German Shepherds, this time in Sweden. The data from these two papers are shown in Tables 40 and 41. Riser (1974) discussed two sires in the Bio-Sensor army programme who were mated to the same bitches. One produced only 35% normal offspring whereas the other had 121 normals (93.8%) in 129 progeny examined.

These kind of results are often confusing to breeders who have an almost child-like faith in hip X-rays. They believe that because a dog has passed some scheme it must, by definition, be normal and if two such dogs are bred together only normal offspring will result. This is clearly untrue. One is dealing with the constant interplay of environment and genetics. A dog, genetically good, may in a poor environment, demonstrate a phenotypic appearance (X-ray) that is bad whereas a dog of poorer genetic merit in a better environment may demonstrate a good phenotype. This has been shown diagrammatically by Lust and Farrell (1977) in a figure reproduced here (Figure 33).

While, in general, one is best advised to use certificated dogs rather than those which fail, it is possible for some failures to be better breeding prospects than some passes and for

Table 40

Proportions of normal and dysplastic progeny from six normal GSD sires

Sire	Progeny		% normal
	grade 0–I	grade II–IV	
A	41	11	78.8
B	39	12	76.5
C	49	20	71.0
D	49	23	68.1
E	25	13	65.8
F	27	15	64.3

Source   Jenny-Gredig *et al* 1970.

considerable difference in the breeding merit of sires or dams which do pass any particular scheme.

   Because hip dysplasia has a medium genetic component of 25–50% it lends itself well to progeny and performance testing. This was recognised by Hutt (1969) and formed the basis of a Canadian scheme put forward by Crawford and Kaye (1973). The need is not only to X-ray stock but also to categorise the breeding merit of the parents of those stock by progeny testing data.

Table 41

Progeny results from nine German Shepherd Dog sires of varying hip status*

Sire Number	Hip status	Number of progeny	% of progeny in each hip Grade		
			Free	I	II–IV
7172	Free	114	78.9	13.2	7.9
7173	Free	205	76.6	15.6	7.8
5378	Free	139	66.2	19.4	14.4
7038	Free	119	59.7	16.8	23.5
3897	Free	143	55.9	35.0	9.1
6150	I	220	48.6	20.5	30.9
6276	Free	309	45.3	18.1	36.6
I	Free	123	35.8	21.1	43.1
5054	Free	118	32.2	33.9	33.9
All	Free	2132	55.0	21.0	24.0
All	I	237	49.4	21.1	29.5

*Figures must be treated with caution as status of dams of progeny is not given and may not, on average, be the same for all sires.
Source   Hedhammar 1976.

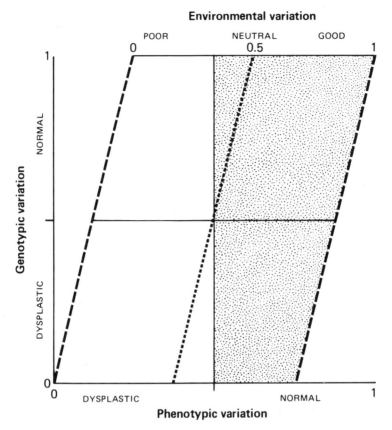

Figure 33   Diagrammatic view of the relationship between genotypic and environmental variations and the phenotypic expression of hip dysplasia. Relative values of 0 through to 1 have been assigned to hypothetical genotypes and environments and the dashed lines were drawn on the assumption that P = 0.25G + 0.75E. On the genotypic and phenotypic axes relative values of greater than 0.5 were normal and values less than 0.5 dysplastic. Normals are thus in the stipled area (after Lust and Farrell 1977).

This will be harder for females than males but the more stock one X-rays the easier it will become to categorise particular sires and dams. The BVA/GSDL scheme was proposed with this in mind since, in time, it will be possible to publish the progeny ranges and mean scores and to see very clearly which sires (dams) are producing the best hips. Once this is available on a wide enough scale we should see a reduction in the use of poorer dogs and increasing use of the better ones with consequent improvement of hip structure.

This scheme is, of course, not compulsory and will depend upon a general willingness to participate. In joining they will have to accept that the hip status of their dog(s) will become common knowledge but they will also gain by having grading of a kind that will enable comparisons between stock in different kennels and they will, if sufficient numbers support the scheme, be able to gain progeny test data. Shepherdists have been among the most vociferous critics of the BVA/KC scheme so they now have gained most of what they want at the price of loss of secrecy. We will now see if they truly have the breed at heart and care about hip dysplasia or whether they are simply 'in it for the money'! If they do not support this scheme then they will have forfeited their right to criticise the BVA in future.

One system of breed progress that should result from the GSDIF initiative will be the gradual decline in use of those dogs with poor hips. Dogs scoring high under the BVA/GSDL scheme can be identified and, hopefully, breeders can discard them from breeding programmes. Each breeder will be able to set his own limits as to what he considers acceptable hip scores and can work from there. It ought to lead to a general reduction in the poorer hips and a steady increase in better ones. Then, as more and more top show dogs become low scoring on hips, we shall see a more rapid progress still.

However, breeders should not anticipate overnight response. Hip dysplasia is not like some minor trait, such as colour, which can be rectified in one generation. We are dealing with a fairly low heritability character and it will take time to take effect. This is clearly shown by the data of Freudiger *et al* (1973b) in Figure 32 and by the results of Swedish work in German Shepherds shown in Table 42.

There is clearly a higher proportion of Free and Grade I stock and a lower proportion of Grade II–IV stock when parental hip status is better. It is interesting that results seem better when the sire is Grade I and the dam Free than in the reverse cross. It may be a spurious finding caused by limited numbers of animals but it appears to be significant, particularly in respect of the higher incidence of Grades II–IV when the dam is herself Grade I.

Hedhammar (1976) followed up this aspect by looking at the pedigrees of a large number of German Shepherds and examining the hip status of individuals and their litter mates and close relatives. His data are shown in Table 43 and very clearly indicate that the progeny of non-dysplastic dams have a better hip status than do the progeny of dysplastic dams. However, within each group, the hips of progeny improve as the pedigree of the mother improves in hip terms and as the hip status of her litter mates improves.

Hedhammar's work not only confirms the previously stated views that progeny testing is important but encourages the collection of information not only on a prospective breeding animal but also on its litter mates.

It is interesting that Hedhammar has compared hip status and temperament in German

Table 42

Breeding results in a hip dysplasia scheme using grading—all German Shepherd Dogs

Parental grade		Number of progeny	Progeny grade (% in each)		
Sire	*Dam*		*Free*	*I*	*II–IV*
Free	Free	1417	58.5	20.9	20.6
I	Free	180	53.3	21.7	25.0
Free	I	509	47.5	20.0	32.4
II	Free	25*	52.0	16.0	32.0
Free	II–IV	222	45.5	22.1	32.4
I	I–II	51*	41.2	21.6	37.3

* Insufficient numbers for percentage figures to be meaningful.
Source   Hedhammar 1976.

Table 43

Status of progeny with regard to hip dysplasia according to dam's pedigree status for hip structure

| | | *Hip status %* | | |
Status	Number of dogs X-rayed	Normal	Grade I	Grade II–IV
Mother free				
Her parents free	986	60.4	18.9	20.7
One or both parents dysplastic	641	53.3	24.0	22.6
Litter mates all free	104	70.2	14.4	15.4
Under 25% litter mates dysplastic	194	64.9	10.8	24.2
25–50% litter mates dysplastic	198	63.1	21.7	15.2
Over 50% litter mates dysplastic	296	57.1	22.0	20.9
Mother dysplastic				
Her parents free	456	48.2	20.4	31.4
One or both parents dysplastic*	321	44.9	21.5	33.6
Under 25% litter mates dysplastic	37	64.9	8.1	27.0
25–50% litter mates dysplastic	49	51.0	10.2	38.8
Over 50% littler mates dysplastic	264	49.2	18.6	32.2

* Or unknown.
Source Hedhammar 1976.

Shepherds and concluded that in general the dysplastic dogs (Grades II to IV) had a poorer temperament score. This is shown in Table 44 and was indicative of the need for further study. More recently Mackenzie *et al* (1985) have looked at the problem in the Bio-Sensor research programme in USA. They looked at 575 dogs over a four year period using 18 different sires and 71 dams. Temperament was scored from 1–9 with higher scores indicating desirability and HD was assessed on a similar scale with higher numbers indicating better hips. However dysplasia was assessed at the 5 to 11 months of age period. Temperament had a heritability of 51% and dysplasia 26% and the genetic correlation between the two was significant at −0.33.

One must not read too much into this work. In the first place a correlation of 0.33 however significant only explains some 11% of the variability between the traits. Moreover a negative correlation could result if sires useful for hips happened to be less good for temperament or vice versa. It would be feasible in a relatively closed group to have concentrated on good character lines that were not as good in hip terms. Additionally the assessment of hips in puppyhood is fraught with danger. The work is cited here for completeness but care is needed in extrapolating to a wider context.

Combating Hip Dysplasia by Non-Genetic Means

Since this book is intended as a genetic text rather than a veterinary one it is not intended to delve into the veterinary aspects of treatment of hip dysplasia. The replacement of hip joints with artificial ones is sometimes attempted but is beyond the scope of this book. It

Table 44

Relationship between hip dysplasia status and low scores for temperament in German Shepherd Dogs

Hip dysplasia status	Number of dogs	% with low scores for temperament
Free	1280	38.5
Grade I	498	38.3
Grade II–IV	565	43.7
Total	2343	39.7

Source   Hedhammar 1976.

does, however, seem appropriate to consider two specific aspects, one involving surgery and the other nutrition.

Since Bardens and Hardwick (1968) implicated the pectineus muscle as a causal factor in hip dysplasia various techniques have been applied to it. Bardens and Hardwick (1968) and Giardina and MacCarthy (1972) claim that tenotomy (cutting of a tendon) or myectomy (resection or removal of part of the muscle) are useful preventative measures in young pups. The evidence for this is by no means universal in terms of acceptance.

Lust *et al* (1972), Bowen *et al* (1972) and Cardinet *et al* (1974) all claim that operations on the pectineus muscle will not necessarily prevent hip dysplasia even when performed as early as 8–10 weeks of age. The last named group found that 58% of coxofemoral joints became dysplastic after pectineal myectomy or tenotomy.

In Britain Vaughan *et al* (1975) studied this kind of operation in 100 dogs aged from three months to eight years but with 71 under 12 months of age. They were of the opinion that in 80% of cases the resectioning of the pectineus muscle gave an improvement in the dog's response to dysplasia (all 100 dogs being dysplastic) but only in 35 instances was the level of recovery a high one. This is in marked contrast with the work of Wallace (1971) who claimed a success rate of 94% with improvement occurring within 24 to 72 hours of the operation being undertaken.

With the exception of the original proponents most workers using the method seem to feel that the operation does not arrest hip dysplasia though it may allow greater freedom to the dog in terms of pain-free movement. The long-term effects of such operations are not fully understood and it is imperative to realise that dogs so treated are likely to be ineligible for further exhibition in the shows run by most kennel clubs. A personal viewpoint is that pectineus resectioning is overused in Britain and is best avoided in the majority of cases. Many dogs treated in this way would very probably have improved in clinical signs even if left untouched.

The nutritional system concerns the work of Belfield (1976) who considered hip dysplasia was an expression of sub-clinical scurvy. This work has been widely hailed by many breeders—especially those with serious hip problems in their stock—as a true answer to their prayers. At the time of writing many breeders, especially in the USA, are using sodium ascorbate in their kennels in the belief that they will eliminate hip dysplasia. I can only view such enthusiasm as both misplaced and premature and some comment seems needed here before breeders lose their way on this issue.

It was once believed that vitamin C was produced by the dog in sufficient quantity as to negate the need for supplementation. It is now generally accepted that vitamin C is involved in bone development and the dog may not be as efficient as was once believed in synthesising its own vitamin C, more particularly ascorbate.

However, accepting this, one must not lose sight of the fact that Belfield's evidence was based upon eight litters of German Shepherds from parents which were dysplastic in some instances and which were presumably normal in others but which had produced cases of dysplasia. In the paper, which was in a non-refereed journal and hence not subject to scientific scrutiny, Belfield gave no numbers for his so-called trials, provided no data as to the ages of dogs treated and used no controls. Such an experiment would not be regarded as acceptable in any refereed journal and cannot be taken as dogmatically as some breeders apparently have done. The fact that Belfield begins by stating that he has 'never found a genetic pattern' in hip dysplasia, throws considerable doubt upon his reading of the scientific literature, the more so when he uses a reference to 1753 as evidence that scurvy affects the joints.

It may be that vitamin C in general and ascorbate in particular is involved in dysplasia but Belfield's work does not prove this to be so and breeders are foolish to accept it as so. Moreover, even if Belfield were correct the use of ascorbate would merely disguise the underlying genetic picture. By seeking to avoid dysplasia by a nutritional means (ascorbate) the breeder may be disguising an underlying increase in adverse dysplasia genes. He might, in due course, find that threshold levels have changed and that even high levels of ascorbate have to be given to counter the increased build up of dysplastic genes. He might also find that playing about with vitamin levels in this fashion will affect other aspects. Breeders take such steps at their peril. Evidence does suggest that vitamin C abuse can be dangerous!

Chapter 9

Genetic Diseases of the Brain and Central Nervous System

Introduction

This chapter is intended to deal with various disorders which are primarily thought to involve disruption of the normal activity of the brain and central nervous system (CNS). In many ways this is too sweeping a category. Hormonal malfunctions like some kinds of dwarfism might logically be included because they are brought about by problems in the pituitary gland of the brain. However dwarfism seems more appropriately discussed in skeletal defects than in this chapter which will be confined to more obvious brain disorders.

Disorders of the CNS are, of course, legion since numerous infectious diseases will adversely affect that part of the animal. However this book is confined to genetic studies and as a result only those diseases known or believed to have some genetic component are included.

Epilepsy

Definition

The term epilepsy indicates a seizure or fit and it is thus a very vague definition for a disease since seizures or fits can take any forms and be occasioned by a multitude of causes.

Epileptic fits are among the oldest brain disorders known to man being recorded in literature for many centuries. They are also known to occur in other species, in particular the dog. This does not mean that the absolute incidence of epileptiform seizures in dogs is high but it could well be higher than in man. According to Forster (1963) the prevalence of epilepsy in man is about 0.5% (5 cases per 1000) whereas in a Californian veterinary hospital study Holliday *et al* (1970) estimated that seizure disorders constituted some 1% of all canine diseases.

The epilepsy with which the breeder is mainly concerned is idiopathic or functional epilepsy, that is seizure disorders of a particular kind that cannot be explained by some other external or internal influence upon the animal.

Before seeking to discuss the problem of idiopathic epilepsy it seems important, indeed essential, to outline some of the other factors which might lead to seizures or epileptiform fits. The subject has been examined by Cunningham (1971) who categorised these factors into extracranial and intracranial causes—inflences which were outside or inside the head. The list which follows is based upon Cunningham's list to which I have added some others.

Extracranial causes

1　Hypoglycaemia: anything which reduces blood sugar levels can cause this complaint and it is known that seizures can result (Cello and Kennedy 1957).
2　Hypoxia: anything which leads to a reduced supply of oxygen to the brain can lead to seizures (Passonneau 1969). These difficulties may arise from heart or lung disease.
3　Liver disease: any severe liver disorder can give rise to seizures (Zeive 1966).
4　Intoxication: the ingestion of strychnine, lead or other poison can lead to epileptiform seizures.
5　Vitamin D: anything which interferes with vitamin D utilisation can lead to parathyroid malfunction which can bring about hypocalcaemia and hence fits. Eclampsia is another condition which resembles a hypoparathyroid state and can give rise to fits.
6　Teething: severe teething troubles could give rise to seizures.

Intracranial causes

1　Tumours: any brain tumour, both parasitic or malignant could cause seizures to occur.
2　Encephalitis: diseases such as distemper can give rise to this problem and indirectly to fits.
3　Trauma: any accidental knock to the head could cause permanent or temporary brain damage which might occasion fitting over a long period of time.
4　Hydrocephalus: a state where excessive fluid exists within the cranial cavity may result in an unusually large head and can be associated with fits.

All the above factors could lead to the production of a dog which has fits. In many cases the removal of the causal factor will lead to recovery from the epileptiform problem. For example Grimm (1974) treated 13 dogs which were suffering from epileptiform seizures following infectious diseases like distemper and claimed a full cure.

Many of the above-named conditions will demonstrate other symptoms than simply seizures, which can be readily checked by any veterinarian. Tumours, for example, are likely to occur in older dogs and may leave the dog with a weak or paralysed limb which would not occur with idiopathic epilepsy. Fits caused by infectious disease will probably be identifiable by leukocyte counts or by the presence of fever. Hypoglycaemia will doubtless be identified by low blood sugar concentration, while accidents such as intoxication or trauma may well have been observed by the owner.

Anderson and Carithers (1975) have emphasised the importance of taking careful histories on each epileptic-type case, recording such things as age, breed, vaccination record, life style and so on and Cunningham (1971) has detailed the step by step procedure to be followed by veterinarians in checking epileptic cases. This is very important because most dogs which have had a fit will not do so on demand for the veterinarian. By the time the practitioner has been called to the dog it may well appear in normal health and it would be dangerous for breeders to immediately assume that they have a genetic problem on their hands.

Only when other possible causes have been checked as far as possible and been eliminated should the breeder begin to consider idiopathic epilepsy. Cunningham (1971) considers that the commonest causes of epileptiform seizures are intracranial ones and that on eliminating all other factors there still remains a large proportion of cases which must be termed idiopathic epilepsy.

True epileptic fits of the idiopathic kind will tend to have a characteristic pattern. They will generally be of short duration (30 seconds to 4 minutes) and at some stage the dog will be unconscious. It will keel over and may urinate and/or defaecate. The limbs may stiffen at some point and make galloping motions at others. The eyes will roll up into the head and the dog will perhaps emit some screaming sounds. It will look as if the animal is in its death throes and it may be a frightening experience for owners who had not expected or experienced it before. In some cases it is known for a dog to go from one fit to another and to die or be destroyed without ever recovering but this is rare. Generally the dog will come to its senses, shake itself and carry on as normal . . . until the next time.

According to Croft (1968b) most seizures will occur in the home or kennel and only rarely when the dog is under stress at a show or other function. In this respect idiopathic epilepsy may differ from seizures induced by flashing lights and other stress factors. It does, however, mean that dogs may have fits in the privacy of their kennel without the owner being aware of the problem and it means the epileptic can be shown (knowingly or otherwise) and win in the show ring.

Stress factors do not have to be obvious ones. Using a breed called the Horak two Czech workers induced fits in 8 dogs simply by keeping them in a darkened room (Martinek and Horak 1970). In a later paper (Martinek and Dahme 1977) similar results were produced on ten dogs (not necessarily new ones) and it may be that these were genuine cases of idiopathic epilepsy. Certainly the dogs were from an experimental breed and hence inbred which might well have led to similar problems being common in the population.

Incidence of Epilepsy and Breeds Affected

Although epilepsy has been mentioned in dogs for years few reliable estimates of incidence are known. Holliday *et al* (1970) placed a value of 1.0% on general incidence of seizures but this would over-estimate idiopathic epilepsy and in any event related to a population attending a veterinary hospital which would, by definition, be atypical of dogs in general.

The first breed to receive publicity on epilepsy was the Keeshond following a letter published by Croft and Stockman (1964) in which they concluded: the vast majority of Keeshonds in this country are either affected with a genetic tendency towards epilepsy . . . or at least carriers of the recessive gene n.

Such a letter was certain to stimulate the Keeshond clubs into taking some action which may have been its objective but it was clearly a gross exaggeration of the facts since neither the incidence nor the genetic nature of the disease was known.

Subsequently Croft published a study on 260 dogs of which 167 were thought to have electroencephalograms (EEGs) typical of epilepsy (Croft 1965). The author presented a table showing the breeds affected which included Poodles, Retrievers, Boxers, German Shepherds and Collies among others. There were 31 Poodles (19% of 167) and 15 Shepherds (9%) and Croft presented alongside these incidence figures some data purporting to be typical of breed representation in the general population, giving the incidence of Poodles and Shepherds as 21 and 7% respectively. Since the 260 dogs were from a larger population of 570 animals suspected of having problems of the CNS it is clear that Croft's sample was atypical and any attempt to derive incidence figures from it would be both dangerous and misleading. The important feature was not the so-called incidence but the fact that more breeds than Keeshonds were involved.

Since that time epileptiform seizures have been seen in the Tervueren in Holland (Van der Velden 1968), in a Beagle colony in the USA (Bielfelt *et al* 1971), in Shetland Sheepdogs (author's observation), in German Shepherds in various countries (Willis 1976) and in Irish Setters, Golden/Labrador Retrievers.

The only reliable incidence figures are those for the Beagle colony cited above in which there were 29 fitting dogs in a population of 1492 animals (1.94%). This figure cannot, of course, be applied to any other breed or population other than that in which it was derived.

It is probable that epilepsy will occur in every breed and that if one searches for it one will find it but the incidence is likely to be low.

The Genetics of Epilepsy
In view of the difficulties surrounding diagnosis of true idopathic epilepsy it is not surprising that the genetics of the disease should be in a confused state. It is, however, regrettable that unproven and nebulous claims should be so readily seen in the literature.

The first author to claim that epilepsy was inherited in the dog seems to have been Iljin (1932) but he offers no evidence yet is cited by Fox (1965) in a review of genetic diseases in the dog. This in turn is taken by Croft (1968b) as evidence of a genetic trait. Croft and Stockman's (1964) reference to a recessive gene is made without proof although Burns and Fraser (1966) do cite unpublished work by Mann in support of a simple autosomal recessive theory. This related to work in which an EEG positive reading was taken as evidence of epilepsy. According to Burns and Fraser (1966) the carrier to affected type of mating (Nn × nn) gave a perfect fit with the expected 10 out of 20 offspring having positive EEG readings. The carrier to carrier matings (Nn × Nn) had only 9 total offspring and seemed to produce more EEG positives than the expected 25%.

The problem with this work is that it assumed an EEG positive reading to be indicative of epilepsy and an EEG negative to indicate normality. There must be doubt on this score. I know of Shepherds with EEG normal readings that have had fits and Croft's own data on Keeshonds (Croft 1968a) was not conclusive in that of 36 dogs with positive EEG readings only 4 had ever actually had a fit. In this connection it is worth pointing out that Croft examined 150 dogs by EEG and 114 appeared normal—a far cry from the original claim in 1964.

Doubts harboured by many of the efficacy of EEG readings were confirmed by Wallace (1975) who examined EEG readings from 321 Keeshond dogs attending Craft's clinic. The study covered dogs born over the period 1956–72 and probably represents the best data available on EEG work in dogs. The Keeshond clubs in Britain were supporting Croft's work and many owners were insisting upon having potential mates EEG tested so that a biased sex sample occurred (229 females to 92 males). Wallace undertook many tests on the data and concluded that EEG readings as made for the study had little or no relation to the occurrence of fits and did not support any autosomal recessive theory. However, she did find some faimily relationships suggesting some genetic component in the aetiology of epilepsy and that while age of onset was variable it generally occurred after 12 months of age. Wallace also found that, while rare, fits were about four times more prevalent in males than in females.

In this connection at least the Keeshond study seemed to bear out findings in other breeds. In their Beagle colony Bielfelt *et al* (1971) observed a male to female ratio of 4.6:1 among dogs with clinical symptoms of epilepsy. Similarly Falco *et al* (1974) had a ratio of 3.6:1 in favour of males in a study made on German Shepherds in Britain. Van der

Table 45

Incidence of fitting progeny among mating groups of Tervuerens

Parental status	Progeny	Fitting progeny	% with fits
Both parents free of fits	46	2	4.3
One parent known to have had fits	48	32	66.7
Both parents known to have had fits	13	11	84.6

Source   Van der Velden 1968.

Velden's (1968) data on the Tervueren do not show this same excessive incidence in males although a higher proportion of males than females were affected. However, the data on Tervuerens was based upon owner information not checked by any veterinary diagnosis and covered varying ages.

Van der Velden's data did show indications of a genetic involvement in that fitting progeny appeared more numerous from the parents which had had fits than those which had not (Table 45).

The Tervueren data, tenuous though they are, do indicate a genetic involvement though not a simple one. In like fashion the Beagle data of Bielfelt *et al* (1971) suggest that offspring from two particular sires had a higher incidence of fitting progeny. These two sires had cumulative incidence rates (allowing for the increasing onset of fits with age) of 10.1 and 15.3% compared with only 5.7% for all other sires.

In the more extensive German Shepherd study Falco and her colleagues had access to 289 pedigrees of which 68 belonged to dogs known to have had some kind of epileptiform seizure not attributable to extraneous causes. They found the average inbreeding of the epileptics to be 7.03% compared with 5.18% for the controls, the difference being significant. One ancestor (No 18) was held to be a causal agent in that a positive association existed between clinical seizures and a high inbreeding coefficient to this animal.

Earlier Stewart (1969) who had been involved with the work claimed that 98% of the pedigrees of epileptic dogs stemmed from a dog of comparative unknown ancestry whom she later (1970) named as Ingosohn of Erol. Whether dog No 18 in the Falco study is Ingosohn cannot be ascertained but if it is the result is very surprising. He was not a dog of 'unknown ancestry' but very well bred from the cream of German stock; he was to be found in almost all British pedigrees and his sire is in most German pedigrees. If Ingosohn is indeed involved then some of the most successful lines in British breeding must have also been involved. Ingosohn lived from 1938–51 so his involvement is now largely academic and breeders have greater interest in more recent dogs. Several of these have been named by Willis (1976) and GSDIF data seem to indicate that German stock are not free of being causal agents of the problem. Some GSDIF data are shown in Figure 34.

Falco *et al* (1974) suggested a distribution of age at first fit which had a preponderance (25%) being between 12 and 24 months of age, a finding confirmed by GSDIF information. Falco and her group also found that age of onset was earlier as inbreeding coefficient of the dog increased (Figure 35) and as the contribution of animal 18 to that inbreeding coefficient increased (Figure 36).

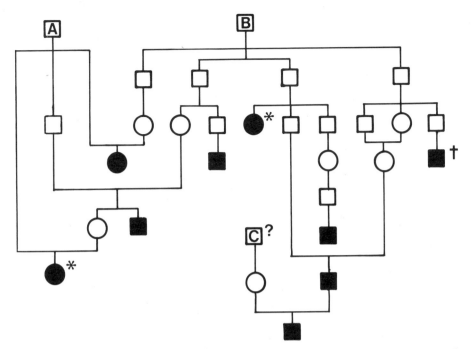

Figure 34 Relationship of two German born German Shepherd dogs (A and B) to epileptics (solid symbols) reported to the GSDIF. The symbol * incidates litter sister to a cryptorchid and † indicates the dog was a cryptorchid. Animal C may have been an epileptic.

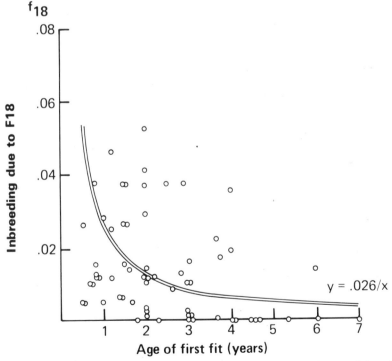

Figure 35 Epilepsy in German Shepherd Dogs. Regression of age at first fit upon inbreeding contribution from a specific ancestor (F18) (from Falco *et al* 1974).

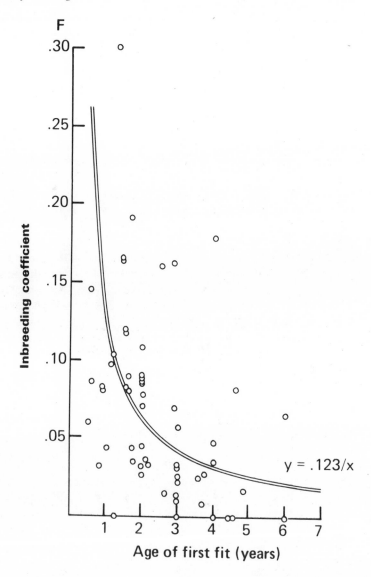

Figure 36 Epilepsy in German Shepherd Dogs. Regression of age at first fit on total inbreeding coefficient (from Falco *et al* 1974).

The increased risk of epilepsy with inbreeding is similar to that in man (see Utin and Danielov 1973) and taken in conjunction with the sex differences suggests a more complex mode of inheritance than was originally propounded by Croft.

Epileptiform seizures in the Beagle have been reviewed by Edmonds *et al* (1979) and they tend to support the theories of Bielfelt *et al* (1971) that the condition in this breed is caused by an autosomal recessive gene but with incomplete penetrance. Additionally it is suggested that there is a sex linked suppressor located on the X chromosome which helps to explain the higher incidence among males. This explanation is not supported by the Falco *et al* (1974) and Wallace (1975) studies in other breeds.

The author has looked at epilepsy in the Welsh Springer where the disease is quite virulent. In the Netherlands Gubbels and Schaap (1981) suggested an autosomal recessive explanation but in a study of some 94 'fitters' in 54 litters Willis (1988b) showed that the Dutch data did agree with an autosomal recessive explanation whereas British data agreed less successfully with this theory. The evidence suggested that male incidence was consistent with the theory but that an insufficient number of females fitted if the theory was to hold for both sexes. It may be that the sex effect results from different hormonal patterns in the two sexes.

One cannot extrapolate easily from one breed to another but it seems likely that several genes are involved, either as major genes or modifying factors and that some sex-limited involvement exists as regards expression. It could well be that the problem is that of a threshold character and that dogs inherit a liability to seizures which will come to light in specific conditions. There is, however, a need to examine more pedigrees and postulate tentative theories before seeking to indulge in some kinds of controlled mating.

Unfortunately in the case of a serious disease like epilepsy which may not be apparent until two years of age any testing programme is costly. Breeders will be more keen to avoid it than to try to understand it and the more they seek to avoid it the less we shall learn about it. There is, in any breed affected, a need to isolate and identify specific problem animals and then avoid or reduce risks by not inbreeding to these dogs or by not doubling up on them. It will not further knowledge but it might keep the incidence to manageable proportions.

Progressive Neuronal Abiotrophy (Ataxia)

The Disease
Progressive neuronal abiotrophy (PNA) was first given prominence in Kerry Blue Terriers in the USA following publication of a report by deLahunta and Averill (1976). This created something of a furore in breed circles in the USA and Britain and a great deal of genetic nonsense has been put forth by breeders which has done little to help either the breed or our understanding of the condition.

The first reaction to the deLahunta work is to consider the condition as something new in dogs but examination of the described symptoms suggests that it may well be similar to diseases previously described in other breeds.

PNA is a disease of the brain, more specifically degeneration of cells of the cerebellum. In young dogs lesions were found in cerebellar tissue called Purkinje's cells. In older dogs degeneration was found in other parts of the cerebellum but little will be gained by any discussion of post-mortem findings in detail since this is a problem for pathologists; breeders will be more directly concerned with clinical symptoms.

The Cornell workers had data on or examined 13 Kerry Blues from a kennel in New York and another in California. All had developed very similar clinical signs at between nine and 16 weeks of age. Pelvic limb stiffness and mild head tremors were the first signs and these progressed in severity until the pelvic limbs were showing incoordinated movements (ataxia). Later the foreleg action became impaired, all movement became jerky and exaggerated and the head tremors became a side to side motion. Eventually dogs could not stand without support and after being put on their feet invariably fell over. In other respects the animals behaved normally but as time passed the difficulty in eating and in movement led to degeneration of the muscles.

In many ways the symptoms were not unlike distemper infection, could have been mistaken for distemper and might well have been in an era when distemper vaccines were not used. The authors likened the symptoms to an earlier case in the breed reported by Mettler and Goss (1946) which had been termed canine chorea but which had ataxia and a widespread loss of Purkinje's cells. It was postulated at the time that the case had been precipiated by a distemper vaccination while the animal was in an unstable state but the evidence for this seems tenuous.

Examination of the literature shows a steady progression of reports on ataxia in various breeds, mostly terriers. These cover a French Bulldog (Bertrand *et al* 1936), two Boston Terriers (Dow 1940), a Scottish Terrier (Verlinde and Ojemann 1946), a Fox Terrier (Frauchiger and Fankhauser 1957), certain Airedale families (Cordy and Snelbaker 1952), Bern Running dogs (Good 1962), Finnish Harriers (Tontitila and Lindberg 1971), Jack Russells (Hartley 1973), Swedish Lapland dogs (Sandefeldt *et al* 1973) and a Gordon Setter (deLahunta *et al* 1980). In most cases where post-mortem details were recorded there was degeneration of the cerebellum and loss of Purkinje's cells. In addition to these cases Bjork *et al* (1957) reported on ataxia in Smooth Fox Terriers in Sweden over a 15 year period where there was loss of Purkinje's cells and degeneration of the spinal cord.

Whether all these diseases are essentially the same is difficult to say. Most cases related to isolated dogs and only in the case of the Smooth Fox Terriers in Sweden, the Swedish Lapland dogs and the 1976 Kerry Blue reports were the same groups of scientists involved in that deLahunta was involved in the Kerry and Lapland cases and Bjork in the Fox Terrier and Lapland cases. All appear to have been considered as distinct diseases by the workers concerned in that the pathological symptoms were somewhat different and age of onset and severity of clinical symptoms varied. However all had Purkinje's cells being destroyed and all had ataxia. In their discussion of the Lapland cases Sandefeldt *et al* (1973) review previous cases and claim that theirs was a totally new disease but in comparing the symptoms with those noted by Bjork *et al* (1957, 1962) and others described as Friedreich's ataxia by Mollaret *et al* (1933) there are several points of similarity and it does not seem to have occurred to any of the investigative groups to consider the fact that the same disease may produce somewhat different symptoms in the distinct genetic situations of different breeds.

Be this as it may, our present interest lies not so much in the discussion of whether these various forms of ataxia are different forms of the same disease as in the mode of transmission of the general disease format.

The Genetics
Only in the case of the Smooth Fox Terriers, Lapland dogs and Kerry Blues were sufficient numbers of dogs available to assess the possible genetic structure of the ataxias observed.

Bjork *et al* (1957) showed that the Smooth Fox Terrier cases occurred in both sexes and appeared to bear no relationship to any nutritional, managerial or environmental features. They did, however, find that in the pedigrees of affected dogs there were common ancestors and they concluded that the most recent dog and a possible causal factor was Dandifino (born 1925) an English dog who won a CC at Richmond in 1927.

It was possible to mate one defective dog to his normal sister which produced four surviving puppies of which one was ataxic. There were, however, data on 23 litters with at least one ataxic pup. In each instance both parents were normal and it was assumed that the disease was a simple recessive condition which would make the parents of such litters Aa in genetic type and ataxic pups all aa. There were, in fact, 91 pups born of which 25% ought to have been affected. In practice 25 pups were suffering from ataxia which was close enough to expected theory to allow the workers to conclude that a recessive gene was the cause.

In the Swedish Lapland dog situation there were 12 litters in which at least one ataxic case appeared and the data are summarised in Table 46.

In the American Kerry Blue case there were 13 affected animals in 5 New York and 3 Californian litters. The pedigrees are shown in Figure 37 which is a redrawing of the deLahunta and Averill (1976) pedigree information with names included and one further case diagnosed in Britain added in. It can be seen that all cases trace back to the litter brothers Tregoads Vicky's Cappy and Victor. In their paper the Cornell workers record a case of a littler in Texas which traced back on both sides to Victor but which did not provide full details for inclusion here. Subsequently an affected case in Ontario was reported by DeForest *et al* (1978) and pedigree data showed it to be heavily inbred on Melbees Chances Are (12.5%).

The statistical assessment of litters is shown in Table 47 assuming a simple autosomal recessive with both parents being Aa in genotype.

DeLahunta and Averill (1976) calculated expected numbers on the basis of 25% of pups being PNA which would have meant only 8.75 PNA cases and on raw data the observed ratios do not fit the 3:1 test. On uncorrected data the simple autosomal recessive theory has to be rejected but the authors propose this without showing any significance tests. They do point out that the lack of litters with no affected stock inflated the number of PNA cases but they do not carry out the correction test which I have done in Table 47. Had they done so they would have found that the chi-squared value (see page 352) was only 0.06 and thus the autosomal recessive theory is quite tenable.

Once the pedigree information shown in Figure 37 became public knowledge in Kerry Blue circles there was some attempt by the US Kerry Blue Terrier Club to present a balanced view of the problem but not all individual breeders adopted the same logical

Table 46

Matings of normal Swedish Lapland dogs in which at least one case of ataxia appeared

Number in Litter	Litters	Progeny		Expected Numbers*	
		Normal	*Affected*	*Normal*	*Affected*
1	1	0	1	0	1.000
3	2	4	2	3.406	2.594
4	1	3	1	2.537	1.463
6	5	20	10	20.875	9.125
7	3	16	5	14.940	6.060
Total	12	43	19	41.758	20.242

*Expected numbers after making allowance for mode of collection (see page 352).
Source   Sandefeldt *et al* 1973.

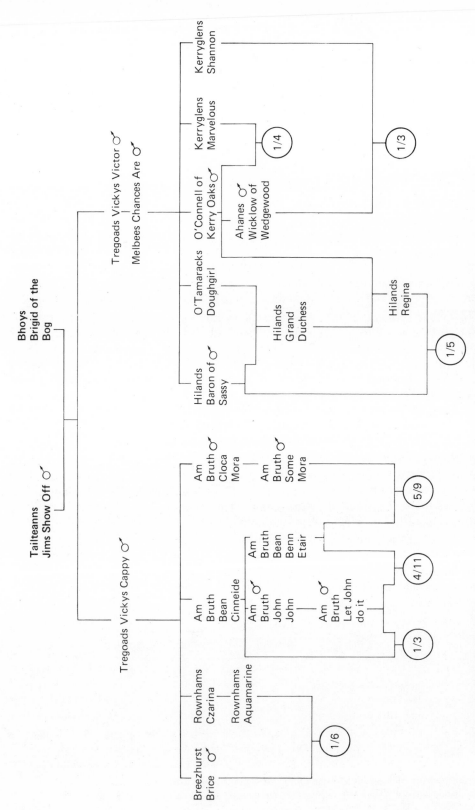

Figure 37 Lines of descent from Tregoads Vickys Cappy and Tregoads Vickys Victor of litters containing Progressive Neuronal Abiotrophy (PNA) pups. Breed is the Kerry Blue Terrier and numbers encircled represent PNA cases in total number born (1/6 = one case in six born) (redrawn, with additions, from deLahunta and Averill 1976).

Table 47

Occurrence of PNA in eight litters of Kerry Blue Terriers

Number in litter	Litters	Progeny		Expected Numbers*	
		Normal	PNA	Normal	PNA
3	3	5	4	5.109	3.891
4	1	3	1	2.537	1.463
5	2	7	3	6.720	3.280
6	2	7	5	8.350	3.650
Total	8	22	13	22.716	12.284

*Expected numbers after correction for method of ascertainment (see page 352). This was not undertaken by the authors concerned.
Source deLahunta and Averill 1976.

viewpoint. One prominent British breeder alleged that the Kerry Blue Terrier Club of England and the Kerry Blue Terrier Association had made strong recommendations that owners of dogs and bitches carrying the bloodlines of the two Tregoad dogs named above and their litter brother Gallant should not breed from them (Attwood-Parker 1977). The same author goes on to say that at the time of writing there were 'Kerries in quarantine who are known carriers'. This last statement suggests that the dogs in quarantine had produced PNA and that does not appear to be the case.

Action to take Against PNA
Whether PNA occurs in Kerry Blues or any other breed it is both undesirable and illogical for breeders to adopt a witchhunt type of action against it. They will rightly want to reduce the incidence or eliminate it, if possible, but they must seek to do this by sound genetic measures and without losing valuable qualities. This means keeping the PNA problem in perspective.

Essentially PNA is a breeders loss in that it has a fairly early age of onset (on average 11 weeks of age). This means that losses will be met by the breeder since he must either destroy the dog early in life or, if sold at about 6–8 weeks, it will quickly develop ataxia and most buyers would have a case in law to reclaim the costs incurred at having been sold an affected animal. This, however, seems eminently desirable since breeders who make wrong decisions ought to be prepared to pay for their mistakes.

On the credit side the very fact that PNA is an early onset disease means that breeding information is quickly known and one does not have to keep a dog for some years before finding out that it has a genetic disease. It is also effectively lethal so that all PNA affected stock will be dead or destroyed prior to sexual maturity. There is thus no risk to the breed from PNA cases. The recessive nature of the condition means that it will be spread by Aa type animals and the breeder needs to be able to identify which animals are of this genotype. He cannot do this, as yet, by any physical means since Aa type animals will be perfectly normal and indistinguishable from AA animals. Any suggestion that Aa dogs should be banned from exhibition or destroyed is ludicrous. If we ban these then there are many other dogs who, for similar clinical reasons, would have to be banned and, carried to a local conclusion, all dog showing and breeding would cease.

By the same token the cry that all descendants of the Tregoad brothers be destroyed or not bred from is illogical. In a simple recessive condition only 50% of the progeny of an Aa type animal will carry the defective a allele, the other 50% will be carrying A. If we were to conclude that the Tregoad stock were of only moderate quality then little harm would result from culling their descendants but it is quite another thing to dispose of bloodlines which are producing many other virtues. Kerry Blues are not a breed on which I can speak with any expertise but it is well-established that the Tregoad line has produced good Kerry Blue Terriers. The dog Melbees Chances Are (a known carrier of PNA) was possibly one of America's greatest sires. To cull him and his offspring might help to reduce the incidence of PNA but at too high a price in terms of breed type.

Furthermore the global disposal of all descendants of the famous litter will not necessarily eliminate PNA. We still do not know from whence the PNA allele reached this litter. It is unlikely to be a mutation in the litter itself but more likely in a parent. The sire was widely used so is probably not to blame and if the dam was in some way involved then it means that other lines of British origin may be implicated. Certainly one pup confirmed by deLahunta as a PNA case had a pedigree entirely free of Tregoad dogs (USKBTC 1976). Then again the 1946 case reported by Mettler and Goss suggests that the defect goes back to a much earlier point in time and probably to Ireland.

The decimation of top bloodlines advocated by some breeders—whatever their motivation—is not sensible. What is needed is a dispassionate and cooperative study of the problem on an international level.

Kerry Blue breeders should begin to compile data on all litters, retaining pups to three months or selling earlier on a guarantee of replacement of PNA results. All presumed affected animals should be checked by a recognised expert and pathology undertaken to ensure that PNA is involved.

Test matings have been advocated but little hope exists in this area. All aa dogs will die so that test mating must be between suspect carrier (A?) and known (Aa). As will be seen later (Table 100 page 356) this means three or four litters with a total of 16 pups before one can be reasonably sure of the genetic make-up of the dog under test. If PNA was at a high incidence in the breed Aa type dogs would be commonplace but if PNA is rare Aa dogs are difficult to identify (see Table 87 page 294). If PNA is rare then there is no serious problem anyway.

I am not convinced that in this case outstanding specimens should be disposed of even if they are proven carriers through I see little point in using known Aa dogs if they are of moderate quality. One has to assess failings against virtues and Kerry Blues will not be helped by hysterical witchhunts on this or any other defect. A register of known carriers to which breeders could have access is a useful record which breed clubs could maintain.

It is interesting that in Sweden a control scheme to attempt to control juvenile neuronal muscular atrophy was set up in the Swedish Lapland breed. Test mating was begun in 1973 and a report on results was produced by Sandefeldt and Nilsson (1986). They showed that by the end of 1983 (ten years of work) some 260 male and 297 female non-carriers had been identified by virtue of siring at least 11 normal pups when mated to a known heterozygote. In 277 litters from 37 non-carrier sires only 38% were classed as non-carriers while from 162 litters ex 56 non-carrier dams some 75% were non carriers. It was reported by these authors that a considerable number of bitches of 'unknown genotype' were mated to non-carrier males, hence the rather slow progress. Incidentally 11 normal pups from a known heterozygote is a 4.22% chance of an actual carrier being recorded as a non-carrier.

Hypomyelinogenesis

Essentially this condition involves inadequate production of myelin around the nerves of the spinal cord and brain. In effect there is a reduced insulation capacity and this leads to symptoms in the dog akin to trembling. It may be connected to diseases reported above and similar diseases are seen in species other than the dog. It has been reported in Tibetan Mastiffs in USA (Abbott 1986) and was seen in Bernese Mountain Dogs in Britain during 1985. To date some dozen or more cases have been recorded and the indications are that the BMD situation, like that in the Tibetan Mastiff involves a simple autosomal recessive (Wallace 1986; Willis 1986). In all cases to date the affected dogs trace back to an imported male on both sides of the pedigree. Programmes to seek to examine the problem and to control incidence have been set up by the British Bernese Mountain Dog clubs.

A similar type of defect has been seen in the Rottweiler in Holland (Wouda and Van Nes 1986) and although the mode of inheritance was unclear a genetic explanation was considered likely.

Cerebellar Degeneration in Rough Collies

This condition was first reported in the Rough Collie in Australia by Hartley *et al* (1978) though it was first identified by breeders in 1966 in a dog who sired some 700 offspring. The pathology of the disease is not dissimilar to PNA and ataxia in that there is loss of Purkinje cells but there is also extensive demyelination on the central nervous system with the initial lesion being a massive destruction of preformed granule cells in the anterior cerebellar vermis. Clinical signs appeared between one and two months of age and involved typical ataxia with swaying of the head and body, especially if any attempt was made to walk or run. Balance became increasingly difficult to maintain, especially if excited or at meal times.

Hartley *et al* (1978) presented data on 34 affected animals from 16 litters by eight different sires, all descendants of the original sire. In addition information was available on a further 36 animals. Proband analysis showed that the segregation frequency lay between 0.22 and 0.30 which encompassed the expected 0.25 and thus confirmed that the condition was a simple autosomal recessive.

Although differences between this and other PNA/ataxia cases exist this may be a reflection of breed differences rather than an indication that these cerebellar degeneration diseases are all unrelated separate entities. Hartley *et al* (1978) point out that all but one of the cases seen by them in Rough Collies were sables but this may reflect the bloodlines used rather than any link with the disease and sable coloration.

Recurrent Tetany or Hyperkinetic Disorders ('Scottie Cramp')

The Disease
This disease was reported as far back as the 1940s (Klarenbeek *et al* 1942) in the Scottish Terrier and would appear to have been sufficiently common in the breed to have received the popular name of Scottie or Scotch cramp. It does not, however, appear to be unique to that breed since Smythe (1945) also reported it in a Wire-Haired Fox Terrier and a Cocker Spaniel and more recently a similar condition was seen in two Dalmatians (Woods 1977).

Insofar as the Scottish Terrier is concerned the subject has been discussed in detail by a variety of authors (Joshua 1956; Meyers *et al* 1968, 1969, 1970) as well as those previously named.

Dogs suffering from the condition undergo transient episodes of muscular hypertension. At rest or during short exercise periods the affected dog will behave and appear normal but when subjected to strenuous exercise or excitement clinical signs become apparent. At first these involve an arching of the back in the lumbar region. A stiff-legged gait then occurs with the hind legs being overflexed and the dog may skip with one or both legs flexed against the body. If the dog is still required to be active there will be a progressive difficulty with movement until in severe cases it will become unable to move and stand still as though carved out of stone. According to Meyers *et al* (1969) there is considerable variation among dogs both in terms of severity of the clinical symptoms and the time taken for their onset. They considered that the mental state of the dog was more important than the amount or intensity of exercise. Excitement and fear tended to increase the problem while anxiety and apprehension might even be inhibitory.

Apparently dogs do not seem to be in pain and they do not lose consciousness but there is an increase in muscle tone and electrical activity of the muscle. If allowed to rest the dog will return to normal and it does not seem that longevity is affected. Age at onset is variable but according to Meyers *et al* (1970) is usually seen about 12 months of age and may be as early as six weeks.

Diseases of this kind are often called myotonias and several are known to occur in man but according to Meyers *et al* (1970) there is little similarity with the condition in Scottish Terriers beyond the clinical symptoms.

Drugs can suppress symptoms quite effectively (Meyers *et al* 1969) and most authors seem to accept that the problem lies with the central nervous system since muscles appear to be physiologically normal. According to Meyers and his colleagues positive diagnosis of the disease involves three stages. The dog should have a clinical history of abnormal gait or seizures during excitement, the typical hyperkinetic episodes should be induced by injection of amphetamine and they should be promptly ended by injection of diazepam or promazine derivatives. Clearly this type of testing must be done by veterinarians but it does seem that diagnosis on this basis is relatively simple.

The Genetics

Most early writers on the subject (Klarenbeek *et al* 1942; Smythe 1945; Joshua 1956) refer to familial patterns of the disease and Smythe considered it to be a recessive genetic trait. However no papers seem to have presented data on the subject prior to Meyers *et al*

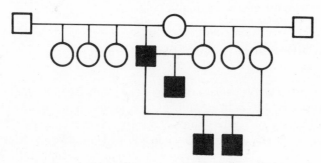

Figure 38   Pedigree of 'Scottie cramp' (solid symbols) (Meyers *et al* 1970).

Table 48

Occurrence of Scottie cramp in litters where both parents were normal but believed to be carriers of the condition*

Litter size	Litters	Litters with affected			Total pups	Affected pups	
		1	*2*	*3†*		*Actual*	*Expected*
1	3	3	0	0	3	3	3.0
2	1	1	0	0	2	1	1.1
3	3	3	0	0	9	3	3.9
4	6	4	0	2	24	10	8.8
5	3	1	2	0	15	5	4.9
6	1	0	1	0	6	2	1.8
Totals	17	12	3	2	59	24	23.5

* Only litters with at least one affected pup are included.
† No litter had more than 3 affected pups.
Source   Meyers *et al* 1970.

(1970). Their data are based upon pedigree studies and breeders' records. A typical pedigree from Meyers' papers is shown in Figure 38 and indicates the recessive nature of the disease because normal parents can give rise to affected offspring. Another case cited by these workers involved a dog who was used to mate two closely related bitches and produced three cases of Scottie cramp, he himself being a sufferer. However, when mated to four unrelated bitches with no known history of cramp in their pedigrees more than 20 normal offspring were produced. Transmission from affected sire to son rules out any sex-linked mode of inheritance and no sex-limited problem seemed to be involved which disagrees with the report by Smythe (1945) that the problem was more common in dogs than bitches.

Meyers *et al* (1970) were rightly cautious in their report as to the exact mode of inheritance but the data given in Table 48 suggest that it is a simple autosomal recessive condition.

Although it seems logical to consider Scottie cramp to be a genetic problem in the Scottish Terrier it does not follow that the cases observed in other breeds are identical. As Burns and Fraser (1966) point out the symptoms are not dissimilar to parathyroid malfunction and it could be that cases in other breeds have a non-genetic base. Any breed group which has problems of this kind should collect and check pedigree records before accepting any genetic basis.

A condition similar to Scottie cramp was reported in Airedales by Kollarits (1924). There was permanent trembling of the hindquarters and tail and the author attributed this to inbreeding depression but offered no real evidence.

In a recent paper in which eight cases of Scottie cramp were investigated two Swedish workers (Andersson and Akerlund 1976) put forward the theory that the ultimate cause of the problem was an abnormal development of the bones of the skull. This seems at variance with other views but is worth further investigation since it suggests a selectional defect.

Quadriplegia and Amblyopia ('Swimmers')

The Condition

A condition in newly-born puppies which seem incapable of standing was first described by Ball and Asquith (1958) in two unrelated Pekingese. The authors attributed a genetic basis to the condition on very flimsy evidence and claimed that it was something which breeders tended to keep hidden. According to Burns and Fraser (1966) the condition was known in many breeds, publicly talked about and, as reported by Smythe (1963), appeared to be similar to a haemolytic disease of newborn puppies described by Young *et al* (1951). This latter problem seemed to produce fading puppies as a result of the ingestion of antibodies from an immunised A-negative mother by her A-positive pups. This would appear to resemble the Rhesus factor situation in humans. It does not, however, conform to the findings of Palmer *et al* (1973) who studied the problem in 18 Irish Setter pups.

These animals, some of which survived to 25 weeks of age, could generally only stand when given assistance. In the main they lay flat and moved rather as would a seal when swimming (hence the term 'swimmers'). Neck muscles appeared weak initially but became stronger and the head could then be raised normally. Head tremors and jerky movements were common and some pups had fits. There was impairment of vision (amblyopia) with no blink reflex or retraction of the head when bright light was shone upon the eye.

Pups were thought to whine for longer than seemed normal but as they aged they became more normal and appeared bright and playful. The eating pattern was abnormal in that the jaws clamped tightly on food but did not immediately commence chewing. Other sensations, apart from vision, appeared normal.

Post-mortem findings on the brains were not conclusive. Only in animals which had survived beyond three months of age were there any obvious abnormalities and these were confined to the cerebellum with, in general, loss of Purkinje's cells. Whether this was the causal problem of the disease or simply a reflection of it was not clear.

The Genetics

According to Parry (cited by Palmer *et al* 1973) 'swimmers' have been known for many years in the Irish Setter and most experienced breeders are able to recognise the symptoms within 3 days of birth. If Parry is correct then it is surprising that the study of Palmer and his colleagues should be the first serious attempt to understand the genetics of the condition.

These authors had access to a total of 11 litters in which 'swimmers' had appeared. There were 96 animals born of which 59 were normal, 30 affected and a further seven destroyed for reasons unconnected with the condition.

The data are shown in Table 49 and relate only to litters in which 'swimmers' appeared. The ratio of 59 normals to 30 swimmers is not in disagreement with 3:1 ratio albeit not a very good fit. If the 7 animals destroyed are included as normal then the goodness of fit improves but, as the authors point out, there is a bias in data where only litters containing affected animals are used. The two final columns in Table 49 represent a correction for this bias and statistical tests show a good fit with the 3:1 ratio.

Of the affected animals 9 did not have their sex determined but there were 13 females and 8 males does not suggest any sex-limited factor. The sex-linked possibility of a gene carried on the X chromosome is discounted because it would necessitate only females being carriers and this is clearly not the case from the pedigree information reproduced in Figure 39. This relates to 14 animals examined at the veterinary clinic concerned.

Table 49

Incidence of normal and affected dogs in litters of Irish Setters containing 'swimmers'

Number in litter*	Litters	Progeny			Expected progeny†	
		Normal	Affected	Total	Normal	Affected
2	1	1	1	2	1	0
5	1	4	1	5	4	0
7	1	3	4	7	12	12
8	4	21	11	32	57	20
9	1	7	2	9	14	2
11	2	14	8	22	54	26
12	1	9	3	12	27	6
Total	11	59	30	89	169	66

* Excludes animals destroyed unchecked.
† After correction for bias due to method of ascertainment.
Source Palmer *et al* 1973.

The authors conclude that 'swimmers' in the Irish Setter are caused by a single autosomal recessive gene with full penetrance and that it is post-natally lethal. The overall degree of inbreeding (see page 320) in the affected pups was 11.78% which is high, approaching a half-sib mating. Several champions were shown to be carriers and the authors assume that several others must be implicated.

It has since been suggested (Cunningham 1975) that 'Swimmers' can be cured by maintaining them in a sling arrangement from birth. If this is true it does not preclude a genetic condition nor does it necessarily invalidate Palmer's assessment of a post-natal lethal since left to their own devices 'swimmers' will die. The wisdom of rearing 'swimmers' must be questioned and breeders would be better advised to destroy them.

Test mating to reduce the incidence of the condition or to eradicate it form lines will have to be based upon Aa × presumptive Aa type matings (see page 356) and will be feasible in a breed with relatively large litters, at least for males. Whether it is worth doing is questionable. If 'swimmers' are left to die only carrier (Aa) type dogs will exist and on average the maximum incidence in the breed could not exceed 25% of pups born and will remain much lower. Since more than enough pups will be born it affords a ready-made inbuilt culling procedure. The Palmer paper relates to two so-called strains and it does not follow that all strains are similarly affected.

The genetics of 'swimmers' in other breeds is unknown but it is logical to assume a similar situation to that of the Irish Setter.

German Shepherd Dog Myelopathy

This disease is a slow and progressive neurologic disorder which is characterised by partial paralysis over a period of from two to eight months. There is a loss of muscle strength and ataxia in the truncal region. Some workers have suggested that it is a 'dying-back disease' (Averill 1973; Griffiths and Duncan 1975). This is a degenerative process in which the

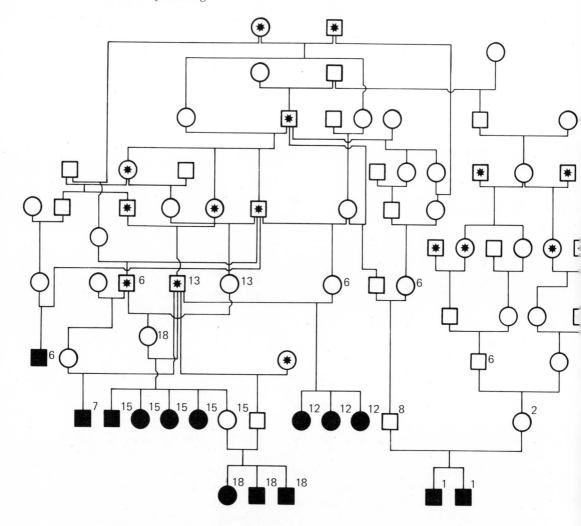

Figure 39   Pedigree of 'swimmers' in Irish Setters. Solid symbols are affected animals and symbols with central stars refer to Champions. Numbers are coefficients of inbreeding (%) (redrawn from Palmer *et al* 1973).

nerve cell is affected by some kind of metabolic disturbance. Nerve cells of the central and peripheral nervous systems may be affected. Morphologically such diseases are characterised by degeneration of long fibre tract systems with the most severe lesions being at the terminal parts of the affected pathways. The larger fibres are generally the main ones affected and lesions are usually bilateral and symmetrical. According to Braund and Vandevelde (1978) lesions in German Shepherd Dog Myelopathy should be concentrated in the cervical and brainstem areas and/or in the lumbar part of the spinal cord. However these workers examined 23 Shepherds (14 affected and nine normals) and found that the 'dying-back' theory was not supported by the pathological findings. They took various measurements of the nerve fibres and although degeneration was found in various regions of the spinal cord the findings were not consistent with a dying-back disease.

More recently Waxman *et al* (1980a,b) have shown that blood lymphocyte activity is impaired in affected dogs with the impairment being greater in more severely affected dogs. The disease is akin to multiple sclerosis in man and the seriousness of the condition is emphasised by the fact that GSD myelopathy does not really respond to therapy and leads to the inevitable destruction of the dog.

Whether this disease is peculiar to the German Shepherd or whether it is similar to degenerative conditions in other breeds as was suggested by Averill (1973) is uncertain. Braund and Vandevelde (1978) have postulated that the fact that this disease occurs in older dogs, and that it is seen in one breed in particular, indicates that genetic factors may be involved. Their suggestion that pedigree analyses be undertaken is sensible but not easy since the need to have detailed morphological data to accompany such pedigrees is obviously not going to be easy to obtain. The average age of the 14 affected dogs in the study of Braund and Vandevelde was 8.2 years with a standard deviation of 1.83 and this means that by the time pathology is undertaken the disease is likely to be well advanced and other secondary effects may complicate diagnosis.

In other species the predisposition of thoracic segments of the spinal cord to degenerative change has been linked to bone changes and invertebral disc prolapse. It is known that viral, nutritional and idiopathic changes can be implicated and although Averill (1973) has suggested that nutritional and vascular disorders are unlikely to be causes of the disease in German Shepherds no real evidence to support this view exists.

If the disease is genetic in origin it is unlikely to be simple in its mode of inheritance and it may be associated with selectional changes brought about by type selection.

Other Traits

Leukodystrophy
This disease is characterized by the gradual and symmetrical destruction of the white matter of the CNS and the demyelination of peripheral nerves. Nerve fibres may be myelinated or not, myelinated fibres being surrounded by a white sheath of fatty material and it is this which is broken down.

The clinical signs reflect the type of degeneration that is taking place. Destruction of the spinal cord leads to loss of limb control, damge to the cerebellum brings about ataxia and trembling and damage to the cerebral hemispheres of the brain causes mental degeneration. According to Fletcher (1969) the disease becomes noticed at from two to seven months of age and death occurs after some two to three months. According to Fletcher (1970) there are certain typical features on the EEG machine and this is a useful diagnostic tool.

The disease is known in Cairn Terriers and West Highland White Terriers and is said to be an inherited defect (Fankhauser *et al* 1963; Hirth and Nielsen 1967) but the evidence for this is tenuous. If it is inherited it is likely to be recessive in nature since affected animals die early in life and cannot thus transmit the problem. The incidence of the disease in either breed, or in others, is unknown.

Juvenile amaurotic idiocy (neuronal ceroid-lipofuscinosis)
This is a degenerative disease in which complex fatty substances accumulate in the CNS. These lead to complete mental degeneration, blindness and wasting of the body. Strictly speaking it is a storage disease in that some intermediate product is not broken down and

eliminated from the body. Either the necessary enzyme is absent or its activity is diminished.

In 1967 Karbe and Schiefer reported a form of this disease in the German Short-haired Pointer. Affected animals died by 10–18 months of age but only males were affected. A sex-linked theory was postulated but needs more proof.

Later, Koppang (1970) reported a form of the problem in English Setters in Norway. He provided clear proof of an autosomal recessive trait. Subsequently Patel *et al* (1974) found that the causal factor was a reduced activity of the enzyme PPD-peroxidase. They were able to detect carriers by laboratory tests which should provide a basis for eliminating the disease. It is not certain that the condition seen was the same as that in the German Pointer.

Spinal muscular atrophy

In 1979 Lorenz *et al* reported a progressive neurologic disease in a family of Brittany Spaniels in the USA. Several dogs were affected at ages from two to eight months. In the earliest stages there was weakness of the pelvic limb muscles with extension thereafter to other areas including muscles of the face and tongue. Affected dogs remained mentally alert and responsive to visual and auditory stimuli and there was no incontinence. Dogs survived and could be bred from so that a breeding colony was set up to investigate the condition. It seems to be unlike other motor neuronopathies found in the dog but akin to problems seen in children.

In a later paper Cork *et al* (1979) examined the genetic aspects and concluded that their data suggested inheritance was of an autosomal recessive kind. However, the possibility of polygenic inheritance was not ruled out.

Progressive axonopathy

Griffiths *et al* (1980) reported on five Boxers which had shown various degrees of hind limb ataxia. Although muscle atrophy was not seen all cases showed a progressive problem and all five were killed. Four of the cases concerned dogs ataxic from puppyhood but one was a five year old animal showing signs from three months previously. It appeared that the axons of the CNS were swollen and peripheral nerves were depleted in myelinated fibres. The condition has not been reported in other breeds but subsequent to the publication of the Griffiths paper the British Boxer Clubs began to collect evidence of further cases. According to unpublished data from Dr B. M. Cattanach (1981) who has worked on all the data located (some 60+ animals) the trait is inherited as a simple autosomal recessive and traces back to specific lines. A publication from the British Boxer Council (1982?) lists several of the known cases and outlines the mode of transmission and the methods recommended for control of the disease.

Chapter 10

Genetics of the Eye

Introduction

Abnormalities of the eye feature prominently in the report by Hodgman (1963) and more recently Barnett (1976) has reviewed a series of eye problems believed to be inherited in the dog. The number of breeds involved in the case of some defects seems very large and it is probable that no breed exists which does not have some degree of susceptibility to at least one eye condition. As with hip dysplasia some of the eye conditions have been subjected to considerable study by the veterinary profession although the genetics of many of these eye conditions is still unclear.

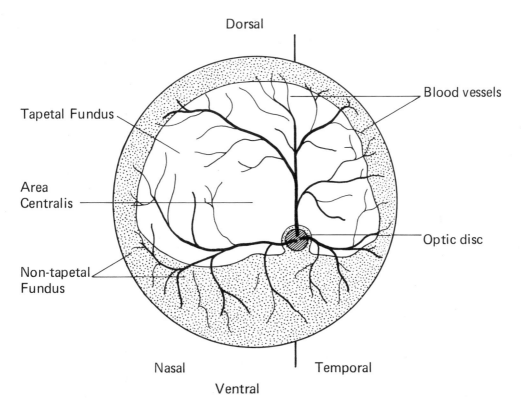

Figure 40 Diagrammatic view of the left eye of the dog as seen in frontal section (redrawn from Hodgman *et al* 1949).

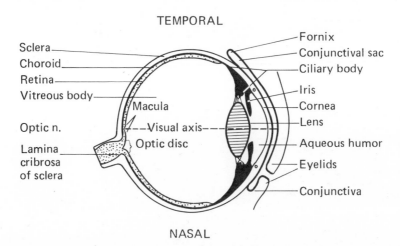

Figure 41   Diagrammatic view of the eye in horizontal section (Gardner *et al* 1963). Reproduced with permission of W. B. Saunders Co Philadelphia.

One might say that more attention has been given to abnormal than to normal eyes since our understanding of the mode of inheritance of eye shape and colour is still very limited. Indeed, on eye shape we know virtually nothing and on eye colour data are sparse and far from being sufficient to allow other than generalisations to be made.

This chapter deals with eye colour and then goes on to discuss the various inherited (or possibly inherited) defects in alphabetical order rather than in any order of importance or severity. Figures illustrating the eye are presented for ease of understanding the nomenclature used (see Figures 40 and 41) and photographs are provided throughout to show the type of picture presented in the animal that is visible to the naked eye or via an ophthalmoscope.

No attempt has been made to provide a comprehensive review of diagnostic techniques since this is a matter for the veterinarian rather than the breeder but clinical symptoms have been given where possible. Breeders are, however, reminded that diagnosis of eye conditions is best done by qualified experts armed with the right sort of equipment and this may not be possible with one's local veterinarian, who may not possess all the expensive equipment needed for diagnosis, but may involve approaching specialists through him.

Genetic studies of eye defects is an area where the breeder, eye specialist and geneticist might well cooperate to good advantage and mutual benefit. It is an area in which breed clubs could usefully organise both the testing of specific dogs for eye defects and the compilation of pedigree data. The problem which will be returned to later is the need to ensure that whole litters are checked. Little will be gained by the collection of pedigrees of affected dogs alone since, in this way, no real testing of genetic hypotheses is possible.

Eye Colour

The colour of the eye (iris) and the colour of the coat are not strictly separate entities in that eye colour can, in some cases, be modified by the type of coat colour genes that are carried (see Chapters 4 and 5).

1. Curly Coated Retrievers illustrating the B/b series. The liver coloured animal carries bb and the black dog is either BB or Bb. One can only distinguish BB and Bb types from pedigrees or progeny information. *(Photo Diane Pearce)*

2. An Isabella or fawn Dobermann. The animal carries two recessive genes in duplicate—bbdd. The bb series prevents black pigment and the dd series dilutes the resultant liver pigment. Note the normal tan markings on the legs and the presence of a brown nose. *(Photo J. Richardson)*

3. A liver (bb) German Shepherd Dog aged 2½ months. This animal was born to a sable dam by a black-and-tan sire. It is probably genetically sable, but the presence of two liver genes has caused the removal of all black pigment and the animal is brown on the nose and pads as well as having lighter coloured eyes. The condition is unacceptable in most standards, but is actually normal in biological terms. *(Photo courtesy Mrs R. C. July)*

4. A litter of German Shepherd Dogs illustrating the effect of dd in this breed. Two of the pups (to the right of the picture) have a 'dusty' appearance. They are black-and-tan animals but carrying dd which causes a 'bluish' dilution effect.

5a, b. Beagles showing different versions of white spotting. The first one is nearly all-white due to the presence of $s^p s^p$ with many minus modifiers. The second dog is less white and is likely to be exhibiting 'plus' modifiers of the s^p allele.

6a, b. Chondrodysplasia in the Alaskan Malamute. The dog on the left shows the condition to a milder degree than the one on the right. Note that although the condition leads to shortened legs the animals are still sizeable. They are dwarfs but not miniatures. *(Photo courtesy Dr Sheilah M. Fletch)*

7. A German Shepherd Dog pituitary dwarf with a normal GSD alongside. The dwarf is about 4 years of age and has lost its puppy coat (at 12 months) but not grown another. It is very typical of this condition. *(Photo courtesy H. Teall)*

8. Pituitary dwarfism in the Karelian Bear Dog. A normal sized animal is shown with two dwarfs which are 1 and 1½ years old. *(Photo courtesy Dr E. Andresen, © Hereditas 1977)*

9a, b. Carpal subluxation (on right) compared with a normal adult from the same colony. This is a sex-linked trait connected with haemophilia A in this colony. *(Photo courtesy Dr J. R. Pick, © Laboratory Investigation and Dr J. R. Pick 1967)*

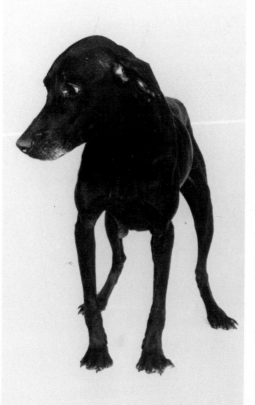

10. Ehlers–Danlos syndrome in an English Springer Spaniel. Note the excess skin and the extreme thinness of the skin. This latter has caused lacerations across the back. *(Photo courtesy Dr G. A. Hegreberg)*

11. *Below left:* Congenital alopecia in a male Miniature Poodle. *(Photo courtesy Dr V. J. Selmanowitz and American Genetic Association)*

12. *Below right:* Hip dysplasia X-ray of a Bernese Mountain Dog female (Redinka Rose). This is classified as a near normal under the BVA/KC old scheme and scored 3/3 under the BVA/GSDL scoring system. The score was made up of 1 on each side for Subluxation and 2 on each side for Cranial Acetabular Edge. Note identification filmed onto the plate. Parents of this bitch scored 3/3 and 5/3. *(Courtesy Mrs H. E. Davenport)*

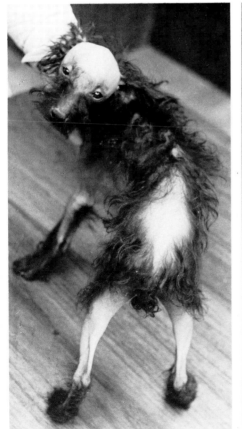

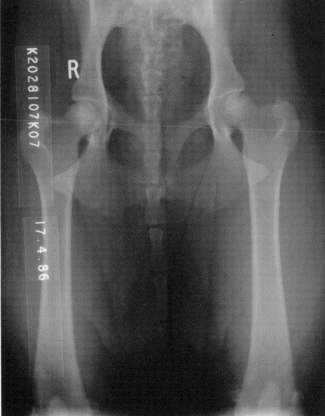

13. A Scottish Terrier suffering from 'Scottie cramp'. Note the arching of the back in the lumbar region. *(Photo courtesy Meyers et al 1970, © American Genetic Association)*

14. Congenital oedema in a Bulldog pup delivered by Caesarian section. Note the tenseness of the skin and swellings of the head and limbs. *(Photo courtesy Dr P. W. Ladds, © Journal of the American Veterinary Medical Association 1971)*

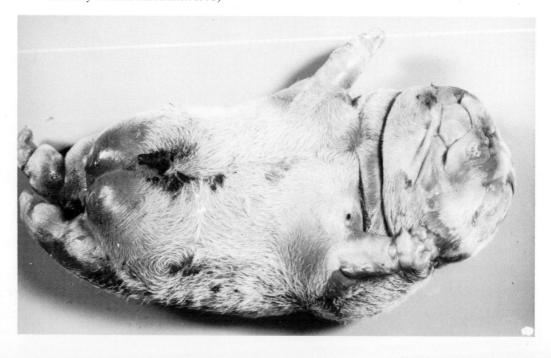

15. Normal appearance of the retina of a dog (Greyhound aged 2 years). *(Photo courtesy Dr K. C. Barnett)*

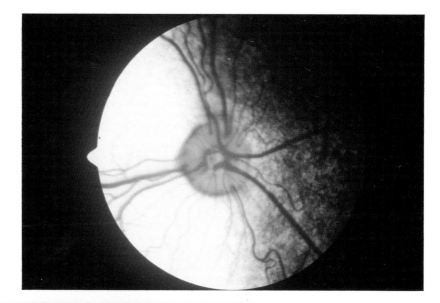

16. Generalised progressive retinal atrophy (Miniature Poodle aged 4 years). *(Photo courtesy Dr K. C. Barnett)*

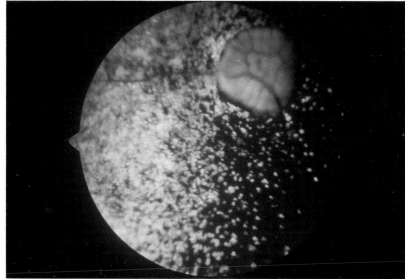

17. Centralised progressive retinal atrophy (Labrador Retriever aged 3 years). *(Photo courtesy Dr K. C. Barnett)*

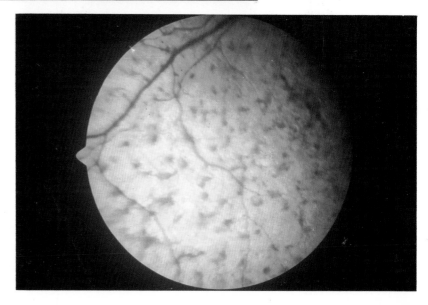

18. An adult Rough Collie affected by cyclic neutropenia. This animal is genetically a tricolour but the colour is diluted on the back where it should be black and on the muzzle and eye spots which ought to be brown. *(Photo courtesy Dr J. E. Lund et al 1970, © American Genetic Association)*

19. Tricolour Rough Collies. The one in the foreground is quite normal but the two others have cyclic neutropenia and the coat colour is diluted from black to grey and from brown to white. *(Photo courtesy Dr J. E. Lund et al 1970, © American Genetic Association)*

Our knowledge of eye colour stems from studies on the Greyhound (Warren 1927; Burns 1943) and the German Shepherd dog (Humphrey and Warner 1934). In dogs with no coat colour dilution factors visible (that is dogs homozygous or heterozygous for non-dilution genes) we see eye colour ranging from very dark brown through to light yellow. Burns and Fraser (1966) suggest that there are three eye colour alleles called Ir, ir^m and ir^y with dominance going in that order. This gives a series of colour combinations:

$$IrIr, Irir^m, Irir^y, ir^mir^m, ir^mir^y, ir^yir^y,$$

with colour being darkest at IrIr and lightest at ir^yir^y. Since dominance is incomplete varying shades will exist and there is the added complication that, in optical terms, the colour of the surrounding coat will influence the judgement of the observer. Thus a brown-faced dog can tolerate a lighter eye colour than can a black-faced animal before being penalised. These eye shades will be inherited independent of coat colour but when dilution genes are present this will not be the case.

The 'blue' dilution gene d will, when present as dd, cause eye colour to become a smokey grey. The liver coat colour allele b will, in the bb state, dilute Ir to chestnut, ir^m to hazel and ir^y to very pale yellow (Burns and Fraser 1966). Then again cc and c^bc^b may produce blue eyes. The merle allele M will give rise to wall-eye if restricted pigment chances to cover the eye although it is not yet certain whether there is a separate factor related to M but producing wall-eye.

Iljin (1926, 1928) reports on a factor called ruby eye which affects retina pigmentation so that a light shone onto the eye is reflected as red rather than the normal yellow-green. This is said to be recessive to normal eye colour. Certain eye diseases such as PRA (see page 221) will alter eye colour.

Many judges seem to be obsessed by eyes in that light-eyed dogs, regardless of other qualities, will be summarily dismissed from the ring. Eye-colour is basically aesthetic and it seems particularly futile to pay more attention to it than to some important structural and mental characteristics.

In their work with German Shepherds, Humphrey and Warner (1934) reported a phenotypic correlation of between -0.50 and -0.79 between eye colour and intelligence. This suggests that between 25 and 62% of the variation in intelligence could be explained by eye colour with lighter eyes being associated with greater intelligence. The data relate to phenotypic correlations and give no clues to underlying genetic correlations and they were produced at a time when statistical analyses were less advanced than now. They may be spurious but they do give added weight to the view that eye colour ought not to be excessively penalised. In this connection it is worth mentioning that my contacts with police officers from the Metropolitan Police dog section have revealed contrary evidence, albeit not subject to any statistical analysis. Police officers who have commented upon eye colour say that light-eyed dogs were invariably unreliable for work and certainly not the most intelligent. This may suggest that Humphrey and Warner were wrong or it may be that the light-eyed (and frequently curly-tailed) German Shepherds observed by the police were not always free of other 'blood' which could as readily account for poor working qualities.

It cannot be overemphasised that insistence upon dark eyes is, in many instances, an attempt to seek the impossible. In dogs which are bb in genotype the very dark eye is genetically impossible to achieve because of the action of the liver coat colour gene upon eye pigmentation. The same is true of the dilution gene d. Several breed standards insist upon dark eyes and in doing so make some coat colours impossible to achieve. Such standards should be revised and their continued existence emphasises the dangers of allowing breeders, with no genetic understanding, free rein on issues they are not competent to decide. It is high time that all standards were examined by geneticists to eliminate such inconsistencies.

Cataract

Definition

Cataract can be defined as opacity of the lens (Duke-Elder 1969). It is said by some workers to be a common eye disorder in the dog and one source (Anon 1967) suggests that almost every dog over eight years of age will develop some degree of lenticular opacity.

Usually a cataract is easily observed by the naked eye, at least in an advanced state. There will be a white opacity of the lens and when fully developed a cataract will present a bluish white or grey appearance with a mother-of-pearl-like sheen. There will be varying degrees of blindness.

Categorisation of cataracts can be made by several methods. Some are acquired as a result of trauma or developmental problems while others are clearly inherited. Some are congenital (present as soon as the eyelids open) while others occur late in life. A final classification can be made according to the position of the cataract in the eye (see Roberts 1973; Barnett 1978).

Despite the comment on naked eye identification, breeders are well advised to consult an ophthalmic specialist since it does not follow that cataract is the primary problem; many are secondary consequences of other eye defects. It is thus important to know whether a dog has primary or secondary cataract and whether or not it is likely to be genetic in origin. Identification of cataract is thus based upon detailed knowledge of the dog's history as well as breed and pedigree information in addition to ophthalmoscopic examination.

Genetic Evidence

Cataracts have been mentioned in the literature for a long time. Nicolas (1925) suggests a hereditary tendency towards the problem in Poodles and Pugs while Westhues (1926) records cases of hereditary cataract in mongrels. A family of German Shepherds was described by Hippel (1930) in which the condition was regarded as a simple dominant. Later a Scandinavian report by Høst and Sveinson (1936) described a condition in Pointers which developed in the 12–24 month period of life and which led to total blindness. It was traced back to a bitch called Lady of Gammelgord but the mode of inheritance was never fully determined. It is perhaps interesting that no further reports on inherited cataracts implicate Pointers.

Smythe (1958) recorded a high percentage of cataracts in Fox Terriers, Collies, Old English Sheepdogs and Sealyhams while in the same year Anderson and Schultz recorded cases in a Beagle colony. In this latter paper there were 1129 animals with only one male affected. Mated to five normal females this male produced 21 affected and four normal offspring. This is a high percentage of cases if the male concerned was a mutant carrying one dominant allele. However he may have carried two dominant alleles and there might have been some variable penetrance. The picture is unclear but suggestive of a dominant rather than any other mode of transmission.

Since 1969 there has been a spate of reports on hereditary cataract in a variety of breeds.

Most cases have been reported by American workers but in many instances the condition is known in the same breeds in Britain (Barnett 1976, 1978).

There does appear to be different genetic forms of cataract in that recessive and dominant forms are known according to the breed concerned. In Miniature Schnauzers a congenital type of cataract which affected the subcapsular cortex and lens equator was reported by Rubin *et al* (1969). Test breedings were made from 47 pups in 12 litters and it was suggested that an autosomal recessive mode of inheritance was involved. This was confirmed by breeding work undertaken by Donovan (1971). According to Roberts (1973) post-natal cataracts are known in this breed but the mode of inheritance, if any, is not clear.

A report on bilateral equatorial cataracts was made on a family of Standard Poodles by Rubin and Flowers (1972) in which signs were visible by 6 to 18 months of age but which were detectable by slit-lamp at 10 weeks. Again the data were indicative of a recessive mode of inheritance as shown in pedigree data in Figure 42. In this instance no other ocular defects were observed.

Nuclear or cortical cataracts or both, positioned equatorially or laterally were reported in Old English Sheepdogs by Koch (1972). Various matings were made (Table 50) and from 115 animals in 29 litters 71 were examined. Of these 44 had cataract, five with accompanying retinal detachment. The relationship between the two defects was uncertain but the mode of inheritance appeared to be recessive and autosomal.

In the Afghan Hound post-natal cataracts were reported by Roberts and Helper (1972). They examined 291 animals and observed lesions in 10 dogs which, during a period of examination, did not progress in the manner common to most inherited cataracts. Five dogs with characteristic total opacity were noted. Test mating two affected dogs produced

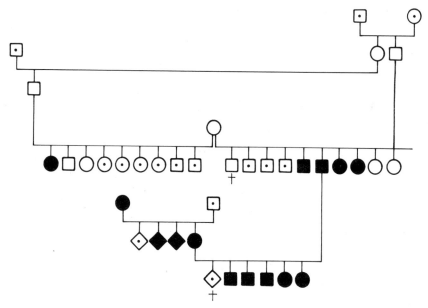

Figure 42 Pedigree of cataract (solid symbols) in Standard Poodles (Rubin & Flowers 1972).
◇| unknown sex   ⊙ not seen   † stillborn

Table 50

Occurrence of cataract in various matings of Old English Sheepdogs

Type of mating	Litters	Dogs	Dogs seen	Number with cataracts
Normal × Normal	1	10	8	5
Normal × Cataract	10	36	27	15
Cataract × Cataract	2	9	3	3
Unknown × Normal	7	21	11	10
Unknown × Cataract	6	32	13	6
Unknown × Unknown	3	7	4	4

Source   Koch 1972.

a litter of 10, all of which developed bilateral cataracts. The earliest case was seen at some 4½ months and the oldest at 23 months. The data are indicative of an autosomal recessive especially when considered with other information presented by these authors. This involved two pairs of normal parents producing progeny with cataracts and a mating of affected to normal dogs which gave both types of offspring. The overall incidence in the breed seemed to be low but represented dogs taken for examination in a scheme run by the Afghan Hound Club of Northern California. Several members with affected stock might not have had their dogs examined. Barnett (1978) reports cases in this breed and stresses that although always bilateral there is not necessarily symmetry. Age at onset can be as late as 36 months.

In Miniature Poodles Roberts (1973) reports cases of cataract occurring at from 2 to 6 years of age. The condition was bilateral but an interval of 12 to 24 months might occur between the first and second eye being affected. No other occular disease was noted but Roberts offered no genetic data.

According to Barnett (1976, 1978) hereditary cataract is known in Britain among Miniature Schnauzers, Old English Sheepdogs, Afghan Hounds, Staffordshire Bull Terriers, Boston Terriers, American Cockers and Golden and Labrador Retrievers. He considers that in both Staffordshires and Bostons an autosomal recessive gene is involved. In both cases the condition is bilateral and generally tends to be symmetrical. Diagnosis can be as early as 8 weeks of age in the Boston, suggesting a congenital trait and can be detected before 12 months of age in Staffordshires although not congenital in this case. According to Formston (1966) the cases in Boston Terriers in Britain stem from a Canadian import Acecourt Wee Michael brought over in 1955. He had cataract but never sired it in Britain suggesting a recessive allele of very low frequency in Britain. However, inbreeding to this dog caused cataract to appear which confirms the recessive nature of the problem bearing in mind other data given by Barnett (1976). More recently Curtis (1984) has described a late onset cataract in the Boston Terrier. The mode of inheritance is unknown at present. According to Barnett (1985) cataract in the Miniature Schnauzer is caused by a simple autosomal recessive gene which supports American work (Gelatt *et al* 1983a, b).

In the Golden Retriever the genetic picture seems more complex. Yakely *et al* (1971) reporting on American cases found variable types of cataract expression ranging from polar to total opacity. According to Barnett (1978) the condition may not always be bilateral and one eye may remain ostensibly normal for years. Barnett (1976) held the view that the condition was dominant in that all affected cases had at least one affected parent and in cases where both parents appeared to be normal ophthalmoscopic examination revealed cataract in at least one of them. In his 1978 paper Barnett states that at a championship show in Britain in 1966 there were 42 cases in 184 (23%) but he held the view that it was being eradicated quickly, an indication of the dominant nature of the problem. Rubin (1974) agrees with the dominant theory and suggests that polar opacity is a sign of the heterozygote and total opacity a sign of the homozygous state. Data on the Labrador Retriever are less common but according to Barnett (1976, 1978) the condition is effectively identical with that in the Golden in both its nature and mode of inheritance.

The picture in American Cockers is less clear. It was reported by Yakely *et al* (1971) in a study based on examining 285 dogs with a high incidence of cataract being found. Age at onset ranged from eight weeks to seven years but breeding studies did not identify the mode of inheritance although it did seem to be dominant in that it occurred from generation to generation and crosses with Brittany Spaniels (no cataract) gave normal and affected stock. If the trait were recessive, and the Brittany Spaniel was free of it, then no cases should have occurred.

One problem in the American Cocker is that various types of cataract are seen. According to Roberts (1973) some of these types are, as yet, unclassified. Barnett (1978) describes some of the types seen and emphasises the variability in both cataract type and age of onset, although generally this tends to be early. No doubt the unclear picture will complicate genetic studies but Buskirk (1977) has put forward ways of identifying inherited and non-hereditary cataract in American Cockers. He claims that the inherited form has a monolayer of cells in the lens epithelium whereas the non-inherited form has a multilayer epithelium. In a survey of 146 American Cockers Williams *et al* (1979) found a 6% incidence of cataracts of various types.

More recently Yakely (1978) detected cataracts in 255 American Cockers in a sample of 1920 examined at clinics during the period 1965–75. Various test matings were made, including some with normal Elkhounds which latter had no ocular defects and were assumed to be free of all cataract genes. In the F_1 generation of eight litters there were 29 progeny which had a mean age of 5.6 years at completion of the study and none had developed cataract. This suggests that a dominant mode of inheritance is unlikely in the American Cocker. Nevertheless backcross data (F_1 to affected Cockers) produced only eight cataract cases out of 34 examined. This is too low for a simple recessive and it suggests that there is either variable expressivity and/or incomplete penetrance. The study did not rule out the possibility of a polygenic mode of inheritance.

In Denmark Olesen *et al* (1974) recorded cases of bilateral congenital partial cataract of a non-progressive nature in Cocker Spaniels. The cases occurred in a kennel of red Cockers and affected about 10% of pups. Only a few per litter were affected and other breeds in the kennel had no such problem. Eight test matings were made (Table 51) and the mode of inheritance was not divulged but was considered to be complex.

Five cases of juvenile lens cataract were reported in the GSD during 1980. These were in Britain from a German imported sire and largely unrelated bitches. Experimental matings were undertaken and the results were indicative of a simple autosomal recessive trait. This has been reported by Barnett (1986).

The BVA/KC in Britain has a scheme for certifying dogs for cataract using temporary

Table 51

Results of test matings for cataract in Cocker Spaniels

Type of mating	Litters	Pups	Pups with cataract	% with cataract
Normal × Cataract	1	2	1	50
Cataract × Cataract	7	32	8	25

Source   Olesen *et al* 1974.

and permanent certificates. Where a dominant form is known to be involved a permanent certificate indicates that the recipient can be safely used. In recessive conditions such a certificate indicates phenotypic freedom only but hereozygotes can receive this. Care must thus be taken in using certified dogs.

Although hereditary cataract presents many genetic problems it does seem to be devoid of sex-limited or sex-linked complications in that in all types and breeds where it has occurred both sexes have been affected.

Collie Eye Anomaly (CEA)

The Disease

This condition was first reported by Magrane (1953) in the USA. It has been reported in Britain (Barnett 1969a) and Australia (Blogg 1970) and possibly is found in all countries of the world where collie breeds exist. It is, as its name implies, a condition found only in collies namely Rough Collie, Smooth Collie and Shetland Sheepdog, though rarely, apparently in the Border Collie.

Various names have been used for this condition, among them being: Chorioretinal dysplasia, Collie ectasia syndrome, Coloboma of the optic disc, Ocular fundus anomaly, Optic disc anomaly or excavated optic disc and Posterior ectasia of the sclera. The term Collie Eye Anomaly (CEA) is less specific but is more commonly used nowadays since it is general enough to cover a defect which has a variable degree of expression.

In a review of over 2000 cases Roberts (1969) considered the ocular defects to be, in order of frequency, the following:

1   unusually tortuous retinal arteries and veins;
2   a pale area of the fundus in specific positions relative to the optic nerve with a
    poorly developed tapetum lucidum;
3   coloboma in the area close to the optic nerve head;
4   streaks on the fundus of young animals;
5   scleral ectasia in the region of the optic nerve and often detachment of the retina;
6   central corneal opacity.

The condition seems to be congenital in that it has been noted in pups aged from one to 14 days of age (Roberts *et al* 1966b) and in embryos of 25–45 days of development (Latshaw *et al* 1969). The problem is bilateral but not symmetrical in that differing symptoms or degrees of problem may appear in the two eyes.

According to Barnett (1969a) a common sign is blood specks in the eye as well as abnormal vision which may vary from slight to total blindness. Such loss of vision may not be progressive but can occur suddenly due to detachment of the retina. Usually there is microphthalmia or small eye size but this may be an associated problem due to the desire among breeders for small eyes in Collies.

Because of the different degrees of CEA, American workers initially attempted to grade the condition into five categories with I denoting the mildest form and V the most severe lesions. This policy seems to have been discontinued and all-or-nothing state of affected or non-affected seems to be the only system of grading adopted.

Breeds Affected
As previously stated the Rough Collie, Smooth Collie and Shetland Sheepdog all suffer from CEA. Barnett (1969a) exonerated the Border Collie but in 1976 reported two cases. In view of the large number of Border Collies examined under the PRA schemes this suggests that incidence in the breed is negligible.

In respect of incidence in the breeds Roberts (1960) felt that 25% of Rough Collies in four prominent bloodlines were affected by CEA. Examination of 300 dogs revealed that up to 30% of the breed was suffering from CEA (Roberts and Dellaporta 1965). In a study of 572 Rough Collies Donovan and Wyman (1965) found an incidence of 79.9% and in a later paper this same group (Yakely *et al* 1968) diagnosed 87% CEA in over 900 dogs examined. Donovan (1965) reported on the results of an examination of over 2500 Collies and considered over 90% to be affected. All these figures relate to US dogs where, over the period concerned some 20–25,000 Collies were being registered annually with the AKC and the breed stood in the first ten in popularity. By 1969 Donovan *et al* had examined over 7000 Rough Collies and were still referring to an incidence in excess of 90%.

Lower incidence of CEA seems to be the case in Smooth Collies and in Shetland Sheepdogs in the USA (Rubin 1969) which were, in any event, numerically less important in the USA than the Rough Collie. A study among Shelties in the Netherlands (Barnett and Stades 1979) showed an incidence of 48.3% in 120 dogs examined. It was noted that among 21 animals from a long-established inbred line no cases were seen. This particular line, inbred for some 40 years, was believed to have never had the problem but it was rather old-fashioned in type in that it was smaller in size, had larger eyes and a more pronounced stop. Such lines could well form the basis for eliminating or reducing the CEA anomaly.

Incidence figures in Britain seem to be less (Barnett 1976) though no real factual evidence exists. It is said by Lawson (1969a) that the Shetland Sheepdog is the most affected breed in Britain with up to 80% of dogs examined at Glasgow University having ophthalmoscopic defects of some kind, albeit minor in most instances.

Even if one accepts the above figures as overestimates based upon the samples seen by veterinarians the overall picture presented is a rather horrifying one and the suggestion that only about 2% of dogs have severe defective vision (Barnett 1976) is no real cause for any apathy about CEA. Nor can any country claim to be free of the problem. Mason and Cox (1971) gave an incidence of 66% in Australia and it is likely that any country looking for the problem will find it.

The Genetics
It is very obvious from all the papers on the subject that CEA is not sex-linked or limited in any way but occurs in both sexes. It also appears to occur in all coat colours including

Table 52

Mating trials with Rough Collies which were phenotypically affected by CEA or which were phenotypically normal

Type of mating		Litters	Pups*	CEA cases	CEA %
Sire	Dam				
Normal × Normal†		3	26	5	19.2
Normal × CEA		12	78	47	60.3
CEA × Normal		2	18	9	50.0

* Pups born dead or not examined (17) excluded.
† In this group some Dobermann 'blood' involved.
Source Wyman and Donovan 1969.

merles and there is no evidence that colours like silver are more prone to the problem than any other colour (Rubin 1969).

Roberts (1967a) did postulate that the merle gene was in some way associated with CEA and merle is known to be involved with eye problems in Collies but there is no conclusive evidence to suggest any particular proneness to CEA in dogs with the Mm genotype. One can thus accept the general view that all colours can be affected.

In respect of the genetic theories Roberts (1960) postulated that it was recessive because affected pedigrees all had a common sire. Later Roberts *et al* (1966a) suggested that the variable expression of CEA was not necessarily an indication of polygenic inheritance but could still be explained by a simple autosomal recessive gene which had pleiotropic effects.

Another group of workers (Donovan and Wyman 1965) suggested a polygenic auto-somal recessive transmission which could be intensified by inbreeding and diluted by outbreeding. This same group of Washington State workers crossed affected Collie females with a normal Dobermann and suggested an autosomal recessive mode of inheritance with variable expression (Yakely *et al* 1968). Some data from this group are given in Table 52. The three phenotypically normal males used by these workers must

Table 53

Mating data relating to CEA in Rough Collies

Type of mating	Litters	Pups seen*	CEA cases % of total	% CEA cases expected
Normal (NN) × Affected (nn)	3	26	0	0
Normal (Nn) × Normal (Nn)	7	48	20.8	25
Normal (Nn) × Affected (nn)	33	174	57.5	50
Affected (nn) × Affected (nn)	21	122	100.0	100

* Approximately 15% of pups not examined because of neonatal death.
Source Yakely 1972.

have been carrying CEA genetic factors since they produced CEA cases when mated to normal but known carrier females. The data are certainly indicative of a recessive trait.

A later paper from this Washington group (Yakely 1972) provided more data shown in Tables 53 and 54. The first of these relates to genetic ratios and the second to the types of lesions observed. The data seem indicative of an autosomal recessive trait. The fact that dogs of similar genotype may have varying degrees of CEA suggests pleiotropy or the interaction with other genes but does not invalidate the basic theory.

Cello (1969) has argued that a grading system is unwise because animals with minor defects may be simply expressing different versions of the same gene. If, as seems likely, pleiotropic effects are operating or there is some interaction with other genes then a Collie with a mild form of CEA will simply be demonstrating a fortuitous situation or a favourable combination of genes. When bred from, the favourable combination will be broken up and serious CEA can result.

American workers (Cello 1969, Wyman and Donovan 1969, Catcott 1969, Yakely 1972) are all agreed that there are simply normal or affected dogs and that all affected animals will transmit CEA. They recommend the non-use of all CEA stock and the careful use of CEA 'carriers'. Cello (1969) even recommended that the AKC not award the title of champion to affected stock.

Because of an early onset of the condition (it is congenital but can be readily identified by 6 weeks of age with a later check at a few months) selection against CEA is not difficult provided that sufficient phenotypically normal dogs exist in the population or can be introduced from another country. However, as a recessive it does mean that normal dogs can carry the CEA allele so progeny testing is essential. Methods for doing this are standard (see Chapter 17) and can readily be applied by test-mating to affected CEA animals.

Breed clubs ought to cooperate on this score or be compelled to do so by the appropriate

Table 54

Percentage of lesions of various types in affected stock from matings of Rough Collies with or without CEA

	Mating type					
	Normal (Nn) × Normal (Nn)		Normal (Nn) × Affected (nn)		Affected (nn) × Affected (nn)	
Type of lesion	RE*	LE†	RE	LE	RE	LE
Choroidal hypoplasia	100	90	95	86	96	96
Tortuous retinal veins	60	50	52	48	52	54
Colobomas	20	10	31	23	15	17
Retinal detachment	0	0	6	7	2	0
Intraocular haemorrhage	0	0	2	1	0	0

*Right eye.
†Left eye.
Note Only animals examined are recorded (15% of litters were not examined due to neonatal death).
Source Yakely 1972.

KC by use of legislation and severe penalties. The argument that only a few dogs are severely affected therefore little need be done in a spurious and dangerous one since retinal detachment when it does occur means total blindness.

The surprising thing is that a recessive allele should have become so prevalent in a breed and this is not to the credit of the breeders and breed clubs involved. That breeding methods will work is shown by Yakely (1972) who recorded a reduction in incidence from 97% in 1967 to 59% in a three year period. The fact that only 33% of the stock examined came from matings where both parents had CEA suggests that breeders were finally beginning to take heed of scientific advice. More recently Hutt (1979) has questioned the accuracy of genetic theories regarding CEA. According to him the condition is polygenic rather than Mendelian and he presents data to justify his views. If this is shown to be true then progeny testing rather than test mating would be a more logical pathway to follow but that will only be possible if breeders agree to cooperate and pool their data. If not then the condition will spread and worsen.

Any breeder seeking to import stock from another country would be wise to ensure that (a) the import is normal for eye structure and (b) comes from normal parents who are genetically normal as proven by progeny test or that the dog is normal and is progeny tested prior to purchase. Any breeder buying a Collie without such safeguards is risking a great deal and if sellers are not prepared to offer such guarantees then their kennels should be avoided.

Corneal Dermoid Cysts

Cysts on the cornea or conjunctiva are developmental anomalies usually seen in young animals. The lesion is generally a small and flat skinlike elevation of the surface of the globe. Hair frequently grows on the surface and causes local discomfort and discharge.

Kittel (1931), reporting the condition in a family of St Bernards, considered it to be a genetic trait but the evidence is sparse. St Bernards have been implicated by Gelatt (1971) as well as by Barnett (1976) who reported three cases in this breed among 26 that he examined. According to Smythe (1958) and other veterinary texts the condition is hereditary and German Shepherds are the breed most commonly affected. Barnett (1976) had seven cases in this breed in his sample while Szczudlowska (1967) also reported dermoid cysts on the conjunctiva of dogs of this breed. The latter author suggested a hereditary influence and considered that overfeeding was also implicated. The evidence for this latter statement arose from the fact that two affected females were mated to the same sire and one bitch (overfed) had seven young with two of these having dermoid cysts while the other bitch (sparingly fed) had five normal young. Such data are highly subjective and neither conclusively support a hereditary or a nutritional pattern.

Barnett (1976) reported cases in the Cocker, Smooth-Haired Dachshund, Shih Tzu, Bulldog, English Setter, Beagle, Basset Hound, Cavalier King Charles Spaniel, Border Terrier, Pug, Pekingese, Whippet and Miniature Wire-haired Dachshund, Incidence seems to be low bearing in mind that Barnett is regarded as a leading eye specialist seeing many hundreds of eye conditions.

Until further data are forthcoming the hereditary nature of dermoid cysts cannot be established.

Corneal Dystrophy

Corneal dystrophy can be defined as an opacity of the eye occurring post-natally without any obvious reason. Usually the condition is bilateral, often non-progressive and there is minimal inflammation. Cases in dogs have been reported regularly since the 1930s (see Barnett 1976) and a type of dystrophy has been associated with the Collie Eye Anomaly (Roberts and Dellaporta 1965).

In their text book Jubb and Kennedy (1963) consider the German Shepherd to be the most commonly affected breed while Wyman and Donovan (1971) implicate Afghan Hounds, Dachshunds and Poodles. Barnett (1976) records 86 cases which, in addition to the breeds mentioned above, involve the American Cocker Spaniel, Boston Terrier, Boxer, Cavalier King Charles, Golden and Flat-coated Retrievers, Griffon, Jack Russell, Pembroke Corgi, Rough Collie, Samoyed, Shetland Sheepdog and Tibetan Spaniel.

Familial relationship appeared in several cases but no real genetic evidence exists. Barnett (1976) refers to an excess of females but the numbers are probably too small to make this finding significant in any way.

An extensive study of corneal opacity was undertaken in the Siberian Husky by MacMillan *et al* (1979). They examined 560 dogs aged from 7 months to 12 years and detected corneal opacity in 78 (14%) of cases. In all but two instances the effects were bilaterally symmetric and there was considerable variation in the intensity of the defects seen between dogs. There was sound evidence for an increase in both incidence and severity with age although blindness appeared likely in only five animals. The condition resembled a defect seen in man that is known to be an autosomal dominant trait. However MacMillan and his co-workers made no conclusions as to the genetics of the trait in the Husky.

Crispin and Barnett (1978) did report corneal opacity in the GSD but considered it to be a secondary aspect of hypothyroidism. Their work was done in the UK where data on hypothyroidism in the GSD is unavailable but Blake and Lapinski (1980) put the incidence of hypothyroidism in the GSD at 19.6% in a sample of 143 dogs. This was US data and the same paper showed sled dogs (including Huskies) to have a 33.3% incidence in 48 animals seen. It may be that the degree of corneal opacity seen in the Husky is a reflection of that breed's apparent predisposition to hypothyrodism but this needs to be fully examined.

Distichiasis and Ectopic Cilia

In man distichiasis refers to a second row of eyelashes but as dogs do not normally have them on the lower lid the term in the dog refers to extra or supernumerary lashes. The term Trichiasis means a third row of lashes and is used to describe misdirected lashes. Ectopic cilia refers to lashes which grow on the inside or outside of the eyelid.

According to Lawson (1973) extra lashes are common in the dog and they have been reported by various authors since the time of Nicolas (1925). In his review Barnett (1976) refers to 84 cases from 21 pure breeds. There was no abnormal sex ratio and age at presentation ranged from 7 weeks to 8 years.

Ectopic cilia were first recorded by Helper and Magrane (1970). Bedford (1971) recorded three cases in Boxers and Barnett (1976) refers to 19 cases in 9 breeds. In all cases the ectopic cilia were located on the upper lid. There seemed to be a preponderance of females but in the small numbers involved such an observation is no doubt spurious.

The genetic evidence is sparse. Burns and Fraser (1966) considered that distichiasis and entropion might be expressions of the same gene and Carter (1972) refers to 11 cases affected with both defects while in Barnett's 84 cases there were nine with both entropion and distichiasis. Barnett (1976) favours a dominant condition but the evidence is too limited to support any genetic theories.

In a survey of 146 American Cockers Williams *et al* (1979) found a 74% incidence of distichiasis, in most instances bilateral. Whether this is due to some specific gene or the result of selection for an abnormal eye with more complex genetic involvement is uncertain. It does suggest a need for breeders to take steps to control the problem.

Entropion and Ectropion

These two conditions are best discussed together because in some dogs they both appear. They are possibly the most widely distributed eye diseases and various breeds are involved (Hodgman 1963). Entropion is the inversion of the eyelid while ectropion is the reverse situation.

Both conditions are readily corrected by minor surgery and the number of dogs which have undergone this type of operation and returned to the show ring may well be legion. Ectropion is not very likely to be painful to the dog but entropion will generally be so because of contact between the lashes and the eye. Unlike most eye diseases entropion and ectropion may be selectional defects in the sense that certain breed standards, if strictly adhered to, will encourage the problem.

According to Barnett (1976) a short eyelid and small slanting eye will often lead to entropion and some breeds have deliberately been selected for this kind of eye. Smythe (1958) considered that 60% of Chows were affected by this problem and although Barnett (1976) considers that selection must have reduced this figure it is by no means certain that this is so. Many Spitz breeds are involved such as Elkhounds and Pomeranians. Bellars (1969) reported eight cases in Huskies taken on the British Antarctic Survey Expedition.

Barnett (1976) considers the gundog group, especially the Retriever breeds, to be implicated in several cases of entropion with Cocker Spaniels being particularly prominent. He argues that the loose skin and low ear carriage with a prominent skull has been developed to excess, especially in golden Cockers. This has led to entropion in the upper lid and ectropion in the lower. He describes cases of senile entropion seen in Cockers from seven years of age.

English Pointers and German Short-haired Pointers have been noted with entropion and the incidence seems to be rising in the latter breed (Barnett 1976). Among other breeds can be listed the Airedale, Bulldog, Dalmatian, Irish Setter, Rhodesian Ridgeback, Sheltie, Old English Sheepdog and in my own experience the German Shepherd Dog and Irish Water Spaniel. Entropion and ectropion are reported in the Boxer and Great Dane and ectropion only in the Beagle, English Springer and Curly-coated Retriever (Barnett 1976).

Several breeds have been selected for a diamond-shaped eye with a kink in both eyelids and this will, according to Barnett (1976), lead to ectropion at the kink and entropion on either side of it. Breeds such as the Basset Hound, Bloodhound, Bull Mastiff, Clumber Spaniel, Mastiff and St Bernard are all bred in this way and Barnett reports on the need to undertake surgery in examples of all six breeds.

Despite the relatively common occurrence of eyelid problems the genetic situation is

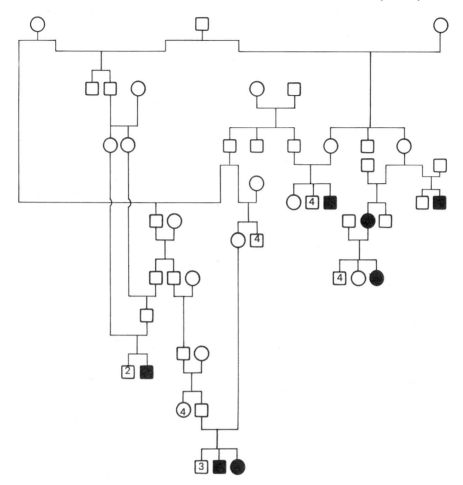

Figure 43 Entropion in British Antarctic sledge dogs (Huskies) (redrawn from Bellars, 1969). Numbers relate to normal animals of this sex in litter.

unclear. Barnett (1976) highlights some of the problems facing any investigator: these include a variable range of incidence ages and considerable variation in severity of the problems. Burns and Fraser (1966) cite a pedigree in an unnamed breed in which entropion appeared to be inherited as a dominant with variable expressivity. They also cite a strain of Pointers in which the condition appeared to be a simple dominant but provide no exact data. Bellars provided pedigree data on seven of the eight cases he observed in Huskies. This is reproduced in part in Figure 43 and is more indicative of recessive than dominant inheritance. However a dominant with incomplete penetrance cannot be ruled out.

Glaucoma

Increased intra-ocular pressure occurs in various animals with the dog being considered the most frequently involved. An eye that is affected by glaucoma will be readily seen to be grossly abnormal. The eyeball will be enlarged and bulging and the cornea will be hazy and lack transparency. The eyeball will be hard to the touch and the pupil will be widely dilated, if visible at all. There will generally be a poor response to light. Most cases end in blindness although temporary alleviation is possible.

Glaucoma can occur as a secondary symptom to some other eye problem so that it can be described as primary or secondary. Only in cases of primary glaucoma should the disease be regarded as an entity in itself.

Barnett (1970a) reviewed the subject and considered that primary glaucoma was a rare condition in dogs. In his later paper (1976) he reports 14 cases in Miniature and Toy Poodles but mainly in aged (6–16 years) animals. There were a further 12 cases in Spaniels (Cockers, English Springers and Welsh Springers) with a lower age incidence (5–10 years). In addition to these breeds the condition was noted in the Basset Hound, Wire Fox Terrier, Jack Russell and Lakeland. Isolated cases were noted in the Boxer, Labrador, Whippet, Elkhound, Maltese, Dandie Dinmont, Dalmatian and Wire-haired Dachshund.

Out of 50 cases there were only 32% males which is a feature noted by Magrane (1957). Another common feature appears to be that the left eye is generally the first to be affected. Surprisingly Barnett (1976) reports no cases in American Cockers although there are several such reports in America (Lovekin 1964; Lovekin and Bellhorn 1968; Magrane 1971). American reports also implicate the Basset Hound (Martin and Wyman 1968) and the Beagle (Gelatt 1972) although the latter report is doubtful as a primary glaucoma situation since lens luxation was involved.

Martin and Wyman (1968) report familial tendency in their data but it is by no means certain that primary glaucoma is inherited at all. However, more recently Cottrell and Barnett (1988) reported 28 cases of primary angle closure glaucoma in Welsh Springer Spaniels. This breed has not previously been implicated. These authors suggested a higher incidence in females than males and suggested a mode of inheritance that was dominant but again their data are not unequivocal.

Hemeralopia

Hemeralopia or day blindness in the dog is characterised by an inability to see in bright light although there is ability to see as the illumination is reduced. The disease was first reported by Rubin et al (1967) who state that it was discovered in 1960 in the Alaskan Malamute and in Poodles. Barnett (1976) also reports a case in the Alaskan Malamute in Britain and what appeared to be an identical case in a two-year-old Great Dane female.

Clinical features have been described in the Alaskan Malamute by Rubin (1971a, b). It appeared to be progressive, varying in age of onset and was usually diagnosed by watching the dog's behaviour in bright light. Generally dogs moving from a dimly lit to a bright environment became blind immediately whereas in the reverse direction they were blind for up to three minutes then began to see apparently normally. There was no ophthalmoscopically visible abnormality. Confirmation of behavioural observations was made by using an electroretinograph (ERG).

Genetic studies undertaken by Rubin et al (1967) in the Alaskan Malamute are summarised in Table 55 and a genealogy is shown in Figure 44. The evidence suggests that the condition is inherited as a simple autosomal recessive in this breed but the mode of inheritance in any other affected breeds is unknown.

Table 55

Occurrence of hemeralopia in various matings of Alaskan Malamutes

			Observed results	
Type of mating*	Litters	Pups†	Normal (HH or Hh)	Affected (hh)
HH × HH	1	11	11(11)	0(0)
HH × Hh	2	13	13(13)	0(0)
Hh × Hh	3	25	17(18.75)	8(6.25)
Hh × hh	5	32	17(16)	15(16)
hh × hh	6	25	0(0)	25(25)

* HH = normal, Hh = normal but carrier, hh = affected.
† Four pups which were stillborn or not ested are excluded.
‡ Figures in parentheses refer to number expected in each category after excluding the four dogs
  mentioned above.
Source Rubin *et al* 1967.

Lens Luxation

Dislocation or luxation of the lens has been known in the dog as far back as 1925 when it was reported by Nicolas. It involves dislocation of the lens, usually in both eyes although Formston (1945) reports than 38% were unilaterally affected cases in his sample of over 100. Clinical diagnosis depends upon noting the abnormal position of the lens and also secondary glaucoma which, according to Barnett (1976) is a very common feature and, in Britain, the most common cause of secondary glaucoma. In terrier breeds the condition is usually bilateral but there may be an interval (a few weeks to several months) before the luxation occurs in the second eye. Age incidence at onset varies from three to ten years of age so that it is essentially a disease of the middle-aged dog (most cases being between three and seven years of age). Sex ratios appear to be normal but some variation does exist between the cases reported by various workers.

Breed incidence seems largely confined to the terrier breeds and to particular ones within this group. Thus Gray (1932) and Wright (1934) highlight a preponderance of cases in the Wire Fox Terrier and Sealyham. Formston (1945) recorded 100 cases of which 10 were Sealyhams and the rest Wire Fox Terriers. Later Knight (1962) reported 103 cases including 28 Wire Fox Terriers and 18 Sealyhams. Lawson (1969b) and Hodgman (1963) had similar findings and both implicated the Smooth Fox Terrier. Lawson (1969b) considered the Jack Russell Terrier to be involved and Barnett (1976) confirms this, noting more cases in this breed than any other. Isolated cases in non-terrier breeds have been seen but usually these are unilateral and are caused by trauma or some other intraocular disease. Recently, however, the Tibetan Terrier, a herding dog rather than a terrier, has been implicated (Barnett and Curtis 1978).

The genetic picture is far from satisfactory although most of the veterinary workers readily agree that it is genetic in terrier breeds. However evidence is more inferred than real and this is certainly true of the idea that it is dominant in its mode of action.

Formston (1945) presents some data which Burns and Fraser (1966) suggest is indicative

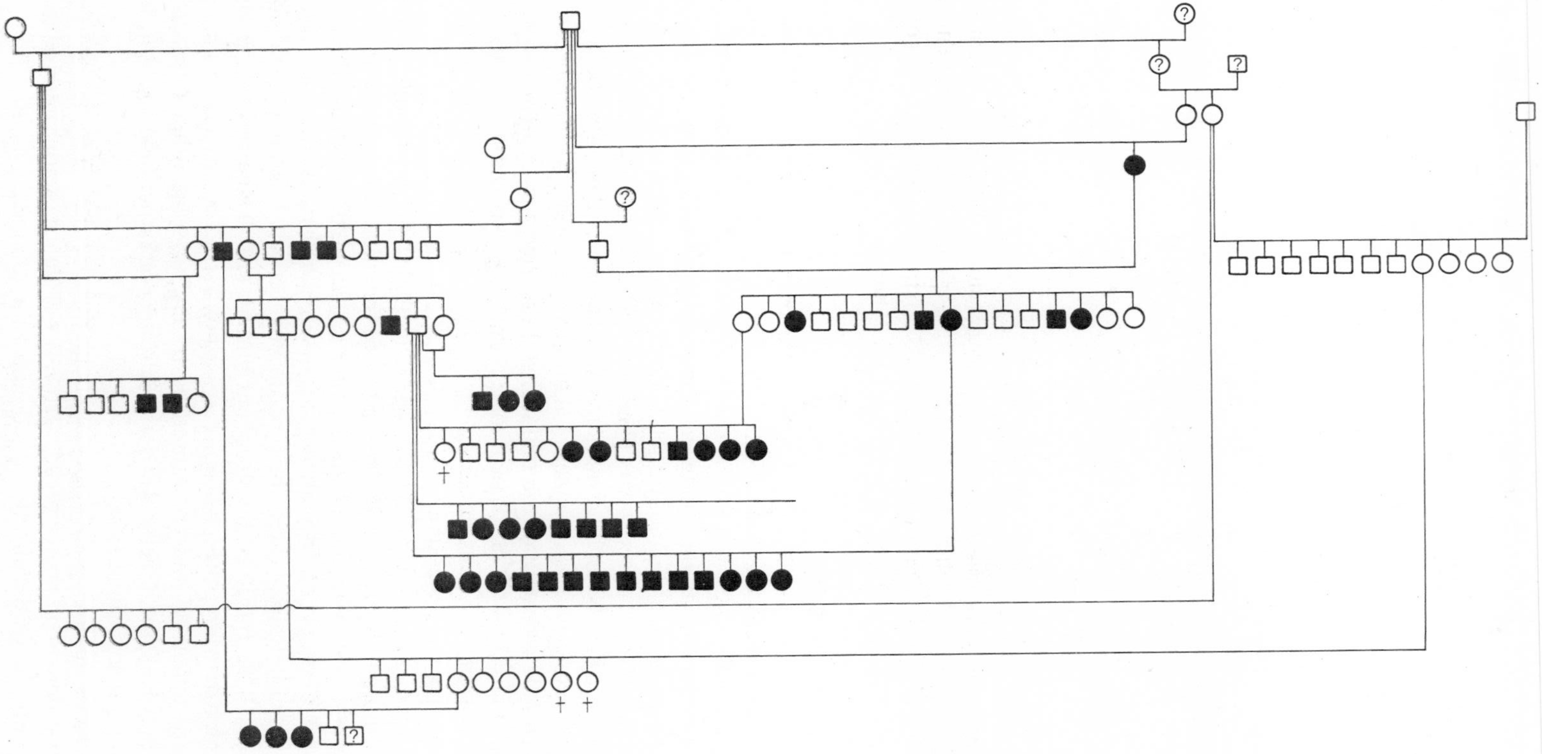

Figure 44 Pedigree of hemeralopia (solid symbols) in Alaskan Malamutes (Rubin *et al* 1967).

○ normal   †stillborn   ? not seen

of a dominant autosomal allele. Barnett (1976) tends to support this view with isolated cases of lens luxation in dam and daughter, dam/son and brother/sister and so on. He emphasises his argument with the view that crossbred Jack Russells are affected and this would be unlikely if the condition were recessive. However this seems invalid in that most Jack Russells are only version of Fox Terriers and hence susceptible to the problem. Knight (1960) suggests that lens luxation was eradicated from Wire Fox Terriers in Denmark by selective breeding. This is indicative of a dominant gene but presupposes that the eradication claimed has indeed occurred. Lens luxation in man is apparently dominant (Sorsby 1970) but that is no reason to accept a dominant theory in the dog.

The most conclusive evidence comes from Willis *et al* (1979) in 27 Tibetan Terriers from Britian and Sweden. Two cases were out of affected dams but all the others were from normal parents and an *a priori* test of segregation ratios (Table 56) showed that the data were consistent with a simple recessive theory. A general proband test on the same data gave a segregation ratio of 0.152 ± 0.0563 which was lower than, but not significantly different from, the expected 0.25 of a simple autosomal recessive. Inbreeding of the 27 cases was high with a mean of $14.3 \pm 5.3\%$ and there was a close relationship to a particular mating pair and one other male related to the female of this pair. The lines of descent of the 27 dogs are shown in Figures 45a and 45b and it can be seen that all dogs trace back on both sides of their pedigree to either the mating pair or to dog number three.

There were 19 females and 8 males out of 50 and 48 respectively which may indicate a greater propensity for lens luxation in females or a failure to report males as easily —perhaps because of pet ownership rather than being in breeding kennels. There may, however, be differential sex expression.

A more recent study in this breed in Sweden by Garmer (1986b) showed that of 929 dogs examined in 1985 46 (4.9%) were affected by lens luxation. Age at onset was between 3 and 6 years and the mode of inheritance was in accordance with British findings.

Table 56

Incidence of lens luxation in litters of Tibetan Terriers

Number in litter*	No. of Litters	Adult progeny			Corrected data†	
		Normal	Lens luxated	Total	Expected normals	Expected luxated
2	3	3	3	6	2.571	3.429
3	5	10	5	15	8.515	6.485
4	4	12	4	16	10.148	5.852
5	3	12	3	15	10.080	4.920
6	2	7	5	12	8.350	3.650
7	1	6	1	7	4.980	2.020
9	2	14	4	18	13.134	4.866
Total	20	64	25	89	57.778	31.222

† Using *a priori* correction for segregation ratio.
* Reaching 24 months of age.
Source Willis *et al* 1979.

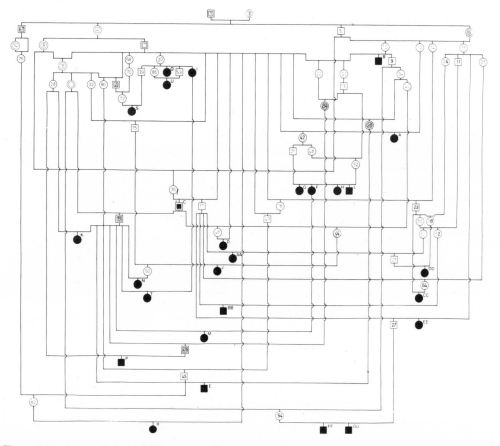

Figure 45a Lines of descent of lens luxation cases (solid symbols) from Tibetan Terrier sire number 1 and dam number 2 (from Willis *et al* 1979). In this figure and figure 45b: Champions □ ○ ■ ; Numbers in circles are animal identifications; Letters relate to identification of lens luxation cases (A–U British, AA–GG Swedish).

Persistent Pupillary Membranes

The pupillary membrane is a sheet of skin covering the anterior surface of the lens and formed during development of the eye. It generally atrophies during foetal life but in some instances it persists into adult life hence the nomenclature.

It was reported by Nicolas (1925) who considered it to be an inherited condition but not until a report by Roberts (1967b) on the condition in Basenjis in America was there any particular concern.

The Basenji seems to be particularly prone to this condition (Roberts and Bistner 1968; Barnett and Knight 1969) but it is noted by Barnett (1976) in the Afghan, Beagle, Boxer, Border Collie, English Springer, Labrador, Newfoundland, Pyrenean Mountain Dog, Sealyham, Shih Tzu, West Highland White and Wire-haired Dachshund as well as in both the Flat- and Curly-coated Retriever breeds. The condition has also been reported in the Cocker Spaniel by Gelatt and Veith (1970).

In Pembroke Corgis Barnett (1976) reports a familial relationship as was the case in

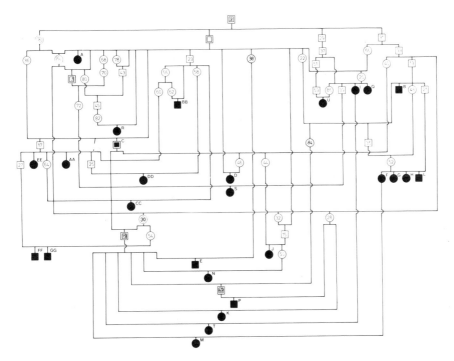

Figure 45b   Lines of descent of lens luxation cases (solid symbols) from Tibetan Terrier sire number 3. (For key see caption opposite.)

some other breeds but most data seem to stem from the Basenji. Barnett and Knight (1969) consider the condition to be caused by an autosomal dominant with a wide range of expression and incomplete penetrance but although they examined 222 Basenjis no genetic data are presented to support their claim. They arrived at their decision on the assumption that persistent pupillary membrane was a typical colobomata (that is, a congenital absence of a portion or structure of the eye). However there is some dispute among specialists as to whether this definition is a correct one (see Bistner *et al* 1971) which throws doubt on the hereditary aspects of persistent pupillary membrane.

Progressive Retinal Atrophy (Generalised)

The Disease
Although Centralised PRA should be dealt with before Generalised PRA if strict alphabetical order is to be adhered to, the Generalised type will be discussed initially because it was the first to be described and studied and only when ophthalmology developed was the Centralised type noted and investigated.

Progressive retinal atrophy was first described by Magnusson (1909, 1911, 1917) in the Gordon Setter in Sweden. Although he did not so name it his descriptions fit those of the Generalised type of PRA as described by Hodgman *et al* (1949). There appear to be various stages in the development of the disease. Initially there is an increased pupil size with slight impairment of night vision that is, apparent blindness on a moonless night. The tapetum becomes more highly reflective and more green in colour while the non-tapetal fundus becomes more grey than normal. At the second stage there is a marked reduction in visual powers at dusk or in dim light. The tapetal changes are more marked and there are changes in the vascular system of the eye. Changes to this latter part mainly affect the secondary blood vessels which become less numerous. In the later stages of the disease the dog becomes totally blind at night and daylight vision is impaired leading to complete blindness. Smaller blood vessels disappear and only the main ones, much reduced in size, remain. The non-tapetal fundus becomes 'pavement-grey' in colour and the tapetal fundus becomes white at the periphery. Because of the original impaired night vision the disease has popularly been known as 'night blindness' but this is a misnomer as blindness is eventually total.

The above description is no more than a general one and can vary considerably according to the original eye colour of the dog and the breed and stage of PRA. Some other diseases of a non-genetic nature may give similar symptoms and it is essential to have any suspect dog examined by a qualified expert.

The Breeds Affected

After the original reports on the Gordon Setter little was mentioned until Hodgman *et al* (1949) reported on the Irish Setter in Britain. Since that time a variety of breeds have been implicated in various countries. Various names have been used such as rod dysplasia, photoreceptive abiotrophy and primary tapetoretinal degeneration.

Breeds known to suffer from this kind of PRA are the Miniature and Toy Poodles, Cocker Spaniel, Elkhound, Miniature Long-haired Dachshund and Tibetan Terrier among others. Priester (1974) in America studied 448 cases of PRA and found a high risk for several breeds but did not differentiate between the types of PRA. His data implicate 46 breeds compared with the 26 breeds affected in 251 cases reported by Barnett (1965a, b). Priester did find an above average risk for Miniature and toy Poodles and Irish Setters and also implicated the Miniature Pinscher at the highest level of risk but on a very low number of cases. He concludes that the risk in Cocker Spaniels was not excessive which is contrary to most views in Britain. Tibetan Terriers did not appear in his list but in Sweden there appears to be a high risk rate since Garmer *et al* (1974) examined 320 animals and found 22 cases with 97 known carriers. This same author (Garmer, 1986a) showed that in Labrador retrievers in Sweden generalised PRA occurred in 74 from a population of 5125 examined.

Although the breeds affected vary considerably in their types and origin the symptoms appear very similar in all with the exception of age at onset. In the Irish Setter the original workers (Hodgman *et al* 1949) found that symptoms could occur by 6–8 weeks but were always detectable by the age of 4 to 6 months. In other breeds the age of onset may be much later which presents obvious problems in terms of genetic studies.

It does, however, seem that late diagnosis is largely due to the use of ophthalmoscopes since more advanced machinery has been able to produce much earlier diagnosis. Electroretinographic methods have been used by some American workers with a very accelerated diagnosis resulting. Thus Aguirre and Rubin (1971) were able to detect PRA in Elkhounds by 6 weeks of age and in Miniature Poodles by 9.5 weeks (Aguirre and Rubin 1972).

The Genetics

Magnusson's early work (1911) suggested that the condition was inherited in Gordon Setters in Sweden and he attributed it to a British import Ranger, who was himself unaffected. The condition in Irish Setters was known to be inherited for some time and Rasbridge (1944) analysed 200 pedigrees and was able to pinpoint animals which had transmitted the condition. The classic paper by Hodgman *et al* (1949) does not give any genetic data but accepts that the condition is an autosomal recessive one, a view borne out by subsequent matings made within the breed. The same theory has been accepted for Generalised PRA in the Bedlington Terrier, Cairn Terrier, Elkhound and Tibetan Terrier as well as in the Miniature and Toy Poodle and Cocker Spaniel.

Barnett (1976) suggests that coat colour in Poodles is a clue to heredity in that most cases were black whilst in Cockers very few were solid coloured reds or blacks and most were parti-coloured. This should not be construed as meaning any linkage between PRA genes and specific colours in the sense that certain colours are more prone to the problem. The colour relationship simply indicates that certain famous, widely-used and carrier (or affected) dogs were of a certain colour. This is certainly known to be the case in Cocker Spaniels, one of the breed's most famous parti-coloured dogs being a carrier of PRA.

Support for the simple autosomal recessive theory comes from Krahenmann (1974) who examined 82 cases of Generalised PRA and isolated seven Swiss breeds, hitherto not reported as having the condition. More recently Wolf *et al* (1978) have studied Generalised PRA in the Rough Collie using both ophthalmoscopy and ERG machines. They found that not only was the condition fairly early in terms of its development (it was identifiable by ERG by about six weeks) but that the mode of inheritance was consistent with a simple recessive trait. Dice (1980) found PRA in 46 out of 400 Samoyeds examined from 1972–7 and various test matings confirmed the accepted theory.

Eradication Schemes
PRA is relatively unique among canine defects in that schemes for eradication or reduction of incidence have been in operation. On publication of the work in the Irish Setter the English KC adopted a very rigid and unusual policy of accepting an Irish Setter Association scheme involving 'test mating' and controlled registration. The test mating involved mating the 'testee' to a known PRA affected (pp) animal and if at least six normal pups were born the animal was considered to be PP (that is, normal non-carrier) in genetic constitution whereas the presence of a single PRA offspring was sufficient to label the 'testee' as Pp.

The scheme was effective in Irish Setters because the age of onset of PRA was relatively early and because most breeders were willing or obliged to cooperate. There are flaws as will be seen in a later chapter (Chapter 17) and Irish Setter breeders did not eradicate PRA but they did markedly reduce the incidence.

In 1966 the BVA/KC introduced a scheme to test Elkhounds for PRA involving the use of a temporary certificate being granted to any dog under a certain age with no PRA signs. Once the dog reached this specific age it was granted a permanent certificate assuming no PRA was visible by ophthalmoscope examination. Later the scheme was extended to cover the Saluki, although this breed may not have inherited PRA, and in 1969 it was extended to cover all breeds (Barnett 1970b).

Black (1969, 1972) has been a fierce critic of the PRA scheme on the grounds that with a recessive condition a clear certificate merely indicates that a dog has one normal gene but does not prove that it has two. Thus a dog can obtain a permanent certificate and be genetically PP and carry PRA. This is beyond dispute but the argument that no scheme is better than an ineffective one is invalid. The PRA scheme will identify pp dogs which can be discarded and, if breeders were to really care about their breeds instead of just paying lip service to the idea they could, by collecting data on pp dogs identify most of the Pp animals and avoid them or use them in very controlled conditions so as to preserve their good points and still eradicate or reduce PRA incidence. Black's (1969) view that highly inbred animals should not be registered seems to suggest a limited understanding of genetics since inbreeding does not cause PRA. A dog can be highly inbred and if it is from PP stock it will be perfectly normal as regards PRA.

The failure to reduce the incidence of PRA is a failure by the breeders themselves who cannot avoid the issue by trying to blame the BVA/KC scheme. The fact that the veterinary profession has the ethical problem of not divulging the names and details of affected stock does not help and I personally do not subscribe to the need for such standards—admirable though they may be in human medicine—being applied to dogs. However, even if veterinarians will not divulge the names of affected stock there is nothing to stop breeders doing it. The argument that to do so would involve the divulgant in legal issues is not one that has been proven and is unlikely to be tested. Breed clubs would do their breed a service if they were to thoroughly document and publish all cases of Generalised PRA so as to clearly identify Pp stock.

Trauner (1971) has described a scheme in the USA aimed at obtaining 1000 pedigrees of PRA affected Poodles which would be coded to enable identification of affected lines. The final effectiveness of the scheme is unknown.

Progressive Retinal Atrophy (Centralised)

The Disease

This form of PRA was first described in various working breeds by Parry (1954) and subsequently confirmed by other workers (see for example, Barnett 1965c). Central PRA differs from the Generalised type in both clinical and ophthalmoscopic appearance as well as in histopathology. There is not the initial night blindness syndrome and it appears to have been noticed originally in gundogs which had no difficulty seeing a shot bird fall but then failed to mark it accurately and had to use their nose to find it after first over-running the bird. The vision is affected centrally so that the dog can see moving objects well enough but then may collide with something stationary placed directly in its path. It can sometimes be demonstrated by placing a low object in front of an affected dog and leading him up to it so that he is aware the object is there. The object is then removed and when trotted up to the point the dog will jump at the place where it recalled the object being.

Peripheral vision is not markedly affected and total blindness may not occur as with Generalised PRA. This makes it harder to detect as far as owners are concerned, especially in working gundogs which, by greater use of their nose, may exhibit no deterioration in retrieving ability. Secondary cataract, common in the other form of PRA is apparently less frequent with Central PRA (Barnett 1965c).

Histopathological changes are, in the early stages, confined to the central retina and only at a very late stage of the disease is the peripheral retina affected with a relatively sudden change from one stage to the other. Ophthalmoscopically there is a very pronounced series of brown pigment spots in the tapetum very similar to retinitis pigmentosa in man. These spots are irregular in shape and size as well as varying in colour and, in an advanced stage of the disease, decline in number and definition and finally disappear. The effects on blood vessels, very noticeable in Generalised PRA, are less obvious in this form and are generally indicative of a late stage of the disease.

The Breeds Affected

Parry (1954) observed the condition in Border Collies and Labrador Retrievers and it is known to appear in several other breeds including the Rough Collie, Golden Retriever, Flat-coated Retriever (Barnett 1965b), German Shepherd, English Springer, Cardigan Corgi (Barnett 1976) and Briard (Bedford 1977). Since a few cases of Generalised PRA have been found in the Cardigan Corgi (Keep 1972, Barnett 1976) and in English Springers (Barnett 1976) it seems that these two breeds may be the only ones with both kinds of PRA. In general, breeds with Central PRA seem to be free of Generalised PRA.

Although various breeds are named above it does not follow that all are equally affected as regards incidence. Barnett (1976) reports only 15 cases in German Shepherds which, in view of the popularity of the breed, suggests a low incidence of the problem. On the other hand, in 100 Labradors examined by Barnett (1976) there were 22 with Central PRA despite the fact that there was no history of eye problems. In 500 Border Collies examined at the 1965 National and International Sheepdog trials there were 12% affected (Barnett and Dunn 1969).

In both Labradors and Border Collies all coat types seem to be affected suggesting that no particular lines are predominating although Burns and Fraser (1966) suggest that in the former breed it is the working strains that are more affected than show lines.

According to Barnett (1976) there is no sex-linked or sex-limited effect in that both sexes can be affected but there is a wide age range in terms of onset. The earliest cases were identified by ophthalmoscopic changes at 15–18 months with most being seen by two years of age but in some instances a dog may not be suspected as a problem until some eight or ten years of age.

The Genetic Evidence

Unlike Generalised PRA the genetic picture is less clearly understood. Pedigree data presented by Barnett (1965b) on Labradors and Rough Collies indicated a strong familial inheritance but the mode of it is unclear. In data presented in 1976 Barnett refers to 568 Labradors from the Bengerbrig lines of which 159 had PRA (28%). There were 69 litters involved, several examined in their entirety. In 108 cases at least one parent was examined and in 92 of these one or both parents were affected. In 16 cases (10 litters) both parents were normal but in seven of these litters one or more of the grandparents had PRA.

The evidence points strongly towards some kind of dominant mode of transmission and this is supported by Barnett's (1976) comments that in eight cases there was direct parent to offspring transmission of PRA for three or four generations. Similarly cases of two PRA affected parents with normal offspring indicate dominant inheritance. However, the fact that some PRA cases arise from normal parents does suggest that a simple dominant situation is unlikely. It is more probable that dominance is incomplete in its penetrance, at least in the Labrador Retriever which is the view accepted by Barnett (1976). It seems to be generally believed that the PRA allele has a penetrance of about 80%. This means that while dogs with two PRA alleles will exhibit the condition only about 80% of those with one allele will suffer from PRA, the remaining 20% appearing to be normal though they may well transmit the problem. Dogs with no PRA allele will be normal and transmit normality when mated to similar normal stock.

The value of 80% penetrance can serve as no more than a guide and does not necessarily apply to other affected breeds but if there is incomplete penetrance of any degree it clearly makes breeding much more difficult.

In the late 1970s the British Briard Club and the Briard Association cooperated with Dr P. G. C. Bedford and the author in an attempt to examine the condition in that breed. Bedford examined over 600 dogs and the evidence (Bedford 1984) is indicative of a simple recessive condition. It may be, however, that CPRA in this breed is not identical with that in the Labrador.

Eradication Schemes

The BVA/KC scheme described in the previous section is applied to Central PRA as well as Generalised. Because one is dealing with a dominant allele a clear certificate in Central PRA-affected breeds will be more useful than in Generalised PRA cases. However, a proportion of 'normal' dogs will carry one PRA allele which is lacking penetrance so care must be taken to identify normal animals which, when mated to other normals, transmit PRA. The methods by which one determines whether the sire or dam or both are the cause of the incomplete penetrance will depend upon pedigree data analyses and results from other matings.

The International Sheepdog Society which controls Border Collie breeding in Britain has been successful in markedly reducing PRA in this breed. All dogs attending trials have been examined ophthalmoscopically since 1965 when Barnett and Dunn (1969) reported a 12% incidence among 500 dogs. In a three year period a total of 1813 dogs were examined and 190 cases (10.5%) of PRA were identified. Dogs aged two years or more with no signs of PRA have their registration certificate so endorsed and the Society went on to insist upon compulsory examination of all breeding stock. By 1973 the incidence of PRA in this breed was down to under 2% (Barnett 1976). This relatively rapid decline is indicative of a dominant situation and also emphasises the extent to which organised schemes can be successful when rigid rules are enforced by a breed society. It is a pity that many Kennel Clubs do not enforce equally rigid rulings upon show dogs when genetic evidence warrants them.

Retinal Dysplasia

Abnormal development of the retina leading to its detachment was first described in the Bedlington Terrier in the USA by Rubin (1964) and ascribed to genetic factors (Rubin 1968). Subsequently it was reported in the Sealyham Terrier (Ashton *et al* 1968) and in the Labrador Retriever (Barnett *et al* 1970). These two breeds were implicated in Britain and, in the case of the Labrador, in Sweden also. Cases have since been reported in Yorkshire Terriers in Holland (Stades 1978). The term retinal dysplasia was used to describe a condition involving retinal folds in the Beagle (Heywood and Wells 1970) but according to Barnett (1976) this is a different condition. There is certainly a difference between the two conditions in that the problem in the Bedlington, Labrador and Sealyham is characterised by total detachment of the retina at birth or shortly afterwards with affected dogs being blind. In the Beagle the condition consists of multiple retinal folds with only minimal effects upon vision in affected dogs. This would suggest that the global term 'retinal dysplasia' ought not to be applied to both cases and the term multifocal retinal dysplasia has been used to cover the cases seen in Beagles and identical cases observed more recently in American Cocker Spaniels (MacMillan and Lipton 1978). True retinal dysplasia has occasionally been termed retinal detachment (Roberts 1959, Rubin 1964) but the preferred term is retinal dysplasia. A case of retinal detachment has been observed in Australian Shepherd Dogs (Veith and Gelatt 1970) but the animals concerned had various ocular defects so there is no real certainty that primary retinal dysplasia was actually involved.

Ashton *et al* (1968) considered their three cases in the Sealyham to be due to an autosomal recessive but data were too sparse to be reliable. However, Barnett (1976) reports other cases and these tend to confirm the initial views. In all known cases the sire and dam were normal, only some pups in each litter had symptoms and in every instance both sire and dam traced back to a certain male born in the late 1940s. This last-named male seems to have been normal.

The Labrador data reported by Barnett *et al* (1970) involved nine British cases and 26 in Sweden with all three colour varieties being affected. All cases traced back on both sides of their pedigree to a male born in 1934. In 15 Swedish matings involving normal parents there were 99 normal and 26 affected progeny with an even sex distribution. This supports a simple autosomal recessive theory. Three matings were made from affected parents and mortality was so high among the 17 pups born that only eight dogs could be examined clinically and nine others histologically. In all cases retinal detachment was detected.

The evidence thus seems overwhelming that retinal dysplasia is a simple autosomal recessive in the three breeds known to be involved. It is a severe defect leading to total blindness early in life and thus eradication is called for whenever possible. This view was accepted by Wikstrom (1986) working in Sweden.

In humans the condition is frequently associated with anomalies of the central nervous and cardiovascular systems (Reese and Straatsma 1958). Similar problems were observed in Labradors by Barnett *et al* (1970) though not in Sealyhams. However, Barnett (1976) does point out that affected pups have unusual behaviour patterns suggestive of mental retardation.

This confirms the need to be severe in culling this defect and with a relatively low breed incidence suggests that affected stock and their parents should be culled from breeding programmes though parental stock can obviously lead a normal life and need not be destroyed.

The multifocal form of retinal dysplasia has been studied genetically by MacMillan and Lipton (1978) who observed it in 96 American Cockers out of some 500 being screened for other ocular defects. It was observed in dogs as young as 3–4 weeks and as old as 7 years. Both sexes and various colour varieties were affected and 71 of the 96 dogs showed close relationships. In 5 litters between affected parents, all 23 pups seen were affected. This is indicative of an autosomal recessive trait as were other mating results present in the paper concerned. However in no case did two normal parents produce affected stock so the recessive mode of inheritance cannot be confirmed and a dominant or polygenic mode of transmission could not be excluded. Extended pedigree data implicated three dogs but without confirmation of the method of transmission this may be spurious. The need to select against multifocal retinal dysplasia is obviously less apparent than in the case of true retinal dysplasia.

Other Eye Anomalies

Coloboma

A coloboma is the congenital absence of a portion of a structure of the eye (Barnett and Knight 1969). Typical colobomata are defects in the region of the embryonic cleft and are due to some problem in the mechanism of closure. Colobomata can thus be said to be typical or atypical in relation to the structure affected but they are likely to be found in many eye defects.

Iljin (1932) considered coloboma to be inherited but unless the type of coloboma is clearly specified and shown to be independent of other defects such a generalisation is meaningless.

Microphthalmia

Microphthalmia is a small eye and can thus be produced by selection for it or may feature as a specific condition not deliberately sought. It is established that microphthalmia is a condition seen in association with merle coloration in various breeds and in those instances represents a pleiotropic effect of the merle gene.

More recently Australian Shepherd Dogs have been found to have a condition involving microphthalmia and multiple colobomata. The first report concerned five cases (Gelatt and Veith 1970) and a later report involved 45 animals (Gelatt and McGill 1973). These animals were produced in various matings undertaken at the University of Minnesota where it was found that all affected dogs had microphthalmia, microcornea and hetero-chromia irrides (light blue eyes). In 62% of dogs there was cataract, in 54% equatorial staphylomas and in 54% detached retinas. All dogs were 30–90% white in colour and blue merle so that it suggests a slightly different version of the merle gene since the white colour appears to be more extensive than is usually the case. The white coat and merle factors were clearly a feature of the case but Gelatt and McGill (1973) report instances of excessively white blue-merles of this breed with no ocular defects. They consider the defect to be a simple autosomal recessive.

A microphthalmic defect in Dobermanns was reported by Wikstrom and Koch (1974) in Scandinavia. There were 3 cases in a litter of 8. The litter was inbred 2:2 on a certain sire and had more distant inbreeding to the sire of this animal, as well as to other dogs. No conclusions can be drawn as to mode of inheritance.

The Merle series

Mention has already been made of the dangers of this M allele in connection with eye disease. The literature has been recently reviewed by Klinckmann *et al* (1986) who also presented their own data on 18 adult Dachshunds. In this breed the M allele leads to dappling and the Hannover Veterinary school has maintained a kennel of dapple Dachs-hunds since 1971. Klinckmann's group examined the eyes of 18 Dachshunds which were 9 (MM), 5 (Mm) and 4 (mm). All the normal mm animals were devoid of eye defects and all the MM animals had a series of eye anomalies. The defects seen varied but included the absence of the Tapetum lucidum, lack of retinal pigment, a rudimentary lens, microphthal-mia, microcornea, microcoria and other more minor anomalies. Although major anom-alies were obvious in MM cases Mm animals also had eye problems similar to those of the homozygotes albeit less severe in most instances. The authors likened the Merle syndrome to the Klein-Waardenburg syndrome of man which is associated with eye/ear defects.

Sorsby and Davey (1954) claimed that the heterozygous merle 'produces little more than a pleasant physiological variant' but Klinckmann considered that it was contrary to animal welfare in that it leads to severely handicapped homozygotes and impaired heterozygotes. They considered that breeding with the Merle factor should be restricted to scientific purposes where it might be a useful model to examine depigmentary disorders in man.

Chapter 11

Genetics of the Circulatory System and Related Systems

Introduction

This chapter deals with defects of the cardiovascular system, the blood and then a series of other problems in related systems. Finally it deals with renal defects which do not fit here but which provide insufficient material to encompass a chapter on their own.

It is not intended to deal in detail with the genetics of blood groups. This is not because of lack of interest in this aspect but rather their limited practical importance at the present time. Blood groups are useful in establishing parentage and in the understanding of the relationship between various canine types and their modern descendants (for example Clark *et al* 1975; Simonsen 1976). Knowledge of blood groups is also useful in respect of veterinary medicine since it is necessary to know whether or not transfusions can be made with any blood or whether incompatibility systems exist as in man.

Work on blood groups has been undertaken by Swisher and Young (1961), Swisher *et al* (1962) and Bull (1974) to which papers the reader is referred for more extensive bibliography. Practical aspects of blood groups have been outlined by Dudok de Wit *et al* (1967) and haemolytic disease in the newborn dog was discussed in detail by Young *et al* (1951).

There appear to be seven blood group systems in the dog A, B, C, D, E, F and G which act as autosomal dominants, much as in man. It would seem for Swisher and Young (1961) that some 99% of dogs are C+ and F+ and hence these groups are unimportant in either parentage checks or in transfusion aspects. Similarly the B, D, E and G systems are weak antigens and rarely cause significant red cell destruction such as leads to haemolytic disease (Young *et al* 1951). This means that in the case of blood transfusions any dog will suffice as the donor. However, if there are to be repeated transfusions some care must be taken with the A group. This has sub-group A1 and sub-group A2 (now called CEA-1 and CEA-2) and of the 63% of dogs that are A+ some 45% fall into category CEA-1. It seems that CEA-1 cells are the more antigenic and cause most of the incompatibility reactions. If A positive blood is given to an A negative patient all will be well but subsequent transfusions could be fatal. In the main, CEA-1 will cause more serious reactions but, as a rule, it is best to use compatible blood groups in respect of the A system. The aspect is not dwelt upon because it is more a medicinal matter than a genetic one.

Similarly, the relationships between breeds and between wild dogs and their relatives is academically interesting but outside the scope of this book. Of greater importance is the testing of parentage. Anyone associated with pedigree livestock will know that blood grouping throws up a proportion of pedigree errors. Some estimates put this at 5% of registrations but in some beef situations on ranch conditions errors can reach 20% or more.

An illustration of this is given by Trommershausen-Smith *et al* (1976) in horses. There is a rule that grey horses must have at least one grey parent and no exceptions should exist. A second rule states that chestnut parents cannot produce black or brown progeny other than in the case of certain situations in palominos and Shetland ponies. Despite this exceptions do occur and Trommershausen-Smith and her colleagues examined 17 so-called exceptions to these rules checking various blood components in the foal and its parents. In nine instances involving chestnuts purported to have produced bays it was found that the pedigree was erroneous, in one instance the dam actually not being the dam! In eight cases involving grey progeny from non-grey parents they were able to exclude the mating in all but one instance. This one instance is not an exception since it merely indicated that the sire *could* have been the father, not that he was.

Such tests are a valuable guide to pedigree frauds and errors which occur in the canine world. Instances of 'impossible' colours in German Shepherds have been cited by Willis (1976) and were shown to be errors (deliberate or otherwise) by genetic theory but it would be more valuable to blood group such cases and thus check the validity of any pedigree. In the Artificial Insemination organisations concerned with cattle no bull calf is bought without checking that his parentage is the true one, yet equally valuable dogs are bought and sold with no such check and much fraud can be carried out. It seems appropriate for the world Kennel Clubs to instigate some blood group checks in any doubtful cases since the pedigree validity is in their hands rather than that of breeders.

Although blood groups are of limited help in the identification of parentage other parameters have been under study in more recent years with much more promising results. Simonsen (1976) reviewed electrophoretic studies on the blood proteins of domestic dogs and other canidae which not only illustrated the close relationship of dogs and wolves but gave other pointers towards breed origins. Gundel and Reetz (1981) and Reetz (1981) showed how with 9 erythrocyte antigens and 4 blood polymorphisms quite high success rates in determining paternity could be achieved. Similar interesting papers were produced by Juneja *et al* (1981a, b) looking at blood plasma proteins and transferrin types. In the latter paper the ability to identify inbreeding levels in certain breeds by means of transferrin frequencies was highlighted.

Perhaps the greatest step forward has been with the so called DNA fingerprints. Developed from human investigations Jeffreys and Morton (1987) working at Leicester University have shown that DNA fragments taken from venous blood would enable paternity to be established in dog breeds with a very high degree of accuracy. It was estimated that the chance of two dogs having identical DNA 'fingerprints' would be less than 2×10^{-21}. This technique is now patented by Cellmark Diagnostics, a branch of ICI, and would have tremendous application to dogs albeit not cheap.

Cardiovascular Diseases

Introduction
Heart disease in dogs was rarely and infrequently reported in the period up to 1950 as is evidenced by a review of cases covering the period 1800–1970 (Patterson 1971) but in the 1950s and 1960s several studies were made on the subject mainly by Pennsylvania Veterinary School. Surveys made at this school and at twelve other North American veterinary clinics led to distribution data on various common heart ailments (Patterson 1968; Mulvihill and Priester 1973) and it was known by this time that several heart ailments

were genetic in origin. Breeding colonies of affected dogs were set up consisting of specimens of the breeds most commonly affected by the various defects and this has enabled not only elaborate genetic studies aimed at elucidating what happens in the dog but has served to assist in the understanding of similar conditions in man.

Before discussing breed incidence figures some data on the relative frequency of specific defects in different species might be of interest and are shown in Table 57. This survey was undertaken by Priester *et al* (1970) and covered 137,717 patients seen in ten different North American colleges over the period 1964–69. The Table shows actual numbers of cases in each category and also the relative risk in any species taking dogs as the base standard. Species other than those named were given by Priester *et al* (1970) in one group but are excluded here.

There are more defects noted among dogs than any other species and the relative risk appears higher but within certain categories of defect such as neurological problems most species are at equal risk and, in terms of urogenital problems, dogs seem relatively free from trouble. Cardiovascular defects appear more common in dogs than other species but that does not mean that their incidence is high. In the survey by Patterson (1968) there were 6.8 cases of congenital heart disease per 1000 patients while in that of Mulvihill and Priester (1973) there were 4.6 cases per 1000 patients. These two surveys covered a population of 174,201 dogs.

The most common heart diseases in the dog are shown in Table 58. It must be remembered that these figures relate to dogs visiting clinics so that diseases leading to early death will not be ranked highly as dead pups will rarely be post-mortemed and will simply be disposed of whereas in human studies checks will be made of all deaths. Thus a defect such as aortic atresia, which causes death in man, is not noted in the dog though it may well occur.

Table 57

Numbers of cases of congenital defects in various species with relative risk (in brackets) taking dog as base line

| Defect category | Species | | | | |
	Dog	Horse	Cow	Pig	Cat
Musculoskeletal	1977	212(0.34)*	40(0.09)*	9(0.12)*	48(0.09)*
Cardiovascular	241	8(0.10)*	20(0.31)*	4(0.51)	16(0.25)*
Urogenital	346	518(5.08)*	162(2.41)*	127(9.69)*	26(0.28)*
Gastrointestinal	149	39(0.79)	30(0.89)	20(3.35)*	8(0.20)*
Neurologic	120	43(1.01)	32(1.25)	2(0.51)	33(1.00)
Organs of special sense	570	34(0.16)*	19(0.16)*	0(0.00)*	26(0.16)*
Other defects	426	248(1.73)*	211(2.09)*	257(13.6)*	71(0.60)*
Multiple defects	245	28(0.40)*	19(0.45)*	3(0.41)	14(0.22)*
Total	4074	1130(0.86)*	533(0.61)*	422(2.63)*	242(0.22)*

*The risk is significantly greater (over 1) or less (under 1) than the corresponding risk in dogs for the same category of defect. In making this statement there is 99% accuracy. Unstarred items have the same risk as in dogs.

Data   From ten North American Veterinary Clinics 1964–69.
Source   Priester *et al* 1970.

In both surveys the diseases were most common in purebreds when compared to mongrels (2–4 times as high) and breed incidence patterns suggest that some breeds have a predisposition to certain defects. This arises because breeds, although of common origin in many cases, have remained isolated for long periods of time with little or no interchanges of genes between them. In most instances there was considerable inbreeding at the start of each breed and thus members of the same breed have many genes in common with each other but distinct from those of other breeds. By inbreeding recessive genes will be more readily brought to the surface in purebreds than would be the case in mongrels. Mutations can account for some defects but they are an unlikely source of defects because of the rarity of mutations and the ease with which non-recurrent mutations can be lost from the population (see page 295). If a breed has a predisposition to a certain heart defect (or any other defect for that matter) it is probable that there is a genetic basis for this, albeit not necessarily a simple one. The exception to this would be when a certain breed is kept in a specific type of environment and it can be shown that such an environment is a factor influencing the defect. In the canine world breeds are maintained in all kinds of environments so that evidence for genetic involvement in diseases that are prevalent in a breed is high, at least circumstantially.

Having isolated breeds with specific tendencies to certain heart defects the Pennsylvania group set up breeding studies to check the genetics of these by breeding together affected lines in various combinations. This has been well summarised by Patterson (1976) and is reviewed here for completeness of the genetic story in dogs. Only defects in which some genetic pattern has emerged are discussed and they are dealt with in order of relative incidence (see Table 58). In all cases sex-linked inheritance is excluded as a mode of inheritance and most defects do not appear to be transmitted by a single gene but in each case are somewhat more complex.

Patent Ductus Arteriosus
According to Patterson and Detweiler (1967) this condition is most common in Poodles, Collies and Pomeranians. Mulvihill and Priester (1973) confirm the predisposition in Poodles and add Shetland sheepdogs to this list.

Table 58

Relative frequency of various anatomical forms of congenital heart disease in dogs presented to veterinary clinics

Type of malformation	Patterson 1968	Mulvihill and Priester 1973
Patent ductus arteriosus	25	36
Pulmonic stenosis	18	11
Ventricular septal defect*	9	10
Aortic stenosis	12	6
Persistent right aortic arch	7	12
Atrial septal defect	4	3
Other defects	25	22

*Includes Tetralogy of Fallot.

The ductus arteriosus is a connection between the aorta and pulmonary artery during foetal life. Normally it will close at around the time of birth but in some instances it persists and is called patent or persistent ductus arteriosus. There is higher pressure in the aorta than in the pulmonary artery and part of the arterial blood is pumped into the pulmonary system. Because of an increased blood supply the lungs, left heart and ascending aorta will dilate and hypertension can result. The disease gives a characteristic murmur and typical ECG readings.

A milder form of the condition is called ductus diverticulum in which there is partial closure of the ductus arteriosus. In this state there is no flow of blood into the pulmonary artery from the aorta and no murmur.

In matings of Poodles, both of which suffered from patent ductus arteriosus, Patterson (1976) records that in 82.8% of offspring (10 litters 35 offspring) there was an incidence of cardiovascular malformation. Of these 82.9% there were 79.3% with complete concordance with the parents (that is, the same type of defect) and in 20.7% there was partial concordance. Ductus diverticulum also occurred emphasising the related nature of these two problems.

Various matings were undertaken (Patterson *et al* 1971) which demonstrated that the patent ductus arteriosus condition is a graded defect. Test data are shown in Table 59.

The conclusions that can be drawn from this table are that although distinct in the form of expression ductus diverticulum and patent ductus arteriosus seem to be genetically similar but there is not much difference between the transmitting ability of each type. It is also obvious that the condition is not a simple dominant one since the incidence of about 21% defective hearts when one parent is normal is too low. If it were a dominant defect then at least 50% of animals would be affected in such matings. The fact that normal

Table 59

Results of test matings in Poodles for patent ductus arteriosus

			Offspring*		
Type of mating	Matings	Normal	Ductus arteriosus	Patent ductus arteriosus	% Affected
Normal × DD†	4	22	5	1	21.4
Normal × PDA‡	18	61	9	8	21.8
Normal†† × DD	6	7	3	9	63.2
Normal†† × PDA	7	13	9	18	67.5
DD × PDA	3	6	0	7	53.8
PDA × PDA	10	6	6	32	82.9
Total	48	115	32	66	46.0

* Surviving offspring only.
† Ductus diverticulum.
‡ Patent ductus arteriosus.
†† Normal, but first degree relative to animals with patent ductus arteriosus. Other dogs labelled as normal had no family history of defect.
Source   Patterson 1976.

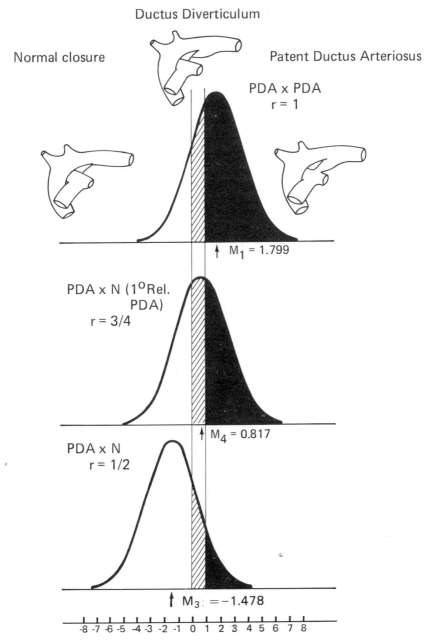

Figure 46 Threshold model for the inheritance of patent ductus arteriosus (PDA) and ductus div-erticulum (DD). The blank areas represent normal animals, shaded areas are DD cases and solid areas represent PDA cases. Reading downwards the three graphs represent the likely distribution of progeny when mating two PDA cases, a PDA case with the first degree relative of a PDA case and the mating of a PDA case to a normal, unrelated animal. The values of r represent the proportion of genes each group of offspring has in common with dogs with PDA. As r decreases the proportion of PDA and DD cases declines. M indicates the mean value in units of standard deviations. (From Patterson *et al* 1972, with permission).

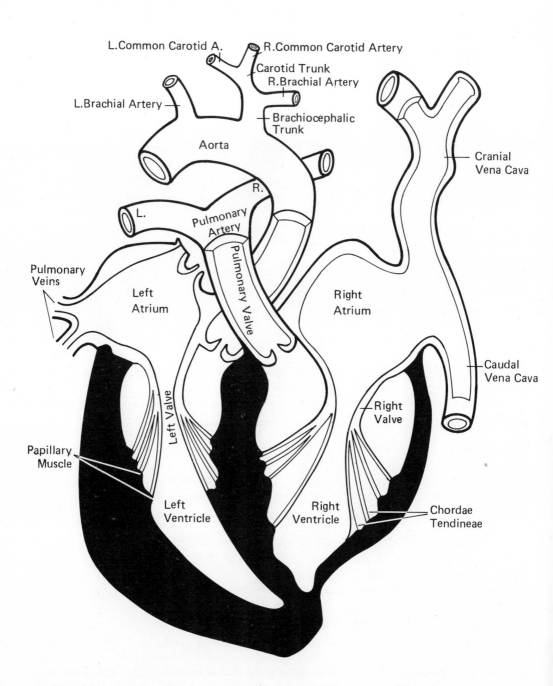

Figure 47   Structure of the heart (Frandson 1965). Reproduced by permission of Lea and Febiger, Philadelphia.

animals with a family history of the defect produce higher proportions of defective offspring when mated to PDA animals than do other normal stock suggests a far from simple mode of inheritance. The data are much more suggestive of some form of polygenic inheritance with additive effects. However, since there are essentially only three grades of problem—PDA, DD or normal—the most likely explanation which is suggested by Patterson (1976) is of a threshold character (see page 30).

The number of genes involved is unknown but there will be two threshold points. When an animal passes the first threshold it will have ductus diverticulum problems and when it has sufficient genes to pass the second threshold it will exhibit full patent ductus arteriosus. Patterson *et al* (1972) illustrates this graphically in a figure reproduced here (Figure 46).

For kennels with such problems the procedure to be followed is that laid down elsewhere (see page 318). Essentially breeding from dogs with, or with a family history for this condition, will encourage the transmission of more of the genes controlling PDA and, as a result, the mean of the population concerned will move to the right and into the area of increasing PDA and DD. In contrast, selection of animals with no evidence of the condition, and little family history for it, will move the population to the left and reduce the incidence of PDA and DD.

Both Patterson (1968) and Mulvihill and Priester (1973) showed a twofold excess of females among animals with PDA. This is indicative of some kind of sex-limiting factor causing greater expression of the defect in females. This complicates breeding methods slightly but does not invalidate them though it suggests that males with several PDA genes may not always demonstrate that fact phenotypically.

In an American study of a family of Salukis Ogburn *et al* (1981) found 15 animals out of 35 examined to have heart defects. All had either PDA or ductus diverticulum but there was a broader spectrum of cardiac malformations. Pedigree analyses suggested genetic implications but no effective theory could be suggested.

Conotruncal Septum Defects
Although heart defects are separately classified in Table 58 it does not follow that they are distinct in genetic terms. Breeding results involving animals suffering from Tetralogy of Fallot suggested that a variety of defects might be caused by a similar genetic aetiology (Patterson *et al* 1974). These were basically defects of the conotruncal septum and included not only Tetralogy of Fallot but also pulmonic stenosis and ventricular septum defects.

Pulmonic stenosis is a defect in which there is interference with the emptying of the right ventricle. As can be seen from Figure 47 the route is via the pulmonary valve into the pulmonary artery and in pulmonic stenosis there is incomplete opening of the valve due to a thickening of the tissue. This causes an abnormal heart sound as blood is forced through the too small opening. Ventricular septum defects imply a problem in the passage of blood through the ventricles. In Tetralogy of Fallot there are usually both pulmonic stenosis and ventricular septum defect. In combination, these have the effect of elevating right ventricular pressure and pulmonary hypertension occurs. The aorta receives blood from both ventricles while pulmonary blood flow is reduced. Mixing of venous and arterial blood causes cyanosis which is worsened by exercise although dogs can live for some years before congestive heart failure occurs. Complete correction involves open heart surgery and is thus expensive.

Pulmonic stenosis has been considered as being a feature of heart conditions in the Bulldog, Beagle, Chihuahua and Fox Terrier (Patterson 1968) and in the Samoyed and

Table 60

Incidence and concordance of heart defects in progeny of defective dogs

Parental defect and breed	Litters	Progeny	% Heart disease	% Concordance* Complete	Partial
Tetralogy of Fallot† (Keeshonds)	4	11	90.0	40.0	60.0
Pulmonic stenosis‡ (Beagles)	10	35	25.7	100.0	0.0

*Both parents had same defect. Complete concordance in offspring means same type of defect as in parents.
 Partial concordance means similar defect related to that of parents or parental defect with other defects.
† Other defects occurring in offspring were problems of conotruncal septum.
‡ No heart defects in offspring other than pulmonic stenosis.
Source   Patterson 1976.

Miniature Schnauzer (Mulvihill and Priester 1973). Tetralogy of Fallot is featured in the Keeshond (Patterson 1968; Mulvihill and Priester 1973) and ventricular septum defects were noted in the Bulldog by Patterson (1968).

   Mating results from certain of these problems are shown in Table 60 while matings with Keeshonds exhibiting conotruncal septum defects are shown in Table 61.

   The Pennsylvania workers rightly assumed that the data in Table 60 are not indicative of any simple genetic mode of inheritance unless incomplete penetrance is involved which is a far from satisfactory explanation. In broad terms the findings resemble those of patent ductus arteriosus in suggesting a polygenic mode of inheritance with threshold points. However, in this instance, the research team were able to associate severity of the disease

Table 61

Conotruncal septum defects (CSD) in Keeshonds

Type of mating			Litters	Progeny	Affected progeny* CSD	Others but no CSD	Total
Normal	×	Normal	2	12	4(33)	1(8)	5(41.7)
Normal†	×	CSD	15	61	39(64)	5(8)	44(72.1)
CSD	×	CSD	39	152	122(80)	10(7)	132(86.8)
CSD	×	Normal (F₁)	9	46	14(30)	0(0)	14(30.4)
CSD F₁	×	Normal	4	21	3(14)	0(0)	3(14.3)
CSD F₁	×	CSD (F₁BC)	2	9	8(89)	0(0)	8(88.9)
Normal F₁	×	CSD F₁BC	5	31	20(65)	2(6)	22(71.0)
Total			76	332	210(63)	18(5)	228(68.7)

*Figures in parentheses relate to percentage of total progeny.
†Normal but related to CSD stock.
Source   Patterson 1976.

Table 62

Conotruncal septum defects in Keeshonds according to grade of parents

Parental grade	Mid parent	Litters	Progeny	Number in Offspring Grade				Mean grade
				0	*1*	*2*	*3*	
0 × 0	0	2	12	8	3	1	0	0.42
0 × 1	0.5	9	36	14	10	6	6	1.11
1 × 1	1.0	6	29	9	7	10	3	1.24
1 × 2	1.5	8	38	10	14	8	6	1.26
0 × 3	1.5	6	25	8	11	4	2	1.00
2 × 2	2.0	2	6	2	1	1	2	1.50
1 × 3	2.0	13	49	6	14	17	12	1.71
2 × 3	2.5	6	19	2	5	4	8	1.95
3 × 3	3.0	4	11	1	2	3	5	2.09
Total	1.58	56	225	60	67	54	44	1.36

Source   Patterson 1976.

in the parents with that in the offspring. To this end they graded all animals into one of four grades (0–3) with 0 representing a normal state and 3 with the most severe form of the problem. On this basis data could be retabulated and there is increasingly greater severity in the progeny as the severity in the parental stock rises (Table 62).

Patterson and his colleagues proposed a threshold situation involving three threshold points which is reproduced in Figure 48. They conclude that malformation of the conotruncal septum is a polygenic trait, inherited as a threshold character and with a high heritability. This suggests that selection against the problem will be effective and rapid.

Subaortic Stenosis

Aortic stenosis is a thickening of the outflow tract of the left ventricle thus slowing down the emptying process and causing hypertrophy of the left ventricle. There is also poststenotic dilation of the ascending aorta. In most cases the valves may not be the primary seat of the problem but narrowing may be occurring just below them, hence the term subaortic stenosis. Narrowing of the opening is caused by a fibro-cartilaginous ring. There is a typical murmur and it can be detected radiographically as well as by ECG readings. It can cause fainting and sudden death.

The Newfoundland and Boxer are known to have a particular breed predisposition (Patterson 1968; Mulvihill and Priester 1973) while the German Shepherd has been implicated by Patterson (1968, 1971). German Short-haired Pointers were implicated by Mulvihill and Priester (1973).

In five matings of Newfoundlands suffering from the defect there were 26 offspring of which 38.5% showed cardiac defects, 80% of which had complete concordance with the parental defect. Valvular pulmonic stenosis was also noted in some offspring. Because there seems to be a grade or range of severity of the problem Pyle *et al* (1976) suggested a grading scheme on the 0–3 basis with 0 representing the normal state and 3 the most severe form of the defect.

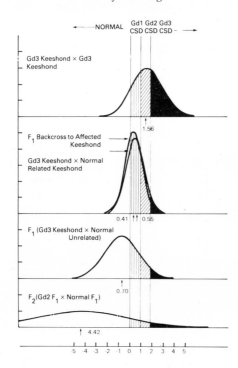

Figure 48 Threshold model for the inheritance of conotruncal septum defects. The graphs represent the proportion of offspring in the Normal, Grade 1, Grade 2 and Grade 3 categories of conotruncal septum defects from various matings. As the parents become more normal so the proportion of normal offspring increases – moving from the upper graph to the lower. (From Patterson *et al* 1974, with permission.)

Test matings ruled out recessive modes of inheritance as affected stock produced normal offspring. The matings between affected and normal dogs and between two affected parents were in good agreement with the expected results from a simple autosomal dominant with 100% penetrance but backcross data were not.

The data are shown in Table 63 and it is interesting that almost half of the stock were dead or destroyed before 3 weeks of age and in no case was subaortic stenosis observed in these dogs. The youngest age at which lesions were identified was 24 weeks, suggesting that the disease is not strictly congenital but develops later. Working only on dogs surviving beyond three weeks of age the data support a fully penetrant dominant but only if the backcross of affected F_1 stock is excluded. Patterson (1976) considers the trait to be a polygenic one or a major dominant gene with modifying factors.

Other Heart Defects

All three surveys reported earlier found the German Shepherd Dog to be predisposed to persistent aortic arch and the Irish Setter was considered so by Patterson (1968). Mulvihill and Preister (1973) recorded a predisposition to tricuspid insufficiency in Great Danes and Weimaraners and to mitral insufficiency in the Bulldog, Chihuahua and Great Dane.

Three matings of German Shepherds with persistent right aortic arch produced 30 offspring of which 10% showed heart defects. Of these three, one showed concordance and one had partial concordance. Other defects noted included pulmonic stenosis, PDA and persistent left cranial vena cava (Patterson 1976). The mode of inheritance is unknown and cannot be assessed from this limited number of matings.

James and Drake (1968) studied 11 Dobermanns which died suddenly. All were found to

Table 63

Test mating results for subaortic stenosis (SAS) in the Newfoundland

Type of mating		Litters	Progeny seen*	SAS Grade in progeny				Mean grade	% SAS
				0	1	2	3		
All progeny†									
Normal	× SAS	3	24	16	0	5	3	0.79	33.3
SAS	× SAS	5	24	10	0	5	9	1.54	58.3
Normal‡	× SAS (F₁)	8	40	32	1	4	3	0.45	20.0
SAS F₁	× SAS	3	31	19	1	8	3	1.37	38.7
SAS F₁	× Normal‡	3	20	20	0	0	0	0	0.0
Totals		22	139	97	2	22	18	0.72	30.2
All progeny surviving beyond 3 weeks									
Normal	× SAS		9	1	0	5	3	2.38	88.9
SAS	× SAS		15	1††	0	5	9	2.47	93.3
Normal‡	× SAS (F₁)		20	12	1	4	3	0.90	40.0
SAS F₁	× SAS		19	7	1	8	3	1.37	63.2
SAS F₁	× Normal‡		19	19	0	0	0	0	0.0
Totals			82	40	2	22	18	1.22	51.2

*In first three mating types a total of 13 animals were sold prior to examination and are excluded.
†Included animals post-mortemed after death at under 3 weeks of age.
‡Normal non-Newfoundland.
††No SAS but suffering from valvular pulmonic stenosis.
Source Patterson 1976.

have the same type of defective heart in that there was degeneration of the His bundle and cartilage and bone formation in the surrounding tissues. Six of the dogs had a common ancestor but this may be fortuitous and no genetic explanation exists. It is thought that these dogs died of what is known as an Adams-Stokes attack caused by interruption of atrioventricular conduction.

Canine Cyclic Neutropenia

This disease, sometimes called the grey Collie syndrome, is a blood disease characterised by a failure to develop any kind of immunity. There is a breakdown of erythrocytes and platelets and there may be an inability to synthesise vitamin K. Mentality is sometimes sub-normal and neutropenia is eventually lethal. The condition is one known in man where it is not lethal and it has been reported in the dog by various authors (Conklin 1957; Ford 1958, 1963).

Most pups die within days but those that survive may appear to be improving by about weaning age. The improvement is illusory because the disease is cylical and bouts of fever, diarrohea, respiratory infection etc will occur. In addition there is necrosis of the bone.

Essentially the disease is caused by a periodic and regular failure in the production of neutrophils (a type of white blood cell) in the bone marrow. Transplanting bone marrow has been tried and seems to alleviate the problem as well as rectifying coat colour defects (Jones *et al* 1975; Yang 1978). Survival for more than six years is reported by Matsas and Yang (1980) following transplants but such dogs must not be used for breeding and it seems pointless to consider this as a true cure in affected dogs which are best destroyed at birth.

The only breed affected seems to be the Rough Collie and it is well established that the condition is a simple autosomal recessive. This was the suggestion put forward by Ford (1958) and by Cheville (1968) as well as Lund *et al* (1967). The main genetic evidence comes from Ford (1969) and Lund *et al* (1970). The data of Ford have already been cited (Table 15 page 86) and those of Lund are given in Table 64. Cheville (1968) showed that in his six cases three left untreated died by 20 weeks of age while three treated dogs survived to between 26 and 106 weeks of age. Ford (1969) confirmed that few dogs survive to adulthood and this was further emphasised by Lund (1969) and Lund *et al* (1967, 1970).

The gene has a pleiotropic effect in that it not only causes problems in the blood but also brings about dilution of the coat; this latter aspect has been discussed under the section dealing with Collie coat colour. It is interesting that Lund *et al* (1970) refute the suggestion of Roberts (1967a) that the grey colour is a version of MM (homozygous merle genotype. Two MM dogs were seen by Lund and his colleagues but, though blind and deaf, they had no blood disorder.

Homozygous cyclic neutropenia can be identified early in life by the specific colour dilutions and affected pups should be destroyed as they will, in any event, die. Any dog which produces cases must be labelled as a 'carrier' animal and should be discarded from breeding programmes if the wish is to reduce the incidence of the problem.

Table 64

Incidence of grey (cyclic neutropenia) pups in Rough Collie litters containing at least one such pup

Litter size	Litters	Total pups born	Total grey pups
2	2	4	2
5	5	25	6
6	2	12	2
7	3	21	8
8	7	56	13
9	5	45	21
10	1	10	2
11	2	22	7
12	1	12	4
Total	28	207	65

Source   Lund *et al* 1970.

Haemophilia (A and B)

Haemophilia is a failure of the blood to clot normally and this arises because there is an impairment of the formation of a substance called fibrin in blood—an essential part of the clotting principle. Fibrin is produced from fibrinogen by the action of an enzyme called thrombin. This enzyme is itself the result of various other reactions and interactions involving a series of substances so that interference with the cycle at any point will produce failure of the whole chemical reaction and impair fibrin production.

In man there is evidence of genetic involvement in the control of several substances in the chain, the two most important ones being termed Factor VIII (Haemophilia A) and Factor IX (Haemophilia B). The first named is the classic sex-linked haemophilia made famous by Queen Victoria who transmitted it to her offspring. The second type is due to a deficiency of plasma thromboplastin and it is very often called the Christmas factor. Haemophilia B is often called Christmas disease.

Both conditions are sex-linked and thus transmitted in the form described in Chapter 1 (see page 10). In dogs McKinna (1936) first reported males with haemophilia and in 1938 Merkens showed that it was transmitted as a sex-linked trait. He worked in Greyhounds but later reports came from Field *et al* (1946) and Hutt *et al* (1948) which confirmed the mode of inheritance.

Symptoms of haemophilia are lameness, swellings (due to internal bleeding) and failure of the blood to clot. Because of these symptoms the death of affected male dogs is frequently inevitable before they reach reproducing age. As a consequence haemophilia is usually transmitted by carrier females and haemophiliac females are rarely produced.

Using special methods, Brinkhous and Graham (1950) did succeed in rearing affected males and thus were able to test genetic theory and, at the same time, provide much information on the coagulation of blood and haemostasis.

Because the conditions are genetically well understood there is no point in detailing numerous items of research. Readers anxious to obtain such information are referred to the excellent review by Dodds (1974, 1978). It seems more relevant to record breeds in which these kinds of haemophilia have been reported. It should be pointed out that the following lists are not necessarily complete and it is probable that haemophilia A and/or B is likely in many breeds were it to be looked for.

Breeds with haemophilia A or B are the St Bernard (Lewis and Holman 1951), Irish Setter (Graham 1952), Labrador Retriever (Archer and Bowden 1959; Howell and Lambert 1964), Cairn Terrier (Mustard *et al* 1960), Beagle (Brock *et al* 1963; Spurling *et al* 1972), Vizsla (Buckner *et al* 1967), Weimaraner and Chihuahua (Kaneko *et al* 1967), Antarctic Sledge Dog (Bellars 1969), French Bulldog (Slappendel 1975), English Springer Spaniel (Bovell 1977) and German Shepherd Dog (Ruff 1978). Other breeds are also affected and a more extensive list of references is given by Dodds (1974). In her later paper (1978) Dodds argues that most breeds of dog are likely to have haemophilia A but she lists only six breeds known to suffer from haemophilia B, which are: Cairns, Cockers, Coonhounds, French Bulldogs, St Bernards and Malamutes. Whichever breeds are involved the condition is unlikely to be very common in view of the early death of affected males. When it does occur breeders are well advised to eradicate it and they can best do this by carrying on bloodlines of carrier females through their normal sons. If they seek to perpetuate the line via females there is a 50% chance that these will be carriers. If a daughter is to be retained care is needed in checking all her sons. The fact that a daughter

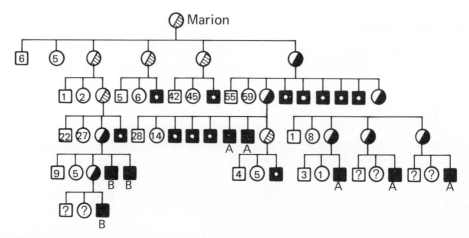

Figure 49 Haemophilia A and B in the female line of a French Bulldog female (Marion) (Slappendell 1975).

  ■ haemophiliac male   ◨ suspect haemophiliac male   ◖ carrier female
  ⊘ suspect carrier female   ⑰ total females descended from the bitch concerned
  ⑱ total males descended from bitch concerned

of a known carrier does not give any haemophiliac males may mean nothing if she has produced a litter largely of females.

One diagrammatic pedigree is reproduced (Figure 49) from a paper by Slappendel (1975) relating to French Bulldogs since it illustrates very clearly the sex-linked nature of the disease. In this outbreak, which was in Holland, both haemophilia A and B were present.

In his work with sledge dogs Bellars (1969) recorded three males with haemophilia in two litters from the same parents which he felt was due to a recent mutation. Symptoms were not identical to those previously reported in other breeds but were considered to be typical enough to diagnose haemophilia. An item worthy of special mention is the fact that Bellars also recorded entropion in this population (see page 215) and he suggests that the relationship was such as to give entropion a more disturbing aspect. This should not be overemphasised and there can certainly be no assumption that haemophiliacs are likely to be from lines with entropion or vice versa. In a small population with linebreeding being practiced it is not unlikely that various recessive genes will segregate out and the occurrence of two defects is likely to be fortuitous rather than an indication of linkage or true association. The same is less true of the association between subluxation of the carpus and haemophilia which was discussed earlier (see page 127).

The way in which Haemophilia A can be spread through a breed has been amply demonstrated in the German Shepherd Dog. Four cases were reported in Germany (SV 1980b) all stemming in the correct lines of descent from Canto v d Wienerau, a popular stud dog dying young in circumstances that suggested haemophilia A. Subsequently cases were reported in France (Poirson 1980), Norway (Thomsen *et al* 1984) Sweden (Fogh *et al* 1984), Denmark (Fogh 1986) and in Britain (Willis 1986b). The subject has been reviewed by Willis (1987) showing that all cases tie in with the original dog Canto. Subsequently cases have been seen in Australia.

Other Haemophiliac Diseases

Stuart-Prower Factor or Canine Factor X Deficiency
Factor X deficiency in man was first described by Telfer *et al* (1956) and in the dog by Dodds (1973). The canine cases involved a Cocker Spaniel kennel in America where, in a period of eight years up to 1968, the breeder lost 58% of males and 55% of females either as stillbirths or up to 2 months of age. The total number of pups born amounted to 142. The kennel had employed extensive inbreeding and was advised to outcross. In 1971 a further spate of stillbirths and deaths in the 7–10 day period began with haemorrhagic complications. Additionally an 11-month-old female died from internal haemorrhage.

Dodds supervised various test matings (Table 65) and there were several lesions as a consequence. Her genetic analyses based on the data from test matings and on blood tests suggested an autosomal dominant allele was implicated. This allele interfered with Factor X—one of the intermediate stages in the thrombin chain—and strictly it appeared to be incompletely dominant rather than dominant since the heterozygotes showed fewer and less severe symptoms than homozygotes which had such severe symptoms as to cause early death.

To date Factor X deficiency has been seen only in Cocker Spaniels where it is known to appear in all colour varieties. According to Dodds (1978) the American Spaniel Club has cooperated with her laboratory in testing breeding stock and over 2000 dogs have been through the scheme. Her paper gives details of her blood testing schemes and explains how breeders can have their animals tested.

Canine von Willebrand's Disease
Like all other bleeder diseases this one is characterised by an excessive bleeding time, largely as a consequence of reduced Factor VIII activity. There is abnormal retention of blood platelets—irregular shaped particles involved in clotting—and a short prothrombin consumption time.

The condition derives its name from a disease found in man and was first reported in the

Table 65

Results of test matings in Canine Factor X deficiency

Mating type	Litters	Progeny			
		Normal*	Mild†	Severe‡	Unknown¶
Normal × Normal	5	24	0	0	4
Normal × Mild	6	8	7	8	10
Mild × Mild	3	1	2	8	4
Total	14	33	9	16	18

* Normal = normal clotting times.
† Mild = mildly affected X factor 25–65%.
‡ Severely affected = X factor less than 25% or dead with evidence of massive haemorrhage at autopsy.
¶ Cause of death unknown but no visible lesions at autopsy.
Note In Dodds' original paper sexes are separated but since no sex-linked or sex-limited factor is involved they are unified here. Sex ratios were normal.
Source Dodds 1973.

dog by Dodds (1970). It occurred in a German Shepherd population in America and was the basis of Dodds' study. Details were published by Dodds in 1975 following various tests to seek better understanding of the mode of inheritance.

There appeared to be different expressions of the disease which Dodds categorised as Mild or Moderately Affected, Incomplete and finally Severely Affected. These were defined by Factor VIII activity, platelet retention and bleeding time. In the Mild and Severe forms there was reduced Factor VIII activity and platelet retention as well as a long bleeding time but in the Incomplete form there was either a reduced Factor VIII activity or low platelet retention with normal Factor VIII activity. Bleeding time was either normal or prolonged. Various other secondary diseases occurred in some of the moderately affected stock which may have been pleiotropic effects of the basic disease or may simply have been the result of other genes since the line was said to be highly inbred.

Twenty-two matings were made and results of live births are shown in Table 66. No sex-linkage or sex-limited problems were seen so sexes have been combined. Indications are that the disease is due to an autosomal dominant allele with variable penetrance and expressivity.

It did appear from tests undertaken that the disease became progressively less severe as the animal aged. Factor VIII activity in 2–4 month old animals was about 80% of that obtained in adults and, except for bleeding time, most haemostatic tests showed values which overlapped the normal range. This was particularly true during pregnancy, a feature also noticed in humans. However, whereas there was a regression towards the base-line post-partum in dogs there was never the complete reversal as in man. Thus pregnancies gradually improved the haemostatic picture.

Only one severely affected pup was born and this bled to death by ten days of age. The stillbirths, appended to Table 66, were much higher when diseased to diseased matings were made and since diseased stock only had one VWD allele it may be that the high stillbirth rate was a reflection of the homozygous form of the disease being lethal. Dodds (1975) came to the conclusion that when both parents had VWD there was about 60% affected offspring whereas when only one parent was affected this percentage was closer to 50. This, of course, was related only to live births and it seems logical to include stillbirth data which, if ranked as affected, increased these figures to 73 and 57% respectively. These

Table 66

Results of test matings for Canine von Willebrand's Disease (VWD) in German Shepherd Dogs

			Progeny numbers			
Mating type	*Litters*	*Pups born**	*Normal†*	*Mild‡*	*Incomplete¶*	*Severe***
Normal × Normal	7	38(2)	38	0	0	0
Normal × VWD	9	47(5)	22	23	2	0
VWD × VWD	6	35(17)	14	14	6	1

* First figure is live births, figures in parentheses refer to stillbirths.
† Normal haemostatic tests (factor VIII activity, platelet retention and bleeding time).
‡ Factor VIII 20–60%, platelet retention < 50%, bleeding time > 12 minutes.
¶ See text.
** Factor VIII 20%, platelet retention < 10%, bleeding time > 30 minutes.
Source   Dodds 1975.

are close to the 75 and 50% expected from simple Mendelian segregations; Dodds is careful to conclude that VWD inheritance may not be a single gene situation but her data are very much in favour of this or at least one major gene.

It is interesting that the line had problems with cryptorchidism and hence reduced fertility but there is no indication of any linkage between the two defects. Von Willebrands disease is not peculiar to the German Shepherd Dog but has also been seen in Golden Retrievers, Dobermanns, Scotties and Miniature Schnauzers (Dodds 1978) and in a Chesapeake Bay Retriever (Johnson *et al* 1980a). Mode of inheritance has been studied only in the GSD but is presumably the same in all breeds.

Afibrinogenaemia
This congenital condition, characterised by severe umbilical bleeding and very low or zero levels of fibrinogen was reported in the dog by Kammermann *et al* (1971), the breed being the Durrbach. It has also been reported by two American workers cited by Dodds (1974) in unspecified breeds. Genetic data is sparse in the extreme since Kammermann and his colleagues had only one case (a 6-year-old male) but, on family data, they suggested an inherited trait was involved, possibly an autosomal dominant.

Factor VII Deficiency
This condition was reported in Beagles in Canada by Mustard *et al* (1962) and then by Garner *et al* (1967), Capel-Edwards and Hall (1968), Poller *et al* (1971) and Spurling *et al* (1972). In all cases the breed involved was the Beagle which may reflect the use of this breed in research more than indicate something peculiar to it. The condition is a mild one causing delayed coagulation. Heterozygotes can be identified by blood tests and the condition is clearly an autosomal one. In reviewing the subject, Dodds (1974) concludes that it is best described as an autosomal dominant because of the ability to identify heterozygotes but that the clinical expression depends upon possession of two Factor VII deficiency alleles and thus it is recessive in clinical entity. According to Dodds (1978) an important aspect of this deficiency is a susceptibility to demodectic mange, several Beagles developing this problem. Dodds' laboratory has now isolated Factor VII deficiency in Alaskan Malamutes.

Factor XI Deficiency
This was first described in Springer Spaniels by Dodds and Kull (1971). It is basically a deficiency of plasma thromboplastin antecedent (PTA) with minor bleeding episodes, severe bleeding after surgery and low Factor XI assay. The case occurred in a female and three of her offspring were heterozygous for the condition suggestive of an autosomal dominant trait. More recently Dodds (1978) has isolated this deficiency in the Pyrenean Mountain Dog. In both breeds the condition appears to be serious in the nature of the haemorrhages following even minor surgery which, in many cases, are lethal.

Canine Thrombocytopathy
This is a disease in which there is an inherited platelet abnormality. Platelet counts were below normal in affected dogs and there was poor clotting time, lengthy bleeding and other defects. It was reported in a family of Otterhounds by Dodds (1967) and inherited as an autosomal dominant with both homozygous and heterozygous states being identifiable (Dodds 1974) in terms of assay and clinical signs. A similar disorder was reported in a

Foxhound (cited by Dodds 1974) and in a Basset Hound family (Lotz *et al* 1972) while a Scottish Terrier was implicated in a third report (Myers *et al* 1972) which suggests that the defect may be more common than generally supposed. Only in the Otterhound case was any genetic theory put forward but Johnstone and Lotz (1969) do suggest that their Basset Hound case was autosomal in fashion.

Other Comments
Although various haemophilic diseases exist in the dog it must not be assumed that all occurrences of haemophilia are genetic in origin. Acquired disease is likely to be more common than inherited problems but it is rarely subjected to scientific study once the cause has been isolated and the animal treated. Dodds (1974) has reviewed several instances of acquired disease in the dog and breeders with haemophilia outbreaks should not immediately assume that they have a genetic mutation or defect on their hands. Checks should be undertaken via veterinary surgeons or clinics before any genetic theory is postulated and only when environmental features have been eliminated should a genetic explanation be pursued. In view of the fact that most haemophilias are likely to be of Factor A or B types a sex-linked explanation is most likely but all other types, though rarer, are autosomal in nature and require different action in genetic terms.

Haemolytic Anaemia (Pyruvate Kinase Deficiency)

This type of anaemia is basically brought about by a deficiency of pyruvate kinase, an enzyme involved in the normal production of red blood cells (erythrocytes). It is known in man and was first reported in American Basenjis by Tasker *et al* (1969). This group of workers observed three cases and, in the same year, Ewing reported eight more cases in this breed whilst in 1971 Searcy *et al* recorded a further seven cases. In all instances the Basenji was the breed involved and, as a consequence, Missouri University set up a breeding colony in 1972 to observe the problem, results from which have been reported by Brown and Teng (1975).

Details of various matings made by the Missouri workers are set out in Table 67. Unfortunately the numbers of litters were not given but progeny numbers were and are

Table 67

Mating results with Pyruvinate Kinase Deficiency (PKD) in Basenjis

Mating type	Progeny in each category		
	Normal	*Carrier*	*Affected*
Normal × Normal	All*	—	—
Normal × Carrier	8	8	0
Carrier × Carrier	6	19	8
Carrier × Affected	0	0	2†

*Number not given but all normal.
†Not tested but dead at birth.
Source   Brown and Teng 1975.

tabulated for ease of understanding. Although actual anaemia was present only in affected stock it did appear that so-called 'carriers' were only superficially normal. Thus the half life of red blood cells was only 6.5 days in haemolytic anaemia pups compared to 16 days in normal pups whereas in 'carriers' the half life was 12 days. In normal adult Beagles kept as controls the corresponding figure was 21 days.

The data presented by Brown and Teng (1975) fit a simple autosomal recessive theory although strictly speaking the deficiency is genetically an additive one, in that one defective allele causes certain changes in the blood while the presence of both defective alleles causes sufficient change to induce anaemia.

More recently Andressen (1977a) has reported the disease in the Basenji in Denmark and in an analysis of ten litters he confirmed the American findings. His pedigree information is reproduced in Figure 50. In a subsequent paper (Andresen 1977b) blood

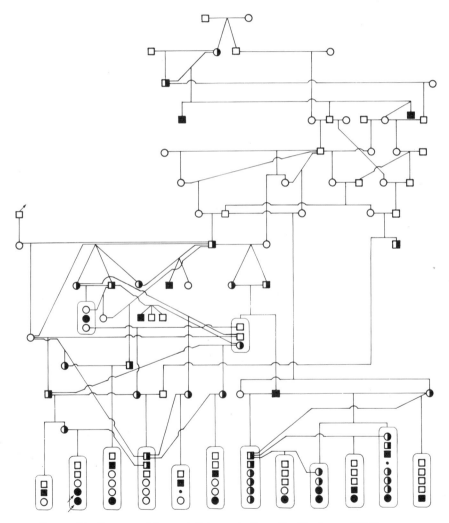

Figure 50   Pyruvate kinase deficiency in Basenjis (Andresen 1978).
●■   affected   ◐◲   carriers   •   stillborn

studies were reported and the terms PK and pk were proposed as gene symbols. Thus PK PK represents a normal animal, PK pk a 'carrier' and pk pk will be an affected dog.

The Danish cases traced back to British stock so the condition is probably present in Basenji stock in most countries. In the USA Brown and Teng (1975) estimated a 19% incidence of 'carriers' following blood tests on 300 dogs. This would suggest an incidence of anaemic animals of about 1%. Whether the picture in other countries is similar is uncertain but it is interesting to speculate as to why the Basenji is the only breed thus far affected. American and Danish workers have postulated a possible link between this and the anaemia in man known as sickle cell anaemia. This latter condition is a recessive genetic trait originating in the part of Africa from which the Basenji derives. In a homozygous state the sickle cell allele causes anaemia in man but in the heterozygous state it affords considerable resistance to malaria and thus had a reasonably high frequency in the human population of the region since non-carriers would be highly susceptible to malaria. It is tempting to suggest that the pyruvate kinase deficiency in the Basenji is linked in some way with disease resistance although in man the target of sickle cell anaemia is the haemoglobin molecule as opposed to the erythrocyte. However there is no evidence to support this theory regarding disease resistance in the dog.

It may well be that in the natural habitat in Africa the pyruvate kinase deficiency allele aided disease resistance in the Basenji. Unfortunately, in the environments to which the breed is now subjected, such resistance may well be of limited value and hence the anaemic condition becomes more serious. This is certainly the case with sickle cell anaemia in man which had beneficial effects in Africa but which, in the negro population of North America (descendants of the original 'carriers' in Africa), was of no value since there was no exposure to malaria.

In view of the fact that 'carrier' Basenjis can be identified by appropriate blood tests (see Andresen 1977b) it would be a fairly simple matter, given appropriate blood testing facilities, to fully categorise the population and then select against the allele by the avoidance or reduced usage of known 'carriers'. The degree to which this can occur will depend upon the incidence in the population but if this is 19% it may not be possible to cull all 'carriers' in one operation. However, outstanding animals which are 'carriers' could be used under strict control conditions to preserve their virtues and at the same time avoid their affected or 'carrier' progeny.

Pelger-Huët Anomaly

The white blood cells (leucocytes) are of varying kinds and it sometimes happens that two kinds of white blood cell (neutrophils and eosinophils) have incompletely segmented nuclei. This condition is known as Pelger-Huët anomaly and is known to occur in both man and the rabbit. Since the white blood cells act as a first line of defence against infection it is possible for sufferers of Pelger-Huët anomaly to have impaired resistance although generally the condition is benign. In man the incidence ranges from 1 in 350 in parts of India (Gehlot and Monga 1973) to 1 in 43,000 in parts of USA (Ludden and Harvey 1962). The trait is inherited as an autosomal dominant in man.

In the rabbit there is incomplete dominance with animals having the homozygous dominant condition dying at birth or shortly afterwards (Nachtsheim 1950).

Schalm *et al* (1975) reported the occurrence of Pelger-Huët anomaly in a redbone hound and later Bowles *et al* (1979) described the condition in an inbred family of English–

American Foxhounds. As in man the condition appeared benign with no excess disease incidence among affected dogs. However it was noted that affected females weaned only some 63% of pups compared with 81% from outcrossed females. The 63% incidence was based upon 20 litters but the number of outcrossed litters was not given. Stillbirths were higher for Pelger-Huët females than outcrosses (11 v 5%) but conception rates were similar (77%) as was litter size (7.3). The suggestion from the data is that this leucocyte anomaly adversely influences foetal survival as well as that of newly born animals. It is uncertain whether the trait in the dog is a dominant one.

Phosphofructokinase deficiency

Mature erythrocytes need energy to maintain the membrane plasticity and thus prevent accumulation of methemoglobin as well as to prevent degenerative oxidation of haemoglobin. Energy requirements are met by anaerobic glycolysis which converts glucose to pyruvate through a complex chain reaction controlled by enzymes under genetic control. Pyruvate kinase deficiency is a breakdown in this chain but more recently Giger and Harvey (1987) have recorded an earlier breakdown in the chain due to a deficiency of phosphofructokinase (PFK). The condition was observed in seven related English Springer Spaniels in USA. Dogs tended to show intermittent darkening of the urine from slightly amber through to brown-black. Additionally there was lethargy, weakness, loss of appetite, fever and weight loss. Such manifestations lasted for period of about a week. Data suggested an autosomal recessive gene was implicated. Affected dogs were PFK deficient and carriers could be identified by measurement of PFK erythrocyte activity which would permit screening for this defect and so make its control relatively easy.

Oedema

Congenital Lethal Oedema
Oedema is a term used to signify an animal or region swollen with fluid. This usually involves the lymph system. This system is a draining system for tissue fluids that parallels and augments the venous circulation. It acts as a defensive mechanism against alien materials, filtering them from the body and producing antibodies against them. Lymph nodes occur throughout the body and the spleen is a lymphatic organ.

In cattle, swine and man there are known to be inherited oedemas with varying degrees of severity. In cattle the condition is mainly seen in Ayrshires where it is known to be a simple autosomal recessive in its mode of inheritance (Donald *et al* 1952; Morris *et al* 1954). In this breed the affected calf is swollen and bloated and the disease is called dropsy with the calves being referred to as 'bulldog' calves because of their appearance. In swine the condition is inherited in a similar fashion (Wiesner 1960) whereas in man the trait seems to be a dominant one (Esterly 1965).

Oedema in the dog was reported in a Schnauzer by Keller (1928) who also said that it was not uncommon in dwarf Bulldogs. More recently Ladds *et al* (1971) reported seven cases of oedema from five bitches in four Bulldog kennels in the USA. All the births involved caesarian section and affected pups were either dead at birth or died soon afterwards.

The figures relating to this report are shown in Table 68 and suggest that caesarian section is almost inevitable as the oedematous foetuses do not enter the pelvic cavity which makes palpation for identification purposes difficult.

Table 68

Occurrence of oedematous Bulldog pups in 5 litters

Litter	Sire	Parity of dam	Pups Normal	Oedematous	Location of pup in uterus	Other defects in litter
1	A	1	7	1	Tip left horn	1 Cleft palate
2	A	1	5	1	Tip right horn	1 Cleft palate
3	B	1	4	1*	Tip right horn	None
4	B	2	2	2	Body/left horn	None
5	C	1	4	2	Unknown	None

* This pup was reported by a veterinarian and was the fourth such animal in a 6-week period. All were from sire B out of first parity dams.
Source   Ladds *et al* 1971.

Ladds and his colleagues offer no genetic explanation but the numbers involved suggest a simple recessive condition as being most likely, the ratio being close to 3 normals per affected pup. The incidence of the problem may be low but the gene frequency will be much higher than most breeders will suspect (see page 294).

Congenital Lymphoedema

An earlier case of oedema was reported in America by Patterson *et al* (1967) with histological and pathological studies being produced by Luginbuhl *et al* (1967). The original case was in a 'mixed Poodle' which was reported as having swollen rear limbs at about eight weeks of age. She did, in fact, have swollen lymphatic system problems and was retained for breeding purposes. At the time of the report she was 5 years of age and had produced 17 pups in three litters. These were to a German Short-haired Pointer and a Poodle (both normal) and to one of her affected sons. This son was also mated to an affected litter sister and to a normal Collie and normal Keeshond.

These six matings produced a proportion of affected progeny (see Table 69) that was consistent with lymphoedema being caused by a simple autosomal dominant gene.

Table 69

Incidence of oedematous progeny in various matings involving congenital lymphoedema

Type of mating	Matings	Progeny Normal	Affected	Region affected* Rear limbs	All limbs	Limbs and trunk
Normal × Affected	5	20	20	9†	5	6
Affected × Affected	1	0	4	0	0	4
Total	6	20	24	9	5	10

* In neonatal period.
† In four of these the oedema had disappeared by three months of age.
Source   Patterson *et al* 1967.

Unlike the Bulldog cases reported above this type of oedema was not always lethal although 11 of the 24 affected animals died prior to weaning compared with only 3 of the 20 unaffected pups.

The oedema was not generalised as in the Bulldog cases but affected the limbs, especially the rear ones, and sometimes the trunk. However in some cases oedema was transient in that after three months of age it was no longer obvious (see Table 69).

The identification of oedema of this kind might not be easy in the case of those animals with only a mild form, which could lead to difficulties in genetic diagnosis. The reasons for differential forms of expression in the dog are unknown. The disease seems to be expressed by some kind of disturbance in the formation of the peripheral lymphatic channels, including the lymph nodes, and a failure to establish the normal contact between these and the more central parts of the lymphatic system. Patterson *et al* (1967) in reviewing the case, and comparing the canine and human forms of the disease, point out an apparent association between lymphoedema in man and the formation of neoplasms. Whether this is true of the dog is unknown.

Kidney Defects and Renal Disease

Kidney diseases are known in many species including the dog but in some instances it is not easy to decide whether they are primary problems or merely secondary symptoms of some other disease. Many kidney diseases are merely acquired problems which need not be discussed here but a few genetic, or possibly genetic, situations are known.

In both Sweden and Germany a problem has been reported by several workers (Krook 1957; Persson *et al* 1961; Freudiger 1965) in each case affecting the Cocker Spaniel. There was a pronounced hypoplasia (size reduction) and in the more severely affected dogs death from uraemia occurred. The Swedish workers did not speculate on the genetics of the problem but Freudiger (1965) did suggest that it was an inherited one since it occurred in specific lines in two kennels where inbreeding had been undertaken.

In a Beagle colony Vymetal (1965) reported a high incidence of defective kidney development similar to that seen in the European Cocker Spaniel data. Again there was hypoplasia of the kidneys and in eight cases out of 770 one kidney was entirely missing. The problem was traced to two sires which were eliminated and this reduced the incidence though it did occur via two daughters of one of these males. The incidence of approximately 1% was not high in absolute terms but important enough to be noted and implies recessive inheritance though not necessarily simple. Robbins (1965) suggested that kidney defects were more common than popularly believed and implied that the occurrence in Beagles was more apparent because of the use of this breed as a research tool.

Renal disease has been reported in a line of Elkhounds in the USA by Finco *et al* (1970). Six dogs were affected and one sired litters to four related females producing a total of 15 pups. Only in the case of a mating to his own dam did renal disease occur with three pups one of five seen developing the defect. In the other cases no problems were noted but only four animals were actually seen by the investigators. In a later paper Finco (1976) reported on 21 cases in this line out of 56 animals examined.

Age at detection ranged from 3 to 48 months. In most cases seen the kidneys were small, white and very firm while urine analyses revealed specific symptoms. Clinically the dogs lost their appetites and showed marked weight losses, osteomalacia of the bones occurred and in most cases death resulted. A genetic explanation may eventually result from this work but is not yet available. Finco does show some pedigree data in the original paper relating to three dogs but it is not possible to combine these into a meaningful diagram.

The Dalmatian is peculiar in the sense that it suffers from an inability or reduced ability to break down uric acid into allantoin when compared with other breeds. As a consequence Dalmatians excrete more uric acid in the urine than do other dogs. Whether this affects them is uncertain. The condition has been known for a very long time (Wells 1918; Onslow 1923; Klemperer *et al* 1938) and at least one worker has suggested that the breed is more susceptible to kidney stones (Keeler 1940). According to Weatherford and Trimble (1940) the breed has fewer intranuclear crystals in the cells of the liver which is a factor known to be associated with high uric acid excretion while blood cells apparently lack the ability to transport uric acid (Harvey and Christensen 1964). According to Trimble and Keeler (1938) the genetic situation is that failure to excrete allantoin is inherited as a simple autosomal recessive. This was determined in crosses with other breeds. It does not appear to be related to coat colour.

Renal disease in the Bedlington Terrier in Scandinavia was reported by Okaanen and Sittnikow (1972). In two litters from the same bitch there were a total of nine pups of which three had renal disease and associated hyperparathyroidism by the age of six months. The litters were inbred 12.4 and 14.1% suggesting possible recessive inheritance.

A renal disease similar to hereditary nephritis in man was described in the Samoyed by Bernard and Valli (1977). They reported five females dying of nephritis by about 7–11 months of age and a female dying at about five years of age from a similar problem. A further five animals showed a milder form of the disease. All were related and the authors suggested that the condition might be inherited and have a different form of expression in females as does human inherited nephritis. A later report (Bloedow 1981) covered a total of 22 male and 2 female cases and produced evidence that supported a genetically controlled and possibly sex-linked mode of inheritance. More data are needed but the fact that treatment was generally ineffective emphasised the need for greater controls.

Chronic progressive renal failure is known to occur in the Soft-coated Wheaten terrier which is not numerically strong in most regions, including Eire from whence it comes. It has been reported in the UK (Nash *et al* 1984) and Norway (Eriksen and Grøndalen 1984). Kidney development in all cases seen was abnormal and the pedigree data were suggestive of a genetic base, albeit currently unclear. The need for breed club involvement is obvious.

Chapter 12

Behaviour

Introduction

The dog was probably the first animal to be domesticated, its association with man going back for some 8 to 10 million years (Zeuner 1963). For only a very brief part of that time has man been recording canine behaviour and making planned breeding attempts to alter canine behaviour patterns but for almost all of the period man has been directly altering the dog. The way in which man has changed the shape is apparent in the myriad forms of dog seen throughout the world but the ways in which he has altered behaviour are possibly less obvious and perhaps less permanent.

It is not the purpose of this book to become involved in any long debate about the ancestry of the modern dog. There are those who advocate theories of descent via jackals, others favour the dingo and yet others seem content to settle for wild dogs. Most of the scientific evidence supports the view that the dog is descended from the wolf. This is a line of argument which does not always go down well with some breeders who consider it a dangerous line to pursue but there is ample evidence to support the wolf theory for most of our breeds and there are several breeds like the German Shepherd Dog and some of the Spitz types which very probably have wolf much closer in their ancestry—certainly no further back than 80 or 100 years.

Be this as it may, the important feature is that behaviour in our modern dogs will be influenced by behaviour paterns in their ancestors. Many studies have been undertaken on wild species and clearly show similar behaviour patterns to those of the dog. We have altered the dog to fit in with man and we have exposed the animal to differing training patterns and environments so that many wild instincts have been curbed or put to alternative uses. The sheep herding pattern of the Border Collie may owe a lot to its trainer but it is based upon the hunting instincts of the wolf—man has simply altered the end result in that the dog no longer kills. It is important that breeders remember these points because we must not forget that the wild animal instincts are still there—dormant and modified they may be but they have not been eliminated. We have, as Scott (1958) points out, trained our dog not to urinate in the wrong place but we have not removed the wild instinct to cock his leg. The male is marking out his territory just as did his wild ancestor.

Behaviour is the most important characteristic of our dogs in the sense that unless a dog's behaviour conforms to that which his owner and society demand of him the dog will cease to survive. There may well be a place for the dog whose beauty does not measure up to the high standards of the show ring but there really cannot be any place for the dog whose temperament and behaviour patterns are unsuitable. Much of this book may well be directed towards the physical appearance of the dog but it should never be forgotten that temperament and behaviour overrule any physical virtues. A Dobermann that has no breed type may not be deserving of the title Dobermann but if he has a vicious or cowardly character he is unworthy of the title dog. Breeders forget this at their peril and it is regrettable that in many breeds there are breeders who have apparently decided to forget about character and seem content to produce dull useless dogs or those with unsuitable temperaments but with alleged physical beauty. In my view such dogs have no place in society and their breeders no place in the canine world.

If, like me, my readers feel that character is important in any breed of dog then our joint problem is one of trying to determine how we can produce the ideal character in a high proportion of our dogs. This is not necessarily easy because we have only limited information available on the genetics of behaviour and much of what does exist suggests that behaviour is a complex trait in which heredity is only one of the influences.

We cannot look at canine behaviour as a genetic trait isolated from the other aspects. Behaviour is dependent upon inherited and acquired characteristics and very much upon the interplay between heredity and environment. It is not a subject solely for the geneticist but involves sociologists, embryologists, ecologists and others. Behaviour is thus a multidisciplinary subject and, hopefully, it will be treated as such in the ensuing discussion.

Since 1946 the Jackson Laboratory at Bar Harbor in Maine has been making detailed investigations into the behaviour of the dog. This long-term project was begun ostensibly because some aspects of canine behaviour were considered analogous to those of children. My own view is that this is an oversimplification and any comparison between man and dog in behavioural terms is no more than superficial but, whatever the motivation, the Laboratory has produced useful work on the behaviour of dogs. Two books on canine behaviour have come from workers who spent some time at this unit—Scott and Fuller (1965) and Fox (1971), the latter a rather complex work. However this school was not the first to enter the field. Before this time Whitney (1929, 1932) had done preliminary studies and the Fortunate Fields Project of Humphrey and Warner (1934) pioneered much of the Bar Harbor unit's work. There were others before this and since and some will be mentioned here but there is no attempt being made to comprehensively review in one chapter a subject that could fill a book on its own. Some of the techniques used in behavioural genetic studies have been outlined by Fuller and Thompson (1960) and are worth reading because they highlight the problems inherent in the field. There are, in particular, peculiar problems of interpretation. This is well illustrated by work undertaken by Tryon (1940) who selected rats on their ability to move quickly through a mechanical maze. He believed that he was selecting for intelligence but later Searle (1949) showed that the dull rats were, in fact, afraid of the maze and thus Tryon had been selecting for a difference in emotional reaction.

This is an important point to remember in dog breeding where breeders tend to talk about intelligence and sensitivity. There may, in fact, be little difference between the sensitivity of a gun-shy and gun-sure dog but what we observe is a marked difference in their reaction.

Behaviour is complex and as such it seems appropriate to deal with it in a different way to that used in other chapters for more clearly defined traits. Accordingly the work of Fortunate Fields and Bar Harbor are dealt with as separate entities and then certain aspects of canine ability are treated in self-contained units.

Fortunate Fields

This particular project, reported by Humphrey and Warner (1934) in book form, was begun on the instigation of Mrs Harrison Eustis with the aim of developing a strain of German Shepherd Dog which would be ideally suited to work as a guide dog and also for police work.

The project began with a study of the breed and then developed ideas on the type of dog that was needed in physical and mental terms. The breed Standard was used only insofar as it appeared to aid the functional ability of the dog and where certain aspects were found to be detrimental the Standard was altered to fit the aims of the project.

All stock bred were scored on a points system which is described in detail by them and they were then tested for various mental traits (Humphrey 1934). Emphasis was given to those traits held to be most important for specific tasks as outlined in Table 70.

Looking at the various traits studied Humphrey and Warner's work can be criticised as being rather oversimplified. They made rather broad judgements about the inheritance of characters and did not emphasise sufficiently their own doubts as to the mode of inheritance of what we now know to be very complex polygenic traits. Thus they categorised dogs as being undersensitive, medium sensitive and oversensitive to sound and/or touch. They postulated a mode of inheritance whereby undersensitivity was genetically NN, medium sensitivity was Nn and oversensitivity was nn. Neither in the auditory nor tactile sense is this likely to be true but the categorisation of dogs in this manner did help in training procedures. They did find that oversensitive (shy) dogs were useless for most forms of work and they classified dogs into one of four broad categories:

a   Undersensitive to sound and touch;
b   Undersensitive to touch, medium sensitive to sound;
c   Undersensitive to sound, medium sensitive to touch;
d   Medium sensitive to sound and touch.

Any dog not so classified was culled but of these four groups the first two had low success rates being difficult to teach. Group (*c*) had a low failure rate and a high level of average dogs. Group (*d*) was the best but very susceptible to being spoiled by training and thus had

Table 70

Traits required in different forms of work undertaken by German Shepherd Dogs

Type of work	Olfactory acuity	Nose obedience	Aggression	Distrust
Police	+	+	++	−
Tracking	++	++	+	−
Liaison	+	+	−	+
Guide dog (blind)	−	++	+	−
Sheep herding	+	+	+	0
Pet	0	0	+	

Note   0 unimportant whether present or not; − undesirable; + desirable; ++ desirable in highly developed state.
Source   Humphrey and Warner 1934.

a high number of superior dogs with a few average ones. It seemed to be a greater deficiency to be undersensitive to touch than to sound.

Aggression was apparent in the ease with which a dog could be trained to attack, the only difficulty being in getting him to stop but it was highly correlated with most other behavioural traits. It did, however, seem only of low heritability.

Distrust was not the same as shyness in that distrustful dogs worked well with people they knew but reacted badly to strangers and often trained poorly as a consequence. It did seem to be inherited, tracing back to two foundation animals.

Intelligence, the ability to learn and retain what was learned was of low heritability though highly correlated with other traits. Willingness, a difficult trait to assess, seemed to trace back to a specific line and included many dogs of good nose obedience. This last trait was not the same as olfactory acuity but depended upon the dogs' ability to follow a track once started on it and not be deviated by other, more interesting, smells.

The success rate of this project was high but the confounded nature of training and selection leaves some doubt as to whether the success was due to one or the other or, more probably, to combinations of both. It very definitely will have overestimated the genetic side.

Bar Harbor

This project, begun in 1946 and reported on by Scott and Fuller (1965) as well as by many others, used five breeds of dog. These were the American Cocker Spaniel, Basenji, Beagle, Shetland Sheepdog and Wire Fox Terrier. All are small to medium breeds in view of the costs of upkeep and it does not follow that these are going to be typical of other breeds. Nevertheless, they did derive considerable information from over 202 litters and 470 animals. They paid attention to biological aspects and to performance, social behaviour and stress testing.

It does not follow that the type of tests used will give similar results in other untested breeds and interpretation of any test results is not easy. Nevertheless, the basic finding from this group seems to have been the splitting up of the animal's life into what are termed critical periods. These were as follows:

1   Neonatal (birth to 21 days). During this stage the pup learns little from experience seeking its mother's milk and little else.
2   Transitional (21–28 days). This was considered to be a crucial period in which daily handling was desirable and when the pup was extremely and increasingly responsive to his surroundings. Pfaffenberger (1963) suggests that it is so crucial as to necessitate that weaning is never undertaken during it but is best after 28 days or even before 21 days rather than during the transitional period.
3   Socialisation (4 to 12 weeks). A most crucial stage. If incorrectly socialised a dog could be ruined. Usually dogs change hands at 6–8 weeks and this seems the best time in psychological terms. Prior to four weeks the dog may not adjust to other dogs and after 12 weeks socialisation is difficult with other people. During this stage the dog *must* be introduced to all kinds of new experiences if he is to develop correctly. Keeping a dog in a kennel with a daily check to see that he is growing shapewise is, it seems, a sure way to spoil the dog's character yet very many breeders do spoil their dogs in this way.

4   Juvenile (12 weeks to sexual maturity). Much of what happens in this period will be determined by what went on before. As training usually begins in this period it is important that the two previous stages have been well managed.

Breed differences existed in minor issues which need not be discussed here but the basic trends were similar across breeds. Some social hierarchy developed in dogs akin to the well-known 'pecking order' in hens. In one experiment James (1951) exchanged some pups from Beagle and Wire Fox Terrier litters at birth. He found that in each group the Terriers dominated and, while Beagles avoided Terriers and preferred to be with other Beagles, Terriers also avoided Terriers and preferred to be with Beagles (which they could dominate). A social hierarchy in Basenjis was more apparent than in American Cockers (Scott and Fuller 1965).

Pfaffenberger (1963), whose San Rafael Seeing Eye breeding kennel was closely connected with the Bar Harbor work, felt that dogs not given a chance to express inherent potential prior to 16 weeks of age would never be as good as they would otherwise have been. Krushinskiii (1962) considered that dogs left in kennels until four months of age would become poorly adapted to any other life and this was the view of Melzack and Thompson (1956) who reared Scottish Terriers in isolation from their keeper to 7–10 months of age. In contrast to normally reared litter mates these Scotties all developed abnormal reactions to situations and had low intelligence scores. They felt that failure to cope with situations in infancy (through non-exposure) did not permit the dog to learn to cope later.

Fuller and Clark (1968) reared Beagles and Wire Fox Terriers in (a) solitary confinement (b) confinement in pairs or (c) as pets and then tested their response to handlers, other pups and toys. They found pet reared stock to be more responsive in the early stages of the tests but as these progressed the paired pups showed a higher response. Isolate-reared Terriers were more active than those which were pet reared but isolate-reared Beagles never did overcome the effects of that system of rearing.

Fox (1964) has shown the relationship between behaviour in the various critical periods and the changes of a neurological type taking place in the Central Nervous System. In his book (Fox 1971) he takes this further. The work of this school has been particularly crucial in our understanding of the development of behaviour but there is very little in respect of breeding information.

We do know, and it seems generally accepted, that there are well defined crucial stages in the development of canine behaviour patterns but we do not know with any certainty what amount of the variation seen is transmitted to the next generation. The breeder is interested in knowing whether dogs with behavioural problems will transmit them and on that score we have only limited information at our disposal.

Fuller and Clark (1966a,b) and Krushinskiii (1962) have shown that isolation rearing will be more damaging to breeds that are essentially passive or timid than to those breeds which are naturally aggressive. It is logical to assume that these breed differences have a genetic basis so this indicates genotype environment interactions are occurring but we do not know if, within a breed, we can easily select for timidity or aggression.

Then again, certain tests may reveal breed differences but these may not necessarily be useful in a practical sense. Thus Elliot and Scott (1965) have looked at the ability of breeds to work their way through a maze. The same five breeds were used at a starting age of about 13 weeks. Each dog was assessed on the minimum time to undertake the test, the minimum

Table 71

Means and standard deviations for breeds in maze tests after correction for other factors

Breed	Number	Minimum time	Minimum errors	Range time	Habit	Time score
Basenji	30	5.1(2.0)	3.1(1.4)	3.9(1.7)	5.4(1.9)	3.1(1.2)
Beagle	29	3.5(1.3)	2.5(1.1)	5.9(2.3)	3.9(1.7)	5.8(1.6)
American Cocker	31	5.5(1.7)	3.5(1.0)	4.8(1.8)	4.8(2.1)	5.5(1.6)
Shetland Sheepdog	19	6.3(1.7)	4.8(1.5)	5.5(1.6)	5.5(2.1)	6.2(2.0)
Wire Fox Terrier	18	4.7(2.7)	3.7(2.2)	6.0(1.6)	5.2(1.8)	5.2(1.2)
Total	127	4.9(2.1)	3.4(1.6)	5.1(2.0)	4.9(2.0)	5.1(1.2)

Source Elliot and Scott 1965

errors, the range in performance, the time score and finally the degree of habit (the extent to which it did the same wrong move in successive tests). Data were scored on a seven point scale with higher numbers indicating poorer performance. The mean scores and standard deviations are shown in Table 71.

The workers concluded that Beagles were not habit-forming but continued to improve whereas Shetland Sheepdogs were the poorest all-round performers becoming emotionally disturbed and hesitant and very habit-forming. Basenjis were confident and scored well in early tests but seemed poorly motivated. Cockers were regularly intermediate while Fox Terriers showed a tendency to try to bite their way out of the maze.

On the whole a poor showing for Shelties, yet they are very probably more trainable than any of the other breeds and can learn to undertake complex tasks under direction. Whether this is a reflection of dependance upon man is uncertain but it indicates the dangers of drawing widespread conclusions from certain tests. Moreover it needs to be realised that in most of the tests between 40 and 72% of the total variation was attributable to the individual and only 9 to 38% to breed.

Swedish Army Work

At their training centre in Solleftea the Swedish Army have been testing and training dogs for several years. Much of the good work on hip dysplasia from Sweden has stemmed from this unit and information or training has begun to appear in the scientific literature.

The kennel produces about 300 dogs per year which are litter recorded to 10 weeks and then placed in private homes until 18 months of age when they are exposed to mental testing. All dogs are scored on their reaction to tests and then retained or discarded. Unlike Britain where little or no use is made of trained population geneticists in Police or Army breeding work, the Swedes have wisely consulted experts from Stockholm University. A paper on the inheritance of mental traits has resulted (Reuterwall and Ryman 1973) based upon tests made on 926 Shepherd Dogs from 168 litters sired by 29 different sires out of 103 different dams. All were tested between 1966 and 1969 by one man and 38% of dogs were rejected on the basis of the tests. The actual tests undertaken are shown in Table 72 together with the heritabilities obtained on a paternal half-sib correlation basis.

Table 72

The heritability of certain mentality traits in German Shepherd Dogs

Trait	Definition of trait	Situation used to assess the trait	Heritability* Males %	Females
A	'Affability'	Dog confronted by an unknown person	17	9
B	Disposition for self defence	Dog is attacked by an unknown person	−11	26‡
C	Disposition for self defence and defence of handler	Dog and handler are attacked by unknown person	4	16
D	Disposition for fighting in a playful manner	Dog fights for a sleeve or stick	16†	21†
E	Courage	Man shaped figure approaches dog	5	13
F	Ability to meet with sudden strong auditory disturbance	Shots fired at some distance and noise made with tin cans just behind dog	−4	15
G	Disposition for forgetting unpleasant incidents	A dog is scared at a certain place and then has to pass it again	10	17
H	Adaptiveness to different situations and environments	Assessed during rest of testing	0	4

* Calculated from 488 males and 438 females.
† This likely to be a true figure 95 times in a hundred.
‡ This likely to be a true figure 99 times in a hundred.
Note Other figures are not significantly different from zero. Negative values have no significance and can be considered zero.
Source Reuterwall and Ryman 1973.

The phenotypic correlations are given in Table 73. Further details on the nature of the tests together with photographic representations are given by Hallgren (1975).

The heritability of most traits tested was low which is very disturbing as it suggests that progress in improving performance will be slow. Reuterwall and Ryman argue that this might be the result of previous selection which has left title additive genetic variance in the population but this seems doubtful. The gentic base was a broad one, imported stock from outside the kennel were used throughout and it is doubtful if any prior selection undertaken by breeders would have been very effective. The fact that the heritability of 60-day weight was moderately high (averaging about 40%) shows that considerable variation existed in that trait. A more likely explanation is that the scoring system is prone to considerable error which would raise the variance due to environment.

Sex differences were noted in that females were affected by gunfire to a greater extent than were males which in turn were more prone to exhibit uncontrolled defence (a sub-classification of Trait C). Traits B, C and D (Table 72) were highly correlated suggesting that they are component parts of aggressiveness.

Table 73

Phenotypic correlations between different components of behaviour*

Components†	A	B	C	D	E	F	G
B	−0.19						
C	−0.08	0.53¶					
D	0.14	0.27ø	0.48¶				
E	0.11	0.09	0.13	0.27ø			
F	0.14	0.03	−0.14	0.16	0.38¶		
G	0.07	0.21‡	0.33¶	0.45¶	0.53¶	0.41¶	
H	0.27ø	0.01	0.05	0.16	−0.09	−0.09	0.03

* Assessed from 183 randomly selected dogs from 183 litters (one per litter).
† For explanation of traits see Table 72.
‡ This is likely to be a true figure 95 times in a hundred.
ø This is likely to be a true figure 99 times in a hundred.
¶ This is likely to be a true figure 999 times in a thousand.
Note   Other figures do not differ from zero.
Source   Reuterwall and Ryman 1973.

Litter size and parity of the dam did not influence any of the variables studied and the proportion of dogs discarded was independent of litter size and was similar in different litters of any dam.

How far one can extrapolate from this data to other populations is uncertain. Most genetic data are applicable only to the population from which they were derived and may not apply to other groups of dogs or even other groups of Shepherd Dogs. Part of the reason for low heritabilities may stem from the way in which tests were made. Many trainers would consider 18 months too advanced to undertake selection and the system of leaving dogs in private homes would increase the environmental variation in the population. Some tests ought to have been undertaken with other assessors in order to measure the effectiveness of the tester.

Hedhammar (1976), working with data from this same Swedish army kennels, has examined the relationship between hip dysplasia and the scores a dog received for temperament. He found that 15–20% of the differences between temperament scores could be attributed to heredity but that the temperament of the dam was more influential than that of the sire insofar as progeny were concerned. This may well be due to some confounding between inherited aspects and the influence of the dam through example to her pups. A more interesting point was that the dogs with better standards of hip structure tended to score higher for temperament. The data were shown in Table 44 but no explanation is forthcoming. Similar findings by Mackenzie (1985) working with US army dogs showed not only a correlation of −0.33 between temperament score and hip dysplasia but did obtain a high heritability of 51% for temperament score suggesting a trait responsive to selection.

Olfactory Acuity

The fact that the dog possesses highly developed powers of olfactory discrimination has been reviewed by various workers (Buytendijk 1935; Humphrey and Warner 1934;

Warner 1936; McCartney 1951) and it is possible that this ability of the dog is its most important attribute when we consider the dog's role in a working capacity. Almost every other thing that the dog can do can be done by man—to a greater or lesser degree—but man cannot compete when it comes to olfactory acuity.

Moulton *et al* (1960) argue that the ability to discriminate between odours is not exclusive to the dog or in excess of that which man can achieve. Neuhaus (1953) has claimed that man can easily detect perspiration on a sheet of paper over which a person wearing shoes has walked. Niccolini (1954) claimed that canine and human olfactory threshold levels were similar and Becker *et al* (1957) were unable to train dogs to respond to concentrations of oil of cloves below those detectable by man. However Neuhaus (1953) concluded that the dog could detect fatty acids in a concentration of one million to one thousand million times lower than can man.

Olfactory acuity is not easy to assess because there is some evidence that dogs will not react to odours which have no biological significance to them such as flower scents (Binet and Passey 1895; Heitzenroeder 1913), but will respond to things like meat, blood, urine, sweat and such like. Thus the failure of a dog to respond does not mean that it cannot discriminate but simply that it does not wish to and man has no means of determining what is happening. Whatever various scientists may have concluded about the ability of man to discriminate between odours there is little practical value in this and we can safely conclude that the dog is a vastly superior instrument in this connection.

Some of the early work on tracking ability in the dog was reported by Most (1925, 1926, 1927, 1928a, b) and by Budgett (1933) all papers unlikely to be available to most readers though Most (1954) is an English book on training in which many of his ideas are summarised. Most was of the opinion that German Shepherds and Bloodhounds both performed badly when expected to work on olfactory discrimination alone and that visual and auditory clues as well as familiarity with the trainers' habits were important factors. Budgett makes the point that the dog is not tracking some nebulous body odour but is making use of scents from bruised vegetation and so on, as a consequence of contact. Only when within wind distance of its quarry will the dog make use of actual body odour in the air.

King *et al* (1964) used a mongrel Fox Terrier and an obedience-trained Weimaraner to test their ability to identify human odour (from contact with a glass slide) after various periods of time and with or without outdoor weathering. With indoor ageing of the scent there was a good rate of success up to about one week (the Weimaraner averaging 91.6% and the Fox Terrier 86.1%) and little, if any, fall-off up to 3 weeks (the Fox Terrier actually doing better in this period). With scent that has been exposed to outdoor weathering the success rate was less (60–70%) and fell markedly after one week.

Budgett (1933) found that various fatty acids found in human sweat were not followed by dogs after about 6–9 hours exposure in a field whereas King and his colleagues did get a response to fingerprints up to a week but no response at all after three weeks. Slides exposed on dull rainless days were found more readily than those exposed to bright sunlight.

The work suffers from the paucity of dogs used. There are bound to be differences in ability between dogs and this cannot be tested if only small numbers are used. Humphrey and Warner (1934) considered that nose obedience was an essential feature of a good tracking dog and Whitney (1955) argued that the superiority of the Bloodhound in tracking was not a result of better olfactory acuity but an inherent nose obedience making it stick to the trail it began on.

Galton (1876) suggested that identical twins might be an interesting test for the dog's olfactory acuity and Kalmus (1955) sought to examine this using various dogs from the Metropolitan Police (4 German Shepherds, 1 Dobermann, 1 Labrador and 1 German Pointer) together with 2 other German Shepherd Dogs. The tests used were complex and cannot be detailed here but they did show that dogs could clearly distinguish between one person and unrelated persons and that the odour of an individual was perceived by the dog even when mixed with another person's body odour. The region from which the body odour came seemed to be unimportant in terms of the animal's abilty to identify it. If twin odours were used simultaneously the dog could distinguish one from the other but when the odour of one was offered in lieu of the other the dog would follow it. It thus seemed that human twins did have similar but not identical odours and that the dog could distinguish between them. It is interesting that one particularly highly trained Shepherd (Kim) was able to distinguish better than most other dogs and this emphasised the need to undertake tests with several dogs.

The above information does not, of course, tell us to what extent olfactory acuity is inherited and there is limited data on this. Geiger (1972) has attempted to produce some information by examining the performance of 726 German Wire-haired Pointers at Working Trials in Germany over the period 1968–70. He looked at 613 male and 573 female progeny of 21 males and 356 females and estimated the heritability of scenting power to be 39%, tracking ability 46% while the ability to point and to hunt were 38 and 41% respectively.

This system is, at best, crude but suggests that tracking and scenting ability may be moderately heritable and thus can be improved fairly rapidly by selection. The problem is deciding upon an effective scoring system to rank animals. Geiger (1972) suggested a 12 point system.

Sheep Herding

There can be few dog breeders who, having watched a Border Collie at work, have not marvelled at the skill that has been shown. Sheep herding is something that has been perfected in Britain and is to be seen in many other countries, especially those populated by British emigrants, and yet it is something on which relatively few books have been written and few of these on aspects of breeding. Kelley (1949) and Longton and Hart (1969) are two which come to mind as telling us something about sheepdogs—but even these are limited in respect of anything genetic.

Many of the characteristics of the Border Collie are inherited and this is obvious when one watches an untrained puppy herding together fowl or other livestock in the farm yard. But these are, in part, the instincts of the hunter which man has sufficiently muted by selection for his own ends. It is, however, important to appreciate that Border Collies still need to be trained for sheep work and that their success as workers is also largely dependent upon the type of sheep they are herding.

Although there are differences between breeds of British sheep, Swaledales, for example, being regarded by some as hard to herd, the different breeds have been selected for their ability to flock when they see a dog approaching. Ewes with lambs at foot will be braver and may attack the dog but in general all breeds will bunch and gradually move away. This is by no means true of sheep in some countries and regions. In parts of Africa and Latin America sheep are not worked by dogs and roam freely through villages and across open country. Their behaviour patterns are more goat-like than those of British sheep and when approached by a dog they will often attack with sufficient vigour to drive it away. This has been described by Burns (1969) and is a personal observation of my own. The success of the Border Collie is thus a feature of the sheep as well as the dog because, as Burns (1969) has pointed out, such dogs may fail hopelessly with African sheep. Even in British conditions problems can arise. I recall once having a sheep that had been left isolated from the flock for several months with an injured leg. When subsequently run with the flock again this ewe would not bunch with the others and created havoc with the dogs working the sheep. I have also known of a case where a dog was actually killed by a Rough Fell ram which, on a hot day attacked it and butted it against a wall causing such injuries as to be fatal. However these are isolated incidents and as Burns (1969) has pointed out most sheep, even foreign ones, can be made to adjust their behaviour to allow working by dogs.

This is not intended as a treatise on training sheepdogs but we are interested in knowing which instincts of the dogs will be inherited.

Instincts in sheepdogs can be categorised as follows:

1 Showing eye. This is the characteristic of staring fixedly at the sheep and half-crouching as if about to pounce. Not all sheepdogs show eye and this does not mean that they lack the ability to round up sheep.
2 'Clapping'. This is the tendency of a dog to crouch down flat when checked by handler or by ovine resistance. 'Clappers' may occasionally rush the sheep and grip it and frequently 'clappers' have considerable eye.
3 Barking. Generally sheepdogs do not bark when working, especially those with 'eye' in which barking has probably been selected against. The type of barking, used to make defiant sheep move is called 'defiance barking' by Burns (1969) to distinguish it from other types of barking discussed later. It seems to be a feature of dogs lacking 'eye'.

Burns (1969) argues that dogs lacking eye are rarely extreme 'clappers' and that upstanding dogs are more frequently barkers than are eyed dogs, a fact I would vouch for in my own limited experience. Burns also speaks of 'powerful' dogs which are those animals which seem capable of stopping a sheep by simply looking at it. In contrast a 'weak' dog needs to show considerable movement. She argues that power is something peculiar to 'eyed' dogs and considers the ability of 'non-eyed' dogs to move sheep to be 'force' rather than power. However she does describe some of her own Cocker Spaniels which had the power to walk among sheep unattacked and which did not have an eye.

Burns (1969) points out that many breeds of dog will round up sheep as opposed to attacking them but few show eye. She argues that most German Shepherds show rounding up ability but without eye. My own view is that eye will be shown by some German Shepherds if they have sufficient sheep-working 'blood' behind them. None of my own dogs have shown eye other than my very first who had a pronounced eye as a pup, crouching and crawling towards other animals and dogs and he had some sheep instincts as an adult. He was, however, inbred (4.5:6.5.4) on Voss v Bern HGH, a sheepworker.

Pil'shchikov (1971) has reported on crossbreeding work with European sheepdogs (all having herding instincts) and Asian sheepdogs (lacking herding instincts and more useful as guards). He held that Asian × Asian breedings resulted in no herding instincts in the progeny but when Asian × European matings were made there were about 72% with herding instinct. In European × European matings about 94% had herding instincts.

Table 74

Defiance barking in Border Collies

			Progeny		
Mating	Sire	Dam	Barkers	Silent	Unknown
1	(A)Barks	Silent(B)	2	1*	2
2	(C)Silent	Barks(D)	1	1	2
3	(C)Silent	Silent(B)	0	6	1

* Barked under extreme provocation, otherwise silent.
Source   Burns 1969.

This work suggested that herding instinct was incompletely dominant to the lack of it and was confirmed in matings between Asian sheepdogs and Border Collies.

Burns (1969) undertook three matings among Border Collies and some of the results are shown below in Tables 74 and 75. The details are necessarily summarised and those interested should see the original paper for details of each dog. It does, however, seem that barking is inherited as something of a dominant trait.

The situation with regard to herding instinct and style of approach was less clear. Mating of two clappers produced some dogs that were upstanding and suggests that the mode of inheritance is more complex. The same was true of eye and power, results of which appear in Table 76. One dog did have eye and power and barked, suggesting that behaviour patterns were not mutually exclusive.

Although the mode of inheritance of herding styles may be complex there does seem to be a rather recessive inheritance of herding itself when crossbreeding is being undertaken. Burns and Fraser (1966) cite unpublished work on comparing the behaviour of three Border Collie pups and four Border Collie × Pointer animals by the same sire as the other three. By five months of age the Border Collies were showing eye but the crosses never did. The purebreds never galloped aimlessly in the field of sheep whereas the crosses did.

Table 75

Herding behaviour in Border Collies

			Progeny*				
Mating	Sire	Dam	SUU	SUC	WUU	FUU	Others
1	(A)FUU*	SUC(B)	1	1	1	—	2
2	(C)SUC	WUU(D)	2	—	—	1	1
3	(C)SUC	SUC(B)	3	2	—	—	2

* S = strong; U = upstanding; C = clapper; W = weak; F = fair. The three letters for progeny and parents relate to strength of herding behaviour, approach and stopping style in that order. Thus SUC means Strong herder, Upstanding style and Clapper on halting. Others refer to progeny not classified or discarded as lacking instinct.
Source   Burns 1969.

Table 76

Transmission of eye and power in Border Collies

Mating	Character	Sire	Dam	Individual progeny*					
1	Eye	(A)None	Strong(B)	None	None	None			
	Power	Great	Very Great	Great	Great	Great			
2	Eye	(C)Medium	None(D)	Strong	Strong				
	Power	Medium	Great	Strong	Medium				
3	Eye	(C)Medium	Strong(B)	Strong	Strong	Strong	Strong	Medium	
	Power	Medium	Very Great	Very Great	Very Great	Great	Medium	Medium	

* Includes only progeny fully classified.
Source Burns 1969.

Kelley (1949) did consider that many herding instincts were inherited and could be bred for by judicious linebreeding. He scored dogs on a seven-point equal interval scale for eye and found that the mean score of progeny was close to the mid-parent value.

The subject is certainly worthy of considerable study in view of the importance of Border Collies as working sheepdogs and although the various attributes have been isolated in Tables 74 to 76 for ease of presentation they need to be studied in unison with least squares techniques of statistical analysis. Some of the many resources devoted to sheep research might readily be diverted towards a study of working sheepdogs with good effect.

Guide Dogs

Although man has been using dogs as guides for the blind for many decades there is still a dearth of information on the genetic aspects involved. Humphrey and Warner (1934) deal with some aspects of behaviour important to such dogs while Pfaffenberger (1963) discusses in general terms the procedures followed at San Rafael Guide Dogs for the Blind. In the early days of that school only 9% of dogs entered were found suitable for the work. By 1958–59 all dogs bred and developed at the school were as good or better than the best dogs produced in 1946. Pfaffenberger claims that 90% became guide dogs even with much stricter requirements then in force. A book on US work has appeared (Pfaffenberger *et al* 1976).

This California school concentrated on the blood of a German Shepherd called Frank of Ledge Acres and claimed good results through inbreeding to him (see page 330). Some tests used are given in Pfaffenberger's book but no genetic data is forthcoming.

In Australia Goddard and Beilharz (1974) produced a paper on some studies undertaken at the Royal Guide Dogs centre. This unit had bred its own dogs since 1967 and began a pilot scheme in 1973 to improve the results. Most dogs were pure-bred Labradors and data on them was presented by Goddard and Beilharz in respect of rejection criteria.

Dogs came from two sources as pups—bred by the Association itself or donated. All were walked with willing households and returned for training at 12 to 18 months of age. Three weeks were then spent on each dog during which time tests were made and acceptance or rejection occurred. A summary of the information appears in Table 77, based on a later paper (Goddard and Bielharz 1982).

Table 77

Reasons for rejecting guide dogs (%)

Rejection reason during walking stage/testing/ training*	Donated pups	Pups bred by the Association
Fearfulness	43.9	26.8
Health or physical	16.8	12.5
Excitability	9.9	6.4
Hip dysplasia	6.1	8.4
Dog distraction	4.8	7.5
Lack of concentration	2.3	0.9
Aggressiveness	1.9	4.3
Over sensitive	2.3	3.2
Lack of initiative	1.5	2.1
Lack of willingness	0.8	1.5
Lacks body sensitivity	1.3	3.6
Other distractions	0.6	0.4
Other	2.7	0.9
Number of dogs	524	466

* Dogs rejected for two reasons included under both.
Source   Goddard and Beilharz 1982.

Dogs were rejected on health and hip dysplasia as well as for behavioural traits but the two groups differed only in respect of rejections for behavioural aspects and basically only in respect of fearfulness which included nervousness and other unstable temperament problems.

One problem encountered by these workers was a significant difference between trainers in their scoring techniques. This would inflate environmental variance in any genetic studies and would need to be corrected though whether by additive values as used

Table 78

Heritability estimates for various traits in guide dogs (%)

Trait	h^2	Standard error
Success	44	13
Fear	46	13
Health	25	10
Hip dysplasia	14	9
Dog distraction	9	8
Excitability	9	8

Source   Goddard and Beilharz 1982.

by Goddard and Beilharz (1974) or by multiplicative methods would need to be determined. Various scoring systems to assess nervousness, distraction, suspicion and body sensitivity were used and dogs which exceeded a specific level on these traits (not necessarily the same level on each) were rejected. It was found that good agreement existed between these criteria and the eventual acceptance or rejection of the dog. A multiple regression of the fifteen scores used gave a correlation coefficient of 0.57.

Heritability studies were undertaken in the 1982 paper using 394 Association bred dogs and pooling sire/dam variances. The heritability estimates with standard errors for pooled variances are given in Table 78 and show quite a high value for overall success at becoming a guide dog.

Specific Aspects of Behaviour

Abnormal Aggression in Bernese Mountain Dogs

That dog bites man is not particularly news but there are few reports aimed at trying to understand aggression against man. In an attack against German Shepherds Joshua (1975) rightly condemns the use of that breed by inadequate personalities seeking to feel somehow more manly but she offers no information on canine behaviour and her apparent approval of control of the breed would have been better directed at control of the people who buy it when they do not understand it.

Mahut (1958) looked at 210 'normally-reared' dogs and put them into two groups termed fearful and fearless. The first group included Collies, German Shepherds, Poodles and Dachshunds while the second group included Boxers, Bedlingtons, Boston Terriers and Scotties. He was, however, working in Canada and, had he worked in Germany, he would have found a different reaction from his German Shepherds.

Rech (1953) looked at 2000 dogs classed as biters of humans and found, obviously enough, that males were more aggressive than females with most aggression from guard or Shepherd Dog types and from gundogs more than hunting dogs. Terriers had medium aggression and Toys none at all. They seemed to all show most aggression in the longer daylight hours.

Much depends upon where studies are carried out because in different countries there is definite selection for different traits even in the same breed. Humphrey and Warner (1934) working in Switzerland found that teaching a German Shepherd to bite was the most difficult task in their police course.

However in 1976 Van der Velden *et al* reported on a peculiar behavioural habit among Bernese Mountain Dogs. Several attacks, often against children, had been noted and the breed society carried out a survey among 800 owners of which some 400 replied. Dogs were classed into one of five categories ranging from no behavioural problem through to intermittent unprovoked attacks on owners. A classification of parental type and progeny classes was undertaken and is shown in Table 79. There appeared from this classification to be some genetic basis for the problem in that the proportion of high ranked (aggressive) animals increased as the ranking of at least one parent increased.

In the original paper Van der Velden and his colleagues did not use the mathematical scores applied in Table 79 and these have been instituted to try to place the data into some kind of perspective. There are obvious flaws in the analysis and the data, not least in the fact that 58.4% of the dogs graded had one or both parents ungraded for behaviour. Nevertheless there are indications that this particular trait was under some genetic control

Table 79

Aggression in Bernese Mountain Dogs

Parents (At least one is)	Progeny	Progeny grades (%)					Mean grade
		1	2	3	4	5	
Grade 1	131	58.8	5.3	28.2	2.3	5.3	1.90
Grade 2	63	41.3	9.5	36.5	6.3	6.3	2.27
Grade 3	136	36.8	4.4	36.8	4.4	17.6	2.62
Grade 4	41	19.5	4.9	51.2	9.8	14.6	1.32
Grade 5	114	25.4	0.9	31.6	6.1	36.0	3.26
Total	485	39.2	4.5	34.4	4.9	16.9	2.56

Source   Van der Velden *et al* 1976.

and none of the diagnostic techniques used, such as EEG examinations, revealed any clues as to the reason for the abnormal behaviour. Investigations are still going on in this breed and we will have to await further information.

Whether these cases of sudden unexpected aggression are associated with hypothyroidism is unknown. Reinard (1978) has described the case of sudden aggression in a two year old Dobermann which was attributed to small thyroid glands following atrophy. The author argues that aggression cases should be examined for this problem particularly if the animal has previously exhibited mental changes such as apathy, dullness and quietness. Whether a genetic or metabolic basis the cause is unknown.

Aversion to Humans in Pointers

One group of workers stationed in Little Rock, Arkansas, have been able to develop two strains of Pointer with district behaviour patterns as regards their reaction to humans. One line (Line E) was descended from a pair of abnormally timid dogs while the other (Line A) was descended from a pair of relatively bold animals. Some inbreeding was undertaken in each line with selection being practiced but, whereas there was introduction of outside 'blood' into Line A, no such policy was used in Line E which became more inbred as a consequence. The behavioural and conditioning tests applied to the animals have been reported by Murphree and Dykman (1965) and by Dykman *et al* (1965, 1966, 1969) while genetic analyses have been discussed by Murphree (1973) and Murphree *et al* (1977).

The lines differed in their reaction to human contact. Line E stock had severe aversion to humans with much catatonic rigidity and quivering and this continued to be true after many years of breeding. In contrast, the Line A dogs had more normal reactions. Some crosses were undertaken between the lines and though earlier analyses showed such crosses to be more like Line A, this was not the case after several generations of breeding. By the tenth year AE and EA dogs resembled the E line, suggesting that heterotic effects of crossing inbred lines were not apparent or that dominant inheritance of nervousness was more likely.

Over a 10 year period 307 animals were recorded from A, E and crossbred lines although the crossbred lines were discarded in that year. Tests undertaken on all dogs in respect of their response to humans showed that differences between the lines became more and more marked as the animals increased in age from 2 to 12 months (Murphree 1973).

Table 80

Heritability of exploratory behaviour in two Pointer strains

Age (months)	Parents	Litters	Regression on	h^2
Three	17	23	Dam	0.49‡
	11	28	Sire	0.41
Six	16	23	Dam	0.27†
	13	23	Sire	0.54†
Nine	15	21	Dam	0.29†
	12	22	Sire	0.69‡
Pooled	29	42	Dam	0.33†
	14	38	Sire	0.65*

*P<0.05.
†P<0.01.
‡P<0.001.
Source Murphree 1973.

Regression analysis of offspring on parent were undertaken and showed higher values for that on the sire. Murphree (1973) felt that this was a reflection of greater selection being practised in later years among males. It was less possible to select on the female side because of the need to preserve fertility at an acceptable level. Some of the heritability findings are given in Table 80.

In considering these heritability figures it must be remembered that dam/offspring regressions can include some non-genetic aspects because of association that cannot be eliminated.

Aside from behaviour patterns it was noted that Line A had fertility problems due to inbreeding and this led to introduction of outside 'blood' but no such problem occurred with Line E. This does not indicate any genetic association between fertility and temperament but rather a differential segregation of genes connected with fertility in one of the populations relative to the other. The E Line had susceptibility to mange between the ages of three and nine months but this was not seen in the A strain.

An increased susceptibility to the mange mite coupled with a reduced heart rate and an increased incidence of atrioventricular (AV) heart block in Line E encouraged the workers to examine the biochemistry of nervousness. De Luca *et al* (1974) examined various biochemical parameters without revealing any statistically significant differences between the strains but mean values did differ enough to suggest trends in this direction. Serum creatine phosphokinase (CPK) activity was higher in the E than in the A Line but correction for age eliminated most of this effect.

Various studies on the biochemical aspects were made by Newton *et al* (1976) and in 1978 Brown *et al* looked at inbreeding effects. In this latest paper there were 294 E dogs and 309 A dogs with inbreeding levels rising as high as 57.2% for litters and 55.5% for dams (see page 320). These high levels were in E Line dogs which were used to examine the effect of inbreeding upon various biochemical and physiological parameters as well as upon morbidity scores. The morbidity score was the sum of assessments of five tests to which dogs were exposed at three, six, nine and twelve months of age. Mean scores in the E Line ranged from 9.5 at three months to 11.8 at twelve months and inbreeding was found to increase (worsen) the scores at nine and twelve months by about 0.11 per 1% rise in inbreeding of the animal. Inbreeding also increased AV blocks by about 0.12 per 1% inbreeding but the general conclusion reached was that much of the variability in human aversion was additively genetic.

Barking

Barking aspects of sheepdogs have already been discussed but there are other barking characteristics which have been subjected to some form of genetic study.

In his book Whitney (1971) postulates that trail barking in the Bloodhound acted as a dominant over mute trailing and he selected a line which trailed silently. He did, however, observe that the hound drawl was always lost when crossed with dogs exhibiting a choppy bark so that the F_1 generation had this choppy bark but he did not consider this to be a simply inherited trait.

The dominance of trail barking was observed in crosses between the vociferous Hound and silent English Pointers. However Marchlewski (1930a) noted that in crosses of German and English Pointers the silent hunting of the latter breed acted as a dominant over the yelping sound of its German cousin.

Barking activity does seem to differ in working breeds according to whether or not they are working. Thus Pfaffenberger (1963) found that some gundogs and hounds would not bark when being trained to find a missing person hidden in bomb-damaged buildings. These same dogs would, however, bark at anyone coming to the door of the house where they lived.

Scott (1964), and others of the Jackson Laboratory, made studies on barking activity of American Cockers and Basenjis together with crosses between them. Cockers gave a high-pitched yap and Basenjis a low 'woof' but, whereas the former would continue, the latter usually stopped after a few barks. It seemed that the Basenjis would bark only under a very strong stimulation. Their data suggested that barking or not under specific stimuli was due to genes which altered the threshold of response. As crosses were made between the breeds and more Cocker 'blood' introduced the threshold level was lowered so that the animals barked more readily at a reduced stimulus.

Coaching Position in the Dalmatian

The Dalmatian is sometimes called the Coach dog and derives this name from an apparent affinity for horses and an eagerness to run under a horse-drawn wagon or carriage. During the last century and in part of this one, the breed seems to have been selected by some breeders for this particular trait. An attempt to relate coaching position to genetic control was made by two Harvard workers in the 1930s (Trimble and Keeler 1939; Keeler and Trimble 1940).

The so-called ideal coaching positions were under the front axle with the dog running very close to the heels of the rear horses, the closer the better. Poor coaching position applied to dogs running under the centre of the carriage, under the rear wheels or actually behind the carriage.

A study was made of a kennel which, for some 25 years, had trained Dalmatians to run with coaches and it was observed that certain dogs had a preference for special positions. In their later paper Keeler and Trimble (1940) give pedigree data on a line descended from a dog of good type but poor coaching habits. A series of matings were analysed from dogs

Table 81

Inheritance of coaching position in Dalmatians

Type of mating in respect of coaching position	Matings	Progeny in each grade						Mean
		1	2	3	4	5	6	
Good × Good	9	7	17	1	1	1	0	1.96
Good × Bad	9	1	6	1	1	7	0	3.44
Bad × Bad	2	0	1	0	0	0	1	4.00

Source Keeler and Trimble 1940.

classified as being good or bad in coaching position and their progeny were assessed on one of six grades with 1 being the most forward (best) position and 6 the rear (poorest) position. A summary of the information appears in Table 81.

The low number of Bad × Bad offspring is unfortunate and stems from the breeder's lack of interest in pursuing a poor coaching line. Nevertheless the trend is for an improved coaching position in the progeny as the parental position improves. (Note that the authors miscalculate the average as 3.23 when it is 1.96 in the Good × Good group.) The data are indicative of polygenic inheritance and not in any way suggestive of the inheritance of acquired characteristics since the good coaching position dogs appear to have been so classified from a natural rather than a trained desire to run in those positions.

Excessive Shyness in Descendants of a Fear-biter

Excessive shyness is not peculiar to any given breed but one case reported in the literature seems to be unusual in that it appeared to follow relatively simple Mendelian lines. The particular case was first reported by Thorne (1940) following studies on the approach and withdrawal behaviour of a motley assortment of dogs studied at Cornell University. Some 178 dogs were studied and a high proportion of these showed signs of extreme fear under what appeared to be quite basic tests that ought not to have stressed any sane dog. In total about 46% of the dogs showed consistent withdrawal behaviour and of these 82 dogs there were 43 which were subsequently found to be descendants of a single Basset Hound called Paula who was extremely shy and a 'bad fear-biter' (Thorne 1944).

She was mated to four normal friendly males (Saluki, Dachshund, Bulldog and German Shepherd) and various inbreedings were done among her stock. In all 59 descendants of this bitch were traced and 43 of these were shy unfriendly dogs with only 16 friendly and good tempered. The lines of descent are shown in Figure 51 and are indicative of a dominant trait.

Whether such high percentages of shy dogs appear as frequently in lines is impossible to say and one cannot exclude the possibility that the physical shapes and forms that would have resulted from the matings might have brought with them abnormal hormonal and behaviour patterns. Nevertheless, as an exercise in how not to breed dogs with poor temperament, the data in Figure 51 might prove salutary. It would, however, be dangerous to assume that defects in temperament are inherited in a similar fashion in all cases. The rearing methods used by Thorne and his colleagues may have pre-disposed stock to poor character and thus helped to confound his data.

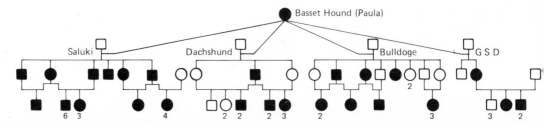

Figure 51   Transmission of extreme shyness (solid symbols) resulting from the mating of a shy Basset Hound female to normal males of four breeds. Numbers beneath symbols indicate number of animals of that sex and type (redrawn from Thorne 1944).

Miscellaneous Aspects

In recent years the journal *Applied Animal Behaviour Science* (formerly *Applied Animal Ethology*) has published many papers on canine behaviour. Not all have genetic overtones and thus need not be covered here in any detail. These include two interesting papers from Australia (Goddard and Beilharz 1984a, b) on the analysis of fearfulness, based on their guide dog work, showing some of the factors influencing fear.

Papers on aggression suggest that it was more likely in males than females (Borchelt, 1983) but that fear-elicited and predatory aggression were less influenced by sex. Similar findings were reported by Beaver (1983) who has reviewed the subject.

Sexual (Ghosh *et al* 1984) and eliminatory behaviour (Reid *et al* 1984) have been examined as has the social interaction between mother and offspring (Wilsson 1984). This latter study was based upon the GSD and has important bearing upon trainability effects.

There have been studies on such things as encounters between domestic dogs and free ranging primates (Anderson 1986) and even studies on the use of the dog to protect rangeland sheep from predators in America (Green and Woodruff 1983). This latter study covered Komondors, Pyrenean Mountain Dogs and the Akbash but was not very encouraging as regards the effectiveness of dogs in this type of occupation.

Chapter 13

Miscellaneous Conditions

Deafness

Deafness is known to occur in many breeds of dog and it does not follow that the occurrence is genetic or that it is related to white coat colour. This last belief is a fairly common one among dog breeders many of whom thought the condition was prevalent in white Bull Terriers.

Burns and Fraser (1966) cite Crew as showing that deafness in Bull Terriers stemmed from the fact that a certain stud dog had passed on a recessive allele for deafness and happened to be a white dog. That deafness is not confined to white dogs in this breed or that not all white dogs are deaf was demonstrated by Hirschfeld (1956). He test-mated Bull Terriers and obtained nine deaf and five normal dogs of which three and two respectively were coloured and the remainder white.

The association of deafness and merle coloration is well established. In the homozygous state the M allele causes Rough and Smooth Collies to be almost white and it was shown by Mitchell (1935) that such dogs are usually deaf and have eye defects.

Work from Hannover on the merle gene in Dachshunds has not only revealed eye problems (Wegner and Reetz 1975; Dausch *et al* 1977) but also impairment of sperm production (Treu *et al* 1976) and hearing problems (Reetz *et al* 1977). Imperfections were not confined to MM animals but were also observed in Mm individuals. Auditory disfunction ranging from slightly hard of hearing through to complete deafness was observed in 54.6% of MM animals and 36.8% of the heterozygote Mm types. This type of information justifies FCI moves to ban the exhibition of merle animals since it suggests that we are dealing not only with an aesthetic colour variant but biological impairment of major functions. Whether these problems seen in Dachshunds apply to all other merle-bearing breeds is not confirmed.

Various other forms of deafness have been recorded in other breeds. Dechambre (1932) discussed a Fox Terrier litter from a white, deaf dam which produced deaf females and normal males. Adams (1956) referred to deafness in a family of Foxhounds which was noted in one hound but had been known in the line over a 14-year period. Kelley, cited by Burns and Fraser (1966) referred to deafness in Border Collies which occurred at about two years of age but which was not associated with white colour. Mair (1976) refers to degenerative deafness in the Dalmatian which he considered to be inherited. This was the view of Anderson *et al* (1968) who examined 53 dogs stemming from an original mating of two related Dalmatians. Hearing tests showed five totally deaf, seven with only remnants of hearing and three with moderate impairment. Only three were females and the authors suggested a sex-linked mode of inheritance with variable penetrance and expressivity—a vague enough explanation to be almost useless as a breeding guide. They showed the source of degeneration to be in the organ of Corti.

Deafness caused by a physical deformity of the ear may be caused by genetic means or may be a legacy of developmental problems and as a consequence deafness is too vague a term to allow authoritative discussion though some forms will undoubtedly be inherited.

Achalasia of the Oesophagus

The Condition

The oesophagus or gullet is that part of the digestive tract running from the back of the pharynx and serving as the route by which food passes down to the stomach. It is made up of a thick muscular wall covered on the outside by fibrous tissue and lined by mucous membrane. Food passes down the oesophagus by a process known as peristalsis. This is a reflexive process consisting of alternate relaxation and contraction of the rings of smooth muscle in the oesophageal wall. In front of any bolus of food there is a wave of relaxation while behind the bolus of food there is a wave of constriction which pushes the bolus forward.

Achalasia exists when the peristaltic movement is uncoordinated at the terminal part of the oesophgaus resulting in retention of food and secondary dilation. Spasms of the oesophagus can occur at various portions of the tract but achalasia is usually used to refer only to malfunction at the caudal end of the tract.

The disease has been known in man since the last century and in the dog for several decades. Most workers seem to be agreed that achalasia is caused by a neuromuscular disturbance but the aetiology of this is uncertain.

The symptoms usually observed by breeders will involve vomiting of food which will be most likely to become apparent soon after the dogs are weaned on to a solid diet. The symptoms will be variable in respect of degree and clinical signs may regress in many pups so that they will become apparently normal but this is not always the case. In those dogs which do not recover spontaneously the oesophagus will become increasingly inflamed and become dilated, elongated and tortuous (Osborne *et al* 1967).

According to Sokolovsky (1972) the most obvious features of achalasia are a thickening of the muscular structure of the oesophageal wall, degeneration of the nerve supply, aperistalsis and a lack of any relaxation of the oesophagus nearest the cardia or entrance into the stomach. Gray (1974) has shown that achalasia involves aberrations of the nerve structure of other organs, not simply of the oesophagus.

A complication is that there seems to be some disagreement among veterinarians as to nomenclature, particularly in respect of the so-called cardiac sphincter, since no sphincter actually exists at the cardial end of the tract.

The Breeds Affected

It is possible that most breeds of dog can exhibit achalasia but certain breeds seem to be more predisposed to it than do others. Some of the breeds implicated are shown in Table 82 with appropriate reference sources.

There does seem to be a particular predisposition in the German Shepherd in that Clifford and Gyorkey (1967) had about half their 33 cases drawn from this breed and Lewis (1977) considered that breed to be the most commonly affected in Britain. Wire Fox

Table 82

Breeds in which achalasia of the oesophagus has been reported

Breed	Source
Boston Terrier	Schnelle 1950
Boxer	Schnelle 1950
Cocker Spaniel	Fitts 1948, Baronti 1950
Dachshund	Lacroix 1949, Kitchen *et al* 1963
Dalmatian	Schnelle 1950
German Shepherd Dog	Lacroix 1940, Brasmer 1953, Lafeber and Beckwith 1956, Stack *et al* 1957, Carlsson and Lumb 1958, Breshears, 1965, Clifford and Gyorkey 1967, Lewis 1977
Great Dane	Lacroix 1949, Kiesel 1951
Greyhound	Spy 1963
Labrador Retriever	Schnelle 1950
Newfoundland	Schwartz *et al* 1976
Poodle	Liegois and Gregoire 1948
Rhodesian Ridgeback	Hofmeyr 1955
Springer Spaniel	Schnelle 1950
Wire Fox Terrier	Strating and Clifford 1966, Clifford and Gyorkey 1967, Osborne *et al* 1967, Sokolovsky 1972

Terriers are also an above-average risk in that Osborne *et al* (1967) reported them to be affected in various states of the USA, Canada, Ireland and Britain.

Despite the breed predisposition, the genetics of achalasia are not well understood. Breshears (1965) suggested a sex-linked situation but this is unlikely as both sexes seem to be affected and are reported to be so by several workers.

Osborne *et al* (1967) examined 6 Wire Fox Terriers and then added information on a further 18 all stemming from the same lines. These authors postulate a single allele causing achalasia and suggest that there is complete phenotypic dominance, but the pedigree data are not supportive of a dominant allele and it could be that the authors meant complete penetrance rather than dominance. In most cases the affected Terriers seem to have been produced by normal parents. Osborne and his colleagues further suggest that affected dogs were some 10% more inbred than the average which is suggestive of a recessive rather than a dominant trait.

Brasmer (1953) reported 3 cases in German Shepherds all by the same sire and out of 3 litters by 2 different dams. Both dams had the same great grandsire but this ancestor was not in the pedigree of their mate.

In their Newfoundland cases Schwartz *et al* (1976) considered that the disease might be developmental although the dam of the affected dogs had signs of a similar disfunction.

It does seem that many dogs recover, especially if fed on a semi-liquid diet, but this does not imply that the condition does not have a genetic basis. There is, however, a need to collect more data if the genetic pattern is to be identified. The fact that one particular sire was an ancestor of 23 out of the 24 cases reported by Osborne *et al* (1967) may be misleading rather than confirmatory of a genetic problem. These workers suggested that

Fox Terriers affected by achalasia should not be bred from but this seems a premature viewpoint and one very likely to be difficult to implement in that dogs affected as pups and then recovering may not be identifiable to their owners if owner and breeder are not the same. In GSDIF data no cases were reported in over 260 litters (Willis 1978a) which may indicate reluctance to report or a genuine failure to observe such cases. It is not improbable that the incidence in any breed is much lower than may seem apparent to veterinarians at clinics seeing a rather specialised sample.

Cleft Palate (Hare-Lip)

Cleft palates are known to occur in a variety of mammals including both man and dog. One of the earliest reports in the dog seems to have been that of Aucante (1970) in Pointers. Since then it has been described in Bernese Sennenhunds (Heim 1914, Weber 1955, 1959), Bulldogs (Wriedt 1925), Cocker Spaniels (Pullig 1952), Shih Tzu (Cooper and Mattern 1970) and German Shepherds (Willis 1978a). It is probable that most breeds of dog have produced such defects but that few cases will be reported in the literature.

The genetics of cleft palate are only vaguely understood. Jurkiewicz (1964, 1965) and Jurkiewicz and Bryant (1968) produced experimental results from dogs but with only hazy conclusions. Koch (1935) postulated that a number of congenital conditions, among which was cleft palate, were all the result of some inherited defect of the anterior pituitary rather than to a series of linked genes. Pullig (1952) had not only cleft palate but also a cranial crevice in her Cocker Spaniel data and it is feasible that these and other defects which occurred were all part of the same basic syndrome. Huber (1950) describes a medium cleft in the intermaxillary bone among skulls seen in Strasbourg museum (breeds affected were the French Bulldog and Mastiff) and this may also be related to cleft palate. The cases in Bernese Sennenhunds described by Weber (1955, 1959) also included nasal clefts and he postulated a dominant gene which caused this problem and cleft palate.

It could well be that various structural defects of the skull are manifestations of the same genetic problem and that the mode of inheritance is not the same in brachycephalic breeds as in others. Some experimental breedings were made in Shih Tzus by Cooper and Mattern (1970) and they observed varying degrees of cleft palate as well as other defects. One such defect was a club foot and the association of hind leg deformities with cleft palate has been seen in Hereford cattle (Shupe *et al* 1967). Some of the Shih Tzu data are given in Table 83

Table 83

Occurrence of cleft palate in matings of Shih Tzu

		Progeny			
		Normal		Cleft Palate	
Parental type	*Matings*	*With leg deformity*	*Without leg deformity*	*With leg deformity*	*Without leg deformity*
Normal × Normal	18	2	26	6	20
Normal × Cleft Palate	1	0	3	0	0

Source   Cooper and Mattern 1970.

and support the idea of a recessive gene but not necessarily a simple situation. Cooper and Mattern suggest that polygenic inheritance is not ruled out and that environmental modifiers may be involved. The occurrence of defects like hernias, missing eyes and extra toes suggests that earlier opinions about a complex syndrome situation may not be far out.

Affected stock are difficult to rear and in any case are best eliminated but at this stage it would be unwise for breeders to cull producers of such defects since we do not yet know the mode of inheritance. Inbreeding on animals known to produce cleft palates might best be avoided as a safety measure. Aggressive tendencies in dogs with cleft palates were noted by Dreyer and Preston (1973) and may reflect abnormal metabolism but this is further support for the destruction of such stock.

In East Germany a large study was undertaken by Turba and Willer (1987) of 1327 litters comprising 10,609 pups. This covered the years 1977–84 and the incidence of hare-lip plus cleft palate was 0.6%. The percentage of litters affected rose from 0.93% in 1979 to 6.62% in 1984. The authors concluded that the abnormalities had a single autosomal recessive mode of inheritance.

Lethal Glossopharyngeal Defect

This particular condition was reported by Hutt and deLahunta (1971) in a breed of dog that was not divulged and in a location in America that was kept equally secret. It was first observed by the breeders of the kennel concerned because apparently normal pups showed no interest in suckling nor could they be induced to do so. They died of starvation within a few days. Because of a long pointed tongue the affected pups were termed 'bird tongues'. Examination showed a very slight oedema of the head and an inability to swallow. There was no apparent jaw defect and only the inward curling margins of the tongue, which made it seem narrower, was noted.

A total of 22 pups was affected and the data are shown in Table 84. The data are suggestive of a simple recessive autosomal trait which is effectively lethal. The frequency in the particular breed would seem to be limited because three carrier males produced 35 litters to unrelated stock and never produced the problem. The mean litter size in the 12 litters was 6.33 suggesting a medium-sized breed was involved.

Table 84

Occurrence of glossopharyngeal defect in 12 litters

		Progeny observed		Progeny expected*	
Litter size	*Litters*	*Normal*	*Affected*	*Normal*	*Affected*
2	1	1	1	0.857	1.143
5	2	7	3	6.720	3.280
6	1	4	2	4.175	1.825
7	7	36	13	34.860	14.140
9	1	6	3	6.567	2.433
Total	12	54	22	53.179	22.821

* Corrected for method of ascertainment. See page 352.
Source Hutt and deLahunta 1971.

Histiocytic Ulcerative Colitis

This disease is essentially an inflammation of the mucosa and submucosa of the colon and rectum. There is usually chronic haemorrhagic diarrhoea in young animals, usually under two years of age. The affected animal will pass small amounts of faeces of variable consistency and fresh blood and mucus will be seen. The disease is a protracted one but loss of body weight and anaemia are not uncommon. According to Hill (1978b) vomiting and loss of appetite will occur in about one third of cases which will further encourage weight loss. Abdominal palpation may reveal a prominent and painful colon and any rectal examination will result in pain.

The disease was first reported in the USA by Van Kruiningen *et al* (1965) in Boxers and there have been several reports since that time in this breed in both the USA and Holland (see review by Hill 1978b).

The aetiology of the disease is unclear but the occurrence in one breed suggests a genetic susceptibility. According to Hill (1978b) the condition may be influenced and exacerbated in certain dogs by stress or trauma and Ewing and Gomez (1973) have suggested that both genetic and environmental factors are involved. Van Kruiningen *et al* (1965) proposed a genetic involvement and most affected animals trace back to two breeding animals instrumental in the development of the Boxer breed in the USA. However, most of the cases seen by these workers came from one kennel and thus had a common environment and it is highly likely that most unaffected stock will trace back to the same two important ancestors.

An effective treatment is not available but empirical methods are suggested by Hill (1978b). It would seem to be a subject deserving of study by Boxer clubs on a world basis if any genetic pathways are to be identified.

A fairly comprehensive review of histiocytic proliferative disorders in the dog was made by Moore (1984) at the same time as he reported six cases of systemic histiocytosis in Bernese Mountain Dogs in California. The animals were aged from 2–8 years at time of examination and all were related with pedigree evidence being presented. At least one case was reported in 1987 in Liverpool and more are suspected in Britain. The genetic nature of the disease, if any, is unclear but warrants attention from the clubs concerned. The BMD cases appear to be unlike those reported in other breeds but lead to anorexia, weight loss, stertorpus respiration and conjunctivitis. A proliferation of nodules over the body was seen but especially in the area of scrotum, nasal apex, nasal planum and eyelids.

Interdigital Cysts

Whitney (1970) has reported on 96 cases of interdigital cysts in dogs occurring in 21 different breeds. He considered the risk to be highest in Border Terriers, Boxers, Staffordshire Bull Terriers, Pekingese, West Highland White Terriers and Scottish Terriers. No cysts were seen in 955 Border Collies or in smaller numbers of German Shepherd Dogs, Greyhounds, Poodles or Retrievers.

The author suggested that the affected breeds were predisposed to cysts by virtue of being more flat-footed which exposed the interdigital web to the accumulation of foreign matter and to injury. If this is true then no genetic predisposition to interdigital cysts really exists and they are a reflection of physical differences of shape and thus a selectional defect, albeit an unintentional one.

Myotonia

A myotonia is the continued contraction of muscle after the voluntary effort or stimulation has ceased. It has been recorded in Irish Terriers (Wentink *et al* 1972), Labradors (Kramer *et al* 1976) and Chow Chows (Griffiths and Duncan 1973; Jones *et al* 1977). Not all cases reported were identical in their symptoms or pathology but most myotonias give characteristic readings on an electromyograph. In the Chow case reported by Jones *et al* (1977) dogs had difficulty in rising but symptoms decreased with exercise. In contrast Kramer *et al* (1976) reported worsening signs following exercise. Generally there is muscle fibre variability suggesting that this condition may be a form of muscular dystrophy. Jones *et al* (1977) reported that elevated serum creatine phosphokinase levels were noted and that percussion on the tongue produced a marked dimple which disappeared only gradually. These workers felt that the desired stiff and stilted gait of the Chow Chow could encourage selection of myotonic animals. They felt the condition had a hereditary basis because of cited reports in Chow Chows from various countries but offer no other evidence. Wentink *et al* (1972) proposed a recessive X-linked mode of inheritance in their Irish Terrier cases but muscle pathology differed from other cases and a sex-linked theory is not in keeping with views in other species like mink (Hegreberg *et al* 1975). More work is needed to clarify this particular series of related defects.

Pancreatic Insufficiency

Normal Function

The pancreas is a gland situated close to the duodenum which has both endocrine and exocrine portions. The endocrine portion consists of small groups of cells, heavily supplied with blood and called the islets of Langerhans. These produce insulin which will pass directly into the bloodstream. The exocrine portion is the major part of the gland and its main duct (duct of Wirsung) opens into the duodenum.

Pancreatic juice is produced under the influence of two hormones produced from the mucosa of the duodenum. One of these hormones is secretin which increases the rate and flow of bicarbonate concentration of the pancreatic juice and the other hormone is pancreozymin which increases the amount of enzyme in the juice. The production of hormone will depend upon the acidity in the stomach. Stimulation of certain nerves can also cause the pancreas to secrete a juice rich in enzymes and eating can bring about such a stimulus.

Pancreatic juice is rich in sodium carbonate and bicarbonate which act to neutralise acidity in the stomach but there are also various enzymes notably trypsin and chymotrypsin which act on peptides and amylase which converts starch to a sugar. Maltase is an enzyme acting upon maltose and converting it to glucose while steapsin hydrolyses fats.

Thus pancreatic juices act to continue digestive processes begun elsewhere and are involved in the breakdown of fats and carbohydrates.

Abnormal Function

Since the pancreas is involved in insulin production and digestion any abnormal functioning of the gland can adversely affect either process. This can lead to diabetes mellitus or digestive malfunction. Problems of diabetes mellitus are dealt with later (see page 283) and here we are concerned with digestive problems.

Canine pancreatic disease is a complex entity of an, as yet, uncertain aetiology (see Hill

1978a). Anything which interferes with normal functioning can lead to the release of activated proteolytic and lipolytic enzymes into the pancreatic tissue and thus lead to pancreatic fibrosis. Many terms have been used to describe the same series of clinial and pathological changes and pancreatic degenerative atrophy is favoured by British workers.

Pancreatic problems can lead to sudden abdominal pains and vomiting but may not be fully apparent until the dog has been affected for months or even years. There will be inadequate digestion and in the advanced cases when there is extensive fibrosis there will be continued loss of condition despite heavy feeding. Flatulence is common, excreta is voluminous, clay-coloured and foul-smelling and will contain much undigested material. In chronic pancreatitis there will be an almost complete absence of pancreatic tissue.

Detailed reviews on the symptoms and chemical tests used in the identification of pancreatic insufficiency have been given by Freudiger and his colleagues in Switzerland (Freudiger 1972, 1975, 1976a, b; Buser and Freudiger 1973). This group have shown that the concentrations of chymotrypsin and trypsin in the faeces were reduced in dogs suffering from pancreatic deficiency (Freudiger and Berger 1971). Generally chymotrypsin was more reduced than trypsin and the reduction was permanent or periodic in occurrence. An increase in amylase levels could indicate pancreatic deficiency but may be caused by other factors though Buser and Freudiger (1973) did not agree with oft-quoted views that damage to the salivary glands leads to an increase in amylase levels. They felt that acute pancreatitis could only be deduced when amylase levels had risen to four times their normal level. In contrast Sateri (1975) felt that serum amylase levels were reduced in affected animals.

More recently Schaer (1979) has given clinopathological details on animals suffering from pancreatic disease. New tests for diagnosis have been suggested by Batt *et al* (1979) and by Westermarck and Sandholm (1980). Batt (personal communication) believes that pancreatic disease is often overdiagnosed and that many animals may be suffering from small intestine problems. He has reviewed the subject (Batt 1980). Anderson and Strafuss (1971) examined 32 dogs suffering from pancreatic disease and found 75% to be affected by chronic pancreatitis while the others had diabetes or pancreatic neoplasms. In this connection Anon (1967) considered pancreatic tumours to be uncommon and to be generally associated with nervous disorders including ataxia and disorientation.

Treatment is possible in many cases. Hill *et al* (1971) felt that diabetes was usually present to some degree in all case of pancreatic degenerative atrophy and that low fat and carbohydrate diets helped. Lyngset *et al* (1975) have suggested treatment with pancreatic enzymes though their effectiveness was not ensured.

Age of onset of pancreatic problems is variable. According to Lyngset *et al* (1975) over 60% of cases were in animals aged four years or more but this may relate to the age at which the problem was first obvious to the owner rather than the actual age of onset. Freudiger (1975, 1976a, b) has suggested that most cases in German Shepherd Dogs were found prior to four years of age, many between six months and two years.

Breed Incidence and Genetics
It is probable that any breed can be affected by pancreatic deficiency but the Freudiger school have mainly worked with German Shepherds and consider this breed to be particularly prone to the problem as does Hill (1978a). Lyngset *et al* (1975) working in Norway found that 60% of their cases were in this breed but the total number seen was not high and could reflect a preponderance of this breed in the country.

The genetics of the disease is unknown but familial ties have been seen. Weber and Freudiger (1977) looked at 19 cases of German Shepherds and traced them back to a dog called Erich born in 1918. All had this dog as common ancestor and 18 were inbred to him. An autosomal recessive was suggested.

This explanation seems to be far too trite. The Erich referred to is undoubtedly Erich v Grafenwerth (born 1918, died 1930) who was born in Germany and travelled to the USA. Examination of breed history (Willis 1976) suggests that this dog is found in the pedigree of every dog alive today and via numerous lines. It would be difficult clearly to identify him as a causal factor of anything at this late date. However there is some circumstantial evidence which suggests that the identification of Erich as a source may not be far from the truth. An early report on the breed, Humphrey (1928), suggested that Hettel Uckermark was difficult to condition and his most famous and influential son, Alex v Westfalenheim, was known to have died of intestinal trouble. Alex was the father of Erich and Hettel was also grandsire of Erich via his dam as well as via Alex. There is some evidence (see Willis 1976) that other lines stemming from Alex v Westfalenheim were prone to digestive upsets and it is not unreasonable to suppose that these upsets were actually pancreatic deficiency though not perhaps recognised as such at the time.

This suggests that the Swiss school may not be far wrong in identifying Erich v Grafenwerth as a source of pancreatic deficiency and that the condition may be under some genetic control. However, it is unlikely that a simple recessive situation exists. Westermarck (1980) has supported the recessive theory with an investigation based upon 59 GSDs but his data are by no means totally convincing and he does not exclude other forms of inheritance.

Diabetes Mellitus

This condition has been well known in man for many centuries. It occurs as a result of insulin deficiency which, in turn, results from pancreatic damage or deficiency. This means that diabetes mellitus is likely to be associated with the previously mentioned pancreatic insufficiency.

Affected dogs are usually found to eat excessively, drink frequently and urinate to excess. These symptoms may be the first to be observed by the owner but will be followed in due course by a rapid loss of weight, particularly in obese animals. Affected dogs thus become emaciated. An acetone odour on the breath and frequent vomiting may be noted and eventually, left untreated, the dog will die in a diabetic coma. Pathological signs are atrophy of the pancreatic gland or its apparent increase in size due to replacement of original tissue with fibrous tissue.

The disease seems to have been first described in the dog by Wilkinson (1960) and according to subsequent reviewers (Lauder 1972; Foster 1977) is increasingly being diagnosed.

In Sweden Krook *et al* (1960) recorded an incidence of 1.5% in some 11,000 autopsies, which is a figure not unlike that for a disease in man. Breed incidence is less obvious but Krook *et al* (1960) considered that the Rottweiler and Dachsbrache breeds were affected to a higher degree than might be expected from their incidence in the general canine population. Lauder (1972) was of the view that Dachshunds, Samoyeds and King Charles Spaniels were similarly prone to the problem. Foster (1977) agreed with these observations on the Dachshund and felt that Toy, Miniature and Standard Poodles were also prone to diabetes. However, as Foster points out, such opinions may reflect geographical distribution as much as genuine incidence.

According to most workers the disease is rarely seen before three years of age and is most common in obese females of eight years and over. It is more common in the female than the male and, in 40% of cases, seems associated with a history of recent oestrus.

Death seems very likely to occur in that Lauder (1972) reported some 40% of animals being dead or destroyed within a month of being examined by the veterinarian and a further 20% being disposed of within six months. Insulin treatment can keep some dogs alive for twelve months or so but very few live beyond four years from first presentation.

As Foster (1977) has pointed out the increasing incidence of diabetes may be a reflection of increasing advances of the veterinary field rather than an increase in occurrence of the disease. This is reflected by his estimate of 54% being kept alive on insulin for 12 months and almost 25% for three years, large increases over the estimates of five years previously cited by Lauder.

In view of breed predisposition it is not improbable that a genetic liability exists but there is no conclusive evidence on this score and it is unlikely that any simple picture will emerge on the genetic side.

Tumours

From the mid 1940s to the present day there has been no shortage of literature on neoplasms in the dog. As a result of these statistical studies various authors have suggested a predisposition to tumours among certain breeds. The obvious difficulty with statistical studies undertaken by examining patients at veterinary clinics, as is the case with most reports, is the fact that the sample may be atypical of the population at large. If 50% of the cases of mammary tumours were in Boxers one could not conclude that this breed was predisposed to such tumours unless the incidence of the breed in the general population was much less than 50%.

Mulligan (1944, 1948a, b, 1949a, b) undertook some of the very early studies in the USA. His work was criticised by Krook (1954) as failing to identify correctly breed incidence in the population at large. This was not the case with Krook's data drawn from Sweden, as the base population was known because breed of dog was included in licensing figures. Burns and Fraser (1966) suggests that the use of AKC registration figures would have served as a base for Mulligan's work but I would dispute this. Any kennel club figures relate to pedigree stock and in many countries large numbers of purebred, non-registered stock exist. It does not follow that the population of purebred, but unregistered, stock is identical with that of registered dogs. Breeds with a high registered popularity, such as the German Shepherd, may also have a high frequency among unregistered stock whereas more expensive breeds are almost always registered and only rarely seen without pedigree papers.

Surveys have been presented in Britain (Cotchin 1951, 1954, 1955; Else and Hannant 1979; Weaver 1983), Scandinavia (Larsson 1956), North America (Nielsen and Cole 1958; MacVean *et al* 1978), Milan (Carrara and Cremagnani 1965), Finland (Rahko 1968), Norway (Grøndalen 1975) and Germany (Bomhard and Dreiack 1977). This is by no means an exhaustive list but for those interested a fuller review can be obtained from the various papers concerned.

In a study undertaken in Sweden from 1983–85 Olsson *et al* (1986) looked at 3100 cases of tumours, some 70% of all cases diagnosed in that country during that period. They found a significantly high incidence of tumours in Boxers, Flat-coated Retrievers, Airedales, Cockers, Irish Wolfhounds, Kerry Blue Terriers, Bernese Mountain Dogs, Scotties, Giant Schnauzers, French Bulldogs, Dobermanns, Welsh Terriers, Standard Schnauzers and Springer Spaniels. In contrast a lower than average incidence was observed in GSDs, Lapland Spitz, Papillons, Harriers, Collies, Greyhounds and Swedish Drevers.

The breeder is interested in knowing whether or not his breed is predisposed to tumours and if so which ones. Hence no attempt is made to comprehensively survey the subject of canine tumours. However, before seeking to discuss particular predispositions it is necessary to briefly review the types of tumours which can occur.

Tumours can be classified as benign (basically harmless) or malignant (cancerous). The former type are usually slow growing, oval or round masses which mainly cause no harm other than that they occupy space in the body and can interfere with other organs or tissues by sheer mechanical means. Malignant tumours, on the other hand, are of many forms and usually invade and destroy normal tissue. They are spread throughout the body via the bloodstream or lymph system.

Carcinomas are tumours of epithelial origin and generally are spread via the lymph system initially and later via the bloodstream. In contrast sarcomas, derived from mesenchymal tissue (middle tissues), are spread directly via the blood. The different nomenclatures used for tumours are shown in Table 85.

Table 85

Types of tumours found in dogs

Name	Location
Skin	
Basal cell carcinoma	Small nodular growth, front half of body
Histiocytomas	Single or multiple nodules usually on legs and feet
Mastocymas	Rear half of body under skin
Melanomas	Oral cavity and around scrotum
Papillomas	Projecting nodules on head, feet and mouth
Squamous cell carcinomas	Near body orifices
Mammary Gland	
These attack female rather than male and most frequently rear glands	
Carcinomas	See text
Sarcomas	See text
Carcinosarcomas	See text
Benign tumours	See text
Other areas	
Adenocarcinomas	Digestive tract, respiratory tract, kidney and testicle
Fibromas	Connective tissue, vagina
Lipomas	Back, abdomen, chest
Hepatomas	Liver
Sertoli-cell tumours	Testicle (especially in retained testicles)
Seminomas	Testicle

Mammary gland tumours are the most common canine neoplasm accounting for between 25 and 50% of all tumours (Bostock 1976). The World Health Organisation has classified mammary tumours into 5 basic grades which are the 4 in Table 85 plus Uncategorised. Each group can be further broken down into several subdivisions based upon the likely behaviour of the particular type of tumour. Some cases have a poor chance of recovery after surgery or other treatment and this will obviously influence breeders in respect of the action they take. Discussion of this is outside the scope of this book but a simple explanation is given by Bostock (1976).

It seems generally agreed by most workers, in whatever country, that the Boxer is predisposed to tumours to a degree that few, if any, other breeds approach. In spite of the criticisms that can undoubtedly be levelled at some of the studies the high risk potential of the Boxer in beyond dispute (Mulligan 1949a, b; Krook 1954; Larsson 1956; Nielsen and Cole 1958; Cotchin 1962; Carrara and Cremagnani 1965; Rahko 1968; Bomhard and Dreiack 1977).

The risk in this breed seems to be a general one but it does seem that the Boxer is particularly prone to thyroid carcinomas, cutaneous tumours and certain tumours of the mesenchymal and nervous tissues. It seems also prone to mammary gland tumours though this was not highlighted by MacVean *et al* (1978).

The Airedale is also a breed at some degree of risk. Krook (1954) considered it to be over-represented in cases of carcinoma while Larsson (1956) felt that Airedales had a high risk for cutaneous tumours and Rahko (1968) did think the breed was constitutionally disposed to tumours.

The Boston Terrier was held to be at high risk for mastocyma by various authors (Mulligan 1949a; Cotchin 1954; Nielsen and Cole 1958; Peters 1969). There seems to be some risk of melanomas in Scottish Terriers (Mulligan 1949a; Cotchin 1954, 1955). The German data of Bomhard and Dreiack (1977) suggested a strong risk of mammary tumour in Dachshunds and Cocker Spaniels, which was also the trend in Rahko's Finnish data (1968).

Some doubt seems to exist regarding the Fox Terrier. Most of Mulligan's work suggested a risk of tumours in this breed but Krook (1954) negates this view and Burns and Fraser (1966) reviewing the data suggest that the implication is that the breed is resistant, at least in Sweden, a view which is confirmed by Rahko (1968) and Larsson (1956).

Testicular sertoli-cell tumours were reported by Weaver (1983) in a study involving 67 cases. He concluded that the Boxer, Cairn Terrier, Border Collie, Shetland Sheepdog and Pekingese had a higher risk than other breeds.

The German Shepherd Dog seems susceptible to cutaneous tumours according to Larsson (1956) but resistant to mammary tumours (Bomhard and Dreiack 1977). The more recent American data of MacVean *et al* (1978) suggested a low incidence of tumours in the German Shepherd, although they did consider their population to be rather young as far as this breed was concerned.

Priester (1967) in a survey of lymphoma showed a high risk for Boxers and an above-average risk in Pointers but a low risk incidence for German Shepherds and Cockers. MacVean *et al* (1978) also considered the Pointer to be at an above-average risk for mammary tumours along with Poodles and Boston Terriers.

Rahko (1968) considered the Finnish Harrier and Finnish Spitz to have a statistically significant resistance to tumours.

According to Grøndalen (1975) some 5% of all tumours were bone tumours and the larger breeds were predominant in terms of those affected. This was a Norwegian study but the risk of bone tumours is well established in large breeds (Cotchin 1954, 1955) and according to Comfort (1960) the risk was not only for greater incidence but an earlier age at onset.

A predisposition for splenic tumours in the German Shepherd has been suggested in Britain (Done and Staton 1978; Mundell and Glynn 1978; Rowland 1978) although it was opposed by Noble and Coulson (1978). Statistical data were provided by Appleby *et al* (1978) and these are reproduced in Table 86. The suggestion that the GSD was more prone to splenic tumour than other breeds seems to be borne out by this information, although it should be realised that in most instances dogs were aged 8–13 years.

Some investigations appear to imply a sex effect in respect of the incidence of tumours but this is not always clear. Frequently it is a reflection of the higher incidence of mammary tumours in the bitches.

Age is an important aspect to consider. Rahko (1968) pointed out that the mean age of dogs showing tumours was high (83% were over 9 years of age) and this is confirmed by the work of Else and Hannant (1979) where the modal age was 10 years. This being the case, it does suggest that tumours are less serious than if they were a common feature of young animals. In respect of mammary tumours, it was demonstrated by MacVean *et al* (1978) that there was a greater incidence among intact as compared to spayed females with the exception of the Pointer. In the British work of Else and Hannant (1979) this greater risk in intact females was less obvious because many of the spayed animals were spayed after having had litters. These authors did, however, show an increased risk of malignant tumours in bitches which had had marked pseudopregnancies.

Rahko (1968) has attempted to explore reasons as to why certain sexes and breeds might have a particular predisposition to specific tumours but the views expressed are, at best, tentative. Genetic predisposition exists but any mode of inheritance must be complex.

It may be that dogs with a predisposition for tumours will transmit this but there is no

Table 86

Incidence of splenic tumours in a canine population of tumour suspects

Breed	Dogs seen	% in population	Cases with splenic tumours	% with splenic tumours
Labrador Retriever	269	10.3	3	1.1
Miniature Poodle	219	8.4	2	0.9
Boxer	205	7.9	0	0
German Shepherd Dog	186	7.1	8	4.3
Cocker Spaniel	111	4.3	0	0
Collie	95	3.6	1	1
Corgi	73	2.8	1	1.4
Other breeds	823	31.6	7	0.8
Mongrels	623	23.9	4	0.6
Total	2604	100	26	1.0

Source Appleby *et al* 1978.

evidence to encourage breeders to take account of this in breeding programmes. In any event most dogs will have completed a full breeding life before their tumour susceptibility is apparent. There is, however, an obvious need for Boxer breeders to approach collectively the problem of data compilation on tumour occurrence and incidence.

Atopic Disease

Hypersensitivity to pollen and inhaled protein particles has been reported in dogs by Halliwell and Schwartzman (1971). From 1809 patients at a clinic 3.31% were diagnosed as having atopic disease with certain breeds seeming particularly prone. An above-average risk seemed apparent in Wire Fox Terriers, West Highland Whites, Scotties, Dalmatians and Sealyham Terriers. In contrast German Shepherds had a below average risk and Dachshunds and Cocker Spaniels seemed free of problems. However the total population of atopic dogs was only 60 and too much should not be read into this risk incidence. Any mode of inheritance is likely to be polygenic and possibly of a threshold nature but no studies seem to have been published.

Thyroiditis

Problems of inflammation of the thyroid gland have been reported by Musser and Graham (1968) in a Beagle colony. In 541 males and 441 females there were 13 and 11% thyroiditis cases respectively. Most were traced back to a female known to be herself affected and there was no apparent association with diet, age, season of year or sex. Stock from other colonies brought into the unit showed an incidence of only 4% in 336 males and 3% in 408 females. However, among purchased stock with the condition, some 42% showed familial relationship to the original affected colony stock. This was strong evidence for a genetic trait and it was supported by data from another Beagle colony.

In the second colony the unit had been a closed one since 1960 consisting essentially of two partially inbred lines. One of these (line A) had been known to have a poorer reproductive performance than the other and it was known to be susceptible to thyroiditis. Poole (1974) was able to show that the A-line Beagles had smaller testes than those dogs with little A-line 'blood'. Later Fritz *et al* (1976) highlighted orchitis (inflammation of the testicles) in this line and showed that orchitis and thyroiditis were in some way related. Both defects were connected to the level of A-line 'blood' in the ancestry of any dog. In total, 69 dogs were affected by one or both conditions, 24% of these having both problems. Both could be considered autoimmune diseases and very clearly have a genetic base although, again, the mode of inheritance is unclear. As with most genetic diseases the problem is likely to be one of polygenic inheritance probably with a threshold level at which the disease becomes apparent. The fact that this problem has been reported in Beagles does not mean that it cannot occur in other breeds.

Copper toxicosis

Hardy *et al* (1975) reported on two cases of Bedlington Terriers which died of advanced cirrhosis of the liver and had very high copper levels in that organ. In a later study of 90 Bedlingtons Twedt *et al* (1979) found that 68 had hepatic abnormalities which included abnormally high copper levels. Genetic studies were undertaken by this group (Johnson *et al* 1980b) and the various matings provided unequivocal support for an autosomal recessive trait controlling this disorder. Johnson *et al* (1980b) suggested that the prevalence of copper toxicosis was probably due to intense inbreeding directed towards reducing retinal dysplasia but they offer no data to support this view of 'intense inbreeding'. Since chemical tests cannot distinguish between normals and carriers a programme of test mating would be needed to combat this disease. Affected stock have more than 1081 μg of copper/g of liver dry matter. The condition is reported in Britain (Kelly *et al* 1984).

Hypothyroidism

Problems of low thyroxine levels have been examined by various authors. Hypothyroidism is defined as a serum concentration of less than 70 ng of triiodothyronine (T_3) per dl or less than 1.5 μg of thyroxine (T_4)/dl or both. Increased ability to measure circulating thyroid hormones in recent years has appeared to indicate an increase in hypothyroidism. In one American review and study of 108 cases Nesbitt *et al* (1980) found that Dobermanns, Great Danes, Poodles, Schnauzers, Irish Setters and Boxers accounted for half of the cases seen. This cannot be taken as evidence that these breeds are more commonly affected than others. However, a more extensive study based on 2033 samples from dogs of 15 breeds undertaken by Blake and Lapinski (1980) showed some breeds to have more hypothyroidism than others. In their sample Beagles, Labradors and sledge dogs (Samoyeds, Huskies and Malamutes) had over 30% of samples with low T_4 levels while for Dachshunds and Schnauzers less than 10% were designated as hypothyroid. Crispin and Barnett (1978) reported a form of corneal opacity in the GSD in Britain but in all cases the eye defect was secondary to primary hypothyroidism. This is an interesting observation in view of corneal opacity seen in the Siberian Husky (see p. 213).

Breed predispositions may indicate genetic differences in thyroidal activity but as yet the underlying genetic principles, if any, remain unknown.

Laryngeal paralysis

The larynx controls inspiration and expiration of air, prevents the inhalation of foreign objects, and is necessary for voice production. Paralysis of the larynx has been described in man by Plott (1964), Watters and Fitch (1973) and by Mace *et al* (1978). This latter group suggested that the condition was inherited as an autosomal dominant.

Vocal fold paralysis has been described in the dog by Venker-van Haagen *et al* (1978) following a laryngoscopy study of 105 Bouvier des Flandres. The dogs comprised 78 males and 27 females all with spontaneous laryngeal paralysis. During the six-year period involved the Dutch-based workers examined 9241 dogs of this breed, suggesting an incidence figure of just over 1%. The condition was seen in a further 25 animals of which 10 were mongrels and 15 purebreds, 11 of the latter being Leonbergers.

Age at examination among the Bouviers was from four months to seven years but 77 of the dogs were aged from four to eight months. Pedigree study was hampered by the accessibility of records and a breeding programme was undertaken and reported on by Venker-van Haagen *et al* (1981).

Mating two affected animals produced five affected offspring out of six born. Subsequent matings of affected son to its mother and affected daughter to its father resulted in a total of 14 animals, all of which were affected. Two females from these F_2 matings were bred to unaffected Greyhound sires and this produced a total of 13 dogs which were all affected. The data are consistent with the defect being caused by an autosomal dominant with complete penetrance provided that one assumes the original parents to have been heterozygotes and the unaffected animal in the F_1 generation to be a homozygous recessive.

Electromyographic recordings of the laryngeal muscles indicated that most animals could be detected by eight weeks of age but one dog did not exhibit signs until three months of age, suggesting some variability of expression.

According to this group of workers the type of paralysis seen in the Leonberger is less severe and occurs at a later age. Whether it is also a simple autosomal dominant is unproven but it seems very logical to assume this to be the case until further data are forthcoming.

O'Brien and Hendriks (1986) have reported laryngeal paralysis in Siberian Husky and Husky cross animals. Test matings suggested a genetic involvement.

Oral eosinophilic granuloma

In 1980 Madewell *et al*, working in California, reported six cases of oral eosinophilic granuloma in Siberian Huskies. The defect took the form of firm yellowish-brown lesions along the sides and undersurface of the tongue. Collagen, a fibrous protein binding cells and tissues together, had degenerated and histologically the lesions were identical to those found in cats suffering from a disease called linear granuloma. All the Huskies were young (under three years) with both sexes affected. The fact that one breed was involved and that one of the cases had had a similarly affected mother suggested genetic involvement but no theories can be reliably put forward at this stage.

Protein losing enteropathy

In 1980 Breitschwerdt and his co-workers reported four Basenjis with symptoms of weight loss, intractable diarrhoea and various neurological signs. They were found to be suffering from excessive loss of protein into the gastrointestinal tract. Any detailed discussion of symptoms is out of place here but it does appear that a similar condition was reported earlier by Flesja and Yri (1977) in the Lundehund, a Norwegian breed used to hunt Puffins. Both sets of workers concluded that there was an inherited basis to the disease, largely on the grounds of familial relationship. The suggestion was of an autosomal recessive but no confirmatory statistical methods were used.

Urinary calculi (urolithiasis)

Calculi, or more simply stones, are concentrations found in any part of the urinary system. They may develop in the bladder and in other regions and can interfere with the passage of urine. Many factors may be involved in the production of stones, including high mineral intake (in feed or water), low vitamin A levels and low water intake. In a study involving some 28 breeds of dog Pobisch (1980) reported that the incidence of calculi was above average in Dachshunds, Fox Terriers, Spaniels, Schnauzers, Spitz, Miniature Dobermanns, Scotties, Maltese Terriers and Pekes. Incidence was below average in GSD,

Boxers, Pointers and Airedales. These differences were significant but whether they would apply outside Austria where the study was done is not certain. Any genetic basis is similarly unproven.

Chapter 14

Selection Objectives and Methods

Introduction

A championship show judge in German Shepherds once went on record as saying that 'if more use was made of the stock which only just made the grade the breed would benefit immeasurably since there would not be this eternal search for new blood' (Theodos 1959a). Taken to task he declared that 'Selective breeding was abhorrent to our way of life!' (Theodos 1959b).

It is difficult to believe that so-called experts should use this kind of terminology but it illustrates the confusion that must exist in the minds of some of the dog-showing community. The minute a breeder decided to retain one animal and sell another or breed from one and not another he is practising selective breeding. The alternative is to allow every dog equal chance of mating every bitch and we will have neither purebreeds nor genetic progress.

Essentially, selection is about the changing of the frequencies of the genes within the population that one is working with. This may be one's own kennel or the breed within a specific region or country or the breed on a world-wide basis. If, for example, more yellow Labradors are used than black ones the frequency of those genes which cause yellow will increase at the expense of those causing black. If we breed from tall dogs at the expense of shorter ones the breed will get taller and so on and so forth. The extent to which frequencies are changed depends upon the intensity of the selection that is being practised and the degree to which the characters selected for are under genetic control.

In the wild animal, selection is being practised by nature, since disease and predators will kill off the weaker and less viable members of the group causing genes carried by them to decline in importance. In some populations there is a gradual increase in numbers during times of plenty and then a rapid decline as disease or starvation wipes out all but the fittest. In species like the wolf this is not the case and population explosions are avoided by a high pup mortality of anything up to 60% or more (Mech 1970) while female fertility is also dampened down.

Because the dog is no longer operating under the rules of natural selection it behoves breeders to understand in some detail the principles of what it is they are doing when they make breeding decisions for their dogs. Veterinary developments and nutritional advances mean that we can keep alive those dogs which once might have died. We need, for the sake of our breeds, to understand which dogs should be retained and why.

There are three basic ways in which gene frequencies may be altered: namely mutation, migration and selection. Man has some control over the last two but effectively none over the first-named. Before dealing with the effects of these phenomena upon gene frequencies it is necessary to examine the situation that prevails in a population where none of these forces is operating. The rules governing such a situation were propounded in 1908 by two scientists working independently in different countries. The law that they produced has borne their joint names ever since and is described below.

The Hardy-Weinberg Law

If we have a large population in which mating is purely at random and there is no mutation, migration or selection then the Hardy-Weinberg Law states that the gene frequencies will remain unchanged from generation to generation.

The Hardy-Weinberg Law applies to any gene series regardless of the number of alleles at the particular locus but it is best understood using a recessive/dominant gene situation. Let us take for this purpose the B/b series governing black/liver colour in several breeds of dog.

Since this series has only two alleles and since B is dominant to b there are three genotypes BB, Bb and bb of which the first two will be black and the last liver-coloured. In practice, genes at other loci might influence the expression of black or liver but for this illustration we will ignore that possibility.

If, in a particular breed, we knew that there were 28% BB, 50% Bb and 22% bb animals then we could calculate the proportion of B and b alleles in the breed. There would, in fact be

$$28 + \tfrac{1}{2}(50) = 53\% \text{ B alleles and}$$
$$22 + \tfrac{1}{2}(50) = 47\% \text{ b alleles.}$$

The percentage of B and b alleles must add up to 100% because no other alleles exist and we can express the data as proportions 0.53 and 0.47 rather than as percentages because this helps with subsequent calculations.

The reader who is conversant with genetic principles may, at this stage, question anyone's ability to know how many BB and Bb dogs there are because both genotypes will appear identical to the eye. This is true but the Hardy-Weinberg Law explains that if we designate the frequency of B and b as being p and q respectively then we can, in the terms of Hardy-Weinberg equilibrium, predict the proportions of animals in each of the different genotypes.

According to Hardy-Weinberg there will be p^2, $2pq$ and q^2 animals for the three genotypes BB, Bb and bb respectively. To the non-mathematical this may seem both complex and irrelevant but, in fact, knowledge of this law means that given an idea of the incidence of a recessive condition in a breed we can calculate the incidence of 'carrier' and 'non-carrier' stock in that breed.

To illustrate this let us take the example of long-coated dogs in the German Shepherd. This is a simple recessive condition caused by nn with Nn and NN being normal-coated (see page 114 for explanation).

Data from the German Shepherd Dog Improvement Foundation (Willis 1978a) suggests that the incidence of long-coated pups in the breed in 1975–76 was about 11%. If this figure was typical of the breed then we can assume that there were 11% nn dogs and 89% NN and Nn. We know from the Hardy-Weinberg Law that nn = q^2 so that if q^2 is 0.11 then q is the square root of 0.11 or 0.33. Since p + q = 1.0 we know that p must be equal to 1.0 − 0.33 or 0.67.

Using values of q = 0.33 and p = 0.67 we can then assess the number of NN and Nn dogs in the breed. The NN dogs will be equivalent to p^2 which is $0.67 \times 0.67 = 0.45$ while the number of Nn dogs will be 2pq or $2 \times 0.67 \times 0.33 = 0.44$.

We can therefore state that in German Shepherds in Britain in 1975–6 there were 11% long-coated dogs (nn) and 89% normal coated dogs of which 45% were NN and 44% were Nn. The incidence of 'carrier' dogs is high so that even if breeders deliberately avoided the use of actual long coats the number of defective coats in that breed would remain fairly high because the proportion of Nn animals is high. It means that any breeder taking his normal-coated bitch to a normal-coated dog (and having no other data available of the genotype of either in respect of coat) will have about a 50% chance that his bitch is Nn and a 50% chance that the stud dog is also Nn. The chance that both will be Nn will be 25% so the chance of producing long coats in the litter will be 6.25%.

The mathematical proof of the Hardy-Weinberg Law need not concern us here but accepting that it is a valid law we can evaluate the relative chances of 'carrier' animals for different proportions of homozygous recessives in the population. This is shown in Table 87 for frequencies of homozygous recessives up to 25%. The data will apply to any trait and it is unlikely that homozygous recessives will be as high as 25% if the character they control is undesirable. In things like coat colour, homozygous recessives may have a higher incidence where they produce a desired colour.

Table 87

Percentages of dogs in each genotype frequency assuming that only two alleles exist and the Hardy-Weinberg Law is operating*

Observed incidence of homozygous recessives (aa)† %	Percentage of dogs that are		Frequency of	
	Heterozygotes (Aa)	Homozygous dominants (AA)	A allele	a allele
1	18	81	0.90	0.10
2	24	74	0.86	0.14
3	28	69	0.83	0.17
4	32	64	0.80	0.20
5	34	61	0.78	0.22
6	36	58	0.76	0.24
7	38	55	0.74	0.26
8	40	52	0.72	0.28
9	42	49	0.70	0.30
10	44	46	0.68	0.32
15	48	37	0.61	0.39
20	50	30	0.55	0.45
25	50	25	0.50	0.50

* Percentages are given to the nearest whole number and frequency values to two decimal places.
† Any gene series can be substituted for the A or a one shown here.

Although the data in Table 87 are shown applying to a dominant/recessive situation they apply equally well to a situation where there is no dominance but in that event the heterozygotes can be identified from phenotypic appearance.

Although there appear to be 50% heterozygotes at an incidence of 20% homozygous recessives this is because of rounding-up numbers. The exact figure is 49.4% and the maximum proportion of heterozygotes is obtained when p and q (A and a in this example) appear in equal numbers in the population. If we were to continue the Table on to higher incidences of aa animals the incidence of Aa and AA dogs would both decline. At the extremes of gene frequency, that is, when there are only A or a alleles in the breed, then all animals will be homozygous AA or aa and hence the appropriate allele A or a will have a frequency of 1.0.

If a particular allele has a frequency of 1.0 in a breed then all dogs of that breed will carry the allele in duplicate and no change will occur unless the alternative allele is introduced. Many colour genes have become 'fixed' in certain breeds. For example the M allele causing merling (see page 69) is absent from most breeds which are thus all mm.

A Hardy-Weinberg situation in the true sense rarely exists unless the alternative alleles are equally acceptable. If, for example, we examined the various blood groups in dogs we would probably find that gene frequencies were static from generation to generation in true Hardy-Weinberg equilibrium. This is because no breeder does any selection for blood groups nor does he select indirectly since there is no evidence that specific blood groups are associated with any particularly desirable or undesirable traits.

Some coat colour genes may be in equilibrium in certain breeds if coat colour is not important and if the alternative colours appear equally acceptable in aesthetic terms. This is clearly not the case with the long-coated German Shepherd illustrated previously. Since long-coated dogs are undesirable fewer long coats are bred from and hence the incidence of long-coated animals should be declining slowly. For this reason the year of assessment 1975–6 was specified. In other years different figures might result according to how well breeders were selecting against the trait.

Mutation

One way in which Hardy-Weinberg equilibrium can be disturbed is by mutation. This is the change of germ plasm in the dog so that it transmits a gene that it did not inherit. Thus a B allele may be changed to b in some of the germ cells and as a consequence a BB animal may, when mated to a Bb or bb animal produce bb progeny which would be impossible in a normal situation.

Many breeders tend to blame mutations for sudden unexpected appearances of specific features that they did not believe existed in their stock. Sometimes a mutation is the true answer but more often than not the breeder was unaware of hidden recessives in his dogs. Natural mutation rates are from 10^{-4} (one in ten thousand) to 10^{-8} (one in a hundred million) and thus rare enough to be safely ignored in most cases.

Generally speaking, mutation rates are low enough to have minimal effect upon Hardy-Weinberg equilibrium except when we are dealing with recurrent mutation where a certain mutational event occurs with a characteristic frequency in each generation and where, in a big enough population, the new mutant is not lost.

Mutations can be caused by man-made agents like radiation and certain chemicals but the direction and effect of such mutations is unpredictable and usually disadvantageous.

Migration

Migration is the introduction of genes from a different population into the population which one is studying. This can mean the influx of dogs from one kennel into another, from one country to another or even from one breed to another.

Migration from one kennel to another may have a big effect on the gene frequencies in the importing kennel but since such transportation is occurring in all directions it is unlikely to have much effect on the breed. Similarly importations from one country to another will not have a major effect unless the gene frequencies in the two breed populations are very different. Importation of 'blood' from other breeds can, of course, be very important but is rarely used except in the development of a breed.

Without going into the mathematics involved it can be concluded that the effect of migration upon gene frequency depends upon two factors. These are the rate of migration and the extent to which the immigrants differ in gene frequency from the native population. The more the immigrants differ genetically and the more of them there are introduced the bigger the effect upon the gene frequencies in the breed.

In the days of Class II registrations when dogs could be entered on the basis of physical appearance it was feasible for extraneous 'blood' to enter the breed but such dogs were rarely influential in any breed in modern times. In those breeds which regularly import from abroad (for example, German Shepherds moving from Germany to the USA and Britain or Boxers from the USA to Britain) there is likely to be a big effect on the gene frequencies of some traits, though not on all. Only where breeds have been isolated from outside influence for a long period of time (when German Shepherd breeders in Australia were prohibited from making any importations from 1928–72) is there likely to be a marked difference in gene frequency for many characters.

Selection

The most important way in which a breeder can influence the genetic make-up of his breed is by selection. The effect which any selection will have depends upon the degree of emphasis in favour of or against some specific trait and the mode of inheritance of that trait.

Dealing with simple traits controlled by one pair of alleles selectivity can vary according to whether we have complete dominance, no dominance or overdominance.

In a complete dominance situation where we are selecting for the dominant trait and against the homozygous recessive then both AA and Aa dogs will be used in preference to aa stock. The coefficient of selection (s) is the strength of that selection. Thus if the AA and Aa dogs are favoured to the extent that for every 100 pups they produce, the aa dogs only produce 80, we are using an s value of 0.2 (20% reduction).

In a no dominance situation we can identify all three genotypes and thus for every 100 pups of type AA dogs, we may have fewer from Aa dogs and fewer still from aa animals.

In an overdominance situation the heterozygote is preferred to either homozygote. This may be true in Kerry Blue Terriers where it is thought, albeit with no definite proof, that the Gg genotype for coat is preferable to the GG and much preferable to the gg which does not turn blue but stays black. In that event greater selection may be made against GG dogs than Gg animals.

The mathematical equations involved become somewhat complex and can be seen in the excellent book by Falconer (1960) but one of them is given here because it has considerable bearing on the selection against undesirable recessives.

If we are dealing with a recessive trait (for the purposes of discussion we can call it aa) and there is complete dominance (AA and Aa appear identical) then we will be selecting against the recessive to some degree. The contribution of each genotype to the next generation will be 1 in the case of AA and Aa and $1 - s$ in the case of aa dogs. If the recessive is lethal then $s = 1$ and no aa dogs will be bred from.

The effect of selection against aa in such a case is that in the next generation the frequency of the a allele will decline by the amount of:

$$\frac{sq^2(1 - q)}{1 - sq^2}$$

This may seem incomprehensible so we will illustrate this with an example involving a gene like the long coat factor in German Shepherds which we will assume occurs in 11% of dogs and which we will select against to the extent, let us say of 30% (that is, $s = 0.3$). If there are 11% long coats this represents q^2 and q is therefore 0.33. If we substitute 0.33 for q and 0.3 for s in the above formula we obtain the following

$$\frac{0.3 \times 0.11 \, (1 - 0.33)}{1 - 0.3 \times 0.11} = -0.0228$$

In other words under these circumstances the long coats in the breed would decline because the frequency of the long coat allele would go from 0.33 to 0.307 (0.33–0.0228) and there would be only about 9.4% long-coated dogs in the next generation (0.307^2).

This is not a very marked reduction and if selection goes on the reduction will become less because as we have seen from Table 87 the more a homozygous recessive is reduced, the more it is being spread by the heterozygotes in the population, which are not easily differentiated from the homozygous dominants except by breeding.

When we are trying to reduce homozygous recessives, the extent to which we can succeed depends not solely on the selection practised against the allele but also the frequency of the allele. The rarer the allele, the more difficult it is to get rid of it.

The number of generations required to reduce the frequency of a particular recessive can be calculated from Falconer's (1960) formula as

$$t = \frac{1}{q_t} - \frac{1}{q_o}$$

where t is the number of generations and q_o and q_t represent the frequencies of the starting and final generation respectively. It also assumes that the recessive is so damaging that it is either lethal or no affected (aa type) animals are bred from (that is, $s = 1$).

Suppose a recessive condition appears in about 1 in every 300 pups ($q^2 = 0.0033$ and $q = 0.0577$) and we want to reduce this to half the frequency, that is, to 1 pup in every 600 by culling all the affected animals, how long will it take us?

A frequency of 1 pup in 600 is a q^2 of 0.00167 and a q of 0.0408. We are thus moving from a q value of 0.0577 to one of 0.0408 and if we substitute in the above formula we have:

$$t = \frac{1}{0.0408} - \frac{1}{0.0577} = 24.509 - 17.33 = 7.179 \text{ generations.}$$

In dogs, a generation is about 4 years which means that it would take a breed 4 × 7.179 or 28.7 years to achieve this relatively small reduction. Most breeders would not be around that long and even after that period of time affected pups would still occur.

If the reader experiments with other figures in the formula he will come to the conclusion that the elimination of recessives is more or less impossible. The task may be accelerated in some degree by test-mating and culling 'carriers' as well as affected dogs but this would increase the generation time and cost involved and, as the allele became rare, fewer 'carriers' would be identified.

This may have been a rather mathematical concept and will bring criticism no doubt from those cynics who believe that dog breeding is an art. Usually such cynics are those who talk about eliminating defects. We can never totally eliminate defects. All we can hope to do is reduce them to such levels of incidence that they are rare enough to cause minimal economic loss within the breed.

The rarer an allele becomes the more difficult it is to reduce it still further, so that the breeder's very success in the early stages makes his task harder and slower in later years. If, for example, we have something as rare as 1 pup in 20,000 it would take us about 59 generations or 236 years to achieve a reduction to 1 pup in 40,000 even if we killed every affected pup. Many recessives in dogs may be more frequent but at least this gives some idea of the enormity of the task. If an allele is so rare that only 1 pup in 20,000 shows it, then a kennel could carry the allele for generation after generation and not be aware of it, although some intense inbreeding might bring it to the surface.

The fact that some particular recessive defect has not been produced in a kennel does not mean that the kennel is actually free of the allele causing the defect. It may be that the breeder happens not to have mated 'carrier' animals together or, when he has done so, the 1 in 4 ratio of affected to normals has not ensued. In many cases, however, particularly in respect of defects not obvious in early life, the breeder may be wrong in thinking that he has never produced it. What he really means is that he has not produced it in dogs he has been able to follow up; the results in dogs he has not seen after selling them are merely conjecture.

Selection for Polygenic Traits

The previous section dealt with the situation of simple characters but as we have seen throughout this book most of the major traits in dogs are not under simple control. We are not concerned with selecting for or against a certain gene because we do not know how many genes there are, or to what degree the character in which we are interested is under environmental, as well as genetic influence.

When a breeder decides to keep certain animals for breeding and to sell or discard the others, what he is hoping to do is divide his available population into two groups of differing gene frequencies. The group he retains for breeding will, he hopes, have a better genetic make-up for those traits in which he is interested than will the group he discards. The extent to which he will succeed in his breeding operation will depend upon his success in making that original selection, in other words—the degree to which he is skilled in breed knowledge and can recognise a good dog when it is staring him in the face. It will also depend upon the extent to which the trait or traits he is selecting for are under genetic control, or more particularly, additive genetic control.

If we are dealing with a polygenic trait following a normal curve pattern then the effect of selection upon the population is shown in Figure 52. The shaded area in the upper figure is the group of dogs selected to be the parents of the next generation and the difference between the mean of this group and the mean of the whole population is termed the selection differential (S). The more superior the parents selected are, relative to the whole population, the greater will be S and the greater S is the smaller will be the group selected since there are fewer individuals the more one moves away from the mean.

The lower curve in Figure 52 shows the population produced from the selected parents in the upper curve and the difference that exists between the original population mean and the population mean of the offspring generation is termed the response to selection (R).

In the particular figure there has been a substantial response but the response is not as high as the original S value. This is due to the fact that not all the superiority of the selected parents was transmitted because it was not all due to additive genetic factors.

The parents we selected were superior not only because of superior genotypes but also because they may have had superior environments as well and the heritability of the character being selected for was not 1 but less than 1.

Response (R) will, in fact, depend upon two main features, namely the heritability of the character (h^2) and the selection differential (S) thus:

$$R = S \times h^2$$

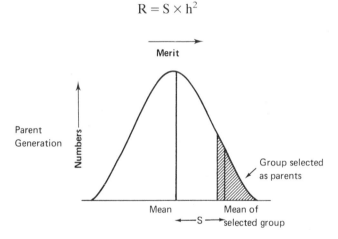

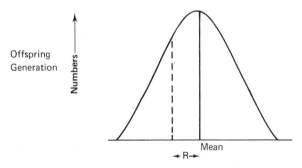

Figure 52   **Illustration of selection differentials (S) and response to selection (R).**

Similarly, if we know the superiority of the parents from the population mean and also know the response obtained, we can assess the heritability as being:

$$h^2 = \frac{R}{S}$$

This is termed the realised heritability and may often be obtained more readily than by normal methods.

It can be seen from the above formulae that the response to selection can be increased if either S or h^2 or both are increased. We can do very little about h^2 other than by being very accurate in our calculations, but we can do something to improve S if we are more selective about what we will or will not breed from. It must be clear by this stage that the original advice criticised at the beginning of this chapter is doomed to failure. If we use as parents more and more dogs which fail to reach the really top flight then we are simply making S smaller and smaller and must have a reduced response as a consequence.

There are, of course, limits as to how selective one can be. It would be illogical, for example, to use only one sire in the population, no matter how outstanding that animal may appear to be, because of potential inbreeding problems. Moreover there are actual physical limits on selection imposed by the number of progeny that can be produced by any animal and hence on the selection that can be undertaken in each sex.

For example, suppose that we had 100 bitches which averaged 3 litters each and produced a total of 24 pups of which half were females. Then we have a total of 1200 bitches born and we will need to keep 100 of these simply to replace their mothers. Our selection intensity cannot be more than 1 in 12 (100/1200) unless we are in a period of breed decline and need fewer bitches to replace the original 100. If we are in a period of breed expansion we must be less selective because we need to retain more females. This philosophy is true even if our bitches do not all produce equal numbers of progeny or 50:50 sex ratios. The main principle is that there is a limit to the number of progeny females will produce on average and hence a limit to selection.

With males, assume that we had 10 dogs each producing 30 litters and a total of 240 pups, half of which are males. In the male case we need to retain 10 males out of the 1200 pups and thus can select up to a rate of 1 in 120 (10/1200) which is ten times as intensely as in females.

This is not to imply that males can be selected 10 times more intensely than females since the above figures are hypothetical. But the fact that we need fewer males than females suggests that we can be more selective in the male sex than in bitches.

Because polygenic traits seem to follow normal curves and because normal curves have certain predetermined limits it is possible to be definitive about the overall merit of the given proportions tha are being selected for breeding. We measure dogs in units such as cm or kg or grades like Excellent, Very Good and so on, and it is obviously difficult to compare selection in wither height made in cm with the intensity of selection made in weight measured in kg. We can, however, relate everything to standard deviations (see page 22) and the amount by which a given proportion of the population exceeds the breed mean in terms of standard deviations is shown in Table 88.

The data in Table 88 are relevant to any normal population in any breed and for any character although obviously the actual standard deviations will vary according to the character and breed being examined.

Suppose, for example, we examine the wither heights of male German Shepherd Dogs in Germany in 1973. We know from an extensive study by Willis (1976) that the mean height was 63.5 cm and the standard deviation was 1.04 cm. Now suppose we were to take the top 10% of dogs in terms of height: looking in Table 86 we see that the top 10% exceed breed average by 1.75 standard deviations. Thus, the top 10% of German Shepherd Dogs for wither height would average 63.5 + 1.75 × 1.04 = 65.32 cm. They would thus be 1.82 cm above the average.

In females, the mean wither height of the breed in the same period was 58.1 cm with a standard deviation of 1.06 cm (Willis 1976) and, if we took the top 50% of bitches for

Table 88

Amounts (in standard deviations) by which certain proportions of the population exceed the breed mean

Proportion of population that is selected	*Superiority of selected group in Standard Deviations**
95	0.11
90	0.20
85	0.27
80	0.35
75	0.42
70	0.50
65	0.57
60	0.64
55	0.72
50	0.80
45	0.88
40	0.97
35	1.06
30	1.16
25	1.27
20	1.40
15	1.55
10	1.75
5	2.06
4	2.15
3	2.27
2	2.42
1	2.67

*This is termed the standardised selection differential or intensity of selection. Although superiority is stated this assumes the 'top' animals in each proportion are kept. If the bottom animals were being kept then the values given would be the amount by which the retained group would be lower than the mean as opposed to being above it. The figures assume large populations. If small populations are involved the values of S will be smaller.

height, they would average $58.1 + 0.80 \times 1.06 = 58.95$ or 0.85 cm above the breed mean for the sex.

If we bred only from the top 10% of males and the top 50% of females for wither height and the heritability of the character was, for example, 40%, then the next generation would have a wither height in dogs of:

$$\frac{1.82 + 0.85}{2} \times 0.40 + 63.5 = 64.03 \text{ cm}$$

while the height of bitches would be:

$$\frac{1.82 + 0.85}{2} \times 0.40 + 58.1 = 58.63 \text{ cm}.$$

In other words, wither height would have increased by about 0.53 cm in each sex in one generation. Clearly one is not suggesting that one should select for wither height in that breed or that one could be as intense as that suggested, but it indicates the use of the data. It also indicates that even fairly intense selection does not yield very rapid progress.

If we had examined a character like litter size in, for instance, the Cocker Spaniel which (from Table 5 page 38) has a mean litter size of 5.64, with a standard deviation of 1.89, we could see the effect of selecting for litter size by breeding only from those dogs and bitches which came from the large litters. Suppose we selected only those bitches from the biggest 50% of litters and those dogs from the top 15% of litters in respect of size. Then, from Table 87, the bitches would exceed breed average by 0.80 standard deviations and the dogs would exceed breed average by 1.55 standard deviations. This would mean that we were taking bitches from litters of size $5.64 + 0.80 \times 1.89 = 7.15$ pups, and dogs from litters averaging $5.64 + 1.55 \times 1.89 = 8.57$ pups. Bitches would thus exceed breed average by 1.51 pups and dogs would exceed the average by 2.93 pups, or a mean difference of 2.22 pups. However, if the heritability of litter size was a mere 10% (0.10), then the next generation would average $5.64 + 2.22 \times 0.10 = 5.86$ pups, an increase of a mere 0.22 pups. If litter increase brought with it more deaths, the net result might be virtually no improvement despite a very intense selection programme.

This illustrates that selection of polygenic traits depends not only on how intensely one selects but also the heritability of the trait under selection. If either intensity or heritability is low, then progress is minimal.

Generation Interval. Selection per Unit of Time

In the previous section the selection of polygenic characters was dealt with on a generation basis. The problem in dealing with selection in this way is that generations are not constant: what the breeder really wants to know is how much progress can be made in a given time. This means that the original formula of $R = S \times h^2$ needs to be altered from a generation basis to a unit time basis which, for want of a better unit, we will call a year.

The formula for genetic progress per unit of time (ΔG) becomes

$$\Delta G = \frac{S \times h^2}{\Sigma L}$$

where ΣL is the generation interval in years. Few calculations of generation interval in dogs have been made. Willis (1976) estimated it to be 48.6 months in German Shepherd Dogs and this is probably a good estimate for medium- to large-sized breeds.

Dogs, can, of course, be bred long before 4 years of age but generation interval is the average age of animals when their progeny are born, not the minimal age at which they can be born.

Looking at the above formula we can maximise progress by having S and h^2 at a maximum and ΣL at a minimum. The older the average age of breeding stock, the higher will be the generation interval but this does not necessarily mean that any reduction in progress is certain. The older the breeding stock, the more the information that we have about them and hence we may be able to have higher S or even h^2 values to counteract the increase in ΣL.

Generally speaking, little is gained by using older stock if the character is of medium to high heritability and thus can be assessed more easily in the phenotypic performance of the individual. In contrast, characters of low heritability or those which cannot, for example, be measured in one sex may benefit from progeny data and thus increase the generation interval.

Clearly, one cannot be dogmatic about what to do in any given situation but breeders should remember that aged stud dogs represent the genetic material of some years previously and should be culled from one's breeding programme—unless they are still superior to the younger studs available.

Litter size can have a big effect on selection procedures as can the number of litters obtained from each bitch. The larger her litters the more selective one can be but, at the same time, one may make most progress per unit time by selecting early rather than by waiting for a bitch to have several litters before selecting stock from her. This is illustrated in Table 89 for three litter sizes. It is assumed that bitches have their first litters at 24 months and every 12 months thereafter. It is also assumed that equal numbers of each sex are born and that the population involved is a large one. The optimal number of litters for maximising genetic progress depends upon the litter size.

In each case in Table 89 the progress per year (i/t) must be multiplied by the heritability but if we assume this to be constant for any given trait, then it will be the same for all litter sizes and numbers.

Table 89

Effect of litter size upon selection intensity and genetic progress per unit of time

Litters reared	t time (years)	Litter size = 8			Litter size = 6			Litter size = 4		
		p*	i†	i/t‡	p	i	i/t	p	i	i/t
1	2	0.250	1.27	0.635	0.333	1.10	0.550	0.500	0.80	0.400
2	3	0.125	1.65	0.550	0.167	1.50	0.500	0.250	1.27	0.423
3	4	0.083	1.85	0.463	0.111	1.71	0.428	0.167	1.50	0.375
4	5	0.063	1.98	0.396	0.083	1.85	0.370	0.125	1.65	0.330

*p = proportion selected (assuming one dog and one bitch are kept from the total number born).
†i = intensity of selection taken from Table 87 for the appropriate proportion selected. Shown in standard deviations.
‡i/t = relative speed of progress assuming that we calculate on a yearly basis. Shown in standard deviations per year.

If we have a litter size of 8 pups then on one litter we would be taking the best 2 out of 8 (25%). If we wait for a second litter we can be more selective in that we can now take 2 out of 16. But, because of the length of time that we have to wait, the relative progress is lessened. The same is true of litter sizes of 6 but, in the case of litter sizes of 4, we will make more progress waiting for 2 litters and taking 2 pups out of 8 than we would do if we took 2 from the first litter. This is true even though we had to wait longer. Had we considered litters of size 2 we would have found greatest progress coming by waiting for 3 litters and taking 2 out of 6 even though we would have to wait 4 years for the pups to be born.

This calculation assumes selection at birth. In fact selection would take place later and thus slightly reduce the progress per year in each case, but proportionately so.

Selection for Multiple Objectives

Thus far selection has been discussed in the context of a breed or population rather than a single kennel and we have assumed selection for a single trait. In practice, breeders rarely select for only one thing but wish to improve several characters at the same time. We thus have to consider the various ways in which we can best select for several traits.

Before doing this it is necessary to emphasise that selection needs to be very carefully decided upon. It is no use deciding to select for so many characters that few, if any, dogs measure up to the required standard. The more characters one wants to select for, the more difficult one's task will become. It is rather like seeking a wife; if you are prepared to settle for a high IQ it isn't that hard to find a suitable girl. If you also want her to be beautiful then some of those with the appropriate IQ fail on looks. If you also want a cordon bleu cook then it becomes more difficult still. If you insist on wanting too many traits you end up a bachelor. The same is no less true of dogs. Keep your demands simple and limit them to the most important aspects and preferably those that are of reasonably high heritability or which are likely to be of that kind.

There are basically four ways of selecting for multiple objectives but one of these is not really applicable to pedigree breeding.

Specialised Lines

A policy very common in most farm livestock species and essentially involves selecting a male line for certain characters, usually those asociated with growth, and a female line selected for fertility traits. The two are then crossed. Clearly, in a pedigree dog breed, this is not likely to be feasible.

Tandem Selection

In this the breeder selects his stock for character A and when he has made an appreciable level of progress he seeks to improve character B and then C and D and so forth. The problem arises when the various traits are negatively correlated. Then, as progress is being made in A, the trait B declines. When selection proceeds on B the progress made in A is gradually lost. If characters are positively related, progress in A brings with it some measure of correlated response in B, but the more traits that are sought the more difficult it is to have them all unrelated or positively related and, as a consequence, Tandem Selection has limited application.

Independent Culling Levels

Many breeders actually use this technique though few might recognise its name. Essentially it consists of setting a minimum standard for each trait in which selection is to be practised. The breeder then selects for breeding those dogs which are above the minimum standard in all the characters sought. This is illustrated in Table 90 using hypothetical examples in Labradors.

The danger with such a system is that unless traits are carefully devised so that major traits are given high standards of excellence, while minor factors are given very loose standards, there is a danger of culling outstanding specimens for failing in some trivial issue. Oppenheimer (1968) has stressed that one needs to breed from those dogs which are outstanding even if they may have some particular obvious failing. He argues that dogs which have very little wrong with them, but also very little outstanding either, are not the ones to choose. In this there is a good deal of common sense which breeders would do well

Table 90

Selection for multiple objectives—use of Labrador Retriever males to illustrate Independent Culling Levels

Trait	Minimum level of acceptability	Dog number							
		1	2	3	4	5	6	7	8
1 Temperament	Correct (OK)	OK	OK	OK	nervy	OK	Fierce	OK	OK
2 General type	Grade of VG	VG	VG	EX	EX	G	VG	EX	G
3 Head and skull	Grade of VG	VG	G	EX	EX	VG	VG	G	VG
4 Bite	Scissors (OK)	OK	OK	OK	OK	OK	OK	Even	Even
5 Teeth	Not more than 2 PM missing	Full set	Full set	2 PM missing	Full set	1 PM missing	Full set	Full set	3 PM missing
6 Colour	Any standard colour	Blk	Blk	Yllw	Blk	Yllw	Blk	Blk	Yllw
7 Eye colour	Brown or hazel (OK)	OK	OK	Light	OK	OK	Light	OK	OK
8 Height	56–57 cm	61 cm	56 cm	57 cm	61 cm	58 cm	56 cm	56 cm	64 cm
9 Coat	Dense or hard (OK)	OK	OK	OK	Soft	OK	Soft	OK	OK
10 Movement	True (OK)	OK	OK	OK	OK	Cow hocked	OK	OK	Close behind
11 Hip status (score)	Not more than 14 total	5/5	0/0	1/1	?	6/7	4/4	15/17	22/22
12 PRA	Interim cert (IC) or permanent cert (PC)	IC	IC	PC	PC	IC	?	?	IC
Final Decision	Reject on	8	3	7	1/8/9 11	2/8/ 10	1/7/9/ 12	3/4/ 11/12	2/4/5/ 8/10/ 11

Note   G, VG and Ex indicate grades of Good, Very Good and Excellent. It is assumed that in all other traits not listed the dogs are equally acceptable.

to follow. Progress comes by using those animals which are far in excess of breed average, even if on some trait they have obvious defects.

Clearly, some things are so crucial that failings in them must invalidate a dog. Temperament must have a high priority as little is gained by breeding from nervous or savage animals. Equally, breed type and general body proportions must rank high. In breeds which have a demand for specific head structures these must rank high also but colour ought to rank low and minor issues, such as eye colour or the odd missing teeth, must not be allowed to assume excessive weighting or you will end up rejecting a superb dog simply because it has a missing premolar and instead use a good average animal with a full set of teeth and no outstanding failings—but no outstanding virtues either.

In the hypothetical example given in Table 90 it is seen that all eight dogs end up being rejected on some score or other. This is very typical of what happens the first time anyone uses such a system and it usually means the would-be breeder has to go back and reassess his standards. It is fairly obvious that dogs 4 to 8 must be rejected because they all fail in some major aspect of type, construction or character as well as in more minor issues. Of the first three dogs the two best are numbers 1 and 3 with number 1 failing in oversize and number 3 in having too light an eye. Overall, dog number 3 is the most outstanding animal being excellent in construction, size and hips. He can be faulted only on the aesthetic issue of light eyes and most breeders with any common sense would use him and thus lower the standard in eyes. Some purists might object to this but they would then end up selecting a poorer specimen. The table illustrates the dangers of being too strict on relatively minor issues with minimal or no effect on the dog's ability to do his job.

Many breeders actually use this method though few actually bother to write things down. They would be well advised to write down the views they have, as set out in Table 90, because in doing so they will see more clearly where they are going and why. They will very definitely see when they are rejecting an otherwise excellent animal for a relatively minor fault.

Selection Index Method
In this all the various points in which one is interested are brought together into an index or single figure and the dog is selected on the basis of that. To use selection indices properly the data must be combined in relation to the heritabilities of each trait, the economic value of each trait and the phenotypic and genetic correlations between traits. It will be immediately obvious to dog breeders that they rarely have such information available and thus cannot use the technique as it should be used. In pig breeding it is developed to a high level of skill with boars being ranked on growth and carcass traits and given a points score where an average boar is designated 100. The top boars selected for major breeding programmes are rarely less than 160 points and frequently exceed 200.

In dogs the sophistication of this is impossible but certain forms of index have been tried such as that by Humprey and Warner (1934). In a sense, the grading of dogs into overall levels of excellence such as is done in many German-based breeds, is an attempt at index selection but since the grade is a general one the heritability of the overall grading must be low and thus likely to be more successful if used in conjunction with progeny testing rather than simple selection of dogs on their own phenotypic appearance. However, no analyses have been published to substantiate the above view of heritability of overall grade.

Aids to Selection—Pedigree

Although every breeder is ostensibly seeking to improve the breed with which he is operating, his principal aim is probably the narrower one of improving his own dogs first. To this extent most of what has been discussed on selection in this chapter will be difficult to apply because the scale of operation of a single kennel is small and most of the theories advanced thus far have been applicable to large populations.

When the breeder decides to mate a particular bitch for the first time the information that he has at his disposal is the bitch herself and her pedigree. Since he will have the pedigree even before that bitch's birth and certainly he will have it while the bitch is too young to assess for phenotypic appearance one can argue that a pedigree represents the first breeding information available to the breeder.

To what extent can a pedigree provide useful information on the breeding worth of a bitch? Usually the breeder will have access to a four or five generation pedigree of his bitch so that he will be able to produce a five or six generation pedigree of her potential litter when he pairs that female's pedigree with a potential stud dog. In some countries, for example pedigrees of German Shepherd Dogs from the SV, the pedigree will contain brief descriptions of the first six ancestors but usually such information is so general as to be of little real value. For the rest a pedigree will be merely a list of names, some daubed with the red ink of show ring fame.

Clearly a pedigree, however long it is, can be of little or no use to a breeder unless he knows something about the names in the pedigree. The more experienced a breeder is in his breed and the more knowledge he possesses about the type and producing ability of the dogs in his breed, the more useful a pedigree becomes. If you can actually visualise the dogs in the pedigree or can produce photographs of them and to this can add material relating to the defects and virtues which the dogs possessed and produced then the pedigree will assume useful proportions and be a suitable guide to what the bitch might produce when mated to a given stud dog.

The accumulation of such knowledge is not easy and there is no short cut method of obtaining it. A breeder who has been 'in the game' a long time may have amassed considerable knowledge about the dogs in the breed but it does not always follow that this is so. Many breeders and judges have learned little of value for all the length of their experience and too few of the really outstanding breeders in a breed have put their knowledge on paper. Those of you who read breed books will know only too well that, in the majority of cases, the books deal only briefly with the major dogs of the breed and rarer still are books which actually attempt to provide pen portraits of such dogs with details of their faults, virtues and producing ability.

If all you know about a pedigree is the names within it then that pedigree is effectively useless as a guide to breeding worth. It would be pointless, for instance, taking some famous ancestor in the pedigree and deciding to inbreed or linebreed to him because if you knew little about that ancestor you could well be in a situation whereby the ancestor had little or no influence on the bitch in whose pedigree he appeared. As a consequence, the inbreeding which is planned would be theoretical but in practice would not really be taking place.

Biologically, pedigrees are useful because an animal receives half its genes from each parent and they in turn receive half from each of their parents and so on. The ideas that an animal receives the genes for colour from the father and construction from the mother and such like are nonsensical and, hopefully, no longer advocated by breeders. A particular parent may *appear* to have had greater influence upon the progeny because they resemble that parent more than the other parent. But this would merely reflect more dominant genes from that parent. It would not alter the fact that 50% of the genes came from each parent and the dog concerned would pass these on in turn.

Galton's Law states that if 50% of the genes come from each parent then 25% come from each grandparent, 12.5% from each great-grandparent and so forth. As a general guide this is a very valid rule but in any particular case it is not necessarily true beyond the parental generation. A dog does get 50% of his genes from his sire but the 50% he gets is a random sample of the sire's genes, having the proviso only that one of each pair of chromosomes must be passed on. The sire could effectively pass on a large number of chromosomes that were from his sire or a large number that were from his dam. On average he will transmit equal numbers from each of his parents so that his son will receive 25% from each grandparent but this is not true in all cases. Once a dog has received a smaller, or larger, proportion of genes from a particular ancestor than might be expected on average the fact is irrevocable.

Many breeders pay a great deal of attention to pedigrees and in particular to the distant parts of pedigrees. In this connection they are usually being unwise. A dog has 78 chromosomes yet in the seventh generation of his pedigree he has 128 ancestors. Unless they have transmitted only a small part of a chromosome many of these ancestors appear in name only in the sense that they have no genes at all in the make-up of the dog in whose pedigree they appear.

If we are dealing with simple genes then pedigree study is of limited value and, once we know accurately the genetic make-up of the dog for that character, we can ignore the pedigree. For example let us assume that we have a black Dobermann and we wish to know his colour genes.

All Dobermanns are $a^t a^t CCEEggmmSStt$ so our particular Dobermann must be the same. We need only to know what he carries at the B and D loci (see page 9). Since he is black he must carry at least one B and one D. If his mother was a red animal we would know he must be BbD–. If his father was a blue (B–dd) then we would know that our particular black must have a formula BbDd, having received Bd from his sire and bD from his dam. Clearly the situation is not always this simple but given the colour of one's dog and knowing something about the colour of his parents we can frequently construct a good deal of the animal's colour formula. Once we have established this with certainty then his pedigree is going to be of little use in terms of adding more data.

The author is frequently consulted about colour in German Shepherd Dogs and, on occasion, is asked about getting grey sables from two black-and-tan animals because one or both of them have grey ancestors close-up in their pedigrees. It is impossible for two black-and-tans to give grey dogs no matter how many greys the pedigree contains because grey is dominant to black-and-tan and if the grey gene was carried by either parent then that parent would be grey and not black-and-tan. If one understands colour then such mistaken beliefs are impossible and the genetic make-up of the dog one is breeding from can be readily worked out.

The same is true of other simple characters but it is clearly not true of traits governed by many genes and by environmental influences. Some breeders seem to infer that pedigree is more crucial than the animal itself. Nothing could be further from the truth.

If you have a pedigree full of beautiful shoulders but the dog concerned has a very steep, forward-placed shoulder then it would be dangerous to assume that he will give good-shouldered progeny. The odds are that he has not inherited the good shoulder factors carried in his pedigree and is thus unlikely to transmit what he does not have. In some instances a dog may have better genes than he appears to have but have been badly reared and thus the phenotypic expression of his genes has been marred. Such a dog will breed better than he looks, but before using him one needs to be certain that one is correct in one's assumption that he was badly reared and not badly bred.

In contrast to this, one can occasionally meet up with very outstanding dogs which appear to have been produced from very moderate ancestors. Such animals may be outstanding as a result of favourable combinations of genes or a very favourable environment. Since a dog can only transmit a sample of his genes such a dog cannot pass on his own combination and may prove a disappointing stud. But this is not always the case.

The more knowledgeable a breeder is about his stock and the breed in general the more valuable can pedigree study become. But the pedigree cannot act as more than a general guide. Once you are using a dog for breeding and have progeny available this will be far more valuable than any pedigree study. If your dog produces rubbish then he is a rubbish dog no matter how beautiful his pedigree may be. If he produces outstanding stock then a less illustrious pedigree can be ignored. No amount of 'red ink' can make a poor specimen or producer into something he is not and breeders forget this at their peril.

Aids to Selection—Performance Testing

Performance testing is effectively the selection of dogs on the physical appearance or performance they demonstrate. If you select a dog with low score for hips you are selecting him on a performance test for hips. If you select your dog because he has a fine head, or is an excellent specimen or can run faster than his contemporaries or on any physical or mental attribute of the dog himself, then you are selecting via performance testing.

The extent to which performance testing works will depend upon two factors. The first is your own accuracy in making the decision and the second is the extent to which the trait is inherited.

If you are one of those breeders who thinks himself a better judge than he really is then you might well end up picking so-called superior dogs that, in fact, are not superior—at least not to the extent you imagined. As a result you will not make much progress by selecting your dogs. On the other hand, if you are effective in your assessment of what constitutes a superior animal, but the character(s) involved has a low heritability, progress will be equally limited.

Clearly, if breeders do not know the extent to which characters are under genetic control it is very difficult to predict the results of selecting the most superior animals for any particular trait. If you operate on a very subjective method of assessment with minimal checks on the consistency of your evaluations, it is likely that any progress will be fortuitous. If you are consistent, and skilled, in your assessments and if you measure those features that can be measured or consistently grade those things that can be graded, it is feasible to make progress in characters of moderate to high heritability.

We do not know which characters these are but, in the light of evidence from other species it seems logical to assume that traits involving weight, height and type may be fairly highly heritable while those involving reproductive traits will be low. Characters which are involved with mental behaviour and temperament may vary from low to high according to the character in question.

It is important in performance testing to be uniform in one's method of assessment. Most breeders actually use performance testing in the sense that they select dogs they consider to be above average in the traits they seek to improve. Unfortunately they often make their assessments at points in time that are not uniform. They may on one occasion select a dog for use on the basis of its being an outstanding pup and on another occasion they will select a mature animal. Unless there is a high correlation between the appearance in puppyhood and the adult appearance such selection methods could be highly inaccurate. In some individual cases an outstanding pup grows into an equally outstanding adult but it is not always so.

Few breeders actually select for height or weight but it is essential that when one does, one is consistent in terms of how it is measured. If you are selecting on height you need to make this evaluation at a consistent age or at maturity. If you are selecting on weight, again, some consistency of age must be made and if you are dealing with weights of pups corrections must be made for litter size and possibly parity of the dam. Without this one's selection may be more apparent than real.

Aids to Selection—Progeny Testing

In a progeny test one selects breeding stock on the basis of the performance of their progeny, rather than on their own performance. This represents a very major difference because when one assesses an animal on its own appearance or performance one is making an estimate of its breeding worth. When one assesses an animal on the basis of its progeny one is actually evaluating the breeding worth of that animal.

The breeding worth of an animal can be defined as twice the deviation of its progeny from the average of the population. Thus if the progeny of a dog are 2 cm taller than the breed average one can assume that the breeding value of that dog for wither height is +4 cm. This arises because an animal can only transmit half of its value to the next generation so that the progeny only measure half that animal's breeding value.

There are several provisos to this statement which need to be borne in mind when assessing animals on the basis of their progeny. The first is that it is assumed that the mates of the animal in question are, on average, typical of the breed and not an exceptionally good or exceptionally bad sample. Clearly, if a sire is mated to top class bitches the progeny will measure not only that sire's deviation from the breed average, but also that of his mates. This is often forgotten when breeders are looking at the show record of a particular sire's progeny. They frequently point out how many CC or stud book winning progeny he has but fail to appreciate how many above average bitches were mated with him. If two dogs each mate 50 bitches but one has 25 CC winning mates and the other only 3 it is not strictly fair to rank their progeny without taking account of the differing quality of the mates which each sire had. Often, a larger sample of mates will help to balance this out, but it does not always follow. Some sires, by virtue of their location or ownership, may get a better sample of bitches than others and comparisons which ignore the dam would be misleading.

It must be assumed that the progeny of a dog are a typical sample of his progeny and not a selected group. Several breed clubs hold stud dog classes in some of their shows but although this is a kind of progeny test it is frequently a biased one since the number of progeny is small and generally carefully selected for quality. Any stud dog, if used often enough and widely enough, will turn up some progeny of merit and if all one assesses are the few meritorious stock an inaccurate assessment of the dog will result. In general, the more progeny seen the less likelihood there is of having a sample that is biased.

Progeny testing also assumes that the progeny of the different sires have been given similar environments. If, for example, two Labradors with low hip scores are being compared on the basis of how well they breed for hip structure but one is used in a kennel which believes in producing fat heavy pups a comparison is likely to be misleading. The dog used in the kennel employing liberal feeding is having his stock exposed to a less suitable hip environment than is his contemporary and as a result is likely to produce poorer hip structure. This poorer hip structure may indeed be due to genetic reasons but, because of the biased environments, one cannot correctly assess this. As in the previous case, the more progeny that a dog has, and the more widespread they are in terms of kennels, the less likelihood there is of bias.

We can conclude that progeny testing to be accurate must involve mating dogs to fairly random samples of bitches which are typical of the breed, taking sufficiently large samples of randomly-selected progeny for examination and rearing such progeny in a wide range of locations. Given these provisos progeny testing can be a very good method of assessing breeding value.

Of course one has to have progeny to do a progeny test and one has to use a dog to have progeny so that any dog who is going to be progeny tested is, to some degree at least, already selected for use. This will generally be on the basis of pedigree and physical appearance but it should be for a limited period until progeny are available for checking. Once a dog seems to be producing well then he should be exploited fully by extensive use if the virtues are to be distributed as widely as possible through the breed.

It must be remembered that progeny testing takes time. One might, for example, performance evaluate a dog by the time he is 12 months of age. In contrast, a progeny test would not be possible until the dog is about 26–28 months of age since he would be used at about 12 months: 14 months would then elapse while one waited for progeny to be born and reach the evaluation age of 12 months.

Progeny testing reduces progress by increasing generation intervals but it increases progress by giving a better method of estimating the amount by which a dog exceeds the breed average. In the case of traits which are not highly heritable the improvement in selection intensity more than offsets the increase in time taken. If one is dealing with highly heritable traits where the phenotypic appearance gives a very good guide to breeding value, one is best selecting on performance and not progeny but in characters that can only be measured in one sex, or which are of very low heritability, one has no alternative but to progeny test.

Although progeny testing is more accurate it must be remembered that, because one is dealing with the means of groups (of progeny), the variance of the groups is less than was the variance of the individuals. The standard deviation of progeny groups will thus be lower than that of individuals.

Progeny testing is obviously much easier to undertake with males because they can have many more progeny from a varied class of mate. Females, on the other hand, cannot have many litters and may have fewer mates if some litters are repeated matings. This makes it much more difficult to get an unbiased sample from a female.

Breeders who attend many shows and take notes on the dogs they see there by specific sires, can undertake some kind of progeny assessment. The more progeny of a dog that you can evaluate, even in very general terms, the better you can assess his potential for transmitting specific traits. If the bulk of the progeny you see are possessed of good shoulders or have correct heads or other virtues then you can assume that the sire is transmitting these features to some degree. Occasional progeny without these virtues should not be taken as a damning feature. All sires will produce inferior stock and it is the overall average that matters together with the proportion of progeny in the upper areas.

Small numbers of progeny cannot be taken as typical of a sire and even fairly large groups may not reveal differences if such groups are selected samples. This is illustrated in Table 90 which covers 321 male progeny by 14 different German Shepherd Dog sires. All 14 sires were top winning dogs in Germany and the progeny represented all males by them in the SV *Körbuch* of 1975 and 1976. The progeny were thus all dogs considered by breed wardens to be fit for breeding. All progeny had certain physical measurements made at maturity (24 months or later) and the data in Table 91 relate to wither height, chest girth and body weight.

Although sires appeared to have distinct progeny means for each trait, and there was some difference in the variability of means for sires and traits, there were significant differences between sires only in respect of progeny body weight. Estimates of heritability were not significantly different from zero. This can possibly be attributed to the fact that the progeny represent selected stock thought good enough to breed from. Stock not in this category were not available for data provision. Since the breed standard sets upper and

Table 91

An example of a progeny test in a breed of dog—all progeny are male German Shepherd Dogs

Name of sire and year of birth	Progeny	Mean value* of progeny for		
		Wither height (cm)	Chest girth (cm)	Body weight (kg)
VA† Bernd v Lierberg 1962	10	63.7(1.9)	79.3(5.2)	36.2(7.2)
VA Mutz vd Pelztierfarm 1966	22	63.9(1.3)	79.2(3.5)	36.2(3.6)
VA Frei vd Gugge 1966	19	63.6(1.2)	78.9(4.4)	35.8(6.8)
Crok v Busecker Schloss 1966	24	63.8(1.2)	78.8(5.1)	36.8(7.9)
VA Arras v Haus Helma 1967	23	63.7(1.1)	79.0(3.5)	35.5(6.3)
Eros v Busecker Schloss 1967	22	63.5(1.3)	79.4(4.9)	37.4(8.3)
VA Quanto vd Wienerau 1967	27	63.8(1.1)	77.7(3.7)	35.9(6.8)
VA Marko v Cellerland 1968	63	63.9(1.5)	79.6(4.0)	37.0(8.9)
Canto vd Wienerau 1968	25	63.7(1.4)	78.9(4.1)	34.7(7.5)
Axel v Grundel 1968	14	63.6(1.0)	77.6(2.8)	34.3(3.6)
VA Pascha vd Bayernwaldperle 1969	13	63.4(1.0)	78.2(4.1)	34.9(8.2)
VA Titus v Eschenzweig 1969	12	64.2(1.2)	81.1(4.1)	36.5(7.3)
VA Hero v Lauerhof 1969	34	63.5(1.9)	78.6(3.8)	36.5(7.3)
VA Reza vd Wienerau 1970	13	64.0(1.7)	80.3(2.2)	36.7(6.9)
Overall	321	63.7(1.4)	79.0(4.0)	36.2(7.6)

* Figures in parentheses refer to coefficients of variation (see page 22).
† VA indicates dogs placed in the select group at the annual German Sieger Show and as such would be considered top show specimens.

lower limits on height it is not surprising that little variation in height occurred. Limits on chest girth and weight do not occur and more variability is seen but still insufficient to give a reliable estimate of sire breeding value. It must, of course, be realised that all the sires were top-class show dogs. Had a wider range of sires been studied more obvious differences might have occurred but poorer sires simply do not have progeny data in readily available form.

This serves to emphasise the need to use random progeny to evaluate a sire if one is going to contemplate using that sire in one's own breeding programme. Some breeders tend to see one or two excellent progeny of a sire and fondly imagine that, because their bitch has similar bloodlines to the dams of these excellent stock, the sire concerned can repeat this production in their kennel. If the sire concerned was appearing to produce well with the bloodlines in a consistent way then the faith in him may be justified but, if the couple of excellent progeny were the only decent dogs in a large assortment of dross, then one would be likely to repeat the dross more than the excellent stock. Only by seeing enough progeny can one hope to determine which particular situation one is in.

Aids to Selection—Family Data

Breeders often use the term 'family' in a very imprecise way. They frequently will cite tail male lines (the top line of the pedigree) or tail female lines (the bottom line of the pedigree) and imply something in this association. If one is wanting to show a line of descent the tail male (or female) lines can be useful ways of presenting this but the genetic meaning is limited. The fact that a champion male had a champion sire who had a champion sire and so on *ad nauseum* may mean no more than that this string of champions was the result of widespread use of the male in each generation. It does not mean that because the tail male line goes back to a famous and successful sire in generation five that the animal whose pedigree we are examining has much in common with that famous ancestor. On average only some 3% of genes will have stemmed from him and 97% will have come from the other animals in the pedigree which one neglects at one's peril.

A family is not formed in this way, nor is it formed because all the dogs have the same prefix. Rather a family represents a close genetic relationship. This means that we can really only talk about full-sib families (those with the same parents though not necessarily from the same litter) and half-sib families (those which have one parent in common). Families less close than this are not really genetically meaningful.

If we are using family selection (either on a full or half-sib basis) then we are selecting or rejecting dogs on the overall performance of the family from which they stem.

The phenotypic value of an individual dog (P), when measured as the deviation by which he differs from the breed mean, is made up of two components. These are the deviation of the family from the breed mean (P_f) and the deviation of the individual from that family mean (P_w). This latter can be called the within-family deviation.

We thus have:

$$P = P_f + P_w$$

If we select on P alone we are giving equal weighting or emphasis to P_f and P_w and we are practicing *individual selection*. If we select only on the basis of the family mean of P_f and ignore P_w we are undertaking *family selection*. If we select on the basis of deviations from family average or *within-family selection* we are using P_w and ignoring P_f. The final method

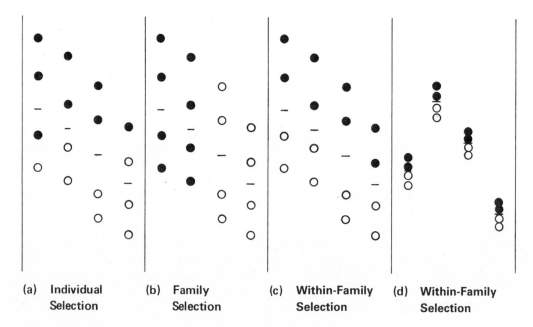

**(a) Individual
        Selection**

**(b) Family
        Selection**

**(c) Within-Family
        Selection**

**(d) Within-Family
        Selection**

Figure 53   Different methods of selection. Each vertical line represents a litter with four individuals which are ranked in descending order of merit. The horizontal line represents the litter mean. Individual selection means taking the best animals (in this case eight in sixteen). Family selection involves taking the best families and within-family selection the best individuals in each family. The final section illustrates the case where within-family selection is likely to be most useful, ie when variation between families (litters) is great and variation within them is small.

is to select on both P_f and P_w but give them different degrees of emphasis and this is termed *combined selection*.

The illustration of individual, family and within-family systems of selection is shown diagrammatically in Figure 53. In each of the first three examples in this situation we are dealing with four litters of four individuals each. Equally, they could be four half-sib groups (all by different sires/dams) but in each case the type of selection being used alters the decisions as to which animals are retained for breeding.

The mathematical advantages and disadvantages of the various systems are quite complex and need not concern us in detail here. In different circumstances each system has advantages but, in the main, the merit of a system will depend upon the heritability of the character being selected for and the phenotypic correlations between individuals.

If we are using family means then we will find that the variation or variance of the character declines compared with individual measurements. This comes about because we are pooling several individual records and thus tending to average out extreme ones. At the same time heritabilities of family means will be altered when compared with individual values.

Generally speaking, individual selection will be preferable to family or within-family selection unless the heritability of the family (within-family) means is increased sufficiently to offset the reduced variance. In general we can assume that with individual selection we will be making most progress unless the heritability of the character is very low, such that the phenotypic performance we are measuring is a poor guide to breeding worth.

Family selection is best undertaken when the heritability is low and common environmental effects among family members are also low. Within-family selection is best undertaken when there is a large amount of variation due to common environment, such that very big differences exist between families but very little variation exists within each family. This is illustrated in column (d) of Figure 53.

The problem with selecting families is that one cuts down one's bloodlines and thus increases the chance of inbreeding unless one has a large population (kennel).

The matter is discussed fully by Falconer (1960) but in the main breeders would be best advised to select individual dogs. They can, however, use data from close relatives of that dog before making their choice and generally will increase the accuracy of their selection more than they will lose it.

If, for example, one has one outstanding specimen in a litter of rather mediocre dogs it could well be that such a dog represents a chance combination of genes more than any real accumulation of desirable additive genes that it can transmit in a predictable way. Such a dog may prove a disappointing sire compared with an animal that is outstanding and stems from a litter (or family) of high-class individuals. By taking into account the performance (appearance) of relatives one can often increase the chances of picking a better breeding prospect.

The mathematical reliability of various selectional aids

Thus far we have looked at the effectiveness of pedigree, performance testing, progeny testing and family data in fairly general terms. When one is seeking to obtain information on a single character it is possible to quantify mathematically the reliability of various items of information. The mathematics of various selectional methods have been described by Searle (1965) and are discussed by Cunningham (1969). Reliability of different techniques will depend upon the heritability of the trait being selected as well as upon numbers of records available. In Table 92 is shown the relative efficiency or reliability (as a percentage) of different items of information.

The derivation of the particular figures need not concern us in this book but it can be seen that as the heritability increases so the reliability of all selection aids increases which is to be expected. It should however be noted that in any single heritability pedigree records are never as useful as a measurement on the dog itself. The more extensive the pedigree records (eg parents and grandparents as opposed to parents only) the more useful records are but once information is available on the dog's own measurements this excels over pedigree data.

Information on full sibs (litter mates) is more useful than pedigree data and that on full sibs more useful than data on half sibs. In both cases, however, value increases with number of siblings. Most useful is progeny data. At 40% heritability the dog's own record (eg his hip score) is a 63% efficient guide to his breeding worth. However 10 random progeny is 73% efficient while 20 are 83% efficient. The more progeny there are the more useful they become but the return on additional progeny declines. It is important that progeny are random samples rather than carefully selected groups.

Data are given for heritabilities up to 70% because values above this are rarely seen.

Table 92

Reliability of various records for selectional purposes at different heritability values (Values as percentages)

| | Pedigree Data* | | | Dog's | Records of Siblings | | | | | | Progeny records | | | | | |
| | | P+ | | Own | Full Sibs | | | Half Sibs | | | | | | | | |
h^2	P	GP	CP	Data	2	4	6	5	10	20	5	10	20	40	80	120
10	22	27	29	32	22	29	35	17	23	29	34	45	58	71	82	87
20	32	37	39	45	30	39	44	23	29	36	46	59	72	82	90	93
30	39	43	45	55	36	45	51	27	33	39	56	70	79	87	93	95
40	45	49	50	63	41	50	55	30	36	41	60	73	83	90	95	96
50	50	53	54	71	45	53	58	32	38	43	65	77	86	92	96	97
60	55	57	57	77	48	56	60	34	40	44	68	80	88	94	97	98
70	59	61	61	84	51	58	62	36	41	45	72	82	90	95	97	98

*P = parents only. P + GP = Parents plus grandparents. CP = complete pedigree. Data in the table relate to a single record per animal. It is assumed that there are zero environmental correlations within and between progeny groups. Reliability is the relationship (in percentage terms) between the additive genetic merit of the dog being evaluated and the phenotypic measure being selected for and being measured.

Numbers can be derived for more progeny/siblings etc and readers are referred to Cunningham (1969) for the formulae.

Variation and Scale Effects on Selection

An essential feature of any selection programme must be a high degree of variation in the population being selected. We have seen that the extent to which progress is made depends upon the heritability of the trait and the selection differential obtained (see page 298). It is also true that given greater variation in a population, and hence greater standard deviations, the same degree of selection intensity will yield a higher absolute value of superiority. This is shown diagrammatically in Figure 54 where two normal populations are shown but with one twice as variable as the other. Taking the same percentage of the population for breeding results in a higher absolute value for parental superiority in the more variable population. The top 20% of any population will be 1.40 standard deviations above the mean (see Table 88) but because the standard deviations differ in absolute value the superiority will be higher in the more variable population.

Let us take, for example, litter size in German Wire-haired Pointers and in Golden Retrievers. According to Lyngset and Lyngset (1970) the two breeds averaged 8.11 and 8.12 pups respectively but had standard deviations of 2.86 and 1.18 pups (see Table 5 page 38).

If we took the top 20% of German Wire-haired Pointers they would have a mean litter size of 8.11 + 1.40 × 2.86 or 12.11 while in Golden Retrievers the top 20% would average 8.12 + 1.40 × 1.18 or 9.77 pups. This represents a difference of 2.34 pups for the same degree of selection and, given similar heritabilities, would lead to faster progress for this trait in the Pointer than the Retriever.

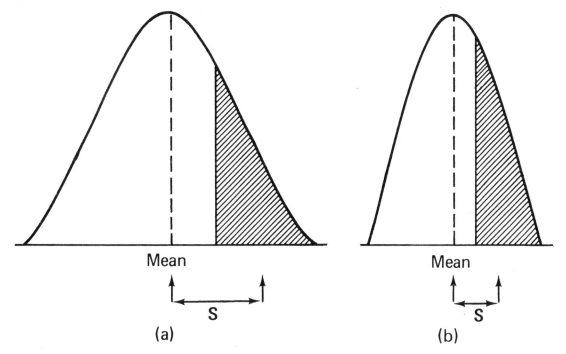

Figure 54   The effect of variation upon selection differentials. In each population the selected group (stipled) represents the top 20% of the population but S in population (a) is twice the value of S in (b).

In this particular instance progress would not be very rapid in either breed because litter size is a character with a low h^2 value and hence most of the variation one sees is due to environmental differences or non-additive genetic factors. The main principle is, however, unchanged—the more variation one has the more progress one will make, other things being equal.

Many breeders seek to advocate uniformity and in many ways a breed is felt to be genetically healthier when the show ring is full of dogs of a uniform type and high quality. One cannot dispute the need for high quality in a breed and the more dogs that reach this level the better but if we have no variation we cannot advance further. Breed standards which are very rigid on every issue will lead to uniformity—assuming that breeders follow them—and no further progress. Specific things of vital importance to a breed, such as temperament, should be fairly rigid in terms of what will be tolerated but on issues of size and structure some latitude is needed in certain areas. To seek, for example, to have all Keeshonden weighing exactly 18 kg would be illogical because many good dogs would exceed or fail to reach this weight and be discarded in favour of inferior specimens with the exact weight. On the question of weight most breeds are liberal in their approach but some of the small-sized breeds are strict and offer limited scope to breeders as a result.

On the question of size we find certain phenomena tend to operate, the first of which is that as a character increases in amount or scale and thus has an increasingly higher value, the variance of the character tends to change in an upwards direction. Not all characters follow this trend but body weight does tend to increase in variance as the mean goes up and

Table 93

Effects of selection for body weight at 60 days in mice—results after 21 generations

Item	Selected for decreased 60-day weight	Unselected	Selected for increased 60-day weight
Mean (g)	11.96	23.06	39.84
Standard deviation (g)	1.71	2.56	5.10
Coefficient of variation (%)	14.3	11.1	12.8

Source   MacArthur 1949.

decrease as it declines and this is illustrated in Table 93 taken from data relating to body weight in mice. Similar data on dogs are not readily available but probably follow the same trend.

The data in Table 93 related to 3 strains of mice, one selected for increased body weight at 60 days and another for decreased 60-day weight while the third line was maintained as a control and bred randomly to remain where it was. After 21 generations the large-sized line had increased 99% on the original control line while the small-sized line had declined by 33%. Standard deviations had increased or decreased accordingly. Selection was asymmetric in that it was more successful in an upwards than a downwards direction. However, if the data had been transformed to logarithms, it would be seen that the effect was simply one of scale and does not therefore mean that complex genetic theories are to be sought.

A useful guide as to whether or not one is dealing with scale effects or more serious changes is to compare coefficients of variation rather than standard deviations. In the example illustrated in Table 93 the standard deviations have increased or decreased with the mean in the same way but the coefficients of variation, which express the standard deviation in terms of the mean, have altered over a narrow range.

Selection for Threshold Characters

The subject of threshold characters was discussed briefly in Chapter 2 (page 30) and when we come to seek to improve such characters one finds oneself in a very difficult situation genetically.

The basis of selection is that one selects those animals which have more of those genes considered desirable and, in the case of most polygenic traits which exhibit continuous variation, the principles are not difficult to apply. By selecting the biggest (if we want to improve size) or the most beautiful (if we seek to improve beauty) we are, in general, selecting those animals possessing more of the desired genes. However, in the case of threshold characters this is not true. In the example of polydactily given on page 30 the threshold point which determined whether a guinea pig had four toes or three toes was 5 alleles. But when we select a four-toed animal we have no idea if it has 5, 6 or 7 or 8 such alleles. Clearly the one with 8 is the better choice if we want to be sure of producing more four-toed animals, but we cannot tell the difference between any of these types because all have the required number of toes. In dogs we are not interested in toe number, although some are born with the occasional extra toe, but we are interested in traits like viability (ability to survive) and we may be interested in traits like disease resistance which will have genetic involvement. Some of the important defects like heart disease, patella luxation, hip dysplasia and umbilical hernia might be considered in the same context as threshold characters. Certainly Robinson (1977) has suggested such an explanation for hernia. Hip dysplasia is less obviously a threshold character since it can be broken down into many grades but in the old BVA scheme it was just placed into three and thus ideally fitted a threshold system.

The problem with threshold characters is to know the incidence of each category and in few, if any, dog traits do we know this. We must thus make do with theoretical or hypothetical examples. One such is shown in Figure 46 and assumes three forms of expression with differing incidence figures. We can plot the graph because we can assume the underlying normal curve and knowing the incidence we can, using tables found in most good statistical books, allocate the threshold points in terms of underlying standard deviations.

Suppose we are dealing with Patent Ductus Arteriosus (PDA) and want to avoid it, and suppose that there are 25% of the population with PDA and a further 10% with Ductus Diverticulum (DD), then we have 65% normal animals to breed from. However, we cannot tell which of these 65% have most or fewest of the defective genes. If we select 20% of these to breed from we will not necessarily be selecting the best 20% but, in actual practice, will tend to select 20% which average exactly what the best 65% averaged. Thus, although we are selecting apparently intensively (20%), we are actually selecting less intensively (the best 65%) and will make less progress as a result.

In threshold traits with only one or two categories of defect it is frequently very difficult to make rapid progress and it can be very disheartening when two apparently normal dogs happen to have a sufficient quantity of defective genes that, bred together, they produce poorer results than might have been expected.

With threshold traits the breeder has to be prepared to follow up his original selections with progeny data. Thus, in the PDA case above, he should discard stock which, though apparently normal themselves, give an above average incidence of PDA in their progeny and concentrate on more extensive use of those parents which give low incidence rates.

In a trait like hip dysplasia, where certain environmental features can encourage dysplasia, it might be argued that exposing stock to a poor hip environment would enable easier identification of those dogs with the best genetical composition for hips which could then be bred. However, it would be expensive and a more logical step might be to grade hips or use a scheme like the BVA/GSDL method. Rearing dogs in ideal hip environments —assuming these were known—would hinder rather than help genetic progress since more poor genotypes would appear as normal and be used as a consequence.

Chapter 15

Inbreeding

Definition

Most breeders will agree that inbreeding is the mating together of closely related animals but there is less unanimity as to what constitutes close relationship. Some will argue that only pairings like parent-offspring or brother-sister are inbred or incest matings while others will also include half-sib matings (that is one grand-parent in common). Less intense matings involving related animals are called linebreeding and many breeders who would baulk at inbreeding seem to be ardent advocates of linebreeding.

The correct definition of inbreeding is mating together of animals more closely related to one another than the average relationship within the population (or breed). As can be seen this is a definition expressed in relative terms and thus it can be argued that inbreeding is not necessarily the same thing in each breed or population within a breed. If, as seems likely, different countries vary in the average relationship to be found between dogs of a specific breed then inbreeding will not be defined alike in each area.

The reason why 'more closely related to one another than the average' has to be included in the definition is obvious if one pauses to think about a pedigree. We begin with two parents then move to four grandparents and eight great grandparents. Each generation the number of ancestors is doubled. By the time generation twenty is reached there will be 1,048,576 animals in the generation and in most, if not all of our breeds there simply were not that many animals in existence twenty generations ago. There must, therefore, have been some duplication of ancestors.

That this is true is readily demonstrated. Finding a dog without common ancestors (that is to say dogs appearing on both sides of the pedigree) is not difficult if we restrict ourselves to three generation pedigrees or even to five. But if we take ten generation pedigrees it is fairly commonplace. Trace back any Boxer pedigree and you will find Lustig v Dom appearing numerous times, just as in any German Shepherd pedigree most male lines will finally end up with Horand v Grafrath.

In any breed a few foundation animals will feature as the origins of the breed and thus all dogs are related in some degree if we take that particular breed. Clearly, therefore, our definition of a closer than average relationship is essential but we need to be able to do more than refer to relationship in vague terms—we also need to measure it.

The Measurement of Inbreeding

Unless we have a precise mathematical definition it is difficult to ascertain which dog is more inbred than another and the more complex a pedigree becomes the more obvious this difficulty. Fortunately Wright (1922b) devised a mathematical model for the definition of inbreeding which he called the coefficient of inbreeding. This is:

$$F_X = \Sigma[(\tfrac{1}{2})^{n_1+n_2+1}(1 + F_A)]$$

where F_X is the inbreeding coefficient of the dog under study, F_A is the inbreeding coefficient of the common ancestor and n_1 and n_2 are the intervening generations between the sire and the common ancestor and between that dog and the dam respectively.

This may seem a rather complex formula for most breeders but if we use the system of calculation devised by Willis (1968) the working out of inbreeding coefficients is not too difficult. Before discussing this system we need to understand certain basic principles.

When we inbreed what we are doing is duplicating an ancestor or ancestors by having that particular animal in both the sire's pedigree and that of the dam. What we are hoping to do is increase the chances of getting the genes carried by that ancestor reproduced in the litter we are breeding. What we are also doing is increasing the chance of having the particular genes that are transmitted occurring in duplicate. In other words the prospective litter will not only have the genes of the famous ancestor but they will have them in duplicate. The higher the inbreeding undertaken the greater the proportion of genes that will be duplicated.

In each generation the genes transmitted to the next are halved in the sense that a dog can only transmit half of what he has to his offspring. The more generations there are between the dog and its descendants the more reduction there will have been of those genes because the halving process will occur each generation. This a dog may transmit 50% of his genes to his son but only 25% to his grandson and 12.5% to his great-grandson. Because of this halving process the value ½ appears frequently in the calculation of inbreeding coefficients and a table of values of $\tfrac{1}{2}^n$ is useful. One such is given in Table 94 for use in the following calculations.

We can begin by looking at a simple pedigree (Figure 55) which relates to a Boxer male Ch Wardrobes Hunters Moon. Only a two generation pedigree is given so any inbreeding further back than this is ignored for the purpose of this illustration.

This dog is a product of a half-sib mating having the same grandsire on each side of his

Table 94

Values of ½n for use in calculating coefficients of inbreeding*

½n	*Actual (approx)*	*As percentage (approx)*
½²	0.250	25.0
½³	0.125	12.5
½⁴	0.0625	6.25
½⁵	0.0313	3.13
½⁶	0.0156	1.56
½⁷	0.0078	0.78
½⁸	0.0039	0.39
½⁹	0.0019	0.19
½¹⁰	0.0009	0.09

* Values less than ½¹⁰ can be safely ignored.

Ch Wardrobes Autumn Haze of Amerglo	Ch Wardrobes Wild Mink
	Merriveen Destiny
Ch Wardrobes Side Saddle of Arnogar	Ch Wardrobes Wild Mink
	Odette of Arnogar

Figure 55   Pedigree of Boxer Ch Wardrobes Hunters Moon.

pedigree. We can thus write out the degree of inbreeding as 2:2 on Wild Mink, that is, Wild Mink appears on the second generation on the sire's side and similarly on the dam's. The colon separates the two sides.

We can calculate the inbreeding by adding the two figures together and subtracting one and then checking this as the value of ½ we must look up Table 94.

The inbreeding of Hunters Moon is thus:

$$\frac{1}{2}^{2+2-1} = \frac{1}{2}^3 = 0.125 \text{ or } 12.5\%.$$

Note that the formula is slightly different from that of Wright because we are looking at actual generations not intervening ones and thus we subtract 1 not add it. If we knew the inbreeding of the common ancestor (Wild Mink) then we would have to multiply the value of 0.125 by 1 + the inbreeding coefficient of Wild Mink. In fact Wild Mink was a brother-sister mating with an inbreeding coefficient of about 0.269. Thus to accurately assess Hunters Moon's inbreeding we have to multiply 12.5 by 1.269 which gives a value of 15.9%.

Winkinglight Jandan Jupiter	Winkinglight Vanquisher	Dutch Ch Faust v Haus Germania
		Ch Orburn Kekeri
	Juno of Robinhalt	Ch Holger v Germania
		Antigone of Quartrefoil
Winkinglight Vesper	Ch Gremlin Inxpot	Axel v Bad Oeyn
		Gremlin Moonbeam
	Ch Orburn Kekeri	Ch Holger v Germania
		Margarethe of Maspound

Figure 56   Pedigree of Boxer Ch Winkinglight Justice.

Let us now study a slightly more complex pedigree, again of a Boxer male Ch Winkinglight Justice, whose three generation pedigree is given in Figure 56.

This time we have inbreeding to Orburn Kekeri 3:2 but we have secondary inbreeding to her sire, Ch Holger v Germania, who appears on the sire's side twice and once on the dam's side. The inbreeding to him is 4.3:3.

Assuming that we have no further data on the pedigree, other than what is given in Figure 56 or can be deduced from it, we can derive the inbreeding to Ch Orburn Kekeri fairly easily thus:

$$\tfrac{1}{2}^{3+2-1} = \tfrac{1}{2}^4 = 0.0625 = 6.25\%.$$

Since we have no knowledge of any inbreeding in Kekeri herself we can ignore the $1 + F_A$ part of the formula. However we must now add to this value the inbreeding to Holger v Germania. The complication here is that he was the sire of Kekeri and thus part of his inbreeding is already calculated. We can write the inbreeding as 4.3:3 and in this instance the appearances that come via Kekeri have been crossed out. We now calculate the inbreeding exactly as before by adding all the figures to the left of the colon to those on the right *except* where the cancelling mark appears on both figures. Thus we do not count the 4 + 3 because this was accounted for via Kekeri, but we do count the 3 + 3 thus:

$$\tfrac{1}{2}^{3+3-1} = \tfrac{1}{2}^5 = 0.0313 = 3.13\%$$

The total inbreeding of Justice is thus 6.25 + 3.13 = 9.38%.

Finally let us turn to an even more complex pedigree, that of the German Shepherd Dog Graf Eberhard v Hohen Esp, an early sire of importance in the breed. His pedigree is given in Figure 57 and shows inbreeding to several ancestors simultaneously. We can write these as follows:

to Nelly II Eislingen   2 : 1

to Hektor v Schwaben   3.3 : 2

to Horand v Grafrath   4.4.4.4 : 3.3

Wolf v Balingen	Pilot	Hektor v Schwaben*
		Thekla I vd Krone*
	Nelly II Eislingen	Hektor v Schwaben*
		Nelly Eislingen*
Nelly II Eislingen	Hektor v Schwaben	Horand v Grafrath
		Mores Plieningen
	Nelly Eislingen	Horand v Grafrath
		Ella Gmund

Figure 57 Pedigree of German Shepherd Dog Graf Eberhard v Hohen Esp (those animals marked * are sired by Horand v Grafrath).

Nelly was inbred 12.5% being a half-sib mating but Horand and Hektor were outbred animals with a zero coefficient. The inbreeding to Nelly II Eislingen is straightforward being:

$$\tfrac{1}{2}^{2+1-1} = \tfrac{1}{2}^2 = 0.25 = 25.0\%$$

which, when account is taken of Nelly II's inbreeding of 0.125, becomes $25.0 \times 1.125 = 28.13\%$.

The inbreeding to Hektor is complicated by the lines already taken account of via Nelly II which are marked with a cancelling line. Thus we count $3 + 2$ but discount $\cancel{3} + \cancel{2}$. The inbreeding via Hektor is thus:

$$\tfrac{1}{2}^{3+2-1} = \tfrac{1}{2}^4 = 0.0625 = 6.25\%$$

The inbreeding to Horand is even more complex because he appears six times but three of these appearances are via Hektor (marked with a cancelling line) while two others are via Nelly Eislingen the dam of Nelly II Eislingen. These have been underlined. We now count each line by adding the figures on the right of the colon to those on the left except when the same cancelling mark appears. Thus we have:

$$\tfrac{1}{2}^{4+\underline{3}-1} + \tfrac{1}{2}^{4+\underline{3}-1} + \tfrac{1}{2}^{4+\underline{3}-1}$$

all other things being ignored. This gives a value of

$$\tfrac{1}{2}^6 + \tfrac{1}{2}^6 + \tfrac{1}{2}^6 = 0.0468 = 4.68\%.$$

The total inbreeding of Graf Eberhard is thus $28.13 + 6.25 + 4.68$ or 39.06% which is a very high inbreeding level indeed.

This may seem very complex but a few calculations will soon familiarise the breeder to this calculation. One must remember that inbreeding only exists if the animal appears on both sire's and dam's side of the pedigree. If inbreeding is calculated to a certain dog then that to his sire and dam is ignored unless appearing via other lines as well. Lines already counted must not be counted twice and when multiplying by the coefficient of inbreeding always use the coefficient not the percentage (that is 0.125 not 12.5%).

What the inbreeding coefficient tells us is the proportion of genes for which the inbred animal is likely to be homozygous, that is, carrying the same allele from each parent. When we mate two Boxers together we get Boxers because many of the genes in the breed are fixed in all Boxers, that is to say, all dogs carry identical genes. Inbreeding will not affect these genes in any way but it will affect those genes for which various alternatives exist. If, for example, there were 2000 pairs of genes in Boxers of which 1000 pairs were identical in all members of the breed then a dog with an inbreeding coefficient of 12.5% would be homozygous for the same 1000 pairs as every other Boxer together with 12.5% of the other 1000, that is, 1125 in total. We do not, of course, know how many genes are involved but the more inbred a dog is, the more inflated his inbreeding coefficient, the more homozygous he will be.

Inbreeding can be divided into current and non-current inbreeding. The current inbreeding can be regarded as that done intentionally by the breeder and the non-current as that which occurs without his knowledge. Thus a breeder will, when planning a mating have a four or five generation pedigree of the prospective litter before him and can see any inbreeding that may be there. He will not be aware of and will not care about earlier inbreeding. In mating two Boxers he might have numerous lines going back to Lustig v

Dom or to Sigurd v Dom but the breeder will not necessarily be aware of them because they will be further back than five generations.

The further back inbreeding is in a pedigree the less intensive it will be. Let us consider a hypothetical example of a dog inbred on Sigurd v Dom with that dog appearing 6.6.6.6.6.6:6.6.6.6.6.6 or twelve times out of a possible 32 in the sixth generation. Despite these twelve lines the inbreeding is only adding up to 1.8% which is quite low.

It is possible to inbreed to several animals at once but this may not be very satisfactory and could almost be a contradiction in terms. The pedigree in Figure 58 shows inbreeding to four animals simultaneously but although the total inbreeding is 12.5% the influence of any one ancestor is limited. If they were very different animals inbreeding would be moving in several directions at once and be rather a pointless exercise.

It is perhaps as well here to explain that linebreeding and inbreeding are essentially the same. They differ only in degree. The old breeding adage that if things go wrong blame it on inbreeding but when things are going well credit it to linebreeding is really without foundation. Both systems involve duplication of the genes from a favoured ancestor or ancestors and thus increase homozygosity but differ in degree. If inbreeding is successful linebreeding will be less so but if inbreeding is dangerous linebreeding may be less so.

When describing inbreeding breeders often say that their dog is inbred or linebred without further qualification. This is a very inadequate description. We need to know which dog the animal is inbred to and the degree of inbreeding. The descriptive form : inbred on Ch Someone from Somewhere 4:3.3 is a useful method as is the use of the coefficient of inbreeding. When pedigrees are very complex the coefficient of inbreeding is the only way of adequately defining an inbred pedigree.

Percentage of Blood

A useful aid to inbreeding coefficients is the term 'percentage of blood' which seeks to measure the genetic composition of a certain ancestor to the dog in question. Each dog

Alpha	Beta	Bill	Prince
			Queen
		Betty	King
			Princess
	Gamma	Tom	Prince
			Queen
		Grace	King
			Princess

Figure 58 **Hypothetical pedigree showing simultaneous inbreeding to four different ancestors in the third generation.**

gives 50% of his genes to his progeny and thus, on average 25% to each grandson and so on. The figures are accurate for one generation but no more. Thus we know for certain that half of a dog's genes come from its sire but we can only estimate that a quarter come from grandsire and an eighth from great grandsire.

Taken overall these percentage of blood figures are of some use but not in any specific case. If we look at the pedigree of Ch Wardrobes Hunters Moon (Figure 55) we see that he has 50% of the blood of Wardrobes Wild Mink because that dog is grandsire on both sides. However it would be possible for him to have had a much lower or much higher figure. He must have Wild Mink's Y chromosome since this will have been transmitted directly via Autumn Haze but Hunters Moon could have nothing else.

When calculating inbreeding coefficients the total inbreeding is assessed by adding together the inbreeding to each ancestor. In making percentage of blood calculations this is more difficult. Thus in the pedigree of Graf Eberhard v Hohen Esp (Figure 57), we can say that Graf has 50% of the blood of Hektor v Schwaben (12.5 + 12.5 + 25) and there is also 50% of blood from Horand v Grafrath (6.25 + 6.25 + 6.25 + 6.25 + 12.5 + 12.5), but these are not added together as Hektor was a son of Horand and thus half of his influence is credited to his sire. If we add them together we would be counting some influences twice. In fact their joint influence counts for 75% of the blood of Graf Eberhard not 100%.

When inbreeding it is useful to try to maximise the percentage of blood of a favoured ancestor without maximising inbreeding. The two pedigrees shown in Figure 59 are both indicative of inbreeding of 12.5% to Am Ch Ingo Wunschelrute but whereas Waldenmarks Nicolette has 50% of the blood of Ingo, Waldenmarks Rhoda has 62.5% of Ingo's blood. These are only average figures but indicate that for the same degree of risk Rhoda has more 'blood' of the favoured Ingo.

Waldenmarks Eric	Am Ch Ingo Wunschelrute
	Am Ch Afra v Heilholtkampf
Waldenmarks Fenja	Am Ch Ingo Wunschelrute
	Levade Preussenblut

Figure 59a   Pedigree of Am Ch Waldenmarks Nicolette.

Am Ch Ingo Wunschelrute	Arry v Burghalderring	
	Lona v Aichtal	
Waldenmarks Inga	Waldenmarks Eric	Am Ch Ingo Wunschelrute
		Am Ch Afra v Heilholtkampf
	Levade Preussenblut	

Figure 59b   Pedigree of Am Ch Waldenmarks Rhoda.

The Genetic Consequences of Inbreeding

Inbreeding is a system of mating which causes the same gene to be duplicated in the animal that is being inbred. The more inbred an animal is the more homozygous it will be in the sense of carrying the same allele at any particular locus. The coefficient of inbreeding is a way of measuring the degree of homozygosity that has arisen in that the higher the coefficient the more homozygous is the animal.

Unfortunately having the same gene duplicated does not mean that the best gene will be duplicated. When we inbreed to a certain dog we are increasing the chance of getting duplicate (desirable) genes of that dog in the litter but these genes can just as easily be undesirable.

If we have a population of AaBbCcDd type then, by inbreeding, we will increase the chances of getting either AA or aa at their locus, BB or bb at another and so on. If the most desirable state is AABBCCDD then we are increasing the chance of getting this by inbreeding but equally we might arrive at aabbccdd which would be less desirable than what we started with.

Inbreeding is a very powerful genetic tool but although we can measure very accurately the degree of inbreeding we cannot predict the direction of it. The importance of inbreeding to good specimens becomes obvious since they will, presumably, have fewer unsuitable genes and thus there will be less risk of duplicating combinations which are not wanted and more chance of obtaining desired combinations.

It is sometimes claimed that inbreeding creates uniformity but this is not true. If our original population was Aa and we inbred we will move towards AA or aa types which will be less uniform than what we started with. If aa types are culled then we may appear to be getting greater uniformity but that is because of inbreeding *with* selection not inbreeding alone.

It is well established that inbreeding tends to be associated with the appearance of defects. This is a true observation but breeders must not imagine that inbreeding creates such defects. Inbreeding is merely bringing to the surface genes that were already in the population. Most defects and anomalies are recessive (not necessarily simple) because dominant defects can be readily removed from the population. When we inbreed we increase the risk that a recessive undesirable gene which has lain hidden in the genetic material of the population will be brought to the surface.

If a condition is frequent in the breed (say, long coats in German Shepherds) then it will be produced frequently whether or not inbreeding is practised because the incidence of the long coat allele in the population is high. If the defect is much rarer (for example, PNA in Kerry Blues) then outbreeding may avoid the problem but inbreeding may bring the two PNA alleles together and cause the defect to be seen in the litter. Even with more polygenically controlled defects like hip dysplasia or epilepsy inbreeding may bring problems to the surface but not always so. In the case of hip dysplasia for example inbreeding on good hipped ancestors with a reputation for producing good hips may result in an improvement of hip status as more of the desired hip genes carried by the famous ancestor are brought together in duplicate.

Very rare defects, like some lethals, will be hidden for years, may not even be known about, and then will come to the surface under an inbreeding programme.

Suppose we have a population of dogs which are Black and mostly carry the genetic structure BB, but where there are occasionally undesirable liver or chocolate stock of formula bb. Let us further assume that the bb stock occur in about 1% of matings. Then we can calculate from Table 87 (see page 294) that there must be 81% BB and 18% Bb dogs in the population, though we may not know which are which. If we begin using brother-sister mating in this population we might find an initial rise in bb stock to 3.25%. We might think that inbreeding produces more problems which would be true but there would now be 83.25% BB and a reduction in Bb stock to 13.5% although this would not be obvious. The breeder would clearly notice the rise in bb but not the decline in Bb. Continued inbreeding with BB and Bb stock would eventually reduce the Bb types still further and decrease bb but once a low level of bb was reached it would decline very slowly thereafter.

Another genetic consequence of inbreeding is that the increase in homozygosity can itself be damaging to a population. This comes about because general viability is dependent upon a heterozygous genetic make-up, at least to some extent. The more inbred a population becomes and hence the more homozygous it is then the less viable it may be. We get what is called inbreeding depression because there is both an increase of homozygosity of inferior alleles and a general increase in homozygosity itself.

The characters most likely to be affected are those which are not additively controlled, that is, those with dominance and epistatic variation assuming a large role. The subject has been discussed in some detail by Lerner (1954) who has argued that populations seek to resist sudden changes in genetic composition by natural means. He terms this genetic homeostasis and it does seem that attempts to move any population too far in the direction of homozygosity are resisted by the organism.

The Practical Consequences of Inbreeding

Very little evidence is available as to the consequences of inbreeding in canine populations so it is necessary to examine some of the effects in other species.

Most breeds, be these dogs or farm livestock, have been evolved following some inbreeding at the start. This was fairly logical in the sense that the early developers of a breed wished to formulate a certain kind of animal and sought to achieve this as rapidly as possible by inbreeding to certain individuals considered to epitomise the breed. This led to fairly rapid fixing of specific breed characteristics when accompanied by the culling of those animals not measuring up to the desired standard.

Unfortunately, excessive inbreeding proved disadvantageous in some cases. Thus, in the Duchess family of Shorthorns, the inbreeding reached such levels that infertility became rife and the line died out. Once a type was established breeders became less eager to inbreed and this was especially true in species where production and fertility traits were of major importance.

Classic experiments using brother-sister matings of guinea pigs for over twenty generations were found to lead to severe retardation of certain traits. Thus Wright (1922a) showed that the number of young born per litter declined from 12.09 in 1906 to a mere 6.79 in 1920. Over the same period the number weaned dropped from 9.83 to 4.29. Despite the reduced litter size there was a decline in birth and weaning weight and the decreases were related to the degree of inbreeding.

In pigs Dickerson *et al* (1946) showed that litter size decreased by 0.26 pigs for every 10% increase in the coefficient of inbreeding and by 56 days of age this decrease had become 0.37 pigs. Thus pigs were not only less fertile but also less able to survive.

In diary cattle Robertson (1954) examined the results of various trials and concluded that inbreeding tended to reduce birth weight, increased early mortality, reduced milk yield and increased the chances of fertility problems. In beef cattle a similar depressing picture was seen (Preston and Willis 1970) with inbreeding depression being, at times, sufficient to negate selection pressure. On the other hand Dinkel *et al* (1968) did notice an improvement in beef cattle conformation with inbreeding, while in some brother-sister mating experiments with rats King (1918–19) found good vigour and fertility even after 25 generations.

A great deal depends upon the species and the population involved as well as the level of inbreeding. Thus Robertson (1954) considered that up to about 20% inbreeding there was only minimal effect upon dairy cows whereas in pigs most scientists have observed difficulties well below this level.

It is logical to assume that in dogs the major effects of high inbreeding will be seen on fertility and general viability which will be depressed whereas traits concerned with beauty may even be improved if we discount any recessive abnormalities that come to light. Data are hard to come by but some information on an inbreeding experiment made in a Beagle colony are shown in Table 95. It can be seen that as the inbreeding rose the neonatal death increased rapidly until at levels of inbreeding in the 67–78% range there was a loss of almost three-quarters of all pups born.

It must, of course, be realised that this level of inbreeding is much higher than that normally reached by pedigree breeders. They will rarely exceed levels of 25–30% even in highly inbred kennels and in most instances will be well below the 20% mark.

In developing his Boveagh strain of Border Collies Kelley (1949) considered that he had no deleterious effects up to 20% inbreeding and in the San Rafael Guide Dogs project in California Pfaffenberger (1963) claimed considerable success from inbreeding to a particular dog called Frank of Ledge Acres. In the most extreme cases litters had inbreeding coefficients of 48% without, according to Pfaffenberger, any ill effects.

This project was aimed at producing guide dogs and Pfaffenberger gives some data showing the scores for retrieving tests in relation to the degree of relationship to Frank of Ledge Acres. These data are shown in Table 96.

Pfaffenberger found that the 'Fetch' test was a good guide to a dog's ability to succeed in the Guide Dog training and his data certainly indicate some trend towards better

Table 95

Effect of inbreeding upon neonatal death in a Beagle colony

Degree of inbreeding (%)	Pups born	Neonatal death (%)
0	489	28.6
0.1–25.0	636	24.8
25.1–50.0	125	32.0
50.1–67.2	401	51.9
67.3–78.5	39	74.4
Overall	1690	34.0

Source Rehfeld 1970.

Table 96

Success in 'Fetch scores' according to relationship to Frank of Ledge Acres

		Percent in each scoring grade			
	Dogs				
Relationship to Frank	*tested*	*Low*	*Medium*	*High*	*Mean**
Less than sire	134	31	47	22	2.32
Sire or equivalent	298	23	52	25	2.54
More than sire	71	11	37	52	3.32

*This is based on crediting 0.5, 2.5 and 4.5 points for Low, Medium and High scores respectively.
Source   Pfaffenberger 1963.

performance as the relationship (and inbreeding) to Frank of Ledge Acres increased. Pfaffenberger tends to play down the effects of harmful genes and does not really give sufficient information to allow a totally unbiased assessment to be made but he is right in assuming that inbreeding to genetically superior animals will be useful. He was clearly lucky in some degree in having access to Frank of Ledge Acres and other lines used in the programme. It may be worth mentioning that one of the foundation lines from Orkos of Long Worth UDT was produced from the Fortunate Fields work of Humphrey and Warner (1934).

In the show ring few studies have been made on inbreeding. My own work with German Shepherds has shown marked differences between the different countries in terms of the degree of inbreeding undertaken. In the early days of breed development the Germans used inbreeding but in modern times tend to avoid it while in Britain, and to a greater extent in the USA, inbreeding is more common. Some data on the levels of inbreeding of British and German-bred German Shepherds have been provided elsewhere (Willis 1976) and here some data are presented on the levels of inbreeding undertaken in Boxers.

The information summarised in Table 97 relates to British Boxer champions for the

Table 97

Inbreeding coefficients of British Boxer champions 1939–75

		Inbreeding coefficient (%)					
Sex	*Total*	*under 1.0**	*1.0 to 4.9*	*5.0 to 9.9*	*10.0 to 14.9*	*15.0 to 19.9*	*20 or more*	*Mean value (%)*
Male	137	65	29	23	9	6	5	4.31
Female	139	75	25	18	7	6	8	4.10
Overall	276	140	54	41	15	12	13	4.20
Percent of total	100	50.7	19.5	14.9	5.4	4.3	4.7	—

*In calculating the average value coefficients less than 1.0 have been included as zero.

period 1939–75 and was compiled from the excellent book produced by the British Boxer Club (BBC 1976). That publication only gives three generation pedigrees but I have extended them where possible in calculating the inbreeding coefficients.

Although the overall average of Boxer champions is a mere 4.2% inbreeding, there are clearly a considerable number of dogs with fairly high levels of inbreeding. No less than 14.4% had inbreeding levels of 10.0% or more, which is higher than the corresponding figure for British champions and CC winners in the German Shepherd breed (9.8% see Willis 1976). Moreover there were 4.7% of Boxer champions inbred to the level of 20% compared with only 0.5% of German Shepherd CC winners.

This illustrates not only the success of inbreeding in producing winning dogs but the differences which exist between breeds. Further examination of Boxer champions shows that no less than 50 (18.1%) had a sire which was inbred to 12.5% or more (that is, at least a half-sib mating) while a further 13 (4.7%) had a dam inbred to this degree and 6 (2.2%) had both sire and dam inbred to this extent. The fact that some 25% of all champions had at least one parent which was inbred to this reasonably high level emphasises the prepotency likely to be experienced with inbred stock.

Ideally, of course, one should check these figures against the overall use of inbred stock but no data exists on this score nor are they readily obtainable from Kennel Club records.

Few studies on the degree of inbreeding in a breed have been published beyond those of the present author. One study was, however, published by McCarthy and Blennerhasset (1972) on the Irish Racing Greyhound. Using the sampling technique proposed by Wright and McPhee (1925) they examined the pedigrees of 21 animals taken at random from the Stud Book. They obtained total inbreeding coefficients averaging 5.7% which, over the generations studied was akin to an average increase of about 0.6% per generation. The implication from the study was that inbreeding depression would be likely to be minimal in this breed, if indeed any had occurred. The number of pedigrees traced back was rather small and might have been atypical but it confirmed breeders' views that inbreeding was generally avoided.

Some breeders have argued that inbreeding, or linebreeding as they prefer to call it, is the only way to success. Thus a famous German Shepherd expert (Brackett 1959) has supported the view that to breed champions one must stick to inbreeding and that to mate dogs and bitches of different bloodlines will produce rubbish in 99% of cases. This man was a highly successful American breeder with a linebred kennel but he is clearly overstating his case with such sweeping claims.

Inbreeding is, as has been shown, a very powerful tool but like all powerful things it can be dangerous in the wrong hands. The novice with a fair sort of animal who imagines he must inbreed her to one of her close relatives is likely to run into more trouble than success. If one is going to inbreed one must have good sound stock and good knowledge of what was behind them.

Taking an ancestor from the pedigree merely because it was a champion is no basis for inbreeding since it might be that the dog one owns has no real inheritance from that champion even though it appears in the pedigree. The better one's stock the more incentive there is to inbreed them during their lifetime because only then can their influence be maintained at a high level even after death. The fact that some inbreeding is undertaken is not necessarily serious since it enables the breeder to realise the hidden defects in his stock and to cull any actual defectives. However, with defects that are late in their onset such as epilepsy or some eye problems inbreeding could cause a breeder some trouble. When it is known that defects of this kind are inherent in the line care must be taken in any inbreeding programme.

The more breeders cooperate in sharing information of their problems the more they can learn about bloodlines and thus seek to avoid major errors in inbreeding programmes. Some of the dangers that would be crucial to a farm livestock breeder such as reduced litter size and such like, are of lesser importance to a dog breeder who can take greater risks as a consequence.

Lush (1945), one of the world's leading population geneticists, held that 'more opportunities for breed progress are lost by not inbreeding when inbreeding would be advisable than are lost by too much inbreeding'. This is not a carte blanche invitation to inbreed at each and every opportunity but emphasises that inbreeding does have virtues that can be exploited on occasion. It must not be forgotten that anyone getting into trouble in an inbreeding programme can, with one outcross bring inbreeding to zero whereas a breeder with an outbred programme who runs into trouble has no logical direction in which to turn for help.

Chapter 16

Other Breeding Systems

Introduction

If we define inbreeding as the mating of animals more closely related than the average for the breed or population then it follows that anything else represents outbreeding. Although inbreeding can be variable in degree, outbreeding is not really divisible into categories to the same extent. However, in the most extreme form outbreeding would involve the mating together of different species (as in mule production) with a less extreme form being the mating together of different breeds of the same species (crossbreeding) and the least extreme form being the mating of unrelated animals of the same breed.

Species crossing is rare in animal breeding and has no real bearing upon dog breeding systems. In contrast crossbreeding is the most widely used method of animal breeding in most livestock species. Beef cattle, pigs and sheep are generally crossbred, at least in the final stages of the production of a slaughter generation. The fact that dairy cattle production is mainly a purebred operation reflects the general superiority of the black-and-white (Friesian/Holstein) cattle which are so far ahead of other breeds that little or nothing will be gained in most instances by crossing them with anything other than another strain of black-and-white cattle. Crossbreeding has been of considerable importance in the early development of some dog breeds but it is now essentially a purebred system that is used within canine circles. Dog breeders are thus concerned with outbreeding systems that involve unrelated animals of the same breed and this chapter is largely confined to the discussion of such methods. However, for want of a better place to put it, some information on certain systems that may have some component of inbreeding are also discussed and a few comments on crossbreeding are included.

The Genetic Principles of Outbreeding

A basic premise of most livestock breeding is that unfavourable alleles are likely to be recessive in nature when compared with more favourable ones. This is a logical belief on the grounds that any alleles that were dominant and undesirable would have been selected out by the simple system of avoiding the use of animals showing the traits concerned.

When we inbreed we increase the chances of bringing together hidden (recessive) alleles that are undesirable. Thus we bring to light defects and abnormalities that have lain hidden (perhaps totally unknown) and at the same time we may bring together genes which do not produce anomalies but which adversely affect the performance or structure of the animal. Hopefully, the matching up of this latter kind of gene will be minimised by careful selection of the partners of such a mating and by careful attention to the quality of their ancestry.

Despite such attention to details it is nevertheless likely that inbreeding, if carried to high levels will increase homozygosity to the point at which inbreeding depression will result. Outbreeding will reverse such trends. Because it is a system which involves mating animals of minimal or no relationship it will tend to increase the chances of heterozygosity, that is bring together different alleles of the various genes. If inbreeding has resulted in depression then outbreeding will tend to reverse this trend. It will thus tend to increase the average merit of the individual but at the same time make it less prepotent and thus adversely affect its breeding merit.

Although outbreeding tends to increase heterozygosity it can only do so for characters in which alternatives exist. If, for example, we mate two totally unrelated Rottweilers there will be no increase in heterozygosity for coat colour because all dogs in this breed are likely to be a^ta^tBBCCDDEEggmmSStt (see page 97) and thus homozygous in every locus with no alternatives. Other genes will, of course, be available in various alternatives and outbreeding will increase the chances of heterozygosity.

If we outbreed, at the extreme level of mating two different breeds, then we will possibly break up most homozygous combinations that exist though not always, because some breeds, though different, have certain genes in common. If, for example, we take the colour situation that results from crossing two non-black breeds like the Irish Setter and Irish Water Spaniel we would obtain solid black dogs in each case. This may come as a surprise to anyone who practices this mating, intentionally or otherwise, but arises from the following colour situation:

Irish Setter (golden chestnut)	AABBCCDDEeeggmmSStt
Irish Water Spaniel (liver)	AAbbCCDDEEggmmSStt
Crossbred (black)	AABbCCDDEeggmmSStt

It can be seen that the two breeds are solid coloured (AA) and differ only in that one is unable to produce black pigment because it has the ee combination while the other is unable to produce black pigment because it has the bb combination. All other genes in the two breeds are identical and are thus unaffected by crossing but in the B/E loci the combinations become Bb and Ee and thus black is now formed. Mating together black dogs of this cross would result in segregation into various black-liver-chestnut combinations but always self-coloured.

Colour combinations are, of course, reasonably easy to work out and the effects of crossbreeding can be predicted with some degree of accuracy in most cases though will admittedly be difficult in several breeds. Of more importance would be the effect of crossbreeding upon other traits where we do not necessarily know how many genes are involved nor their individual effects.

If we cross two different breeds then we would expect to obtain an F_1 generation that was intermediate between the two. This would not apply to colour but would be anticipated in the case of size, structure and so on. If we have a crossbred that is exactly on the mid-parent level in performance then we have totally additive inheritance or nearly so. Thus if mating between two breeds in which adult males average 64 and 60 cm in wither height and we produce males which average 62 cm when adult we have produced the exact mid-point and have an additive situation. It must, of course, be based upon many matings to arrive at effective figures. If, in contrast, the above mating gave progeny that were 63 cm in height then we have exceeded the mid-point and obtained what is called hybrid vigour or heterosis.

Heterosis occurs when the progeny exceed the mid-parent average by a statistically significant amount. They do not have to excel over the superior parent though this can and does sometimes occur. Whether or not heterosis will occur cannot be reliably predicted for any given mating but we do know certain general rules. There are two basic ones which are that heterosis depends upon there being a difference in gene frequencies between the parents and that there should be directional dominance.

The first of these rules is fairly obvious. If the parental stock are similar in genetic make-up then minimal variation from the mid-parent values will be seen in the offspring. The concept of dominance is more complex. Basically heterosis depends upon traits being influenced by interactions of alleles at specific loci, that is, dominance. If a trait is not controlled by any dominant genetic action then heterosis is not likely to occur. In polygenic traits dominance may occur for some genes in one direction and for other genes in the opposite direction. When added together these effects may cancel out so that no overall heterosis may be noted. When dominant effects do occur in a specific direction then the character is likely to respond with heterosis.

Thus, like inbreeding depression heterosis depends upon there being dominant control of genes. Traits which are largely additive are unlikely to exhibit much heterosis and we do not expect much in those characters known as luxuriant traits, that is to say, not directly crucial to the future of the species. In contrast traits which are concerned with viability are likely to exhibit considerable heterosis.

As a general rule traits of moderate to high heritability—largely additive traits—do not show much heterosis and traits with low heritability show considerable heterosis. Thus fertility, viability, disease resistance and most traits of this kind are likely to exhibit heterosis at highish (over 10%) levels. Traits concerned with growth, weight, carcass composition and the like are not generally associated with much heterosis.

Although heterosis is more likely in fertility traits it must not be assumed that there will always be heterosis in such traits. As was explained earlier much depends upon the differences between the parental stocks. If these differences are minimal then even in characters controlled by a high degree of dominance there will be little or no heterosis.

When we are dealing with crosses between breeds it is reasonable to assume that there will be marked differences in genetic composition of the parental breeds and hence potentially high heterosis. In the main this will be true although it will be less true when the breeds concerned have similar origins. When we are dealing with unrelated members of the same breed it is unlikely that major genetic differences will occur between the individual dogs. They may look very different but these differences will be for relatively minor issues in genetic terms, however crucial they may seem to be in the show ring.

There are possible exceptions such as was seen in the German Shepherd in Australia which from 1928 to 1972 was closed to any importation. This meant that the breed there avoided the bloodlines of Utz v Haus Schuetting who was used in every other country in the world. As a consequence genetic frequency differences might have developed over the years.

Such exceptional situations are not going to occur very often and outbreeding within a breed is not therefore a means of making major advances in heterotic traits though outbreeding is very probably going to avoid the problems seen in kennels where high levels of inbreeding are in operation.

The Mating of Unlike to Unlike

Definition and Genetic Consequences

The mating of animals which are dissimilar in appearance is a mating system much used in the canine field. It can be used to cover compensatory mating which is something that almost every breeder will use at some stage of his dog-breeding life. No animal is ideal and hence attempts will be made to mate it to some partner which will compensate where the first fails.

One can, of course, speak of unlike to unlike in broad terms or in specific terms. The mating of two dogs which are dissimilar in shoulder construction is unlike to unlike mating in respect of the particular physical trait but if the animals are similar in other respects is not an example of compensatory mating in the broad sense.

Genetically, the mating of dissimilar animals increases the degree of heterozygosity and lowers the resemblance between parents and offspring. Also, since extremes are being mated together in the sense that they are different in particular traits, there is a trend towards uniformity in the offspring so that the population may show fewer extreme types than before. However the degree to which these things take place is not very marked and reaches a limit very early on.

In respect of simple characteristics, such as colour, then the mating of unlike colours may not produce intermediates. Thus a solid-coloured dog (SS) mated to a dog with Irish spotting ($s^i s^i$) will produce solid-coloured offspring which in colour terms resemble the first parent more than the second. It is in polygenic traits that we generally see the consequences described previously.

It must be remembered that because dogs differ in appearance it does not follow that they differ genetically. A lot will depend upon environmental aspects and their influence on the trait. Thus two dogs may differ in their X-rays yet be very similar in their genotype for hip structure but are the consequence of differing environments. This will often account for supposedly 'odd' results when using dogs with good hip status.

The Practical Consequences

As an outbreeding system unlike mating is not easy to predict in terms of its consequences. Intermediate types are not always to the breeder's wishes. An oversized, excessively long bitch might be mated to a short cobby male and give some offspring that have the mother's overlong body and the father's excessively short legs.

Given knowledge of one's bloodlines and the breed it is easier to predict some consequences and as a general rule it is wise to avoid excesses in compensatory matings. In other words the dog that is too long is better mated to a correctly proportioned partner than to one that is too short.

A fallacy often put forward in canine circles in respect of compensatory matings is that the pedigree of the mate matters more than the mate itself. If a bitch fails in some trait it is most essential to find not only a stud with a good pedigree for this particular trait but also one which himself excels in that trait.

One should not be worried about using a stud with failings where the bitch does not fail provided that he compensates her main deficiencies and that his own failings are not major ones. It is better to use a proven stud with a progeny record to demonstrate what he is throwing, although in the case of a young dog pedigree and appearance must suffice. Sometimes the stud chosen will not compensate because the bitch's failings are more dominant than his virtues or, more probably, because he was not as good as one had imagined.

Compensatory mating as a general policy is not an ideal one. It produces progeny that—however good they look—carry hidden defects which cannot safely be ignored when choosing their mates in due course. The fact that a sire has compensated some bitch's poor shoulder does not mean that the offspring do not carry some of their mother's poorer qualities, albeit hidden from sight. Thus shoulder construction would still need to be considered in future matings even though the animals appeared good in this respect. This means that the products of compensatory mating are unlikely to breed as well as they may look.

Like to Like Mating

Definition and Genetic Consequences

Animals can be alike in pedigree or in appearance. If they are alike or similar in pedigree then they are effectively related dogs and their mating constitutes inbreeding which has been dealt with. Like to like mating really relates to animals which are similar in appearance though not in relationship—at least not closely.

In canine circles a good breeding adage is 'breed the best to the best' and in essence like to like mating is this. It also, of course, implies mating 'worst to worst' and hopefully most breeders would not mate the 'worst' to anything, certainly not to anything other than the 'best'.

This means that like to like mating is generally a mating policy with selection thrown in, in that the breeder has culled out certain animals. It can be applied to individual traits or to the whole dog. Thus, mating two animals of good head structure is like to like mating while mating two dogs graded 'Excellent' would also be a form of like to like mating.

If we mate related animals (alike in pedigree) then we are breeding together animals likely to have similar genes. When we mate animals that look alike it does not follow that this is true. Animals may be similar in appearance through similar genes or by similar results from dissimilar genetic make-ups. We know, for example, that dogs can be of similar colours yet be produced by different genetic pathways. The mating of non-black Irish Setters and Irish Water Spaniels will give all black progeny illustrating that similar colours mated together can give very unlike results.

Phenotypic appearance is not always a good guide to the underlying genotype because of epistatic effects (as in many colours) or environmental influences (as, for example, in hip structure). If we mate animals which look alike but which are dissimilar in their genetic make-up then the result is unlikely to be homozygosity in our stock.

For simple traits like coat colour like to like mating can give very unlike results. For more polygenic traits like to like mating is going to increase homozygosity in the stock subject to two main rules. These are the number of gene pairs (n) which control the trait and the correlation between the hereditary values of the two animals (m). If n is low and m is high then an increase in the homozygosity is likely. In most cases, however, n is likely to be high especially if we are dealing with a broad character like overall grading (Excellent, Very Good and so on) while m is likely to be low, and lower still if we are seeking many characters at once.

Thus mating of like to like will not increase homozygosity very much, though it will slightly. It will, however, increase the resemblance between parents and offspring. This arises because any offspring will show some resemblance to its parent and if its parents are phenotypically similar to start with then resemblance is increased.

In its fullest extent (best to best, worst to worst) like to like mating will increase variation in the population. In most cases this does not occur because the breeder only mates best to best and best to worst so this reduces the extent to which variation is increased.

The Practical Consequences

In view of the large number of traits in which a breeder is seeking improvement he cannot expect to get a high relationship in mates as regards similarity. This means that, though alike in some aspects, mates will be dissimilar in others. Moreover, if breeders are not united as regards the standard there is the complication that groups will head in divergent directions. This means that like to like mating is occurring but what one group consider 'best to best' would be held to be 'worst to worst' by another group. This is very common in Britain and similar countries where judges do not undergo any testing and where all-rounder judges of limited knowledge of any specific breed are placing to the fore animals which specialist judges do not consider ideal. Breeders will follow different lines and end up going in various directions with the breed becoming variable as a consequence.

Most German breeds in their own country are bred using a policy of little inbreeding but much like to like breeding and—with selection—this has resulted in a very uniform type of dog as far as the show ring is concerned. Generally, however, such dogs fail very frequently to impose their type upon English stock when they are imported. This is because English stock are mainly inbred to some degree and thus homozygous to some extent whilst the 'like to like' German import is lacking this degree of homozygosity. As long as imports of this type are bred to animals which are similar in appearance to them some degree of similarity will result but only minimal success on this score is likely with matings to dissimilar inbred stock.

Like to like mating can be successful but breeders must not lose sight of the fact that because a dog is like his parents, which in turn were like theirs so that he has a pedigree full of similar dogs, it does not mean he will be prepotent for this specific type.

Outcrossing

Definition and Genetic Consequences

Outcrossing is the mating of unrelated animals of which one is or both are inbred (or linebred). Most breeders will use this system if they have followed an inbreeding programme and run into some kind of problem. They will choose some unrelated animal to rectify the defect which has cropped up and hence will outcross.

Inbreeding can, if carried on long enough, fix certain traits in the population in the sense that all members of the population carry the particular genes in duplicate. To break up this homozygosity an outcross with an unrelated line or dog is needed. This can bring in different alleles of the genes that are fixed and allow the breeder to continue his programme by breeding back to his main line but with the proviso that he will try to retain the new alleles that were introduced from outside.

The Practical Consequences

Outcrossing is not an essential feature of an inbreeding programme. The popular rules like inbreed for two generations and outcross for one are neither logical nor valid. If a breeding programme using linebreeding or inbreeding as its theme is being successful in that it produces the kind of dog sought then no outcross is needed. Only when some defect is present and seems to be widespread in the line and apparently immutable does an outcross become necessary.

The sex of the outcross is immaterial in genetic terms but is generally a male because it is easy to use a male without buying him and one does not want to buy an animal that will be used for only a single specific purpose. Moreover one can use a male more or less simultaneously on several bitches in the kennel.

Ideally the male chosen should be a good specimen in all-round appearance but he must excel in the area where the home line is now defective. If he is a proven sire known to be producing stock which excel in this particular area so much the better. If he is not a proven sire then he ought to have a pedigree that is excellent for the particular character sought.

Once chosen the dog can be mated to several bitches and the offspring carefully assessed to retain those excelling in the trait which was hitherto defective. As an outcross it is possible that very good stock may result but they should not necessarily be kept for this reason. It is essential to retain stock which are visibly showing rectification in the area for which the line was defective. It matters little which sex is kept but females may be the wisest choice for practical purposes. They should then be mated back to the main line of the kennel taking care to select to retain the particular improvement without losing the original virtues the line had.

Breeders should beware of seeing such good results from a particular outcross that they change their breeding policy. Outcross stock can often be very good in appearance but they will rarely be as predictable as breeding stock as was the original inbred line: changing horses in mid-stream like this can be damaging to the whole kennel success.

If both animals in an outcross are inbred but inbred to very different lines we are dealing with the crossing of inbred lines. It is genetically identical to the first case but can often give some extra virtues. If the lines concerned are quite highly inbred they may be showing signs of inbreeding depression in viability and reproductive traits. Crossing them can sometimes (but not always) give a big boost to such traits.

There is no way of knowing which lines will 'nick' with which and breeders can only find out by the paradoxical situation of mating them to see. Frequently one finds after doing the mating that one would have been wiser not to do it!

Breeders do talk of lines 'nicking' together and it is probable that such things occur. When they are identified breeders can exploit them by making such matings but they must be sure that 'nicking' is occurring. The fact that mating sire A to daughters of sire B has been successful a couple of times may be purely chance. Too often breeders see such results and forget—or never knew—about the ten other similar matings which churned out dross.

Inbred lines crossed together break up homozygosity so that the progeny may be superior in appearance to their parents but less so as breeding prospects. If we have two inbred strains that have become homozygous for several different traits we may by crossing them break up the homozygosity but give rise to offspring which excel in all traits rather than in the few for which each parental line excelled. This is shown below:

        Strain 1:   AABBccddEEFFggHH
        Strain 2:   aabbCCDDEEffGGHH
        Cross: AaBbCcDdEEFfGgHH.

In this illustration Strain 1 is defective in traits c, d and g (assuming upper case letter represents superior/dominant character) while Strain 2 is defective in traits a, b and f. The crossbred is excellent in all eight traits but can transmit a very wide range of different genetic combinations ranging from the highly desirable ABCDEFGH to the highly undesirable abcdEfgH. As such, the cross will be less predictable and prepotent than either strain though it will be physically superior to either.

Bruce Lowe Theories

Bruce Lowe was an Australian who, in the last century, propounded various theories about breeding based on studies made upon horses, notably thoroughbreds. His ideas have found favour among dog breeders, in particular those of certain breeds.

He held the view that the tail male and tail female lines were the principal ones in a pedigree. These are the top and bottom lines of a pedigree running from sire through his sire to his sire and the same from dam to her dam and so on. Oppenheimer (1968) writing on Bull Terriers put forward the view that the Bruce Lowe theories held no word of sense and I will support Oppenheimer on this score. Often, for convenience, we list tail male lines to show descent from the original start of a breed but we must not confuse this convenience with any scientific theory. The tail male and tail female lines are no more important than any other lines in the pedigree and anyone who is fooled into thinking he will be successful by paying attention only to them has only himself to blame for the bad results that ensue.

The important aspects of a pedigree are the most recent animals in it. The closer they are to the dog or litter being considered then the more important they will be and the further back one goes, the less crucial an ancestor becomes. It is true that one sees a leading dog which was the son of a leading dog and so on back for several generations. Breeders, seeing such an occurrence should appreciate that this is a reflection of usage rather than anything magical about the tail male line. If a sire is held to be outstanding then it follows he will be well used and among his stock it is likely that a top-class son will result. He in turn will be widely used and produce another leading son but this is inevitable from the laws of chance and eventually the line will peter out. Whether or not it does, the distant descendants will have little genetically in common with the original outstanding dog.

A second idea of Bruce Lowe was that certain sires produced very outstanding daughters rather than sons. As a consequence theories have arisen in which the exploitation of such sires can be made. This involves having the sire of the dam also being the sire of the dam's dam. One such pedigree is shown in Figure 60 with the hypothetical sire Epsilon being held to be a sire of top bitches.

The pedigree can be more intense by making a dam/son mating. Thus if the bitch Beta was mated to a son of hers Epsilon would appear in the same positions but the pedigree would be 25% inbred as opposed to the 6.25% shown in Figure 60.

I have put against each animal the sex chromosomes they would carry since it seems to me that the theory depends upon the sex chromosomes. If we make the mating shown in Figure 60 then it is possible to produce a litter in which some bitches carry the X chromosome of Epsilon in duplicate. It occurs in this way.

Delta and Beta both carry the X chromosome of Epsilon and there is a 50% chance that Beta will transmit it to a daughter while there is a 50% chance that Delta will pass it on to a son who will automatically pass it on to his daughters. If the X chromosome from Beta links up with one from Alpha that comes from Epsilon then the bitch will have been produced with two X chromosomes from Epsilon. There are, of course, many chances that it will not happen but if we sought it to occur then this is the best way of achieving that objective.

The problem is that even if achieved it will be a pointless exercise. The X chromosome is largely inert. Only a few alleles are carried on the X chromosome and certainly there is little evidence that any traits important to shape and type and performance are sex-linked in this way.

Dogs which seem to sire good bitches are known but it is unlikely to be due to sex-linkage and more probably due to some deficiency in the dog which makes it harder for him to produce good males. Even if it was certain that a sire of good bitches existed and Bruce Lowe pedigrees were constructed any success would be more sensibly credited to inbreeding than to the particular pedigree construction.

males YX females XX	Proposed litter	Alpha YX	Gamma YX	
			Delta XX	Epsilon YX
				Sigma XX
		Beta XX	Epsilon YX	
			Pi XX	

Figure 60 Hypothetical pedigree to illustrate the Bruce-Lowe system. Epsilon is believed to be a sire of outstanding females.

Telegony

Telegony is the belief that a particular mating (especially to a dog of a different breed) can influence subsequent litters of the bitch. It is a theory that one would not imagine exists today as a tenable one but, in 1978, I was asked to appear as an expert witness in a civil action to speak in favour of a litigant who believed it. Needless to say I had to refuse because the theory is totally without foundation. If a bitch is mismated then any resultant litter will be influenced by that particular sire but only for that particular litter. If she is mated again to another dog there will be no legacy of the previous mismating to consider. No dog breeder would believe that a woman marrying for a second time will have children resembling the first husband and it is thus hard to imagine they believe similar things about their dogs.

It is, of course, possible for a bitch to be mated to two sires during the same oestrus period and to produce pups by each in the same litter but this is because fertile sperm is present from each at the crucial stage. Any individual pup will have only one father but it may be a different one to his mates. This will only apply to the litter in question and not to future litters.

Chapter 17

Developing a Breeding System

Introduction

Thus far this book has been mainly concerned with the results of work undertaken by scientists and breeders. The basic principles involved in genetics have been discussed, the mode of inheritance of particular traits examined and the various mating systems have been elaborated upon in terms of the possible consequences of using any one. It seems appropriate to close with a chapter dealing in practical terms with ways in which breeders might operate in their aim to breed better dogs or to understand what is happening in their particular breed.

The geneticist is interested in what is happening within a specific population or breed. Given certain data he can predict with considerable accuracy what will happen to the population as a consequence of certain actions. What he cannot do is accurately predict the results of an individual mating. He can make certain estimates as to the chances of one thing or another taking place but he cannot speak with certainty. The breeder is, of course, vitally interested in the net result of specific matings and this is often a source of conflict between breeder and scientist when the latter refuses to be specific about an individual mating.

A breeder with few bitches and only infrequent litters has very obviously a vested interest in trying to predict the consequences of the matings he makes but there is no way that he can do so with total accuracy any more than can the geneticist. However, if he is a breeder knowledgeable in his breed and about his own stock he may be able to make reasonable guesses as to the consequence of certain actions. If he understands genetics he will be better able to make these predictions because he will not, for example, waste his time believing that two black-and-gold German Shepherds will produce grey because they were themselves from grey parentage. In this respect this book should have helped the breeder. Where it cannot have helped and where it was not intended to help was in respect of breed knowledge. As a German Shepherd enthusiast for over 35 years I can claim some expert knowledge of that breed and what I have learned I have tried to put on paper elsewhere (Willis 1976). I am not equally an expert in any other breed and I would argue that if a breeder is to be successful in the predictions game he must be an expert in his breed and be skilled in genetic understanding.

To many, success is the production of champion stock and in most countries there are those who have been able to churn out a few champions in their chosen breed(s) and as a consequence consider themselves successful. Occasionally they carry this to the point of constantly telling everyone about their success and attribute it entirely to their own skill.

To my mind success is not simply about producing a few winners—even a few champions—but rather it is about producing a generally high standard of stock. Dogs that will not only win in the show-ring but are also well-adjusted animals fitting into the family life and able to undertake specific tasks if they belong to a working breed. This does not mean that working dogs or gundogs must be trained to undertake that specific task but they ought at least to be capable of being so trained. The breeder who can point to dogs which work for the police or act as eyes for the blind or serve as gundogs to the shooter can take as much pride in these as in his ring champions, particularly if the workers are good physical specimens typical of their breed.

Given sufficient time, money and facilities anyone with only moderate ability can churn out a few show-ring winners, even a few workers. A breeder cannot be categorised as successful if he has produced a few useful dogs in a veritable sea of dross. He is successful if the general standard of his stock is high in both beauty and brains and it achieves what he wanted it to achieve; this requires more than just financial backing—it also requires a fair measure of luck and a good deal of sound knowledge of his specific breed.

There are many ways in which knowledge of a breed can be gained and it does not follow that all involve long periods of apprenticeship. I do not believe that it takes thirty or forty years to become an expert. All dog breeders are different and some will learn in five what another might take twenty years to comprehend although the man who has learned a lot in five years should be even more knowledgeable after twenty.

Reading about one's breed is a good start, particularly if one does so with a critical approach. Visiting shows is another, especially if one sits with an acknowledged expert and has the benefit of his or her guidance. Breeding is another way to add to knowledge; exhibiting, training, judging—all are ways in which an enthusiast will learn more about what is happening in his breed and how his breed responds and performs to given sets of circumstances. Many of our best breeders have learned their trade in this fashion but very few of them have written down what they have learned and as we age the memory dims. I would thus suggest that, as a first resort, breeders should commit to paper those things which they observe, especially about the dogs they have bred or are interested in.

This chapter deals with systems of recording that can be used by an individual breeder and which collectively can be useful to a breed group or club. There is then some discussion on the way genetic data can be interpreted and some elaboration of test-mating methods.

Simple Recording Systems

There are many ways in which one can keep records and the system suitable to one person may not prove acceptable to another. It would serve no useful purpose to describe a whole series of recording systems when each must really be geared towards the particular objective of its user. Whichever system is used it must be as comprehensive as is needed but not excessively so. If the records relate only to the breeder's own stock then the elaboration of them can be greater than is the case for records intended to relate to the breed as a whole. Whatever system is used must be relatively simple to follow and it must be such that information sought can be obtained easily and quickly.

In my own breed, the German Shepherd Dog, I have attempted to compile a fairly comprehensive series of records which would enable me to obtain a picture of what was happening in that breed in all countries of the world. The records thus comprise information on the broad scale rather than on the detailed level. The records kept are described below and might serve as a guide to anyone seeking to bring together a similar collection on this or any other breed. The records are:

1   All books published on the breed in English (and a few in other languages). Not all are equally useful. Some are little more than novice texts but others are valuable sources of information.

2   Breed magazines published in many countries. The value of these varies but they are a useful source of photographic information. Even if one is interested in dogs within a specific country the magazines of other countries can be useful in that they include information on dogs of similar bloodlines to those used in the country of interest.

3   A photographic collection of German Shepherds. This now runs to over 55,000 animals covering all countries and the period 1895 to date. Mostly they are gleaned from magazines as my photographic ability is atrocious. Maintaining magazines is expensive in library space and leads to very great difficulty in finding data. My magazines are all cannibalised by photocopying useful articles (filed by subject) and then removing all photographs which are fixed to the back of a record card (20×12.7 cm). The front of a sample card is shown in Figure 61 and would have some photographs of the dog on the back. Not all cards are equally as informative but the aim is to make them as useful as possible. They are filed alphabetically under affix and by region (Britain, Germany, North America and so on). A separate 15.25×10 cm card is maintained for each sire for which I have photographic cards of progeny. Sons are listed by name on the front and daughters on the back. In each case the name of the dam is appended. These cards are useful in compiling photographic pedigrees and serve as a guide to the producing ability of any sire.

4   Judges' reports on all championship shows. These are of very variable quality depending upon the judge. Some are virtually useless but others are a valuable guide as to the faults and virtues of dogs, especially when used in conjunction with the photographic records. My own collection goes back to 1920 and only included championship shows because these are numerous enough in my breed. In other breeds it might be useful to also collect major open show reports.

5   Kennel Club Stud Books, AKC Stud Books, German Züchtbucher and German Korbücher. KC registrations are also kept and transcribed by sire to give a record of all registered stock together with date of birth and dam (and her sire). This enables very easy compilation of any pedigree.

The above records are geared towards general breed information and a breeder may adapt these to cover only his own dogs or those dogs featured in his pedigrees or in which he has particular interest. He may also desire to keep more detailed records on dogs bred by him. To this end the litter recording system used by the GSDL is a valuable guide. It is based upon my own records modified by the GSDL Council and the litter recording card used for the KC abnormalities record is an improved version of this. One of the KC litter records is shown in Figure 62 completed for a litter of mine.

In addition to the litter record and adult record is intended for each dog reaching maturity and the KC form is again shown in Figure 63 duly completed for a dog from the litter recorded in Figure 62.

UK   **Ch Avon Prince of Alumvale**

				Ingo v Piastendamm
Born	12.8.1948		Ingosohn of Erol	
Died	7.11.1957			Franze vd Secretainerie
UK Champ	27.5.1950	Arno of Saba		
				Erich of Buckleberry
			Empress of Leeda	
				Token of Ivel
				Ingosohn of Erol
			Frido Secretainerie	
				Pirina of Mericourt
		Briarville Crystal of Trystlynn		
				Chorltonville Consol
			Chorltonville Cyclone	
				Chorltonville Chum

KCSB	2389AG	F = 6.4% Ingosohn 2:3 Odin Stolzenfels 4.6:5
Colour	Black/Fawn	Adrian; Admiral; Alexis; Arno; Andy Boy; Alicia; Anita; Annette; Astrid.
Breeder	E. Carver	*Career* JW; Top GSD 1951, 1954; Top Male 1952, 1953; Puppy 5; Open 26–14–2; BIS 1; BOB 22.
Owner	E. Carver	*Type* Overlong; Excess hind angulation; Steep upper arm; Broad croup; Large feet; Round eye; Reaching gait; Sound temperament; Glamour; Good shower.
CC/RCC	26 CC 15 RCC	*Progeny* Pale colours; Whites; Cryptorchids; Length; Steep upper arms; Poor Feet; Broad croups; Large size; Round ribs; Round eye; Coarse hocks; Prominent ruff; Character OK.
Sons CC	6–5–39	
Daughters CC	14–12–64	*Litters* 129. Mixed well with Danko 'blood'.

Figure 61   Record card as used by the author for German Shepherd Dogs. Most items are self explanatory on the card giving dates of birth, death and titles, pedigree and CC or RCC wins (for British dogs). 'Type' and 'Progeny' refer to the main type features of the dog and his progeny respectively. Against 'Sons CC' the figures 6–5–39 indicate 6 CC winning sons of which 5 became Champions and the total CCs won by sons was 39—similarly for daughters. 'Puppy 5' indicates the dog won 5 puppy classes at Championship Shows whilst 'Open 26–14–2' means that at Championship Shows he was first, second or third in Open Class this number of times. 'BIS' and 'BOB' refer to Best in Show wins at Championship Shows (general) and Best of Breed wins at Championship Shows. 'F' indicates the degree of inbreeding and is followed by the names of ancestors to which he was inbred. 'Litters 129' indicates that he sired 129 litters registered with the Kennel Club.

KENNEL CLUB CANINE ABNORMALITIES SURVEY

LITTER FORM

BREED	AFFIX:	BREEDER'S NAME:	ADDRESS:
GSD	CAUTO	Dr M.B.Willis	17, Whitecliff Close Tynemouth, ENGLAND

DATE OF BIRTH OF LITTER: 17.3.1974	AGE OF DAM: 42 months	AGE OF SIRE: 82 months	PARITY OF DAM: SECOND	WHELPING DETAILS: (Delete as applicable) NORMAL/DIFFICULT/VETERINARY ASSISTANCE/CAESARIAN

Sire: VERUS vd ULMER FELSWAND

BODO v LIERBERG	VELLO zd SIEBEN FAULEN	Lex v Drei Kinder Haus	Yasko vd Tide
			Frikka vd Schwarzen P.
		Grille zd S.Faulen	Held zd S.Faulen
			Ina v Osnabruck.Land
	BETTY v ENINGSFELD	Arko v Riedersknapp	Heiko v Boehmenhof
			Burga v Cinkushof
		Delfi v Kleistweg	Hein v Richterbach
			Adda v Reiffeck
DINA v LAHNBLICK	VALET v BUSECKER SCHLOSS	Arno v Haus Gersie	Edo v Gehrdner Berg
			Delia v Walburgitor
		Daja v Bernstein Strand	Lido v Friedlichenheim
			Asta vd Wallenstein
	ISA v ESCHENBORN	Alf v Walddorf Emst	Rolf v Osnabruck.Land
			Elga v Villosahaus
		Freia v Behringsweg	Cello vd Pfaffenau
			Nerry v Machtor

Dam: TANFIELD ERLA

VIKKAS SCIPIO av HVITSAND	VERUS vd ULMER FELSWAND	Bodo v Lierberg	Vello zd S.Faulen
			Betty v Eningsfeld
		Dina v Lahnblick	Valet v B.Schloss
			Isa v Eschenborn
	VIKKAS KATIA av HVITSAND	Ludwig of Charavigne	Cent zd Funf Giebeln
			Hella of Charavigne
		Uschi v Affecking	Edo v Haus Geltinger
			Pura v Affecking
TANFIELD FANCY	ILK vd ESCHBACHER KLIPPEN	Klodo ad Eremiten-klause	Arras v A.Riesenzw.
			Halla ad Eremitenk.
		Carin vd Eschbacher Klippen	Harald v H.Tigges
			Carin vd Wester. Muhle
	TANFIELD ANJA	Vikkas Saracen av Hvitsand	Cent zd Funf Giebeln
			Vikkas Glenda av H.
		Vega of House Romulus	Volker v Z.Haus
			Gundi zd S.Faulen

For office use only
INBREEDING   Verus Ulmer Felswand 1:3

F.VALUE
S O | D 4.6% | 12.5%

DETAILS OF SIRE

COLOUR: Black/Tan saddle
COAT TYPE: Normal
(long, short, normal)
EAR CARRIAGE: Correct
BITE: Correct
DENTITION (complete, or if missing, state how many and which): Complete.

TESTICLES: Entire/~~Monorchid~~
H.D.: Certificate/~~Letter~~/~~Year~~
P.R.A.: –
CATARACT:
OTHER COMMENTS:

DETAILS OF DAM

COLOUR: Black/Tan saddle
COAT TYPE: Normal
(long, short, normal)
EAR CARRIAGE: Correct
BITE: Correct
DENTITION (complete, or if missing, state how many and which): Complete.

H.D. ~~Certificate/Letter~~/Fail
P.R.A. –
CATARACT:
OTHER COMMENTS:

LITTER DETAILS (including dead animals)

NO	NAME (exclude affix)	SEX M/F	WEIGHT Birth	WEIGHT 57 days	COLOUR	Any obvious defects apparent should be noted here. Also note stillbirths/deaths.
1	Ahnuhi	M		8.6	B/m	Long Coat. Entire
2	Arapaho	M		10.5	B/T	Coat OK. Entire. No Missing Teeth
3	Blackfoot	M		8.6	Black	Coat OK. Unilater.Crypt. No Missing Teeth
4	Cheyenne	M		10.5	Black (White spot on chest)	Coat OK. Entire. (see adult form)
5	Delaware	M		7.3	B/T	Coat OK. Entire.
6	Chippewa	F		8.6	B/m	Coat OK. Epilepsy at 22 months. Killed.
7	Cree	F		7.3	B/m	Coat OK. No Missing Teeth
8	Shawnee	F		8.6	Black	Coat OK. No Missing Teeth
9	––	F		–	B/T	Died 2 days. Crushed by dam.
10						
11						
12						
13						
14						
15						
16						
17						

NOT WEIGHTED AT BIRTH (Weighed 28/57 days)

When completed, please return this form to:-

KENNEL CLUB,
CANINE ABNORMALITIES SUB-COMMITTEE,
1 CLARGES STREET,
LONDON, W1Y 8AB

Signature of breeder:
....

Date: ....

Figure 62 Kennel Club litter form for reporting abnormalities. This has been completed for one of the author's German Shepherd Dog litters. In the comments on the litter several items have been included which would generally not be apparent at 9 to 10 weeks, when the litter would be reported, but they have been included for interest. It is important to note that in such surveys litters with no defects are just as useful as those with problems and all should be reported. It is particularly important to record pups which do not survive and the reasons for this non-survival. Note that the dental status of all pups is not given. This does not mean that it was defective but that these had not been seen. Unless a fact has actually been checked it should not be recorded.

ADULT FORM

KENNEL CLUB CANINE ABNORMALITIES SURVEY

ADULT DETAILS ON ANIMALS REPORTED ORIGINALLY AS LITTERS

K.C. NAME OF DOG:___CAUTO CHEYENNE_____ SEX: M~~/FX~~   ~~K.C. REGN. No.~~ *BREED* G.S.D.

BREEDER: _Dr M.B.Willis___   OWNER:___as breeder_____

ADDRESS:__17 Whitecliff Close_____
Preston Grange,_____
Tynemouth, England_____

K.C. REG. NAME OF SIRE:_____Verus vd Ulmer Felswand_____

K.C. REG. NAME OF DAM:_____Tanfield Erla_____

DATE OF BIRTH OF DOG REPORTED ON HERE:___17.3.1974_____

DETAILS OF DOG:

AGE AT THIS REPORT:_____4 $\frac{1}{2}$ years_____

ADULT HEIGHT AT WITHERS:_____   ADULT WEIGHT:_____

HIP STATUS: CERTIFICATE/~~BREEDERS LETTER/FAIL~~ (delete which is not applicable)

AGE AT X-RAY:___19___months.   IF FAILED: GIVE DETAILS _____
(See Instructions) _____

EPILEPSY: HAS THIS DOG HAD A FIT?   YES/NO   No (Litter sister did)

IF YES, AT WHAT AGE AND FREQUENCY:__Not applicable_____

TESTICLES: Both descended/none descended/right only descended/left only descended   Entire

BITE:_____   Correct

TEETH:_____   Complete dentition

EAR CARRIAGE:_____   Excellent

COAT TEXTURE:_____   harsh thick

ADULT COLOUR:_____   Black. Slight grey tan on feet and faint white spot chest

P.R.A. DETAILS: _____ -

CATARACT DETAILS: _____ -

IF DEAD, GIVE AGE AT DEATH AND CAUSE IF KNOWN: _____

ANY OTHER COMMENTS: (use other side if needed)_____
Has slight curl to end of tail when gaiting
In litter of 8 reared three X-rayed and all obtained BVA certificate.
Temperament sound but very aggressive to other males

Signature of Owner or Breeder:_____

Date: ____24.7.1978_____

When completed, please return this form to:-

KENNEL CLUB,
CANINE ABNORMALITIES SUB-COMMITTEE,
1 CLARGES STREET, LONDON, W1Y 8AB

Figure 63   Kennel Club adult form for reporting abnormalities. This has been completed for one of the dogs reported in the litter form shown in Figure 62.
Note: breed is missing from the form and should be included.

A more acceptable record in my view is the adult form used by the GSDL (Figure 64). This is a composite form used by the GSDL in surveying dogs. It is based upon the German SV survey form modified by myself and the GSDL Council. It is intended to be filled in by an independent judge but a breeder could readily adapt it to his own breed and complete it himself on each dog he breeds. Obviously completion must be undertaken without using rose-coloured spectacles and in a consistent fashion. It ought also to include as many dogs as possible from those bred. Very often a breeder claims never to have produced specific faults or defects. What he really means is that among adult stock he has bred *and* seen he has not noted the fault, but only rarely has he seen all the stock he has bred. Often he has never observed some dogs beyond the age of eight weeks. He should, wherever possible, seek to follow up all dogs he has bred and he can add a photographic record to the individual form for good measure.

It must, however, be realised that a breeder cannot ever hope to be comprehensive on his own. He does not breed on a large enough scale to fully assess what is happening and the minute he uses stock from another breeder he will not have the records on that dog that he has maintained on his own.

Organisations like the GSDL and the British Briard Club are using systems like those described above and some of the data presented in this book are derived from such schemes. Doubtless in later editions it will be possible to add considerably to our knowledge of these breeds because present-day breeders have had the courage to record and pool, for the benefit of all, the good (and bad) results that they have obtained.

Genetic Studies

The prospect of breeders working together for the common good takes us logically to the subject of genetic studies of breeds carried out on breeders' data. This is not a new idea in that most of the papers summarised in this book have arisen as a consequence of breeders approaching scientists with a problem. Analysis of pedigree data has then led to an understanding of the mode of inheritance of the problem. On other occasions surveys have been undertaken on breeders' kennels to examine specific issues. Thus, much of Little's excellent book on coat colour (1957) depended upon survey data supplied by breeders.

There are, of course, many problems inherent in such studies. Not all breeders are equally skilled and they do not all agree on their definitions. Some flaws in Little's book occur because of this as, no doubt, they will occur in the present volume.

Safeguards can, however, be built into the data collecting system and it is essential that breed clubs hoping to examine any particular problem seek genetical advice first in order that data collected can be of maximum value.

The first stage of any examination of a breed problem is to have accurate diagnosis. Vague terms like blindness, fits or heart trouble are too imprecise to be of much help. Wherever possible there should be veterinary confirmation of defects which may not always be easy. Idiopathic epilepsy, for example, is not something the dog will 'lay on' for the veterinarian. By the time expert help is called the dog will have recovered and it will be on the owner's description of symptoms that the veterinarian will have to work. Similarly with dead pups it may be expensive to have them post-mortemed but if the problem in the breed is serious enough it will be worth while—if only to prove that they did not die of the particular problem under review.

There are many veterinarians and veterinary schools who will be only too happy to assist

THE GERMAN SHEPHERD DOG IMPROVEMENT FOUNDATION

ADULT ASSESSMENT REPORT   Date.................................

KC Reg Name.. KC Reg No................................

Date of birth..............................Sex.....................................

Sire ....Dam ....

Breeder's Name/Address ....

Owner's Name/Address...

BVA/GSDL Score ....Breeder's Letter...................................

Testicles descended: Both/One/None

MEASUREMENTS: Height at withers .... Length of foreleg ....

Chest depth........................... Chest girth ....

Overall length ....| Weight ....

DENTITION: Complete. Missing (details) ....

GENERAL IMPRESSION: ....

....

Sex Impression ....Colour/pigment ....

Expression: Typical. Alert. Noble. Disinterested. Anxious.

Coat Texture: Correct. Short. Long. With underwool. Without underwool. Fine.

DETAILS:

Head/Neck:	*Head.*	Correct for sex. Coarse. Fine.
	Eyes.	Dark, matching. Light. Almond. Round. Prominent.
	Ears.	Firm. Correct Size. Well placed. Soft. Too large. Too small. Wide.
	Muzzle.	Good. Weak. Lippy. Too long. Too short.
	Neck.	Correct. Swan. Stuffy. Throaty.
Forequarters:	*Forechest.*	Well developed. Over developed. Lacking.
	Shoulder.	Well laid. Slightly forward. Forward. Loaded.
	Upper arm.	Angle correct. Too acute. Too oblique. Length correct. Short. Long.
	Leg bone.	Strong. Weak. Very fine. Straight. Bowed.
	Pasterns.	Correct spring. Upright. Weak. Turned.
	Feet.	Correct. Hare. Long. Flat. Open.
	Nails.	Dark. Pale.
Middlepiece:	*Back.*	Firm. Reasonably firm. Soft. Dip behind withers. Short. Long.
	Withers.	Correct slope. Steep. Flat. Short.
	Loin.	Strong. Correct. Narrow. Long.
	Underline.	Clean with slight tuck-up. Too tucked up. Level.
	Ribbing.	Correct. Slabsided. Barrel.
Hindquarters:	*Croup.*	Correct. Long. Short. Steep. Round. Flat. Square.
	Thigh.	Broad. Narrow. Powerful.
	Stifle.	Well turned. Short second thigh. Overlong second thigh.
	Hock.	Short. Medium. Long. Cow. Bow. Sickle.
	Angulation.	Pronounced. Sufficient. Over. Lacking.
	Tail.	Correct. Gay. Hooked. Curling. Short. Overlong.
	Tailset.	Clean. Low. High. Rooty.
Movement:	Coming towards	....
	Going away	....
	Side gait	....
	Outline in action	....

OVERALL CLASSIFICATION OF CONSTRUCTION: ....

TEMPERAMENT:...

Signed (1) .... (2) ....

       (3) ....

Figure 64 Breed survey form from the GSDIF. Each breed would need to have a specific form devised. It is very easily completed by inserting appropriate figures or deleting terms which do not apply. The GSDIF classifies the dog overall into a category on construction and one on temperament separately since this facilitates genetic studies. Grades would be Excellent, Very Good, Good, Satisfactory and Poor with + or − categories in each if desired.

an organised group in the study of a problem and often at minimal or no cost provided the scientist concerned is able to publish scientific results. Geneticists are more hard to come by, especially those engaged in dogs though there are several in the USA and a handful of us in Britain. If the problem is thought to be genetic then genetical help is essential.

Even if we have accurate diagnosis the development of a genetical theory is not necessarily easy. The fact that a defect is present at birth does not make it genetic and the fact that it arises later in life does not make it purely environmental. That it may occur in certain kennels or specific bloodlines so that there is familial relationship among affected stock is an indication of possible genetic involvement but it is not proof. Even the fact that one specific ancestor is implicated in every case may not mean that the condition is inherited or that the ancestor concerned is involved. A dog may be so widely used in a breed that he appears in every pedigree in due course so that mere presence does not damn him as a causal factor. He must appear more frequently in affected than non-affected pedigrees or at a higher level in the former than the latter before he can be condemned.

Breeders often feel that recording defects is sufficient in itself but nothing could be further from the truth. I am often asked to assist some group or other in seeking to understand some defect or some type of colour inheritance and am unable to do so other than in very general terms because the only data available relate to affected animals.

If we are to understand the mode of inheritance of some kind of anomaly of construction or colour we need to be able to assess incidence of the condition relative to the normal. We also need to be able to decide on the role of various other factors. To this end complete litter data—or at least most members of the litter—is essential. We need to know sexes in order that such things as sex-linked or sex-limited inheritance can be assessed. Age or parity of the dam is useful information because some defects may be more prone to occur in later litters than earlier ones or in older rather than younger dams. Five generation pedigrees are more or less essential so that inbreeding coefficients can be calculated because these may shed light on the nature of the problem.

Pedigree charts, such as have been presented throughout this book, will be a useful starting point since they may give some clues as to the mode of inheritance. A trait that seems to be shown in parents (at least one) and offspring is likely to indicate dominant inheritance while one that is seen in only a proportion of offspring from normal parents is likely to be recessive. However, characters that are dominant with incomplete penetrance can easily be confused with recessives if numbers involved are few.

Given certain litter data the geneticist can formulate various theories and then test whether or not the data fit these particular formulations. This will involve making assumptions as to the genetic composition of certain parental matings and then testing whether or not the proportions of offspring in normal and affected categories agree with Mendelian ratios. A test known as chi-square test is used in most cases and this is readily explained in any elementary statistical text book while the necessary tables for testing chi-square will appear in texts like Fisher and Yates (1963) or White *et al* (1974).

It is perhaps important at this stage to highlight one problem met with in this kind of investigation which concerns the way in which data is made available. Usually the investigator has a series of litters in each of which at least one affected animal appears. If he is dealing with parents that are normal in each case, he will assume that he is dealing with a recessive trait, with affected animals being nn in the type of genotype, while their parents are Nn. He will logically assume that in Nn × Nn matings there will be a ratio of three normal (NN or Nn) to one affected (nn) and expects his data to fit this ratio.

Unfortunately, in most instances matings of Nn to Nn where no nn stock appeared are not included and he thus has data which tend to overestimate the expected ratio. In the data on coat length in German Shepherd Dogs presented on page 115 there were several Nn × Nn matings included where no long coats appeared and thus a normal analysis can be made to test 3:1 ratios. However in most other tests some corrections need to be made for the fact that such matings are excluded by virtue of the way data were collected.

There are several ways in which data can be collected. These are:

1   Complete selection: taking a random sample of parents, a method usually not feasible except when checking a dominant.
2   Truncate selection. All affected animals in population are included by complete check.
3   Single selection. Probability of an affected individual is so low that never more than one per litter occurs.
4   Multiple selection. A stage intermediate between 2 and 3 where more than one case per litter occurs but not all affected cases are probands.

In methods 2, 3 and 4 no matings of Nn × Nn type are included where only normal stock resulted. There are various ways by which corrections of data can be made (see Bailey 1961; Cavalli-Sforza and Bodmer 1971; Stern 1973). Two of the methods can be discussed here as they are the most relevant to canine data.

One system is called the Weinberg proband method. This is an attempt to compensate for the loss of N– individuals by discounting from the analysis an appropriate number of nn individuals. Generally it means discounting one affected animal per litter and working on the new data.

The second method is the system used for correcting pooled data based on *a priori* expectation. It presupposes a certain ratio, for example 3:1, and seeks to check this with the data observed after correction using the formula:

$$p' = \frac{p}{1 - q^s}$$

where p is the proportion of nn offspring expected (in this case one quarter), q is the proportion of N– offspring (three-quarters) and s is the litter size. Applied to a litter of 3 we have the likely fraction of nn pups as being:

$$p' = \frac{\frac{1}{4}}{1 - (\frac{3}{4})^3} = 0.432.$$

It can be seen that p' is higher than the value of p. In Table 98 are shown the appropriate values of p' expected for this type of ratio in litters of size 2 through to 12. The item p' × s is the expected number of nn animals per litter.

Using this table, extended to higher litter sizes if needed, it is possible to make allowance for the fact that affected cases are going to be more prevalent than would be the case if the total population was sampled. An example of the use of this table appears in Table 99 using data from Andresen (1977a) on haemolytic anaemia in the Basenji.

In both instances the test is not significant (NS) suggesting that the 3:1 hypothesis proposed is suitable but the goodness of fit is better with corrected data and in many cases the uncorrected data will not produce a good fit.

Table 98

Corrected numbers of pups expected to be nn in matings of Nn × Nn parents assuming at least one member of the litter is nn

Number in litter(s)	Value of p'	Value of p' × s
2	0.571	1.143
3	0.432	1.297
4	0.366	1.463
5	0.328	1.640
6	0.304	1.825
7	0.289	2.020
8	0.278	2.222
9	0.270	2.433
10	0.265	2.649
11	0.261	2.871
12	0.258	3.096

Note The *a priori* probability of nn is 0.25.

Table 99

Test of 3:1 ratio with haemolytic anaemia in the Basenji with or without correction for mode of ascertainment

Litter Number	Progeny observed		Expected (no correction)		Expected (corrected)	
	Normal	Anaemic	Normal	Anaemic	Normal	Anaemic
1	2	1	2.250	0.750	1.703	1.297
2	2	1	2.250	0.750	1.703	1.297
3	4	2	4.500	1.500	4.175	1.825
4	2	1	2.250	0.750	1.703	1.297
5	4	2	4.500	1.500	4.175	1.825
6	4	1	3.750	1.250	3.360	1.640
7	3	2	3.750	1.250	3.360	1.640
8	4	1	3.750	1.250	3.360	1.640
Total	25	11	27.000	9.000	23.539	12.461

Note Chi-squared test (uncorrected) $= \dfrac{(25-27)^2}{27} + \dfrac{(11-9)^2}{9} = 0.59$ NS

Chi-squared test (corrected) $= \dfrac{(25-23.539)^2}{23.539} + \dfrac{(11-12.461)^2}{12.461} = 0.26$ NS

Source Andresen 1977a.

Once a theory has been proposed from specific data such as those given above it is useful to undertake various controlled matings to confirm that the test is valid. This may include Affected to Affected and Affected to Normal matings whenever these are biologically feasible and in each case all progeny born should be checked.

This type of testing need not necessarily be applied only to defects but is, of course, equally valid in testing coat colour theories which are currently no more than tenuous ones in many breeds. In many breeds there are certain colours which are more important than others and in some cases certain colours are regarded as disqualifying ones, yet in many of these same breeds colour inheritance is not understood by the breeders. Breed clubs which collect carefully monitored data on colour could, with genetical help, elaborate acceptable theories as to the mode of inheritance and benefit themselves as well as genetic under-standing in the process.

The Elimination of Anomalies

Most breeders would agree, at least in principle, that it is desirable to eliminate genetic anomalies but the methods often proposed are far from genetically sound or even racially desirable in terms of their effect upon the breed.

The first stage of any action against a genetic anomaly must be to determine the relative importance of the 'defect' in relation to other traits. If we are dealing with an aesthetic defect like colour then I would argue that much less attention should be given to reducing the incidence of the undesirable colour than would be given to defects of character or construction. If the colour concerned has side effects, such as those associated with Merle then action against the colour has to be more severe. It is, however, important to determine at the outset whether or not an undesirable colour is free of association with other more sought after colours. Not all colour effects are isolated from one another but are instead epistatic so that genes at one locus influence what happens at another locus. It is pointless seeking to eliminate an aesthetically undesirable coat colour if that colour is part and parcel of another more desirable effect.

With more obvious constructional and character failings action to reduce their incidence is more logical but before that action can be taken it is necessary to determine whether one is dealing with a dominant or recessive trait or whether there is a polygenic or threshold type form of inheritance. If we are dealing with the last two forms of genetic transmission then test mating and other frequently advocated policies are not valid. We simply have to use sound breeding theories outlined in Chapters 14, 15 and 16. If we want to reduce a polygenically inherited problem we will do so by selecting for breeding more of those dogs that do not exhibit the failing and reducing the number of those showing the defect. The more heritable the trait is and the harder we select against it the more effective will the operation become as has been discussed.

In the case of a dominant trait that is transmitted in a simple autosomal manner the problem is simply one of identification of affected animals. If the trait is dominant all animals carrying the gene will exhibit this fact and can be selected against. This may sound easy enough and so it would be if the defect has an early age of onset but, in some instances, this does not occur. For example, Central PRA may not become obvious until the dog is well into adult life and may well have been bred from many times, transmitting its own problem into many lines before being identified. In this instance there is the added complication of incomplete penetrance whereby some animals carrying the affected allele do not ever exhibit this fact. Sometimes, if the age of onset of a problem is late in life an affected animal may have been used and died long before the age at which it would have demonstrated its own genetic structure.

All these aspects of dominant inheritance will complicate the breeder's life but they are not insurmountable. If breed clubs organise some kind of genetic clearing house for data it is possible to make predictions as to potential risk on each pedigree and thus reduce the incidence of dominant genes. Given sensible planning it ought to be easy to reduce the incidence of a dominant gene very quickly provided that it is reasonably early in age of onset and there is a widespread programme to identify and publicly record the affected cases.

With recessive traits the situation is more difficult. Merely culling out the affected stock will not help very much towards reducing the incidence of the recessive allele as was shown on page 296. If the incidence is high there will be quick response to the culling of nn type dogs but as the incidence of nn animals declines more of the cases will be spread by Nn type animals or 'carriers'. The proportion of Nn to NN animals has been shown in Table 87 and it can be seen from that how a relatively low incidence of nn stock can still mean a high proportion of Nn animals.

In some anomalies, for example haemolytic anaemia in the Basenji (see page 248) it is possible to identify Nn and NN animals from blood tests. This means a fairly early chance to cull Nn stock exists and ought to enable the rapid reduction, or even total elimination, of the defective allele. In most cases this is less true. The Nn type dog will only be identified when it produces nn progeny and in the case of a bitch with limited mating potential she may be Nn but never produce any defect simply because all her mates are NN or because even when mated to an Nn type dog there is, by chance, no nn offspring in the litter. Males with greater use might well turn up the occasional nn progeny but only if there are sufficient Nn carriers in the population at large to ensure that a proportion of his mates are of this kind.

The complication of late onset of disease applies just as well to recessives as to dominants (for example Generalized PRA) which means that nn stock may be used considerably before the genetic problem comes to the surface. Use of machines like the ERG may enable much earlier identification of nn stock and might, in time, even help to identify Nn stock which would help to reduce the incidence of PRA at least.

The alternative to mechanical or blood testing systems of identification is to test mate suspect stock. Test mating is often advocated by breeders but it is by no means as straightforward as breeders seem to think.

The ideal way to test mate is to breed the suspect dog (N?) to an affected (nn) animal. If the suspect is NN then no defective progeny will result. If the suspect is Nn then half the progeny should be Nn and the other half should be nn. The appearance of only one affected offspring is sufficient to condemn the dog as being Nn in his genotype, assuming that the genetics of the condition support a simple autosomal recessive. Of course chance operates and a dog may be Nn but not produce nn stock when mated to an nn animal simply because of luck. We therefore need to be certain that sufficient offspring have been produced to ensure a reliable test. In Table 100 are shown the expected chances than an animal is Nn even though he has produced no nn stock in the test mating. Three kinds of test mating are shown—to affected (nn) mates, to non-affected but known carrier (Nn) mates and to its own offspring. These tests can be undertaken using suspect males and females but very obviously it is harder to test mate a female because she does not produce

Table 100

Test mating for a simple autosomal recessive—percentage chances of being wrong in assuming that an N? dog is NN when no abnormal progeny result

Normal pups seen*	Mating to affected female (nn)	Mating to carrier female (Nn)	Mating to own daughter (N?)
1	50.0	75.0	88
2	25.0	56.3	78
3	12.5	42.2	71
4	6.25	31.6	66
5	3.13	23.7	62
6	1.56	17.8	59
7	0.78	13.3	57
8	0.39	10.0	55
9	0.20	7.51	54
10	0.10	5.63	53
11	0.05	4.22	52
12	0.02	3.17	52
13	0.01	2.38	51
14		1.78	51
15		1.34	51
16		1.00	51
17		0.75	50
18		0.56	50
19		0.42	50
20		0.32	50

*If even one affected pup is seen then the dog under test is known to be Nn.

enough offspring in each litter and has to be mated several times which spreads the testing over a long period of time. It is thus generally feasible only to test mate males.

From Table 100 it is apparent that mating to nn stock needs about six offspring to be born, all of them normal, before the dog can be assumed to be NN in genotype. It is, however, important to realise that there is still a 1.6% chance that the dog is really Nn and so in every 200 dogs tested in this fashion on six offspring there will be three which will slip through the net. Back in the 1950s the Irish Setter breeders in Britain test mated stock against Generalized PRA on the basis of six normal offspring from such matings. Some tested dogs did undoubtedly slip through the net and the PRA incidence, though drastically reduced, was not eliminated completely and is now being seen once more in the breed.

With some diseases the nn type is lethal or semi-lethal and thus N? × nn matings are impossible. In this instance it is necessary to mate the N? dog to known Nn mates but, as is seen in Table 100, this needs about 16 offspring before the risk of error is reduced to 1.0%. In some breeds this could mean as many as four or five mates and if a lot of dogs are to be tested there may be insufficient Nn mates. This is the situation with regard to PNA in Kerry

Blues where the nn type is lethal but few known Nn bitches exist so that testing is well nigh impossible. In that instance father-daughter matings might be done.

The final column in Table 100 shows the effect of testing by mating a sire to his own daughters. The values given have to be multiplied together so that if we mate a sire to five daughters which produce 3, 4, 4, 5 and 6 pups all of them normal the chance of an error is:

$$0.71 \times 0.66 \times 0.66 \times 0.62 \times 0.59 \times 100 = 11.3\%.$$

Thus after this many matings there is still a risk of an 11% error, too high to be very acceptable.

Test mating is only useful if the time taken is reasonable. Testing for PRA in the Irish Setter was possible because by about six months of age any PRA cases would have been identified. If PRA does not reveal itself until some four or five years of age then test mating is impracticable since the dog will by then be aged and his best stud years already passed. Early identification of PRA cases by ERG would enable more effective test mating.

The complication of not being able to test females is not so serious provided that males are tested. Once a male has been shown to be NN in genotype he can be mated to any female, even Nn types, and still not produce any defective pups but, of course, they in their turn will have to be test mated. Only when both parents are proven to be NN is the need to test mate progeny eliminated.

Test mating, even if feasible, is not the end of the story. Once an animal has been identified as being Nn because it has produce nn stock there is the question of what to do about it. There can be no hard and fast rules laid down since breeding decisions have to be made on the basis of many factors not simply on one.

There are some who would advocate immediate slaughter of the Nn dog or, at best, no further use, particularly if the animal concerned is owned by a rival kennel. Others advocate wholesale disposal of the dog and all his close relatives which is a very severe policy and not necessarily a wise one. In my view one has to assess the defect that is carried against the virtues of the dog concerned and the incidence of the problem in the breed.

If we are dealing with a problem of fairly high incidence that is seriously disadvantageous to the dog then we act differently to the situation where the defect is of low incidence or of minor importance. Defects which are obvious at birth or soon afterwards are, in my view, less crucial than those which appear later in life. A PNA Kerry Blue can be destroyed at about 16 weeks but a PRA Labrador might not reveal it until about four years of age when time, money and love have been expended and when the dog may well be serving as a guide dog or working to the gun. Its disposal at this point is tragic and costly and better not to have to be faced if the risk can be reduced by breeding fewer such dogs.

As a general rule I would think that action against Nn type dogs must be severe where the defect is late in age of onset and serious such as blindness of any form but it can be less severe if the nn type is congenital and effectively lethal but where Nn and NN are identically healthy. This is particularly true if the defect concerned has a low incidence in the breed although it can be argued that if the defect has a low incidence the loss of a few good dogs can be safely borne whereas with a high incidence this is harder to achieve.

If one is dealing with colour defects the issue is minor in importance and must be influenced by the quality of the dog. A superb animal in type and character who throws a colour defect is much more worthy of use than a mediocre dog of sound genetic merit for colour.

Whatever action an individual takes the important thing is to ensure that data are made available to breeders. If we all spend our time hiding problems we are building up an explosive situation that will, eventually, rebound upon everyone and do the breed no good at all. Most breeders profess to be 'in it for the good of the breed' and the best test of whether they are in the response they make when they find one of their dogs is throwing some serious defect. Admitting to a defect is not easy and may even be financially damaging but in the long run there is more to be gained for the breed by honesty than by deceit.

Future developments are likely to bring about screening for genetic disease by biochemical methods. If the underlying biochemical anomaly is known then laboratory techniques may be used to identify those animals which are carrying a single dose of a recessive gene. Such techniques have been applied to certain diseases of cattle and to some blood diseases in the dog. The area has been reviewed by Jolly and Healy (1986) who discuss its application to such diseases as fucosidosis in the Springer spaniel. The techniques are complex and do not lend themselves to every disease but in specific cases could be used and could have a major effect on the reduction of the diseases involved. Alas, as yet, the application is limited to a few specific features but future use may be quite extensive.

Where defects are selectional in the sense that they have come about because of deliberate selection for a type of dog that is not really soundly constructed the solution is more difficult. If, as seems likely, breeds like the Chow have eye troubles because of deliberate selection for small eyes the need to change direction and seek a more normal eye is obvious but this will involve polygenic methods not any test mating procedures.

More culling needs to be done by breeders in that mediocre or defective pups should be destroyed not sold. This is particularly true if a breeder is using inbreeding where more defects might come to the surface. Inbreeding is a useful and powerful tool but it needs to be used with ruthless selection against the weak and defective stock that may be produced alongside the good.

Above all breeders need to learn to work together. One can be rivals in the ring and in the breeding field in the sense of trying to do better than anyone else but unless breeders learn to cooperate they will not be able to do much against defects. No breeder is operating on a big enough scale to discover everything and only when records are pooled do things become obvious. This is very true in the case of selectional defects where judges have an important role to play. The dogs which win, especially those winning titles, influence the next generation of breeding stock and judges must be aware of their responsibilities. It is not sufficient to imagine that the judge is there simply to identify best of breed for the 'big ring'. The public spectacle of dog shows should be of minor concern to the breeder and ought to be to a judge. My opinion is that in this connection, all-rounder judges are to be deplored as generally being unable to perform a suitable task. A judge must be a total expert and, in my view, it is impossible to be an expert in the 150 breeds that a Kennel Club may recognise. Superficial ability to see a few aspects of alleged soundness is not enough; the judge must be fully involved in the breed concerned and know it inside out. The same applies to so-called specialists who are frequently bigoted about certain defects—often minor—and fail to see more important issues as a consequence. They are often tolerant of poor character and excuse or even encourage exaggeration.

Kennel Clubs must, of course, bear the brunt of the blame in that they often make no attempt to train and examine judges but just muddle on tolerating mediocrity and frequently ignoring the opinions of specialist clubs who are asked to comment on judges and then have their comments ignored. Much of the problem we see in the construction of dogs today can I believe be laid at the door of judges who have failed to rigidly penalise the variations from the standard and thus have allowed breeders to believe that their type of dog is acceptable and worthy of reproduction. Standards themselves are often badly worded, seemingly composed by men and women who had little understanding of anatomy and none of genetics. Many breed standards could be usefully rewritten—not to fit the dogs—but to make the standard indicative of what an outstanding dog should look like. This is epitomised by the new Kennel Club proposals for a standard in Border Collies. These seek the absence of a tuck-up in the loins and advocate a Terrier-like mode of action, neither of which will help to maintain the working potential of the breed since pig-like bodies and Terrier gaits will be useless in herding sheep. Additionally there is a requirement for dark eyes. Evans (1978) in a study of 56 working dogs found that only 12 had dark eyes while the vast majority were amber or pale. She is correct in pointing out that dark eyes are impossible with some colour varieties like liver-and-white for reasons explained in this book. No doubt the alleged experts will have their way and another working breed will be converted into an obedience automaton or a show ring ornament.

This book has contained much about defects and it is important not to leave the reader with the impression that hereditary defects are legion in dogs. This is unlikely to be the case, at least in respect of serious defects. Only limited information does exist on the subject because little or no attempt has been made to collect it. Many laymen and not a few veterinarians talk about defects in dogs as though they occurred in every litter and in almost every dog. When studies have been made on particular populations this is generally not the case. Thus Smith and Scammell (1968) reported on a Beagle colony which, in the period 1959–67 produced 2855 pups. Up to 1963 there were only two abnormal pups. Since that date 54 (38 litters) were produced and of these 40 (30 litters) were attributable to one sire entering in 1961. Among the 1538 descendants of this dog there was a 2.6% incidence compared with a 1.06% incidence rate in 1317 dogs that did not descend from him. Defects included umbilical hernia, limb deformity, cardiac defects, eye anomalies and bulldog heads. The paper illustrates some of the damage that can result from one unwisely used animal but also emphasises the rather low rate of problems. I am quite confident that if we studied more populations and breeds we would find in most of them a relatively low rate of such anomalies. Let us hope that this book will help to keep it that way.

References

Abbott, D. P. 1986. Canine inherited neuropathy of Tibetan Mastiffs (C.I.N.). Mimeograph published in USA (unknown source).

Abbott, H. 1959. Breeders report on congenital hip dysplasia in the German Shepherd Dog. *The Shepherd Dog Rev.* 37(2): 18.

Adams, E. W. 1956. Hereditary deafness in a family of Foxhounds. *J. Am. Vet. Med. Ass.* 128: 302–3.

Aguirre, G. D. and Rubin, L. F. 1971. Progressive retinal atrophy (rod dysplasia) in the Norwegian Elkhound. *J. Am. Vet. Med. Ass.* 158: 208–18.

Aguirre, G. D. and Rubin, L. F. 1972. Progressive retinal atrophy in the Miniature Poodle: an electrophysiologic study. *J. Am. Vet. Med. Ass.* 160: 191–202.

AHT 1965. *Inherited abnormalities of dogs.* Animal Health Trust, London.

Aitchison, J. 1963. Changing incisor dentition of Bulldogs. *Vet. Rec.* 75: 153–4.

Aitchison, J. 1964. Incisor dentition in short-muzzled dogs. *Vet. Rec.* 76: 165–9.

Alexander, J. E. 1963. Anomaly of craniopharyngeal duct and hypophysis. *Can. Vet. J.* 3: 83.

Allan, G. and Nicholas, F. 1975. The current status of HD in NSW. *Otter tales.*

Allen, G. M. 1914. Pattern development in mammals and birds. *Am. Nat.* 48: 385–412, 467–84, 550–66.

Almlof, J. 1961. On achondroplasia in the dog. *Zbl. Vet. Med.* 8: 43–6.

Alvesalo, L. and Tigerstedt, P. M. A. 1974. Heritabilities of human tooth dimensions. *Hereditas* 77: 311–18.

Andersen, A. C., McKelvie, D. H. and Phemister, R. 1962. Reproductive fitness of the female Beagle. *J. Am. Vet. Med. Ass.* 141: 1451–4.

Andersen, A. C. and Schultz, F. T. 1958. Inherited (congenital) cataract in the dog. *Am. J. Path.* 34: 965–75.

Andersen, S., Andresen, E. and Christensen, K. 1988. Hip dysplasia selection index exemplified by data from German Shepherd Dogs. *J. Anim. Breed. Genetics.* 105: 112–19.

Anderson, H., Henricson, B., Lundquist, P. G., Wedenberg, E. and Wersall, J. 1968. Genetic hearing impairment in the Dalmatian dog. An audiometric, genetic-morphological study in 53 dogs. *Acta oto-lar.* Supp. 232: 34pp.

Anderson, J. R. 1986. Encounters between domestic dogs and free-ranging non-human primates. *App. Anim. Behaviour Sci.* 15: 71–86.

Anderson, N. V. and Strafuss, A. C. 1971. Pancreatic disease in dogs and cats. *J. Am. Vet. Med. Ass.* 159: 885–91.

Anderson, P. and Carithers, R. W. 1975.   History as a diagnosis in canine epilepsy. *Iowa State Univ. Vet.* 37: 6–9.

Andersson, B. and Akerlund, L. E. 1976.   Scottie cramp and splay—functional disorders of Scottish Terriers, probably with a common aetiology. *Svensk. Vet.* 28: 733–8.

Andresen, E. 1977a.   Haemolytic anaemia in Basenji dogs. *Hereditas* 85: 211–14.

Andresen, E. 1977b.   Haemolytic anaemia in Basenji dogs. 2 Partial deficiency of erythrocyte pyruvate kinase (PK; EC 2.7.1.40) in heterozygous carriers. *Anim. Blood Grps biochem. Genet.* 8: 149–56.

Andresen, E. 1978.   Herkunft und Verbreitung von hypophysärem Zwerwuchs beim Hund und Grundlage zur Ermittlung von Anlageträgern verschiedener genetisch bedingter Krankheiten unter Anwendung biochemischer Methoden. *Kleintler Praxis* 23: 65–74.

Andresen, E. and Willeberg, P. 1976a.   Pituitary dwarfism in German Shepherd Dogs: additional evidence of simple autosomal recessive inheritance. *Nord. Vet. Med.* 28: 481–6.

Andresen, E. and Willeberg, P. 1976b.   Pituitary dwarfism in Karelian Bear Dogs: evidence of simple autosomal recessive inheritance. *Hereditas* 84: 232–4.

Andresen, E., Willeberg, P. and Rasmussen, P. G. 1974.   Pituitary dwarfism in German Shepherd Dogs: genetic investigations. *Nord. Vet. Med.* 26: 692–701.

Angus, K. and Young, G. B. 1972.   A note on the genetics of umbilical hernia. *Vet. Rec.* 90: 245–7.

Anon. 1917.   The hairless dog. *J. Hered.* 8: 519–20.

Anon. 1967.   *The Merck Veterinary Manual.* Merck & Co, Rathway, NJ.

Anon. 1971.   Presenting a slightly different view of canine hip dysplasia. *Pure-Bred Dogs.* Oct. 26–8.

Anon. 1973.   Canine hip dysplasia defined. *J. Am. Vet. Med. Ass.* 162: 662 Abstr.

Apgar, C. S. 1940.   The anatomical basis for certain postpartum reactions of the bitch towards her pups in various types of dog. *Anat. Rec.* 76 (Supp. 2): 61.

Appleby, E. C., Hayward, A. H. S. and Douce, G. 1978.   German Shepherds and splenic tumours. *Vet. Rec.* 102: 449.

Appleton, C. and Appleton, D. 1977a.   Husbandry versus hip dysplasia. *Our Dogs.* 1st Sept.

Appleton, C. and Appleton, D. 1977b.   Environment and medication in relation to hip dysplasia. *Our Dogs.* 15th Sept.

Archer, R. K. and Bowden, R. S. T. 1959.   A case of true haemophilia in a Labrador dog. *Vet. Rec.* 71: 560–6.

Arlein, M. D. 1947.   Generalised acute cutaneous asthenia in a dog. *J. Am. Vet. Med. Ass.* 111: 52–3.

Arwedsson, G. 1954.   Arthrodesis in traumatic plantar subluxation of the metatarsal bones of the dog. *J. Am. Vet. Med. Ass.* 124: 21–4.

Ashdown, R. R. 1963.   The anatomy of the inguinal canal in the domesticated mammals. *Vet. Rec.* 75: 1345–51.

Ashton, N., Barnett, K. C. and Sachs, D. D. 1968.   Retinal dysplasia in the Sealyham Terrier. *J. Path. Bact.* 96: 269–72.

Attwood-Parker, L. 1977.   Kerry Blue Terrier notes. *Terrier Talk.* Spring 15–16.

Aucante, M. 1970.   Lettre sur une production monstrueuse. *J. med. chir. pharm.* 32: 13–16.

Averill, D. R. 1973. Degenerative myelopathy in the ageing German Shepherd Dog. Clinical and pathologic findings. *J. Am. Vet. Med. Ass.* 162: 1045–51.

Badinand, F., Szumowski, P. and Breton, A. 1972. Etude morphobiologique et biochimique du sperme du Chien cryptorchide. *Rec. Med. Vet.* 148: 655–89.

Badoux, D. M. and Hoogeveen, P. 1976. Some notes on the biomechanics of the normal and dysplastic canine acetabulum. *Proc. Koninkl. Nederl. Akad. van Wetenschappen.* Series C 79: 97–111.

Bagnall, B. G. 1977. Recent advances in canine dermatology. *Vet. Ann.* 17: 191–4.

Bailey, N. T. J. 1961. *Introduction to the mathematical theory of linkage.* Clarendon Press, Oxford.

Baker, E. 1955. Congenital hypoplasia of the pituitary and pancreas glands in the dog. *J. Am. Vet. Med. Ass.* 126: 468.

Ball, W. Jr and Asquith, R. L. 1958. Flat pup syndrome. *Veterinarian* 19: 135–7.

Bane, A. 1970. (Sterility in the male dog.) *Nord. Vet. Med.* 22: 561–6.

Banks, W. C. and Bridges, C. H. 1956. Multiple cartilaginous exostoses in a dog. *J. Am. Vet. Med. Ass.* 129: 131–5.

Bardens, J. W. and Hardwick, H. 1968. New observations on the diagnosis and cause of hip dysplasia. *Vet. Med./Small Anim. Clin.* 63: 238–45.

Barnett, K. C. 1962. Hereditary retinal atrophy in the Poodle. *Vet. Rec.* 74: 672–5.

Barnett, K. C. 1965a. Canine retinopathies—II. The Miniature and Toy Poodle. *J. small Anim. Pract.* 6: 93–109.

Barnett, K. C. 1965b. Canine retinopathies—III. The other breeds. *J. small. Anim. Pract.* 6: 186–96.

Barnett, K. C. 1965c. Two forms of hereditary and progressive retinal atrophy in the dog. I. The Miniature Poodle. II. The Labrador Retriever. *Anim. Hosp.* 1: 234–45.

Barnett, K. C. 1969a. The Collie Eye Anomaly. *Vet. Rec.* 84: 431–4.

Barnett, K. C. 1969b. Genetic anomalies of the posterior segment of the canine eye. *J. small Anim. Pract.* 10: 451–5.

Barnett, K. C. 1970a. Glaucoma in the dog. *J. small Anim. Pract.* 11: 113–28.

Barnett, K. C. 1970b. The British Veterinary Association/Kennel Club Progressive Retinal Atrophy scheme. *Vet. Rec.* 86: 588–92.

Barnett, K. C. 1976. Comparative aspects of canine hereditary eye disease. *Adv. Vet. Sci. Comp. Med.* 20: 39–67.

Barnett, K. C. 1978. Hereditary cataract in the dog. *J. small Anim. Pract.* 19: 109–20.

Barnett, K. C. 1985. Hereditary cataract in the miniature Schnauzer. *J. small Anim. Pract.* 26: 635–44.

Barnett, K. C. 1986. Hereditary cataract in the German Shepherd Dog. *J. small Anim. Pract.* 27: 387–95.

Barnett, K. C., Bjorck, G. R. and Koch, E. 1970. Hereditary retinal dysplasia in the Labrador Retriever in England and Sweden. *J. small Anim. Pract.* 10: 755–9.

Barnett, K. C. and Curtis, R. 1978. Lens luxation and progressive retinal atrophy in the Tibetan Terrier. *Vet. Rec.* 103: 160.

Barnett, K. C. and Dunn, W. L. 1969. The International Sheepdog Society and Progressive Retinal Atrophy. *J. small Anim. Pract.* 10: 301–7.

Barnett, K. C. and Knight, G. C. 1969.   Persistent pupillary membrane and associated defects in the Basenji. *Vet. Rec.* 85: 242–9.

Barnett, K. C. and Stades, F. C. 1979.   Collie eye anomaly in the Shetland Sheepdog in the Netherlands. *J. small Anim. Pract.* 20: 321–9.

Baronti, A. C. 1950.   Congenital esophageal dilation in a Cocker puppy. *N. Am. Vet.* 21: 666–7.

Barrows, W. M. and Phillips, J. M. 1915.   Color in Cocker Spaniels. *J. Hered.* 6: 387–97.

Batt, R. M. 1980.   The molecular basis of malabsorption. *J. small Anim. Pract.* 21: 555–69.

Batt, R. M., Bush, B. M. and Peters, T. J. 1979.   A new test for the diagnosis of exocrine pancreatic insufficiency in the dog. *J. small Anim. Pract.* 20: 185–92.

Bayer, O. 1936.   (Measures for the prevention of the spread of deleterious hereditary characters and of degeneration in dog breeding.) *Praktierarzt. Arch.* 16: 229–38.

BBC, 1976.   *The British Boxer Club Record Book 1939–1975.* British Boxer Club, London.

Beachley, M. C. and Graham. F. H. 1973.   Hypochondroplastic dwarfism (Enchondral chondro-dystrophy) in a dog. *J. Am. Vet. Med. Ass.* 163: 283–4.

Beaver, R. V. 1983.   Clinical classification of canine aggression. *App. Anim. Ethology* 10: 35–43.

Becker, R. F., Markee, J. E. and King, J. E. 1957.   Studies on olfactory acuity in dogs. 1. Discriminatory behaviour in problem situations. *Brit. J. Anim. Behav.* 5: 94–103.

Bedford, P. G. C. 1971.   Eyelashes and adventitious cilia as causes of corneal irritation. *J. small Anim. Pract.* 12: 11–17.

Bedford, P. G. C. 1977.   Talk to the British Briard Club. British Briard Club Forum, Cheltenham.

Bedford, P. G. C. 1984.   Retinal pigment epithelial dystrophy (CPRA): a study of the disease in the Briard. *J. small Anim. Pract.* 25: 129–38.

Belfield, W. O. 1976.   Chronic subclinical scurvy and canine hip dysplasia. *Vet. Med./Small Anim. Clin.* 10: 1399–401.

Bellars, A. R. M. 1969.   Hereditary disease in British Antarctic Sledge Dogs. *Vet. Rec.* 85: 600–7.

Bennett, D. 1974.   Canine dystocia—a review of the literature. *J. small Anim. Pract.* 15: 101–17.

Bergsten, G. and Nordin, M. 1986.   Osteochondrossom ersattningsorak i ett material forsakrade hundar. *Svensk Veterinartidning* 38: 97–100.

Bernard, M. A. and Valli, V. E. 1977.   Familial renal disease in Samoyed dogs. *Can. Vet. J.* 18: 181–9.

Bertrand, I., Medynski, C. H. and Salles, P. 1936.   Etudes d'un cas d'agenesie du vermis cerebelleux chez le chien. *Rev. Neurol.* 66: 716–33.

Bielfelt, S. W., Redman, H. C. and McClellan, R. O. 1971.   Sire- and sex-related differences in rates of epileptiform seizures in a purebred Beagle dog colony. *Am. J. Vet. Res.* 32: 2039–48.

Binet, A. and Passey, J. 1895.   Contributions a l'etude de l'Olfaction chez le chien. *C. R. Ass. Franc. Av. Sci.* Part 2, 659–61.

Bingel, S. A. and Riser, W. H. 1977.   Congenital elbow in the dog. *J. small Anim. Pract.* 18: 445–56.

Birkeland, R. 1967.   Osteochondritis dissecans in the humeral head of the dog. Comparison of results achieved with conservative and surgical treatment. *Nord. Vet. Med.* 19: 294–306.

Bistner, S. I., Rubin, L. F. and Roberts, S. R. 1971.   A review of persistent pupillary membranes in the Basenji dog. *J. Am. Anim. Hosp. Ass.* 7: 143–57.

Bjork, G., Dyrendahl, S. and Olsson, S. E. 1957. Hereditary ataxia in Smooth-haired Fox Terriers. *Vet. Rec.* 69: 871–76.

Bjork, G., Mair, W., Olsson, S. E. and Sourander P. 1962. Hereditary ataxia in Fox Terriers. *Acta. Neuropath.* Supp. 1. 45–8.

Black, L. 1969. The progressive retinal atrophy scheme. *Vet. Rec.* 85: 694–5.

Black, L. 1972. Progressive retinal atrophy. A review of the genetics and an appraisal of the eradication scheme. *J. small Anim. Pract.* 13: 295–314.

Blake, S. and Lapinski, A. 1980. Hypothyroidism in different breeds. *Canine Pract.* 7(2): 48, 51.

Bloedow, A. G. 1981. Familial renal disease in Samoyed dogs. *Vet. Rec. 108*: 167–8.

Bockelmann, H. 1920. Untersuchungen an Wolfsbastarden nach Zuchtungsversuchen im Haustiergarten zu Halle. Dissertation cited by Iljin 1941 (see reference).

Blogg, J. R. 1970. Collie eye disease. *Aust. Vet. J.* 46: 530–2.

Bohme, R., Schonfelder, E. and Schlaaf, S. 1978. Prognostische Untersuchungen zur Verbreitung der Hüftgelenkdysplasie beim Deutschen Schäferhund in der DDR. *Monat. Veterinarmedizin.* 33: 93–6.

Bohning, B. H., Sutter, P. F., Hohn, B. and Marshall, J. L. 1970. Clinical and radiological survey of canine panosteitis *J. Am. Vet. Med. Ass.* 156: 870–3.

Bomhard, D. von and Dreiack, J. 1977. Statistiche Erhebungen über Mamma-tumoren bei Hundinnen. *Kleinter Praxis* 22: 250–9.

Bone, D. L. 1980. Canine panosteitis. *Canine Pract.* 7(4): 61–8.

Borchelt, P. L. 1983. Aggressive behaviour of dogs kept as companion animals: classification and influence of sex, reproductive status and breed. *App. Anim. Ethology* 10: 45–61.

Bornfors, S., Palsson, K. and Skude, G. 1964. Hereditary aspects of hip dysplasia in German Shepherd Dogs. *J. Am Vet. Med. Ass.* 145: 15–20.

Bostock, D. E. 1976. The prognosis of canine mammary neoplasia. *Vet. Ann.* 16: 194–8.

Bovell, D. 1977. Personal communication.

Bowen, J. M., Lewis, R. E., Keller, S. K., Wilson, R. C. and Arnold, R. A. 1972. Progression of hip dysplasia in German Shepherd Dogs after unilateral pectinal myotomy. *J. Am. Vet. Med. Ass.* 161: 899–904.

Bowles, C. A., Alsaker, R. D. & Wolfe, T. L. 1979. Studies of the Pelger-Huët anomaly in Foxhounds. *Am. J. Pathol.* 96: 237–45.

Boxer Breed Council of the UK (1982?). Progressive axonopathy (PA) of Boxer Dogs. Advisory leaflet.

Brackett, L. C. 1959. Here we go again. *The Shepherd Dog Rev.* 37(2): 29; 37(3): 20; 37(4): 60; 37(5): 22.

Bradley, W. A. 1975. Selection and management of a Beagle colony for experimental dogs. *J. Inst. Anim. Tech.* 25: 43–54.

Bradney, I. W. 1967. Non union of the anconeal process in the dog. *Aust. Vet. J.* 43: 215–16.

Brandsch, H. 1964. Vergleichende Untersuchungen zur Vererbung des Kryptorchismus und der Intersexualität bei Haustieren. *Kuhn-Archiv.* 77: 324–425.

Brasmer, T. H. 1953. Congenital esophageal dilation. *N. Am. Vet.* 34: 36–8.

Brass, W. 1988. Personal communication.

Brass, W., Freudiger, U., Muller, L. F., Paatsama, S., van der Velden, N. A. and van de Watering, C. C. 1978.   Bericht der Hüftgelenkdysplasie Kommission. *Kleinter Praxis* 23: 169–80.

Braund, L. G. and Vandevelde, M. 1978.   German Shepherd Dog myelopathy—A morphologic and morphometric study. *Am. J. Vet. Res.* 39: 1309–15.

Breitschwerdt, E. B., Halliwell, W. H., Foley, C. W., Stark, D. R. & Corwin, L. A. 1980.   A hereditary diarrhetic syndrome in the Basenji characterised by malabsorption, protein-losing enteropathy and hypergammaglobulinemia. *J. Am. Anim. Hosp. Ass.* 16: 551–60.

Breshears, D. E. 1965.   Esophageal dilation in six week old German Shepherd Dog pups. *Vet. Med.* 60: 1034–6.

Briggs, L. C. 1940.   Some experimental matings of color-bred White Bull Terriers. *J. Hered.* 31: 236–8.

Briggs, L. C. and Kaliss, N. 1942.   Coat color inheritance in Bull Terriers. *J. Hered.* 33: 222–8.

Briggs, O. M. and Botha, W. S. 1986.   Color mutant alopecia in a blue Italian Greyhound. *J. Am. Anim. Hosp. Ass.* 22: 611–14.

Brinkhous, K. M. and Graham, J. B. 1950.   Haemophilia in the female dog. *Science* 111: 723–4.

Brock, W. E., Buckner, R. G., Hampton, J. W., Bird, R. M. and Wulz, C. E. 1963.   Canine haemophilia. *Arch. Path.* 76: 464–9.

Brown, C. J., Murphree, O. D. and Newton, J. E. O. 1978.   The effect of inbreeding on human aversion in Pointer dogs. *J. Hered.* 69: 362–5.

Brown, R. V. and Teng, Y-S. 1975.   Studies of inherited pyruvate kinase deficiency in the Basenji. *J. Am. Anim. Hosp. Ass.* 11: 362–5.

Brunsch, A. 1956.   Vergelichende Untersuchungen am Haarkleid von Wildcaniden und Haushunden. *Z. Tierzucht. Zucht Biol.* 67: 205–40.

Bruyerë, P. 1970.   La maladie de Legg-Perthes-Calve-Waldstrom, affection idiopathique de la hanche chez le chien. *Ann. Med. Vet.* 114: 67–74.

Buckner, R. G., Hampton, J. M., Bird, R. M. and Brock, W. E. 1967.   Haemophilia in the Vizsla. *J. small Anim. Pract.* 8: 511–19.

Budgett, H. M. 1933.   *Hunting by scent.* Eyre & Spottiswoode, London.

Buer, A. W. 1943.   *Norsk. Vet. Tidsskr.*

Bull, R. W. 1974.   New knowledge about blood groups in dogs. Mimeo.

Burgisser, H. and Hintermann, J. 1961.   Kystes dermoides de la tête chez le Boxer. *Schweiz. Arch. Tierheilk.* 103: 309–12.

Burnez, C., Burnez, S. and Surnet, Y. 1972.   Le coleur noire recessive chez Berger Belge. *Berger Belge* (1972) 61–73.

Burnez, S. and Burnez, C. 1972.   La transmission hereditaire des coleurs chez les Berger Belge. *Berger Belge* (1972) 2–9.

Burns, M. 1943.   Hair pigmentation and the genetics of colour in Greyhounds. *Proc. Roy. Soc. Edin.* B 61: 462–90.

Burns, M. 1969.   The mutual behaviour of sheep and sheep dogs in Ghana. *Trop. agric.* 46: 91–102.

Burns, M. 1977.   Review of 'The German Shepherd Dog; its history, development and genetics', by M. B. Willis. *Anim. Breed. Abstr.* 45: 217–18.

Burns, M. and Fraser, M. N. 1966.   *Genetics of the dog. The basis of successful breeding.* Oliver & Boyd, Edin.

Buser, J. C. and Freudiger, U. 1973. L'Amylase et la lipase chez le chien—leur rôle dans diverses maladies, spécialement dans les affections pancréatiques. *Schweiz. Arch. Tierheilk.* 115: 81–94.

Buskirk, R. van. 1977. The lens epithelium of American Cocker Spaniels with inherited and non-inherited lens cataract. *Res. Vet. Sci.* 22: 237–42.

Butler, H. C., Wallace, L. J. and Ladds, P. W. 1971. *J. Am. Anim. Hosp. Ass.* 7: 81.

Buytendijk, F. J. J. 1935. *The mind of the dog.* Allen & Unwin, London.

BVA. 1954. Cryptorchidism with special reference to the condition in the dog. *Vet. Rec.* 66: 482–3.

BVA. 1955. Cryptorchidism in the dog. *Vet. Rec.* 67: 472–4.

BVA. 1976. Hip dysplasia. Consolidated report of the Small Animals Committee working parties on the BVA/KC hip dysplasia control scheme. *Vet. Rec.* 100: 484–7.

BVA. 1977. Personal communication.

BVA. 1978. Hip dysplasia: trial scheme for German Shepherd Dogs. *Vet. Rec.* 102: 220.

Campbell, J. R. 1969. Non-fracture injuries to the canine elbow. *J. Am. Vet. Med. Ass.* 155: 735–44.

Campbell, J. R. 1971. Luxations and ligamentous injuries of the elbow of the dog. *Vet. Clin. N. Am.* 1: 429.

Campbell, J. R., Bennett, D. and Lee, R. 1976. Intertarsal and tarsometatarsal subluxation in the dog. *J. small Anim. Pract.* 17: 427–42.

Capel-Edwards, K. and Hall, D. E. 1968. Factor VII deficiency in the Beagle dog. *Lab. Anim.* 2: 105–12.

Cardinet, G. H., Guffy, M. M. and Wallace, J. J. 1974. Canine hip dysplasia: effects of pectineal myectomy on the coxofemoral joints of Greyhounds and German Shepherd Dogs. *J. Am. Vet. Med. Ass.* 165: 529–32.

Carlsson, W. D. 1961. *Veterinary radiology.* Balliere, Tindall and Cox, London.

Carlsson, W. D. and Lumb, W. V. 1958. Esophageal invagination of the stomach in a dog. *Mod. Vet. Pract.* 39: 65.

Carlsson, W. D. and Severin, G. 1961. Elbow dysplasia in the dog; a preliminary report. *J. Am. Vet. Med. Ass.* 134: 295–7.

Carnahan, D. L., Guffy, M. M., Hibbs, C. M., Leipold, H. W. and Huston, K. 1968. Hip dysplasia in Hereford cattle. *J. Am. Vet. Med. Ass.* 152: 1150.

Carrara, O. and Cremagnani, A. 1965. Rilievi statistici sulla incidenza delle neoplasie nel cane del setorato di Milano. *Atti. Soc. ital. Sci. vet.* 18: 401–6.

Carrig, C. B. and Morgan, J. P. 1974. *J. Am. vet. Radiol. Soc.* 15: 28.

Carrig, C. B., Morgan, J. P. and Pool, R. R. 1975. Effects of asynchronous growth of the radius and ulna on the canine elbow joint following experimental retardation of longitudinal growth of the ulna. *J. Am. Anim. Hosp. Ass.* 11: 560–77.

Carrig, C. B. and Seawright, A. A. 1969. A familial canine polyostotic fibrous dysplasia with superiosteal cortical defects. *J. small Anim. Pract.* 10: 397–405.

Carter, J. D. 1972. Combined operation for noncicatricial entropion with distiachiasis. *J. Am. Anim. Hosp. Ass.* 8: 53–8.

Carver, E. A. 1984. Coat colour genetics of the German Shepherd Dog. *J. Heredity* 75: 247–52.

Catcott, E. J. 1969. Summary and conclusions to CEA symposium. *J. Am. Vet. Med. Ass.* 155: 877–8.

Cattanach, B. M. 1978.   Personal communication.

Cattanach, B. M. 1981.   Personal communication.

CAVA. 1967.   Inherited defects in dogs and cats in Australia. *Aust. Vet. J.* 43: 221–4.

Cavalli-Sforza, L. L. and Bodmer, W. F. 1971.   *The genetics of human populations.* Freeman, San Francisco.

Cawley, A. J. and Archibald, J. 1959.   Un-united anconeal processes of the dog. *J. Am. Vet. Med. Ass.* 134: 454–8.

Cello, R. M. 1969.   Comments on the paper by Wyman and Donovan 1969. *J. Am. Vet. Med. Ass.* 155: 870–1.

Cello, R. M. and Kennedy, P. C. 1957.   Hyperinsulinism in dogs due to pancreatic islet cell carcinoma. *Cornell Vet.* 47: 538–57.

Charlton, J. 1976.   In *Hips* by J. Macan. Private publication (1978).

Cheville, N. F. 1968.   The grey Collie syndrome. *J. Am. Vet. Med. Ass.* 152: 620–30.

Christie, D. W. and Bell, E. T. 1971.   Some observations of the seasonal incidence and frequency of oestrus in breeding bitches in Britain. *J. small Anim. Pract.* 12: 159–67.

Clark, P., Ryan, G. E. and Czuppon, A. B. 1975.   Biochemical markers in the family Canidae. *Aust. J. Zool.* 23: 411–17.

Clayton-Jones, D. G. 1974.   Hindleg lameness in the dog. *Vet. Ann.* 14: 167.

Clayton-Jones, D. G. and Vaughan, L. C. 1970a.   Disturbances in the growth of the radius of dogs. *J. small Anim. Pract.* 11: 452–68.

Clayton-Jones, D. G. and Vaughan, L. C. 1970b.   The surgical treatment of osteochondritis dissecans of the humeral head in dogs. *J. small Anim. Pract.* 11: 803–12.

Claxton, J. H. and Yeates, N. T. M. 1972.   The inheritance of cryptorchidism in a small crossbred flock of sheep. *J. Hered.* 63: 141–4.

Clifford, D. H. and Gyorkey, F. 1967.   Myenteric ganglial cells in dogs with and without achalasia of the esophagus. *J. Am. Vet. Med. Ass.* 150: 205–11.

Comfort, A. 1956.   Longevity and mortality of Irish Wolfhounds. *Proc. zool. Soc. Lond.* 127: 27–34.

Comfort, A. 1960.   Longevity and mortality in dogs of four breeds. *J. Geront.* 15: 126–9.

Conklin, E. H. 1957.   Recessive inheritance and the grey Collie. *J. Canine Genet.* March 1–8.

Cooper, H. K. Jr. and Mattern, G. W. 1970.   Genetic studies of cleft lip and palate in dogs (a preliminary report). *Carnivore Genet. Newsl.* No. 9: 204–9.

Cordy, D. R. and Snelbaker, H. A. 1952.   Cerebellar hypoplasia and degeneration in a family of Airedale dogs. *J. Neuropath. Exp. Neurol.* 11: 324–6.

Cork, L. C., Griffin, J. W., Munnell, J. F., Lorenz, M. D., Adams, R. J. and Price, D. L. 1979.   Hereditary canine spinal muscular atrophy. *J. Neuropath. Exp. Neurol.* 38: 209–21

Corley, E. A. 1978.   Canine hip dysplasia and the Orthopedic Foundation for animals. *Norden News* 53(2): 14–17.

Corley, E. A. and Carlsson, W. D. 1965.   Radiographic, genetic and pathologic aspects of elbow dysplasia. *J. Am. Vet. Med. Ass.* 147: 1651.

Corley, E. A., Carlsson, W. D., Sutherland, T. M., Flint, J. A. and Newkirk, H. M. 1963.   Elbow dysplasia, a genetic and pathologic study. In *1963 Ann. Rept. AM 06597–01 USDHEWPHS, Washington.*

Corley, E. A. and Hogan, P. M. 1985. Trends in hip dysplasia control: Analysis of radiographs submitted to the Orthopedic Foundation for Animals, 1974 to 1984. *J. Am. Vet. Med. Ass.* 187: 805–9.

Corley, E. A., Sutherland, T. M. and Carlsson, W. D. 1968. Genetic aspects of canine elbow dysplasia. *J. Am. Vet. Med. Ass.* 153: 543–7.

Cotchin, E. 1951. Neoplasms in small animals. *Vet. Rec.* 63: 67–78.

Cotchin, E. 1954. Neoplasia in the dog. *Vet. Rec.* 66: 879–88.

Cotchin, E. 1955. Melanotic tumours in the dog. *J. Comp. Path.* 65: 115–29.

Cotchin, E. 1962. Problems of comparative oncology. With special reference to the veterinary aspects. *Bull Wld. Hlth. Org.* 26: 635–48.

Cotter, S. M., Griffiths, R. C. and Lear, L. 1968. Enostosis of young dogs. *J. Am. Vet. Med. Ass.* 153: 401–10.

Cottrell, B. D. and Barnett, K. C. 1988. Primary glaucoma in the Welsh Springer Spaniel. *J. small Anim. Pract.* 29: 185–199.

Craft, W. A. 1930. Pigs inherit swirl hair. *Bienn. Rep. Oklahoma A & M. Coll. Agric. Exp. Sta.* p. 36.

Craig, P. H. and Riser, W. H. 1965. *J. Am. vet. Radiol. Soc.* 6: 40.

Crawford, R. D. and Kaye, M. M. 1973. A proposed Canadian selective registration for the control of canine hip dysplasia. *J. Am. Vet. Med. Ass.* 162: 668 Abstr.

Crawford, R. D. and Loomis, G. 1978. Inheritance of short coat and long coat in St Bernard dogs. *J. Hered.* 69: 266–7.

Crispin, S. M. and Barnett, K. C. 1978. Arcus lipoides corneae secondary to hypothyroidism in the Alsatian. *J. small Anim. Pract.* 19: 127–42.

Croft, P. G. 1965. Fits in dogs: a survey of 260 cases. *Vet. Rec.* 77: 438–45.

Croft, P. G. 1968a. The use of the electro-encephalograph in the detection of epilepsy as a hereditary condition in the dog. *Vet. Rec.* 82: 712–13.

Croft, P. G. 1968b. Epilepsy in the dog. An edited version of a talk to the Alsatian League. *League Mag.* June p. 8.

Croft, P. G. and Stockman, M. J. R. 1964. Inherited defects in dogs. *Vet. Rec.* 76: 260–61.

Cunningham, E. P. 1969. *Animal Breeding Theory.* An Foras Taluntais, Dublin 272 pp.

Cunningham, J. G. 1971. Canine seizure disorders. *J. Am. Vet. Med. Ass.* 157: 589–97.

Cunningham, P. L. 1975. *Dog World* 17th Jan.

Curtis, R. 1984. Late onset cataract in the Boston terrier. *Vet. Rec.* 115: 577–8.

Curtis, R. L., English, D. and Kim, Y. J. 1964. Spina bifida in a 'Stub' dog stock selectively bred for short tails. *Anat. Rec.* 148: 365 Abstr.

Dausch, D., Wegner, W., Michaelis M. and Reetz, I. 1977. Ophthalmologische Befunde in einer Merlezucht. *Dtsch. Tierarztl. Wschr.* 84: 469–75.

De Boom, H. P. A. 1956. Anomalous animals. *S. Afr. J. Sci.* 61: 159–71.

Dechambre, P. 1932. La transmission hereditaire des caracteres lies au sexe. *Rev. Zootech.* 12: 363–70.

DeForest, M. E., Eger, C. E. and Basrur, P. K. 1978. Hereditary Cerebellar Neuronal Abiotrophy in a Kerry Blue Terrier Dog. *Can. vet. J.* 19: 198–202.

deLahunta, A. and Averill, D. R. 1976.   Hereditary cerebellar cortical and extrapyramidal nuclear abiotrophy in Kerry Blue Terriers. *J. Am. Vet. Med. Ass.* 168: 1119–24.

de Lahunta, A., Fenner, W. R., Imdrieri, R. J., Mellick, P. W., Gardner, S. and Bell, J. S. 1980. Hereditary Cerebellar Cortical Abiotrophy in the Gordon Setter. *J. Am. Vet. Med. Ass.* 177: 538–41.

Deluca, D. C., Murphree, O. D. and Angel, C. 1974.   Biochemistry of nervous dogs. *Pavlovian J.* 9: 136–48.

Denny, H. R. 1980.   Die chirurgische Behandlung der Osteochondrosis dissecans und des losen Processus coronoideus ulnae im Ellbogengelenk des Hundes. *Kleiner Praxis* 25: 343–8.

Denny, H. R. & Gibbs, C. 1980a.   Osteochondritis dissecans of the canine stifle joint. *J. small Anim. Pract.* 21: 317–22.

Denny, H. R. & Gibbs, C. 1980b.   The surgical treatment of osteochondritis dissecans and ununited coronoid process in the canine elbow joint. *J. small Anim. Pract.* 21: 323–31.

De Pugh, R. B. 1956.   Growth and development. *J. Canine Genet.* Sept. 7–30.

Dice, P. F. 1980.   Progressive retinal atrophy in the Samoyed. *Mod. Vet. Pract.* 61: 59–60.

Dickerson, G. E., Lush, J. L. and Culbertson, G. C. 1946.   Hybrid vigor in single crosses between inbred lines of Poland China swine. *J. Anim. Sci.* 5: 16–24.

Dinkel, C. A., Busch, D. A., Minyard, J. A. and Trevellyan, W. R. 1968.   Effects of inbreeding on growth and conformation of beef cattle. *J. Anim. Sci.* 27: 313–22.

Distl, O., Windisch, E. and Kräusslich, H. 1985.   Zur Verbreitung und Erblichkeit der Hüftgelenksdysplasie bei den Hunderassen Hovawart und Boxer in der Bundesrepublik Deutschland. *Zentralblatt fur Veterinärmedizin* A 32: 551–60.

Dodds, W. J. 1967.   Familial Canine Thrombocytopathy. *Thromb. Diath. Haemorrh.* Supp. 26: 241–8.

Dodds, W. J. 1970.   Canine von Willebrand's disease. *J. Lab. Clin. Med.* 76: 713–21.

Dodds, W. J. 1973.   Canine factor X (Stuart-Prower factor) deficiency. *J. Lab. Clin. Med.* 82: 560–6.

Dodds, W. J. 1974.   Hereditary and acquired haemorrhagic disorders in animals. In *Progress in Haemostasis and Thrombosis* (ed. T. H. Spaet). Vol. 2: p. 215–47.

Dodds, W. J. 1975.   Further studies of Canine von Willebrand's disease. *Blood* 45: 221–30.

Dodds, W. J. 1978.   Inherited bleeding disorders. *Canine Pract.* 5(6): 49–58.

Dodds, W. J. and Kull, J. E. 1971.   Canine factor XI (plasma thromboplast in antecedent). *J. Lab. Clin. Med.* 78: 746–52.

Donald, H. P., Deas, D. W. and Wilson, A. L. 1952.   Genetical analysis of the incidence of dropsical calves in herds of Ayrshire cattle. *Brit. Vet. J.* 108: 227–45.

Doncaster, L. 1906.   On the inheritance of coat colour in rats. *Proc. Camb. Philos. Soc.* 13: 215–28.

Done, S. H., Drew, R. A., Robins, G. M. and Lane, J. G. 1975.   Hemivertebra in the dog: clinical and pathological observations. *Vet. Rec.* 96: 313–17.

Done, S. H. and Staton, J. F. 1978.   German Shepherds and splenic tumours. *Vet. Rec.* 102: 224.

Donovan, E. F. and Wyman, M. 1965.   Ocular fundus anomaly in the Collie. *J. Am. Vet. Med. Ass.* 147: 1465–9.

Donovan, R. H. 1965.   *Proc. Am. Soc. Vet. Ophthal.* 8.

Donovan, R. H. 1971. *Proc. Am. Coll. Vet. Ophthal.*

Donovan, R. H., Freeman, M. M. and Schepens, C. L. 1969. Anomaly of the Collie eye. *J. Am. Vet. Med. Ass.* 155: 872–5.

Douglass, E. M. 1981. Hip dysplasia in a timber wolf. *Vet. Med.* March 402–3.

Dow, R. S. 1940. Partial agenesis of the cerebellum in dogs. *J. Comp. Neurol.* 72: 569–86.

Drew, R. A. 1974. Possible association between abnormal vertebral development and neonatal mortality in Bulldogs. *Vet. Rec.* 94: 480–1.

Dreyer, C. J. and Preston, C. B. 1973. Abnormal behaviour patterns in dogs with cleft palates. *S. Afr. J. Med. Sci.* 38: 13–16.

Druckseis, H. 1935. Geschlechtsverhältnis und Wurfgrösse beim Hund. *Vet. Med. Diss.* Univ. Munich.

Dudok de Wit, C., Coenegracht, N. A. C. J., Poll, P. H. A. and Linde, J. D. vd. 1967. The practical importance of blood groups in dogs. *J. small Anim. Pract.* 8: 285–9.

Duke-Elder, S. 1969. *Systems of Ophthalmology.* Vol. 2. Henry Kimpton, London.

Dykman, R. A., Mack, R. L. and Ackerman, P. T. 1965. The evaluation of autonomic and motor components of the non-avoidance conditioned response in the dog. *Psychophysiol.* 1: 209–30.

Dykman, R. A., Murphree, O. D. and Ackerman, P. T. 1966. The evaluation of offspring of nervous and stable dogs. II. Autonomic and motor conditioning. *J. Nerv. Ment. Dis.* 141: 419–31.

Dykman, R. A., Murphree, O. D. and Peters, J. E. 1969. Like begets like; behavioral tests, classical autonomic and motor conditioning, and operant conditioning in two strains of Pointer dogs. *Ann. N.Y. Acad. Sci.* 159: 976–1007.

Edmonds, H. L., Hegreberg, G. A., VavGelder, N. M., Sylvester, D. M., Clemmons, R. M. and Chatburn, C. G. 1979. Spontaneous convulsions in Beagle dogs. *Federation Proc.* 38: 2424–8.

Elliot, O. and Scott, J. P. 1965. The analysis of breed differences in maze performance in dogs. *Anim. Behav.* 13: 5–18.

Ellsworth, H. A. 1927. The inheritance of carpal displacement. *J. Hered.* 18: 133.

Else, R. W. and Hannant, D. 1979. Some epidemiological aspects of mammary neoplasia in the bitch. *Vet. Rec.* 104: 296–304.

Endres, B. 1977. (Congenital luxation of the patella in dogs. Treatment and results in the period 1966–75.) *Diss. Univ. Munich.*

Engstrom, D. 1966. Tyrosinase deficiency in the Chow Chow. In *Current Veterinary Therapy Small Animal Practice* (ed. R. W. Kirk), W. B. Saunders Co, Philadelphia.

Eriksen, K. and Grøndalen, J. 1984. Familial renal disease in Soft-coated Wheaten terriers. *J. small Anim. Pract.* 25: 489–500.

Esterley, J. R. 1965. Congenital hereditary lymphoedema. *J. Med. Genet.* 2: 93–8.

Evans, J. M., Lane, D. R. and Hendy, P. G. 1974. The profile of small animal practice. *J. small Anim. Pract.* 15: 595–607.

Evans, M. J. 1978. Personal communication.

Ewing, G. O. 1969. Familial nonspherocytic hemolytic anaemia of Basenji dogs. *J. Am. Vet. Med. Ass.* 154: 503–7.

Ewing, G. O. and Gomez, J. A. 1973. Canine ulcerative colitis. *J. Am. Anim. Hosp. Ass.* 9: 395–406.

Falaschini, A. 1941.   Sul comportamento ereditario dello sperone in Canis familiaris. *Nuova Vet.* 19: 126–9.

Falco, M. J., Barker, J. and Wallace, M. E. 1974.   The genetics of epilepsy in the British Alsatian. *J. small Anim. Pract.* 15: 685–92.

Falconer, D. S. 1960.   *Introduction to quantitative genetics*. Oliver & Boyd, London.

Fankhauser, R., Luginbuhl, H. and Hartley, W. J. 1963.   Leukodystrophie von Typus-Krabbe beim Hund. *Schweiz. Arch. Tierheilk.* 105: 198–207.

Feldmann, D. B., Bree, M. M. and Cohen, B. J. 1968.   Congenital diaphragmatic hernia in neonatal dogs. *J. Am. Vet. Med. Ass.* 153: 942–4.

Field, R. A., Richard, C. G. and Hutt, F. B. 1946.   Hemophilia in a family of dogs. *Cornell Vet.* 36: 285–300.

Finco, D. R. 1976.   Familial renal disease in Norwegian Elkhound dogs: physiologic and biochemical examinations. *Am. J. Vet. Res.* 37: 87–91.

Finco, D. R., Kurtz, H. J., Low, D. G. and Perman, V. 1970.   Familial renal disease in Norwegian Elkhound dogs. *J. Am. Vet. Med. Ass.* 156: 747–60.

Fisher, R. A. and Yates, F. 1963.   *Statistical tables for Biological, Agricultural and Medical Research*. Oliver & Boyd, Edin.

Fitch-Daglish, E. 1959.   Do not sidetrack the main issue. *Dog World* 31st July.

Fitts, R. H. 1948.   Dilation of the oesophagus in a Cocker Spaniel. *J. Am. Vet. Med. Ass.* 112: 343–4.

Flesja, K. and Yri, T. 1977.   Protein-losing enteropathy in the Lundehund. *J. small Anim. Pract.* 18: 11–23.

Fletch, S. M., Pinkerton, P. H. and Brueckner, P. J. 1975.   The Alaskan Malamute Chondrodysplasia (Dwarfism-Anemia) syndrome—a review. *J. Am. Anim. Hosp. Ass.* 11: 353–61.

Fletch, S. M., Smart, M. E., Pennick, P. W. and Subden, R. E. 1973.   Inherited chondrodysplasia of the purebred Alaskan Malamute: a clinical and pathological description. *J. Am. Vet. Med. Ass.* 162: 357–61.

Fletcher, T. F. 1969.   Leukodystrophy in the dog. *Minnesota Vet.* 9: 19–22.

Fletcher, T. F. 1970.   Electroencephalographic features of leukodystrophic disease in the dog. *J. Am. Vet. Med. Ass.* 157: 190–8.

Fogh, J. M. 1986.   Haemofili A (blodersygdom hos schaeferhunde i Danmark. *Dansk Veterinaertidsskrift* 69: 938–40.

Fogh, J. M., Nygaard, L., Andresen, E. and Nilsson, I. M. 1984.   Hemophilia in dogs with special reference to Hemophilia A among German Shepherd Dogs in Denmark. *Nord. Vet.-Med.* 36: 235–40.

Foley, C. W., Lasley, J. F. and Osweiler, G. D. 1979.   *Abnormalities of companion animals: analysis of heritability*. Iowa State Univ. Press. Ames. 270pp.

Ford, L. 1958.   Possible pleiotropic effects of the grey gene in Collie dogs. *Proc. 10th Int. Cong. Genet.* 83: 1–2.

Ford, L. 1963.   Serial blood studies of lethal grey Collie puppies. *Mod. Vet. Pract.* 44: 52–3.

Ford, L. 1969.   Hereditary aspects of human and cyclic neutropenia. *J. Hered.* 60: 293–9.

Ford, L. 1971.   Genetic potential for longevity. *Dog World* 19th Feb.

Formston, C. 1945. Observations on subluxation and luxation of the crystalline lens in the dog. *J. Comp. Path.* 55: 168–84.

Formston, C. 1966. *Aspects of comparative ophthalmology* (ed. O. Graham-Jones) Pergamon, Oxford.

Forster, F. M. 1963. *Synopsis of neurology.* Mosby, St Louis.

Foster, S. J. 1977. Diabetes mellitus: coming to terms with the disease in the dog. *Vet. Ann.* 17: 187–90.

Fox, M. W. 1963. Inherited inguinal hernia and midline defects in the dog. *J. Am. Vet. Med. Ass.* 143: 602–4.

Fox, M. W. 1964. The ontogeny of behaviour and neurologic response in the dog. *Anim. Behav.* 12: 301–10.

Fox, M. W. 1965. Diseases of possible hereditary origin in the dog. A bibliographic review. *J. Hered.* 56: 169–76.

Fox, M. W. 1971. *Integrative development of brain and behavior in the dog.* Univ. Chicago Press, Chicago.

Frandson, R. D. 1965. *Anatomy and physiology of farm animals.* Lea & Febiger, Philadelphia.

Frauchiger, E. and Fankhauser, R. 1957. *Vergleichende Neuropathologie des Menschen und der Tiere.* Springer, Berlin.

Freak, M. J. 1948. The whelping bitch. *Vet. Rec.* 60: 295–301.

Freak, M. J. 1962. Abnormal conditions associated with pregnancy and parturition in the bitch. *Vet. Rec.* 74: 1323–39.

Freudiger, U. 1965. Die kongenitale Nierenrinderhypoplasie beim bunten Cocker Spaniel. *Schweiz. Arch. Tierheilk.* 107: 547–66.

Freudiger, U. 1972. Die diagnose der chronischen exokrinen Pankreasinsuffizienz. *Schweiz. Arch. Tierheilk.* 114: 476–87.

Freudiger, U. 1973. Uber die Zuverlässigkeit des Vorröntgens zur Beurteilung der Hüftgelenks-dysplasie. *Schweiz. Arch. Tierheilk.* 115: 507–15.

Freudiger, U. 1975. Untersuchungen über die chronische exocrine Pankreas-Insuffizien (CPI) speziell des Deutschen Schaferhundes. *Effem. Fors. fur Kleintier.* No. 1.

Freudiger, U. 1976a. Epidemiologie, Atiologie, Klinik und Diagnose der chronischen exokrinen Pankreasinsuffizienz. *Praktische Tierarzt.* 5: 301–8.

Freudiger, U. 1976b. Untersuchungen über die chronischen Pankreaserkrankungen des Hundes. *100 Jahr. Kynolog. Forsc. der Schweiz.* Bern.

Freudiger, U. and Berger, G. 1971. Über die Bestimmung der Trypsin und Chymotrypsinaktivität im Kot von Hunden und ihre Bedeutung für die Diagnose der chronischen exokrinen Pan-kreasinsuffizienz. *Schweiz. Arch. Tierheilk.* 113: 169–83.

Freudiger, U., Scharer, V., Buser, J. C. and Muhlebach, R. 1973a. Die Hüftgelenksdysplasie: Bekämpfungsverfahren und Frequenz bei den verschiedenen Rassen. *Schweiz. Arch. Tierheilk.* 115: 69–73.

Freudiger, U., Scharer, V., Buser, J. C. and Muhlebach, R. 1973b. Die Resultate der Hüf-telenksdysplasie—Bekämpfung beim D. Schäfer in der Zeit von 1965 bis 1972. *Schweiz. Arch. Tierheilk.* 115: 169–73.

Fritz, T. E., Lombard, L. S., Tyler, S. A. and Norris, W. P. 1976. Pathology and familial incidence of orchitis and its relation to thyroiditis in a closed Beagle colony. *Exp. Mol. Path.* 24: 142–58.

Frost, R. C. 1963.   Observations concerning ovarian and related conditions in bitches kept as domestic pets. *Vet. Rec.* 75: 653–4.

Fuller, J. L. 1956.   Photoperiodic control of oestrus in the Basenji. *J. Hered.* 47: 179–80.

Fuller, J. L. and Clark, L. D. 1966a.   Effects of rearing with specific stimuli upon postulation behaviour in dogs. *J. Comp. Physiol. Psychol.* 61: 258–63.

Fuller, J. L. and Clark, L. D. 1966b.   Genetic and treatment factors modifying the postulation syndrome in dogs. *J. Comp. Physiol. Psychol.* 61: 251–7.

Fuller, J. L. and Clark, L. D. 1968.   Genotype and behavioural vulnerability to isolation in dogs. *J. Comp. Physiol. Psychol.* 66: 151–6.

Fuller, J. L. and Thompson, W. R. 1960.   *Behavior Genetics.* John Wiley, New York.

Gaines, F. P. and Van Vleck, L. D. 1976.   The influence of Beagle sires on gestation length, litter size, birth weight and livability. *Carnivore. Genet. Newsl.* 3(2): 75–9.

Galton, F. 1876.   The history of twins and the criterion of relative powers of nature and nurture. *Anthrop. Inst. J.* 5: 391–406.

Gardner, D. L. 1959.   Familial canine chondrodystrophia foetalis (Achondroplasia). *J. Path. Bact.* 77: 243–7.

Gardner, E., Gray, D. and O'Rahilly, R. 1963.   *Anatomy.* W. B. Saunders Co, Philadelphia.

Garmer, L. 1986a.   Progressive retinal atrofi (PRA) hos labrador retriever. *Svensk. Veterinartidning.* 38: 120–3.

Garmer, L. 1986b.   Linsluxation hos tibetansk terrier. *Svensk Veterinartidning.* 38: 132–3.

Garmer, L., Kagerman-Pekkari, M., Schauman, P. and Tigerschiold, A. 1974.   Progressiv retinal atrofi hos tibetansk terrier. *Svensk. Vet.* 26: 158–60.

Garner, R., Hermoso-Perez, C. and Conning, D. M. 1967.   Factor VII deficiency in Beagle dog plasma and its use in the assay of human factor VII. *Nature (Lond.)* 216: 1130–1.

Gaspar, J. 1930.   Analyse der Erbfaktoren des Schädels bei einer Paarung von Ceylon-Nackthund x Dakel. *Jena Z. Naturw.* 65: 245–7.

Gee, B. R. and Doige, C. E. 1970.   Multiple cartilaginous extoses in a litter of dogs. *J. Am. Vet. Med. Ass.* 156: 53–9.

Gehlot, G. S. and Monga, J. N. 1973.   Prevalence of Pelger-Huët anomaly of leukocytes in Adivasi population of Western Madhya Pardesh. *Indian. J. Med. Res.* 61: 653–62.

Geiger, G. 1972.   (Testing procedure and inheritance of performance in the German Wirehaired Pointer (population studies based on the German Working Dog and German Wirehaired Pointer breed registry).) *Giessener Beitrage Erbpath. Zuchthyg.* 4: 40–3.

Gelatt, K. N. 1971.   Bilateral corneal dermoids and distichiasia in a dog. *Vet. Med.* 66: 658–9.

Gelatt, K. N. 1972.   Familial gaulcoma in the Beagle. *J. Am. Anim. Hosp. Ass.* 8: 23–8.

Gelatt, K. N. and McGill, L. D. 1973.   Clinical characteristics of microphthalmia with colobomas in the Australian Shepherd Dog. *J. Am. Vet. Med. Ass.* 162: 393–6.

Gelatt, K. N., Samuelson, D. A., Bauer, J. E. Das, N. D., Wolf, E. D., Barrie, K. P. and Andresen, T. L. 1983a.   Inheritance of congenital cataracts and microphthalmia in the Miniature Schnauzer. *Am. J. Vet. Res.* 44: 1130–2.

Gelatt, K. N., Samuelson, D. A., Barrie, K. P., Das, N. D., Wolf, E. D., Bauer, J. E. and Andresen, T. L. 1983b.   Biometry and clinical characteristics of congenital cataracts and microphthalmia in the Miniature Schnauzer. *J. Am. vet. Med. Ass.* 183: 99–102.

Gelatt, K. N. and Veith, L. A. 1970. Hereditary multiple occular anomalies in Australian Shepherd Dogs. *Vet. Med. small Anim. Clin.* 65: 39–42.

Ghosh, B., Choudhuri, D. K. and Pal, B. 1984. Some aspects of the sexual behaviour of stray dogs, *canis familiaris*. *App. Anim. Behaviour Sci.* 13: 113–27.

Giardina, J. F. and MacCarthy, A. W. 1972. Salvaging the predysplastic puppy for use as a working dog. *Vet. Med. small Anim. Clin.* 67: 785–8.

Gibbs, C. 1977. Traumatic lesion of the mandible. *J. small Anim. Pract.* 18: 51–3.

Giebel, C. G. 1859. *Die Saugetiere.*

Giger, U. and Harvey J. W. 1987. Hemolysis caused by phosphofrucktokinase deficiency in English Springer Spaniels: Seven cases (1983–1986). *J. Am. Vet. Med. Ass.* 191: 453–9.

Glembockii, J. A. 1941. *Cryptorchidism in Precoce sheep and its control.* Moscow State Pub. House, Moscow.

Glenney, W. C. 1956. Canine and feline spinal osteoarthritis (spondylitis deformans). *J. Am. Vet. Med. Ass.* 129: 61–5.

Goddard, M. E. and Bielharz, R. G. 1974. A breeding programme for guide dogs. *World Cong. Genetics, Madrid.* 1: 371–6.

Goddard, M. E. and Beilharz, R. G. 1982. Genetic and environmental factors affecting the suitability of dogs as guide dogs for the blind. *Theor. Appl. Genet.* 62: 97–102.

Goddard, M. E. and Beilharz, R. G. 1984a. A factor analysis of fearfulness in potential guide dogs. *App. Anim. Behaviour Sci.* 12: 253–65.

Goddard, M. E. and Beilharz, R. G. 1984b. The relationship of fearfulness to, and the effects of sex, age and experience on exploration and activity in dogs. *App. Anim. Behaviour Sci.* 12: 267–78.

Goggin, E., Li, A–S. and Franti, C. E. 1970. Canine invertebral disc disease: characterization by age, sex, breed and anatomic site of involvement. *Am. J. Vet. Res.* 31: 1687–92.

Good, R. 1962. Untersuchungen über eine Kleinhirnrindenatrophie beim Hund. *Thesis. Univ. Bern.*

Graham, J. B. 1952. Further observations on canine hemophilia. *J. Elisha Mitchell Sci. Soc.* 68: 153.

Gray, G. W. 1974. Acute experiments on neuroeffector function in canine esophageal achalasia. *Am. J. Vet. Res.* 35: 1075–81.

Gray, H. 1932. Some medical and surgical conditions in the dog. *Vet. Rec.* 12: 1–10.

Green, J. S. and Woodruff, R. A. 1983. The use of three breeds of dog to protect rangeland sheep from predators. *App. Anim. Ethology* 11: 141–61.

Grenn, H. H. and Lindo, D. E. 1969. Hemivertebrae with severe kyphoscoliosis and accompanying deformities in the dog. *Can. Vet. J.* 10: 215–15.

Griffiths, I. R. and Duncan, I. D. 1973. Mytonia in the dog. A report of four cases. *Vet. Rec.* 93: 184–8.

Griffiths, I. R. and Duncan, I. D. 1975. Chronic degenerative radiculomyelopathy in the dog. *J. small Anim. Pract.* 16: 461–71.

Griffiths, I. R., Duncan, I. D. and Barker, J. 1980. A progressive axonopathy of Boxer dogs affecting the central and peripheral nervous systems. *J. small Anim. Pract.* 21: 29–43.

Grimm, G. 1974. (Treatment of epileptiform fits in dogs.) *Kleinter Praxis.* 19: 196 and 201.

Grøndalen, J. 1973.   Malformation of the elbow joint in an Afghan Hound litter. *J. small Anim. Pract.* 14: 83–9.

Grøndalen, J. 1975.   Tumores i skje pettsystemat. *Norsk. Vet.* 87: 30–7.

Grøndalen, J. 1976.   (Disorders of the shoulder and elbow joint in young rapidly growing dogs.) *Norsk. Vet.* 88: 309–16.

Grøndalen, J. 1979a.   Arthrosis with special reference to the elbow joint of young rapidly growing dogs 1. A review of the literature. *Nord. Vet. Med.* 31: 62–8.

Grøndalen, J. 1979b.   Arthrosis with special reference to the elbow joint of young rapidly growing dogs 11. Occurrence, clinical and radiographical findings. *Nord. Vet. Med.* 31: 69–75.

Grøndalen, J. 1979c.   Arthrosis with special reference to the elbow joint of young rapidly growing dogs 111. Ununited medial coronoid process of the ulna and osteochondritis dissecans of the humeral condyle. *Nord. Vet. Med.* 31: 520–7.

Grounds, O. V., Hegedoorn, A. L. and Hoffman, R. A. 1955.   Hereditary subluxation. *J. Canine Genet.* Jan. 1–23.

Grull, F. and Henschel, E. 1973.   (Dislocation of the elbow in the Basset Hound: a breed deformity of the shoulder). *Kleinter Praxis.* 18: 217–20.

Grundmann, I. 1954.   Zur frage der Genetik der Polydaktylie beim Haushund. *Vet. Med. Diss. Freie Univ. Berlin.*

Grüneberg, H. and Lea, A. J. 1940.   An inherited jaw anomaly in Long-haired Dachshunds. *J. Genet.* 39: 285–96.

Gubbels, E. J. and Schaap, W. W. 1981.   *Hereditary epilepsy in the Dutch Welsh Springer Spaniel population: a first analysis.* Welsh Springer Spaniel Club in the Netherlands.

Gundel, H. and Reetz, L. 1981.   Exckusion probabilities obtainable by biochemical polymorphisms in dogs. *Anim. Blood Groups/Biochem. Genet.* 12: 123–32.

Gustafsson, P. O. 1968.   Hip dysplasia in the Greyhound. A study of estradiol induced skeletal changes. *J. Am. Vet. Med. Radiol. Soc.* 9: 47–56.

Gustafsson, P. O., Olsson, S. E., Kasstrom, H. and Wennman, B. 1975.   Skeletal development of Greyhounds, German Shepherd Dogs and their crossbreed offspring. *Acta. Radiol.* No. 366. Supp. 81–107.

Hackman, G. W. 1953.   Arvsanlaget for tigerteckningen hos taxer. *Suom. Mayrakoirakerh. Julk.* 3: 2–5.

Hall, D. S., Amann, J. F., Constantinescu, G. M. and Vogt, D. W. 1987.   Anury in two Cairn terriers. *J. Am. Vet. Med. Ass.* 191: 1113–15.

Hallgren, A. 1975.   *Hund och manniska. Om hundens arv. anpassning och miljo.* Bonniers, Stockholm.

Halliwell, R. E. W. and Schwartzman, R. M. 1971.   Atopic disease in the dog. *Vet. Rec.* 89: 209–14.

Hancock, J. L. and Rowlands, I. W. 1949   The physiology of reproduction in the dog. *Vet. Rec.* 61: 771–9.

Hanlon, G. F. 1962.   Normal and abnormal bone growth in the dog. *J. Am. Radiol. Soc.* 3: 13–16.

Hansen, H. J. 1952.   A pathologic-anatomical study on disc degeneration in the dog. *Acta. Orthopaed. Scand.* Suppl. No. 11 117pp.

Hansen, H. J. 1964.   The body composition of dogs and its importance for the occurrence of disease. *Nord. Vet. Med.* 16: 977–87.

Hardy, R. M., Stevens, J. B. and Stowe, C. M. 1975.   Chronic progressive hepatitis in Bedlington Terriers associated with elevated liver copper concentration. *Minn. Vet.* 15: 13–24.

Hare, T. 1932.   A congenital abnormality of hair follicles in dogs resembling trichostasis spinulosa. *J. Path. Bact.* 35: 569–71.

Hare, W. C. D. 1976.   Intersexuality in the dog. *Can. Vet. J.* 17: 7–15.

Hare, W. C. D., McFeely, R. A. and Kelly, D. F. 1974.   Familial 78 XX male pseudohermaphroditism in three dogs. *J. Reprod. Fert.* 36: 207–10.

Harper, R. C. 1978.   Congenital black hair follicular dysplasia in Bearded Collie puppies. *Vet. Rec.* 102: 87.

Hartl, J. 1938.   Die Vererbung des Kryptorchismus beim Hund. *Kleintier u. Pelztier.* 14: 1–37.

Hartley, W. J. 1973.   Ataxia in Jack Russell Terriers. *Acta Neuropath.* 26: 71–4.

Hartley, W. J., Barker, J. S. F., Wanner, R. A. and Farrow, B. R. H. 1978.   Inherited cerebellar degeneration in the Rough Coated Collie. *Austr. Vet. Pract.* 8: 79–85.

Harvey, A. M. and Christensen, H. N. 1964.   Uric acid transport system: apparent absence of erythrocytes of the Dalmatian Coach Hound. *Science* 145: 826–7.

Harvey, C. E. 1977.   Anal and perineal disease of the dog. *Vet. Ann.* 17: 150–5.

Hauck, E. 1949.   Ist Grösse und Aufrichtung des Ohres aus der Delle des Postorbitalfortsatzes erschliessbar? *Wien. tierarztl. Mschr.* 36: 607–9.

Hauptman, J., Cardinet, G. H., Morgan, J. P., Guffy, M. M. and Wallace, L. J. 1985.   Angles of inclination and anteversion in hip dysplasia in the dog. *Am. J. Vet. Res.* 46: 2033–6.

Hayes, H. M. 1974.   Congenital umbilical and inguinal hernias in cattle, horses, swine, dogs and cats: risk by breed and sex among hospital patients. *Am. J. Vet. Res.* 35: 839–42.

Hayes, H. M., Selby, L. A., Wilson, G. P. and Hohn, R. B. 1979.   Epidemiologic observations of canine elbow disease (emphasis on dysplasia). *J. Am. Anim. Hosp. Ass.* 15: 449–53.

Hayes, H. M., Wilson, G. P. and Tarone, R. E. 1978.   The epidemiologic features of perineal hernia in 771 dogs. *J. Am. Anim. Hosp. Ass.* 14: 703–7.

Heape, W. 1908.   Notes on the proportions of the sexes in dogs. *Proc. Camb. Phil. Soc.* 14: 121–51.

Hedhammar, A. 1976.   (Hip dysplasia and temperament. Inheritance or environment.) *Svensk. Vet.* 28: 1057–64.

Hedhammar, A. 1986.   Dagsläget avseede bekämpning av hoftgesdsdysplasi i Sverige. *Svensk Veterinärtidning* 38: 68–77.

Hedhammar, A., Olsson, S. E., Andersson, S. A., Persson, L., Pettersson, L., Olausson, A. and Sundgren, P. E. 1979.   Canine hip dysplasia: a study of heritability in 401 litters of German Shepherd Dogs. *J. Am. Vet. Med. Ass.* 174: 1012–16.

Hedhammar, A., Wu, F. and Krook, L. 1974.   Discussion—overnutrition and skeletal disease. *Cornell Vet.* 64: 113–27.

Hegreberg, G. A. and Padgett, G. A. 1967.   Ehlers-Danlos syndrome in animals. *Bull. Path.* 8: 247.

Hegreberg, G. A., Padgett, G. A., Gorham, J. R. and Henson, J. B. 1969.   A connective tissue disease of dogs and minx resembling the Ehlers-Danlos syndrome of man. II. Mode of inheritance. *J. Hered.* 60: 249–54.

Hegreberg, G. A., Padgett, G. A., Ott, R. L. and Henson, J. B. 1966.   Cutaneous asthenia in dogs. *Proc. 16th Gaines Vet. Symp.* 1–4.

Hegreberg, G. A., Padgett, G. A., Prieur, D. J. and Johnson, M. I. 1975.   Genetic studies of a muscular dystrophy of mink. *J. Hered.* 66: 63–6.

Heim, A. 1914.   *Die Schweizer Sennerhunde.* Zurich.

Hein, H. E. 1963.   Abnormalities and defects in pedigree dogs. 2. Hereditary aspects of hip dysplasia. *J. small Anim. Pract.* 4: 457–62.

Heitzenroeder, C. 1913.   Über das Verhalten des Hundes gegen einige Riechstoffe. *Z. Biol.* 62: 491–507.

Helper, L. C. and Magrane, W. G. 1970.   Ectopic cilia of the canine eyelid. *J. small Anim. Pract.* 11: 185–9.

Henricson, B., Ljungren, G., Olsson, S. E. and Kasstrom, H. 1973.   Hip dysplasia in Sweden. Controlled breeding programme. *J. Am. Vet. Med. Ass.* 162: 667–8. Abstr.

Henricson, B., Norberg, I. and Olsson, S. E. 1966.   On the aetiology and pathogenesis of hip dysplasia. *J. small Anim. Pract.* 7: 673–88.

Henricson, B. and Olsson, S. E. 1959.   Hereditary acetabular dysplasia in German Shepherd Dogs. *Medlemsbl. sverig. Vet. Forb.* 11: 101–4.

Heywood, R. and Wells, G. A. H. 1970.   A retinal dysplasia in the Beagle dog. *Vet. Rec.* 87: 178–80.

Hickman, J. 1964.   *Veterinary orthopaedics.* Oliver & Boyd, Edinburgh.

Hill, F. W. G. 1978a.   Pancreatic disorders of dogs. *Vet. Ann.* 18: 198–212.

Hill, F. W. G. 1978b.   Histiocytic ulcerative colitis of Boxer dogs. *Vet. Ann.* 18: 213–16.

Hill, F. W. G., Osborne, A. D. and Kidder, D. E. 1971.   Pancreatic degenerative atrophy in dogs. *J. Comp. Path.* 81: 321–30.

Hippel, E. von. 1930.   Embryologische Untersuchungen über Vererbung angeborener Katarakt, über Schichtstar des Hundes sowie über eine besondere Form von Kapselkatarakt. *Graefes Arch.* 124: 300–24.

Hirschfeld, W. K. 1956.   Fokkerij op genotype. *Genen en Phaenen.* 1(3): 1–5.

Hirth, R. S. and Nielsen, S. W. 1967.   Familial canine globoid cell leukodystrophy (Krabbe type). *J. small Anim. Pract.* 8: 569–75.

Hitchin, A. D. and Morris, I. 1966.   Geminated ontodone—caination of the incisors of the dog—its etiology and ontogeny. *J. dent. Res.* 45: 575–83.

Hodgman, S. F. J. 1963.   Abnormalities and defects in pedigree dogs. 1. An investigation into the existence of abnormalities in pedigree dogs in the British Isles. *J. small Anim. Pract.* 4: 447–56.

Hodgman, S. F. J., Parry, H. B., Rasbridge, W. J. and Steel, J. D. 1949.   Progressive retinal atrophy in dogs. 1. The disease in Irish Setters (Red). *Vet. Rec.* 61: 185–90.

Hoerlein, B. F. 1971.   *Canine neurology, diagnosis and treatment.* Saunders, Philadelphia.

Hoerlein, B. F. 1979.   Comparative disk disease: man and dog. *J. Am. Anim. Hosp. Ass.* 15: 535–45.

Hofmeyr, C. F. B. 1955.   Cardioplasty for achalasia in the dog. *Vet. Med.* 51: 115–18.

Hofmeyr, C. F. B. 1963.   Dermoid sinus in the Ridgeback dog. *J. small Anim. Pract.* 4: 5–8.

Holliday, J. A., Cunningham, J. G. and Gutnick, M. J. 1970.   Comparative clinical and electro-encephalographic studies of canine epilepsy. *Epilepsia* 11: 281–92.

Holt, P. E. 1974.   Ligamentous injuries to the canine hock. *J. small Anim. Pract.* 15: 457–74.

Hoppe, F. and Svalastoga, E. 1980. Tempromandibular dysplasia in American Cocker Spaniels. *J. small Anim. Pract.* 21: 675–8.

Høst, P. and Sveinson, S. 1936. (Hereditary cataract in the dog.) *Norsk. Vet. Tiddskr.* 48: 244–70.

Howard-Peebles, P. N. and Pryor, J. C. 1980. The R-banding pattern of the canine karyotype. *J. Hered.* 71: 361–2.

Howell, J. M. and Lambert, P. S. 1964. A case of haemophilia in the dog. *Vet. Rec.* 76: 1103–5.

Hubbard, C. L. B. 1948. *Dogs in Britain.* MacMillan, London.

Huber, W. 1950. Sur unde fente médiane intéressamt l'os intermaxillaire chex le chein. *Arch. Klaus-Stift VererbForsch.* 25: 514–18.

Huber, W. and Schmid, E. 1959. A cryptorchid genealogy in the St Bernard dog. *Arch. Klaus-Stift VererbForsch.* 34: 252–6.

Humphrey, E. S. 1928. Shepherd prepotency. *The Alsatian*, various issues.

Humphrey, E. S. 1934. Mental tests for Shepherd dogs. *J. Hered.* 25: 128–36.

Humphrey, E. S. and Warner, L. 1934. *Working dogs.* Johns Hopkins, Baltimore.

Hutt, F. B. 1969. Advances in canine genetics with special reference to hip dysplasia. *Can. Vet. J.* 11: 307–11.

Hutt, F. B. 1979. *Genetics for dog breeders*, Freeman, San Francisco.

Hutt, F. B. and DeLahunta, A. 1971. A lethal glossopharyngeal defect in the dog. *J. Hered.* 62: 291–3.

Hutt, F. B., Rickard, C. G. and Field, R. A. 1948. Sex-linked hemophilia in dogs. *J. Hered.* 39: 2–9.

Ihemelandu, E. C., Cardinet, G. H., Guffy, M. M. and Wallace, L. J. 1983. Canine hip dysplasia: differences in pectineal muscles of healthy and dysplastic German Shepherd Dogs when two months old. *Am. J. Vet. Res.* 44: 411–16.

Iljin, N. A. 1926. (Ruby eye and its inheritance. 2. Ruby eye in mammals.) *Trud. Lab. eksp. Biol. (Mosk.)* 1: 121–7, 129.

Iljin, N. A. 1928. (Ruby eye in dogs.) *Dog breeding and training.* USSR 1(18) 1–3.

Iljin, N. A. 1932. *(Genetics and the breeding of dogs.)* Seljskohozgiz, Moscow.

Iljin, N. A. 1937. La variabilité parallèle dans la phénogenese da la conque de l'oreille chez les canidae. *C. R. (Dokl.) Acad. Sci.* USSR. 17: 379–83.

Iljin, N. A. 1941. Wolf dog genetics. *J. Genet.* 42: 359–414.

Ingeberg, K. E. 1960. Lidt om den Karelske Bjørnehund. *Hunden* 70: 95–8.

Innes, J. R. M. and Saunders, L. Z. 1957. Diseases of the central nervous system of domesticated animals and comparison with human neuropathology. *Advan. Vet. Sci.* 3: 33–196.

Jaeger, O. and Kamphans, S. 1968. Uber Zuchtleistungen von Beagle-Hunden. *D. Tierarz. Wochen* 75: 145–7.

James, T. N. and Drake, E. H. 1968. Sudden death in Dobermann Pinchers. *Ann. Intern. Med.* 68: 821–9.

James, W. T. 1951. Social organisation among dogs of different temperaments. Terriers and Beagles reared together. *J. Comp. Physiol. Psychol.* 44: 71–7.

Jeffreys, A. J. and Morton, D. B. 1987 DNA fingerprints of dogs and cats. *Anim. Genetics* 18: 1–15.

Jenny-Gredig, V., Kielger, J., Muller, A. and Eggenberger, E. 1970.   The incidence of hip dysplasia in Switzerland. *Schweiz. Arch. Tierheilk.* 112: 487–90.

Jensen, E. C. 1959.   Hypopituitarism associated with cystic Rathke's cleft in the dog. *J. Am. Vet. Med. Ass.* 135: 572–5.

Jessen, C. R. and Spurrell, F. A. 1973.   Heritability of canine hip dysplasia. *J. Am. Vet. Med. Ass.* 162: 663. Abstr.

Jochle, W. and Paeske, W. 1963.   (Genetically determined disturbances in fertility in Greyhounds.) *Kleinter Praxis.* 8: 4–5.

Johnson, G. S., Lees, G. E., Benson, R. E., Rosborough, T. K. and Dodds, W. J. 1980a.   A bleeding disease (von Willebrand's disease) in a Chesapeake Bay Retriever. *J. Am. Vet. Med. Ass.* 176: 1261–3.

Johnson, G. F., Sternlieb, I., Twedt, D. C., Grushoff, P. S. and Scheinberg, I. H. 1980b.   Inheritance of copper toxicosis in Bedlington Terriers. *Am. J. Vet. Res.* 41: 1865–6.

Johnston, E. F., Zeller, J. H. and Cantwell, G. 1958.   Sex anomalies in swine. *J. Hered.* 49: 255–61.

Johnstone, I. B. and Lotz, F. 1969.   An inherited platelet function defect in Basset Hounds. *Can. vet. J.* 20: 211–15.

Jolly, R. D. and Healy, P. J. 1986.   Screening for carriers of genetic diseases by biochemical means. *Vet. Rec.* 119: 264–7.

Jones, B. R., Anderson, L. J., Barnes, G. R. G., Johnstone, A. C. and Juby, W. D. 1977.   Myotonia in related Chow Chow dogs. *N.Z. Vet. J.* 25: 217–20.

Jones, J. B., Yang, T. J. and Dale, J. B. 1975.   Canine cyclic neutropenia: marrow transplantation between littermates. *Br. J. Haematol.* 30: 215–23.

Joshua, J. 1956.   Scottie cramp. *Vet. Rec.* 68: 411–12.

Joshua, J. 1975.   Breeding for temperament. *Vet. Rec.* 96: 228.

Jubb, K. V. F. and Kennedy, P. C. 1963.   *Pathology of domestic animals.* Vol. 2. Academic Press, New York.

Juneja, R. K., Christensen, K., Andresen, E. and Gahne, B. 1981b.   Frequencies of transferrin types in various breeds of domestic dogs. *Anim. Blood Group/Biochem. Genet.* 12: 79–88.

Juneja, R. K., Reetz, I., Christensen, K., Gahne, B. and Andresen, E. 1981a.   Two-dimensional gel electrophoresis of dog plasma proteins: Genetic polymorphism of an α,—protease inhibitor and another postalbumin. *Hereditas* 95: 225–33.

Jurkiewicz, M. J. 1964.   Cleft lip and palate in dogs. *Surgical Forum.* 15: 457–8.

Jurkiewicz, M. J. 1965.   A genetic study of cleft lip and palate in dogs. *Surgical Forum.* 16: 472–3.

Jurkiewicz, M. J. and Bryant, D. L. 1968.   Cleft lip and palate in dogs. A progress report. *Cleft Palate J.* 5: 30–6.

Kaiser, G. 1971.   Die Reproduktionsleistung der Haushunde in ihrer Beziehung zur Körpergrösse und zum Gewicht der Rassen. *Z. Tierzücht. Züchtbiol.* 88: 118–68, 240–53, 316–40.

Kaiser, G. and Huber, W. 1969.   Beziehungen zwischen Körpergrösse und Wurfgrösse beim Haushund. *Rev. Suisse Zool.* 76: 656–73.

Kalmus, H. 1955.   The discrimination by the nose of the dog of individual human odours and in particular the odours of twins. *Brit. J. Anim. Behav.* 3: 25–31.

Kaman, C. H. and Gossling, H. R. 1967.   A breeding program to reduce hip dysplasia in German Shepherd Dogs. *J. Am. Vet. Med. Ass.* 151: 562–71.

Kammermann, B., Gmür, J. and Stünzk, H. 1971.   Afibrinogenamie beim Hund. *Zentralbl. Veterinaermed.* 18A: 192–205.

Kamphans, S. 1967. *Uber Zuchtkeistungen von Beagle*.

Kaneko, J. J., Cordy, D. R. and Carlson, G. 1967. Canine hemophilia resembling classic hemophilia. *J. Am. Vet. Med. Ass.* 150: 15–21.

Karbe, E. and Schiefer, B. 1967. Familial amaurotic idiocy in male German Short-haired Pointers. *Path. Vet.* 4: 223–32.

Kasstrom, H. 1975. Estrogens, nutrition and hip dysplasia. *Thesis. Royal Vet. Coll. Stockholm.*

Kawakami, E., Tsutsui, T., Yamada, Y. and Yamauchi, M. 1984. Cryptorchidism in the dog: occurrence of cryptorchidism and semen quality in the cryptorchid dog. *Jpn. J. Vet. Sci.* 46: 303–8.

Kay, R. S. 1969. Progressive retinal atrophy. *Vet. Rec.* 84: 50–1.

Keeler, C. E. 1940. The Dalmatian psyche. *J. Hered.* 31: 112.

Keeler, C. E. and Trimble, H. C. 1938. The inheritance of dew claws in the dog. *J. Hered.* 29: 145–8.

Keeler, C. E. and Trimble, H. C. 1940. Inheritance of position preference in coach dogs. *J. Hered.* 31: 50–4.

Keep, J. M. 1972. Clinical aspects of Progressive Retinal Atrophy in the Cardigan Welsh Corgi. *Aust. Vet. J.* 48: 197–9.

Keller, K. 1928. *Geburtshilfe bei den kleineren Haustieren*. Urban & Schwarzenberg, Berlin.

Kelley, R. B. 1949. *Sheep dogs. Their breeding, maintenance and training*. Angus & Robertson, Sydney.

Kelly, D. F. 1973. Functional disorders of the adrenal gland in dogs. *Vet. Ann.* 14: 174–81.

Kelly, D. F., Haywood, S. and Bennett, A. M. 1984. Copper toxicosis in Bedlington terriers in the United Kingdom, *J. small Anim. Pract.* 25: 293–8.

Kiesel, G. K. 1951. Congenital esophageal dilation in a Great Dane puppy. *Cornell Vet.* 41: 36–7.

King, H. D. 1918–19. Studies on inbreeding. *J. Expl. Zool.* 26: 1–54, 335–78; 27: 1–36; 29: 711–12.

King, J. E., Becker, R. F. and Markee, J. E. 1964. Studies on olfactory discrimination in dogs. 3. Ability to detect human odour trace. *Anim. Behav.* 12: 311–15.

Kitchen, R. H., Kehler, W. H. and Henthorne, J. C. 1963. Megaesophagus in a dog. *J. Am. Vet. Med. Ass.* 143: 1106–7.

Kittel, H. 1931. Uber Dermoide der Kornea ad Spaltbildungen der Lider am Auge von Bernhardinerhunden. *D. Tierarzt. Wschr.* 52: 793–7.

Klarenbeek, A., Koopmann, S. and Winsser, J. 1942. (Muscular disturbances in Scottish Terriers). *Tijdschr. Diergeneek.* 69: 14–21.

Klemperer, F. W., Trimble, H. C. and Hastings, A. B. 1938. The uricase of dogs, including the Dalmatian. *J. Biol. Chem.* 125: 445–9.

Klinckmann, G., Koniszewski, G. and Wegner, W. 1986. Light-miscroscopic investigations on the retinae of dogs carrying the Merle factor. *J. Vet. Med.* A. 33: 674–88.

Klingeborn, B. 1986. Indikationer pä en ärftlig bakgrund till armbägsled sföröndringar hos berner sennenhund. *Svensk, Veterinartidning* 38: 102–7.

Knight, C. G. 1960. Canine intraocular surgery. *Vet. Rec.* 72: 642–6.

Knight, C. G. 1962. The indications and technique for lens extraction in the dog. *Vet. Rec.* 74: 1065–70.

Knight, C. G. 1963.   Abnormalities and defects in pedigree dogs. 3. Tibio-femoral joint deformity and patella luxation. *J. small Anim. Pract*. 4: 463–4.

Koch, S. A. 1972.   Cataracts in interrelated Old English Sheepdogs. *J. Am. Vet. Med. Ass*. 160: 299–301.

Koch, W. 1935.   Neue pathogene Erbfaktoren bei Hunden. *Z. indukt. Abstamm u. Vererblehre*. 70: 503–6.

Kock, M. 1984.   *Statistiche und erbanalytische Untersuchungen zur Zuchtsituation, zu Fehlern und Wesensmerkmalen beim Deutsch-Langhaarigen Vorstehhund*. Vet Thesis. Tierarztliche Hochschule, Hannover. 151pp.

Kodituwakku, G. E. 1962.   Luxation of the patella in the dog. *Vet. Rec*. 74: 1499–1507.

Kohn, F. G. 1911.   Beitrag zur Kenntnis der Haut des Nackthundes. *Zool. Jb. Anat*. 31: 427–8.

Kollarits, J. 1924.   Das Dauszittern mancher Rassenhunde als Heredodegeneration. *Schweiz. Med. Wschr*. 54: 1131–2.

Koppang, N. 1970.   Neuronal ceroidliofuscinosis in English Setters. Juvenile amaurotic familiar idiocy (AFI) in English Setters. *J. small Anim. Pract*. 10: 639–44.

Koroveckaja, N. N. 1938.   Izucenie nekorpryh nasledstvennyh urodstv u svinei. *Usp. Zooteh. Nauk*. 5: 19–39.

Krahenmann, A. 1974.   Progressive netzhautatrophie bei Schweizer Hunderassen. *Schweiz. Arch. Tierheilk*. 116: 643–52.

Kral, F. and Schwartzman, R. M. 1964.   *Veterinary and comparative dermatology*, Lippincott, Philadelphia.

Kramer, J. W., Hegreberg, G. A., Bryan, G. M., Myers, K. and Ott, R. 1976.   A muscle disorder of Labrador Retrievers characterised by a deficiency of Type II muscle fibres. *J. Am. Vet. Med. Ass*. 169: 817–20.

Kreipe, U. 1967.   Missbildungen innerer Organe bei Thalidomidembryopathie. *Arch. Kinderh*. 176: 33–61.

Krempl, H., Muller, S. and Stur, I. 1988.   Hip joint dysplasia investigated in a Hovawart population. *Animalis Familiaris* 3: 3–9.

Krook, L. 1954.   A statistical investigation of carcinoma in the dog. *Acta. path. microbiol. Scand*. 34: 407–22.

Krook, L. 1957.   The pathology of renal cortical hypoplasia in the dog. *Nord. Vet. Med*. 9: 161–76.

Krook, L. 1969.   Metabolic bone diseases of endocrine origin. In *Handbook of the special pathological anatomy of domestic animals* (Eds. J. Dobberstein, G. Pallaske and H. Stunzi). Paul Parey, Berlin.

Krook, L., Larsson, S. and Rooney, J. R. 1960.   The interrelationship of diabetes mellitus, obesity and pyometra in the dog. *Am. J. Vet. Res*. 21: 120–4.

Krushinskiii, I. V. 1962.   *Animal Behavior: its normal and abnormal development* Consultants Bureau, New York.

Krzyzanowski, J., Malinowski, E. and Studnicki, W. 1975.   Badania nad czasim triania ciazy u suk niektoryck ras psow hodowanyck w Kraju. *Med. Weterynaryjna*. 31: 373–4.

Lacroix, J. V. 1940.   Cardiospasm in a puppy. *N. Am. Vet*. 21: 673–5.

Lacroix, J. V. 1949.   Congenital dilation of the oesophagus. *N. Am. Vet*. 30: 29–30.

Ladd, M. F. C. and Robinson, P. M. 1983.   Coat colour inheritance in dogs: determination of genotype from phenotypic observations. *Theor. Appl. Genet.* 64: 283–8.

Ladds, P. W., Dennis, S. M. and Leipold, H. W. 1971.   Lethal congenital edema in Bulldog pups. *J. Am. Vet. Med. Ass.* 159: 81–6.

Ladrat, J., Blin, P. C. and Lauvergne, J–J. 1969.   Ectromelie bithoracique hereditaire chez le chien. *Ann. Genet. Selec. Anim.* 1: 119–30.

Lafeber, T. J. and Beckwith, J. 1956.   What is your diagnosis? *J. Am. Vet. Med. Ass.* 128: 85–6.

Larsen, J. S. and Corley, E. A. 1971.   Radiographic evaluations in a canine hip dysplasia control program. *J. Am. Vet. Med. Ass.* 159: 989–92.

Larsen, J. S. and Selby, L. A. 1981.   Spondylosis deformans in Large dogs—relative risk by breed, age and sex. *J. Am. Anim. Hosp. Ass.* 17: 623–5.

Larsson, B. 1956.   Statistical analyses of cutaneous tumours in dogs, with special reference to mastocyma. *Nord. Vet. Med.* 8: 130–9.

Latshaw, W. K., Wyman, M. and Venzke, W. G. 1969.   Embryologic development of an anomaly of ocular fundus in the Collie dog. *Am. J. Vet. Res.* 30: 211–17.

Lau, R. E. 1977.   Inherited premature closure of the distal ulnar physis. *J. Am. Anim. Hosp. Ass.* 13: 609–12.

Lauder, I. 1972.   Canine diabetes mellitus. *Vet. Ann.* 13: 152–60.

Lawson, D. D. 1961.   Inter-tarsal subluxation in the dog. *J. small Anim. Pract.* 1: 179–81.

Lawson, D. D. 1963.   The radiographic diagnosis of hip dysplasia in the dog. *Vet. Rec.* 75: 445–6.

Lawson, D. D. 1969a.   The Collie Eye anomaly. *Vet. Rec.* 84: 618.

Lawson, D. D. 1969b.   Luxation of the crystalline lens in the dog. *J. small Anim. Pract.* 10: 461–3.

Lawson, D. D. 1973.   Canine distichiasis. *J. small Anim. Pract.* 14: 469–78.

Lee, R. 1970.   A study of the radiographic and histological changes occurring in Legg-Calvé-Perthes' disease (LCP) in the dog. *J. small Anim. Pract.* 11: 621.

Leighton, E. A., Linn, J. M., Williams, R. L. and Castleberry, M. W. 1977.   A genetic study of canine hip dysplasia. *Am. J. Vet. Res.* 38: 241–4.

Leinhart, R. 1932.   Contribution à l'étude de l'hérédité chez les chiens anoures et brachyures. *C. R. Soc. Biol. Paris.* 110: 1164–8.

Lerner, A. B. 1959.   Vitiligo. *J. Invest. Dermatol.* 32: 285–310.

Lerner, I. M. 1954.   *Genetic homeostasis.* Oliver & Boyd, Edinburgh.

Letard, E. 1930a.   L'hérédité mendélienne du caractère 'peau nue' chez le chien. *C. R. Soc. Biol. Paris.* 103: 1135–6.

Letard, E. 1930b   Le Mendélisme expérimental. Expériences sur l'hérédité du caractère 'peau nue' dans l'espèce canine. Observations sur la transmission de quelques autres attributs. *Rev. Vét. (Toulouse).* 82: 378.

Lewis, D. G. 1977.   Personal communication.

Lewis, E. F. and Holman, H. H. 1951.   Haemophilia in a St Bernard dog. *Vet. Rec.* 63: 666–7.

Libbey, J. A., Hanson, J. O. and Solac, R. B. 1970.   Age of animal at definitive diagnosis of hip dysplasia. *Vet. Med. Reporter.* No. 25. Univ. Minnesota Agric. Esp. Sta.

Liegois, F. and Gregoire, C. 1948.   Ectasie oesophagienne chez le chien. *Ann. Med. Vet.* 92: 56 9.

Lindstedt, E., Hedhammar, A., Lundeheim, M. and Swenson, L. 1986.   Skelettrubbningar hos schäfer—arv eller miljo? *Svensk Veterinärtidning* 38: 108–12.

Little, C. C. 1914.   Inheritance of coat color in Pointer dogs. *J. Hered.* 5: 244–8.

Little, C. C. 1920.   A note on the origin of piebald spotting. *J. Hered.* 11: 12–15.

Little, C. C. 1934.   Inheritance in Toy Griffons. *J. Hered.* 25: 198–200.

Little, C. C. 1949.   Genetics in Cocker Spaniels. *J. Hered.* 40: 181–5.

Little, C. C. 1957.   *The inheritance of coat color in dogs.* Howell, New York.

Little, C. C. and Jones, E. E. 1919.   Coat color in Great Danes. *J. Hered.* 10: 309–20.

Lochte, T. 1963.   Untersuchungen am Haarkleid der Ungarischen Hirtenhunde. *Z. Saugertiek.* 28: 267–78.

Loeb, E. 1969.   Best of breed competition at the National Speciality. *The German Shephed Dog Rev.* 46(12) 52.

Loeffler, K. 1964.   Lenkanomalien als Problem in der Hundezucht. *D. Tierarztl. Wschr.* 71: 291–7.

Loeffler, K. and Meyer, H. 1961.   Erbliche patellar-luxation bei Toy Spaniels. *D. Tierarztl. Wschr.* 68: 619–22.

Longton, T. and Hart, E. 1969.   *Your sheepdog and its training.* Alan Exley, Battle, Sussex.

Lord, L. H., Cawley, A. J. and Gilray, J. 1957.   Mid-dorsal dermoid sinuses in Rhodesian Ridgeback dogs: a case report. *J. Am. Vet. Med. Ass.* 131: 515–18.

Lorenz, M. D., Cork, L. C., Griffin, J. W., Adams, R. J. & Price, D. L. 1979.   Hereditary spinal muscular atrophy in Brittany Spaniels: clinical manifestations. *J. Am. Vet. Med. Ass.* 175: 833–9.

Lotz, F., Crane, S. and Downie, H. G. 1972.   A study of a specific congenital platelet functional abnormality in dogs. *3rd Int. Congr. Intern. Soc. Thrombosis and Haemostasis.* p. 220 Abstr.

Lovekin, L. G. 1964.   Primary glaucoma in dogs. *J. Am. Vet. Med. Ass.* 145: 1081–91.

Lovekin, L. G. and Bellhorn, R. W. 1968.   Clinicopathologic changes in primary glaucoma in the Cocker Spaniel. *Am. J. Vet. Res.* 29: 379–85.

Ludden, T. E. & Harvey, M. 1962.   Pelger-Huët anomaly of leucocytes: Report of a case and survey of incidence. *Am. J. Clin. Pathol.* 37: 302–4.

Ludwig, G. 1968.   (Studies on the breeding history of the German Boxer.) *Vet. Med. Diss. Univ. Munich.*

Luginbuhl, H., Chacko, S. K., Patterson, D. F. and Medway, W. 1967.   Congenital Hereditary lymphoedema in the dog. II. Pathological studies. *J. Med. Genet.* 4: 153–6.

Lund, J. E. 1969.   *Canine cyclic neutropenia.* PhD thesis. Washington State Univ.

Lund, J. E., Padgett, G. A. and Gorham, J. R. 1970.   Additional evidence on the inheritance of cyclic neutropenia in the dog. *J. Hered.* 61: 47–9.

Lund, J. E., Padgett, G. A. and Ott, R. L. 1967.   Cyclic neutropenia in grey Collie dogs. *Blood* 29: 452–61.

Lush, J. L. 1945.   *Animal breeding plans.* Iowa State Coll. Press, Ames.

Lush, J. L., Jones, J. and Dameron, W. H. 1930.   The inheritance of cryptorchidism in goats. *Texas. Agric. Exp. Sta. Bull.* 407.

Lust, G. and Baker, J. A. 1970.   Altered protein metabolism in muscle and cartilage associated with malformation of hip joints in dogs. *Fed. Proc.* 29: 551. Abstr.

Lust, G., Craig, P. H., Ross, G. E. and Geary, J. C. 1972.   Studies on pectineus muscle in canine hip dysplasia. *Cornell Vet.* 62: 628–45.

Lust, G. and Farrell, P. W. 1977.   Hip dysplasia in dogs: The interplay of genotype and environment. *Cornell Vet.* 67: 447–66.

Lust, G., Farrell, P. W., Sheffy, B. E. and Van Vleck, L. D. 1978.   An improved procedure for genetic selection against hip dysplasia in dogs. *Cornell Vet.* 68 (Suppl. 7): 41–7.

Lust, G., Geary, J. C. and Sheffy, B. E. 1973.   Development of hip dysplasia in dogs. *Am. J. Vet. Res.* 34: 87–91.

Lust, G. and Kindlon, C. C. 1960.   Biochemical studies on hip dysplasia in dogs. *19th Gaines Symp.* Purdue Univ. Lafayette pp. 16–21.

Lyngset, A. 1973.   The influence of the male dog on litter size. *Nord. Vet. Med.* 25: 150–4.

Lyngset, A. and Lyngset, O. 1970.   Litter size in the dog. *Nord. Vet. Med.* 22: 186–91.

Lyngset, A., Owren, T. and Yru, T. 1975.   (Chronic exocrine pancreatic insufficiency in the dog. Review and case report.) *Norsk. Vet. Tiel.* 87: 381–7.

Macan, J. 1978.   *Hips.* Privately published.

MacArthur, J. W. 1949.   Selection for small and large body size in the house mouse. *Genetics* 34: 194–209.

Mace, M., Williamson, E. and Worgan, D. 1978.   Autosomal dominantly inherited adductor laryngeal paralysis—a new syndrome with a suggestion of linkage to HLA. *Clinical Genetics 14*: 265–70.

Mackenzie, S. A. 1985.   Canine Hip Dysplasia. *Canine Practice* 12(2): 19–22.

Mackenzie, S. A., Oltenacu, E. A. B. and Leighton, E. 1985.   Heritability estimates for temperament scores in German Shepherd Dogs and its genetic correlation with hip dysplasia. *Behaviour Genetics.* 15: 475–82.

MacMillan, A. D. and Lipton, D. E. 1978.   Heritability of multifocal retinal dysplasia in American Cocker Spaniels. *J. Am. Vet. Med. Ass.* 172: 568–72.

MacMillian, A. D., Waring, G. O., Spangler, W. L. & Roth, A. M. 1979.   Crystalline corneal opacities in the Siberian Husky. *J. Am. Vet. Med. Ass. 175*: 829–32.

MacVean, D. W., Monlux, A. W., Anderson, P. S., Silberg, S. L. and Roszel, J. F. 1978.   Frequency of canine and feline tumours in a defined population. *Vet. Pathol.* 15: 700–15.

Madewell, B. R., Stannard, A. A., Pulley, L. T. & Nelson, V. G. 1980.   Oral eosinophilic granuloma in Siberian Husky dogs. *J. Am. Vet. Med. Ass. 177*: 701–3.

Magrane, W. G. 1953.   Congenital anomaly of the optic disc in Collies. *N. Am. Vet.* 34: 646.

Magrane, W. G. 1957.   Canine glaucoma II. Primary classification. *J. Am. Vet. Med. Ass.* 131: 372–8.

Magrane, W. G. 1971.   *Canine ophthalmology.* Lea and Febiger, Philadelphia.

Magnusson, H. 1909.   Om nattblindhet hos hund sasom falid of släkskapsafvel. *Svensk. Vet. Tidskr.* 14: 462.

Magnusson, H. 1911.   *Arch. Verg. Ophthalmol.* 2: 147.

Magnusson, H. 1917.   *Albrecht Graefes Arch. Ophthalmol.* 93: 404.

Mahaffey, M. B., Yarbrough, K. M. and Munnell, J. F. 1978.   Focal loss of pigment in the Belgian Tervueren Dog. *J. Am. Vet. Med. Ass.* 173: 390–6.

Mahut, H. 1958.   Breed differences in the dog's emotional behaviour. *Can. J. Psychol.* 12: 35–44.

Mair, I. W. S. 1976.   Hereditary deafness in the Dalmatian dog. *Arch. Oto-Rhino. Laryngology.* 212: 1–14.

Mann, G. F. and Stratton, J. 1966.   Dermoid sinuses on the Rhodesian Ridgeback. *J. small Anim. Pract.* 7: 631–42.

Manning, W. K. 1950.   Biotin deficiency as the causative agent of induced cryptorchidism in albino rats. *Science* 112: 89.

Marchlewski, T. 1930a.   Genetic studies on the domestic dog. *Bull. Int. Acad. Polon. Sci. Lett. Cl. Sci. Math. Nat.* B(1): 117–45.

Marchlewski, T. 1930b.   Craniology of the domestic dog. *Bull. Int. Acad. Polon. Sci. Lett. Cl. Sci. Math. Nat.* B(11): 511–48.

Martin, C. L. and Wyman, M. 1968.   Glaucoma in the Basset Hound. *J. Am. Vet. Med. Ass.* 153: 1320–7.

Martin, S. W., Kirby, K. and Pennock, P. W. 1980.   Canine hip dysplasia: breed effects. *Can. Vet. J.* 21: 293–6.

Martinek, Z. and Horak, F. 1970.   (Development of so-called genuine epileptic seizures in dogs during emotional excitement.) *Physiol. Bohems.* 19: 185–95.

Martinek, Z. and Dahme, E. 1977.   (Spontaneous epilepsy in dogs in long term studies on a group of genetically related animals.) *Zentralblatt. Vet.* 24A: 353–71.

Marsboom, R., Spruyt, J. and Van Ravestyn, C. H. 1971.   Incidence of congenital abnormalities in a Beagle colony. *Lab. Anim.* 5: 41–8.

Mason, T. A. 1976.   A review of recent developments in hip dysplasia. *Aust. Vet. J.* 52: 555–60.

Mason, T. A. 1977.   Cervical vertebral instability (Wobbler syndrome) in the Dobermann. *Aust. Vet. J.* 53: 440–5.

Mason, T. A. 1978.   Cervical vertebral instability in dogs. *Vet. Ann.* 18: 194–7.

Mason, T. A. and Cox, K. 1971.   Collie eye Anomaly. *Aust. Vet. J.* 47: 38–40.

Matsas, D. J. & Yang, T. J. 1980.   Karotype analysis of leucocytes of gray Collie (cyclic neutropenia)—normal bone marrow transplant chimeras six years after transplantation. *Am. J. Vet. Res.* 41: 1863–4.

McCartney, W. 1951.   Olfaction in animals. *Int. Pefam.* 4: 3–10.

McCarthy, J. C. and Blennerhasset, T. 1972.   A preliminary estimate of the degree of inbreeding in Irish Racing Greyhounds. *J. Dept. Agric. (Eire).* 69: 3–7.

McClave, P. L. 1957.   Elimination of coxofemoral dysplasia from a breeding kennel. *Vet. Med.* 52: 241–3.

McKinna, W. R. 1936.   On haemophilia. *Vet. J.* 92: 370.

McKusick, V. A. 1971.   *Mendelian inheritance in man. Catalogs of autosomal dominant, autosomal recessive and X-linked phenotypes.* John Hopkins Press, Baltimore.

McPhee, H. C. and Buckley, S. S. 1943. Inheritance of cryptorchidism in swine. *J. Hered.* 25: 295–303.

McPhee, H. C. and Wright, S. 1925.   Mendelian analysis of the pure breeds of livestock. 3. Shorthorn. *J. Hered.* 16: 205–15.

Mech, D. L. 1970. *The wolf: the ecology and behavior of an endangered species.* Natural History Press, New York.

Melzack, R. and Thompson, W. R. 1956. Effects of early experience on social behaviour. *Can. J. Psychol.* 10: 82–90.

Merkens, J. 1938. Haemophilia bij honden. *Ned. Bl. Diergeneek.* 50: 149–51.

Mettler, F. A. and Goss, L. J. 1946. Canine chorea due to striocerebellar degeneration of unknown etiology. *J. Am. Vet. Med. Ass.* 108: 377–84.

Meutstege, F. J. 1971. Die Behandlung der intertarsalen Subluxation beim Hund durch gedeckte Arthrodesis von Os tarsi fibulare und Os tarsale IV. *Kleinler Praxis.* 16: 12.

Meyers, K. M., Lund, J. E. and Boyce, J. T. 1968. Muscular cramping of central nervous system origin in Scottish Terrier dogs. *Fed. Proc.* 27: 611.

Meyers, K. M., Lund, J. E., Padgett, G. A. and Dickson, W. M. 1969. Hyperkinetic episodes in Scottish Terrier dogs. *J. Am. Vet. Med. Ass.* 155: 129–33.

Meyers, K. M., Padgett, G. A. and Dickson, W. M. 1970. The genetic basis of a kinetic disorder of Scottish Terrier dogs. *J. Hered.* 61: 189–92.

Miessner, K. 1964. Ist die lockenentwicklung der Pudelhunde eine Pluripotenzerscheinung. *Zool. Anz.* 172: 448–72.

Milton, J. L., Horne, R. D., Bartels, J. E. and Henderson, R. A. 1979. Congenital elbow luxation in the dog. *J. Am. Vet. Med. Ass.* 175: 572–82.

Mitchell, A. L. 1935. Dominant dilution and other colour factors in Collie dogs. *J. Hered.* 26: 424–30.

Moch, R. and Hasse, G. 1953. Hypofunktion der adenohypophyse eines Hundes. *Tierarztl. Umsch.* 8: 242–4.

Mollaret, M. M., Robon, V. and Bertrand, I. 1933. Maladie héréditaire du chien, homologue de l'hérédoOaxatie de Pierre Marie et de la maladie de Friedriech (Etude anatomique). *Rev. Neurol.* 40: 172–5.

Moltzen-Neilson, H. 1937. Calvé-Perthes-Kranheit, malum deformans juvenilis coxae bei Hunden. *Arch. Tierheilk.* 72: 91.

Monie, I. W., Nelson, M. M. and Evans, H. M. 1957. Abnormalities of the urinary system of rat embryos resulting from transitory deficiency of pteroylglutamic acid during gestation. *Anat. Rec.* 127: 711.

Moore, P. F. 1984. Systemic histiocytosis of Bernese Mountain Dogs. *Vet. Pathol.* 21: 554–63.

Morgan, J. P. 1968. *J. Am. Vet. Radiol. Soc.* 9: 21–

Morris, B., Blood, D. C., Sidman, W. R., Steel, J. D. and Whitteb, J. H. 1954. Congenital lymphatic oedema in Ayrshire calves. *Aust. J. Exp. Biol. Med. Sci.* 32: 265–74.

Most, K. 1925. Beitrage zur Frage der Verwendung von Hunden im Kriminaldienst. *Eisenach. Deutsch. Schaferhund. Verband. Berlin.* pp. 70.

Most, K. 1926. Neue Versuche über Spurfähigkeit. *Hund* 20–2.

Most, K. 1927. Die Versuche auf menschengleichen aber von menschengeruch-freien Spuren. *Hund* 469–75, 505–8.

Most, K. 1928a. Das problem der Spurenreinheit auf der menschlichen Spur im Lichte der zummal mit der Fahrtenbahn erzielten Versuchsergebnisse. *Hund* 31–5.

Most, K. 1928b. Die Prüfung des Polizeihundes 'Roland a.d. Baderstrasse' auf Spurenreinheit am 9, 10 und 11 Juli in Kummersdorf bei Berlin. *Hund* 319–24.

Most, K. 1954.   *Training dogs. A manual.* Popular Dogs, London.

Moulton, D. G., Ashton, E. H. and Eayrs, J. T. 1960.   Studies in olfactory acuity. 4. Relative detectability of n-aliphatic acids by the dog. *Anim. Behav.* 8: 117–28.

Muhlebach, R. and Freudiger, U. 1973.   Rontgenologische Untersuchungen uber die Erkrankungsformen der Spondylose deim Deutschen Boxer. *Schweiz. Arch. Tierheilk.* 115: 539–58.

Muller, G. H. and Jones, S. R. 1973.   Pituitary dwarfism and alopecia in a German Shepherd Dog with a cystic Rathke's cleft. *J. Am. Anim. Hosp. Ass.* 9: 567–72.

Muller, G. H. and Kirk, R. W. 1976.   *Small Animal Dermatology.* W. B. Saunders Co, Philadelphia.

Müller, L. F. and Saar, C. 1972.   (First results of veterinary and breeding measures to control hip dysplasia in the Hovawart.) *Tierarztl. Umsch.* 27: 176–7.

Mulligan, R. M. 1944.   Some statistical aspects of canine tumours. *Arch. Path. (Chicago)* 38: 115–20.

Mulligan, R. M. 1948a.   Statistical and histologic study of one hundred and twenty canine neoplasms. *Arch. Path. (Chicago)* 45: 216–28.

Mulligan, R. M. 1948b.   Neoplastic disease of dogs. II. Mast cell sarcoma, lymphosarcoma, histiocytoma. *Arch. Path. (Chicago)* 46: 477–92.

Mulligan, R. M. 1949a.   *Neoplasms in the dog.* Williams and Wilkins, Baltimore.

Mulligan, R. M. 1949b.   Types of neoplasms in five breeds of dog. *N. Am. Vet.* 30: 26–8.

Mulvihill, J. J. and Priester, W. A. 1973.   Congenital heart disease in dogs: epidemiologic similarities to man. *Teratology* 7: 73–7.

Mundell, J. D. C. and Glynn, K. M. 1978.   German Shepherds and splenic tumours. *Vet. Rec.* 102: 248.

Murphree, O. D. 1973.   Inheritance of human aversion and inactivity in two strains of the Pointer dog. *Biol. Psychiat.* 7: 23–29.

Murphree, O. D., Angel, C., DeLuca, D. C. and Newton, J. E. O. 1977.   Longitudinal studies of genetically nervous dogs. *Biol. Psychiat.* 12: 573–6.

Murphree, O. D. and Dykman, R. A. 1965.   Litter patterns in the offspring of nervous and stable dogs. 1. Behavioral tests. *J. Nerv. Ment. Dis.* 141: 321–32.

Musser, E. and Graham, W. R. 1968.   Familial occurrence of thyroiditis and pure-bred Beagles. *Lab. Anim. Care.* 18: 58–68.

Mustard, J. F., Rowsell, H. C., Robinson, G. A., Hoeksema, T. D. and Downie, H. G. 1960.   Canine haemophilia B. (Christmas disease). *Brit. J. Haemat.* 6: 259–66.

Mustard, J. F., Secord, D., Hoeksma. T. D., Downie, H. G. and Rowsell, H. C. 1962.   Canine Factor VII deficiency. *Brit. J. Haemat.* 8: 43–7.

Myers, L. J., Pierce, K. R., Gowling, G. M. and Leonpacher, R. J. 1972.   Hemorrhagic diathesis resembling pseudohemophilia in a dog. *J. Am. Vet. Med. Ass.* 161: 1028–9.

Nachtsheim, H. 1950.   The Pelger-Huët anomaly in man and rabbit. A Mendelian character of the nuclei of leukocytes. *J. Hered.* 41: 131–7.

Nash, A. S., Kelly, D. F. & Gaskell, C. J. 1984.   Progressive renal disease in Soft-Coated Wheaten terriers: possible familial nephropathy. *J. small Anim. Pract.* 25: 479–87.

Nassar, R. and Mosier, J. E. 1980.   Canine population dynamics: a study of the Manhattan, Kansas, canine population. *Am. J. Vet. Res.* 41: 1798–803.

Nesbitt, G. H., Izzo, J., Peterson, L. and Wilkins, R. J. 1980. Canine hypothyroidism: a retrospective study of 108 cases. *J. Am. Vet. Med. Ass.* 177: 1117–22.

Neuhaus, W. 1953. Uber die Riechsharfe des Hundes fur Fettsauren. *Z. vergl. Physiol.* 35: 527–32.

Newton, J. E. O., Chapin, J. L. and Murphree, O. D. 1976. Correlations of normality and nervousness with cardiovascular functions in Pointer dogs. *Pavlovian J.* 11: 105–20.

Niccolini, P. 1954. Lo stimulo olfattorio e la sua recezione. *Arch. Ital. Sci. Farmacol.* 4: 109–72.

Nicolas, E. 1925. *Veterinary and comparative ophthalmology*. H. & W. Brown, London.

Nicholas, F. 1975. The current status of hip dysplasia. *Otter tales* (NSW).

Nicholas, F. 1978. Pituitary dwarfism in German Shepherd Dogs: a genetic analysis of some Australian data. *J. small Anim. Pract.* 19: 167–74.

Niedermeyer, R. 1984. Rontgenologische Untersuchungen über die Entwicklung arthrotischer Veranderungen bei verschiedenen Graden der Huftgelenksdysplasie des Hundes. *Thesis.* Tierarz. Hochschule. Hannover. 45pp.

Nielsen, S. W. and Cole, C. R. 1958. Canine mastocyma—a report of one hundred cases. *Am. J. Vet. Res.* 19: 417–32.

Noble, R. J. and Coulson, A. 1978. German Shepherds and splenic tumours. *Vet. Rec.* 102: 268.

Nordby, J. E. 1932. Inheritance of whorls in the hair of swine. *J. Hered.* 23: 397–404.

O'Brien, J. A. and Hendriks, J. 1986. Inherited laryngeal paralysis. Analysis in the Husky Cross. *Vet. Quart.* 8: 301–2.

O'Brien, T. R., Morgan, J. P. and Suter, P. F. 1971. Epiphyseal plate injury in the dog: a radiographic study of growth disturbances in the fore-limb. *J. small Anim. Pract.* 12: 19–36.

Ogburn, P. N., Peterson, M. & Jeraj, K. 1981. Multiple cardiac anomalies in a family of Saluki dogs. *J. Am. Vet. Med. Ass.* 179: 57–63.

Okaanen, A. and Sittnikow, K. 1972. (Familial nephropathy with secondary hyperparathyroidism in three young dogs.) *Nord. Vet. Med.* 24: 278–80.

Olesen, H. P., Jensen, O. A. and Norn, M. S. 1974. Congenital hereditary cataract in Cocker Spaniels. *J. small Anim. Pract.* 15: 741–50.

Olsson, S. D. 1965. *Canine surgery*. Am. Vet. Publ., Santa Barbara.

Olsson, S. E. 1958. Acetabular dysplasia and Legg-Perthes disease. *Proc. Nord. Vet. Möt.* Helsinki. 948.

Olsson, S. E., Bjurstrom, S., Ekman, S., Jonsson, L., Lindberg, R. and Reiland, S. 1986. En epidemiologisk studie av tumorsjukdomar hos hund. *Svensk Veterinartidning* 38: 212–14.

Olsson, S. E. and Schnelle, G. B. 1973. Another look at the hip dysplasia question. *The German Shepherd Rev.* 51(3): 54.

Onslow, H. 1923. Endogenous uric acid and hematopoiesis. *J. Biol. Chem.* 86: 223–30.

Oppenheimer, R. H. 1968. *McGuffin and Co.* Dog World, Ashford, Kent.

Oppenheimer, R. H. 1969. Unilateral cryptorchidism. *Alsatian League & Club Handbook* 22–3.

Osborne, C. A., Clifford, D. H. and Jessen, C. 1967. Hereditary esophageal achalasia in dogs. *J. Am. Vet. Med. Ass.* 151: 572–81.

Owen, L. N. and Nielsen, S. W. 1968. Multiple cartilaginous extoses (diaphyseal aclasis) in a Yorkshire Terrier. *J. small Anim. Pract.* 9: 519–21.

Paatsama, S. 1963. Hereditary acetabular dysplasia in dogs. *Finsk. Vet. Tidskr.* 69: 144.

Paatsama. S., Rissanen, P. and Rokkanen, P. 1968. Changes in the hip joint induced with certain hormones. An experimental study in young dogs. *J. small. Anim. Pract.* 9: 433–40.

Padgett, G. A. and Mostovsky, U. V. 1986. Animal model: the mode of inheritance of craniomandibular osteopathy in West Highland White Terrier Dogs. *Am. J. Medical Genetics.* 25: 9–13.

Palmer, A. C., Payne, J. E. and Wallace, M. E. 1973. Hereditary quadriplegia and amblyopia in the Irish Setter. *J. small Anim. Pract.* 14: 343–52.

Palmer, A. C. and Wallace, M. E. 1967. Deformation of cervical vertebrae in Basset Hounds. *Vet. Rec.* 80: 430–3.

Palmer, C. S. 1970. Osteochondritis dissecans in Great Danes. *Vet. Med.* 65: 994–1000, 1002.

Parry, H. B. 1954. Degeneration of the dog retina. VI. Central progressive retinal atrophy with pigment epithelial dystrophy. *Brit. J. Ophthal.* 38: 653–68.

Passonneau, J. V. 1969. Energy metabolites in experimental seizures. In *Basic Mechanism of the Epilepsies* (Eds H. H. Jasper, A. A. Ward and A. Pope), Little Brown & Co, Boston.

Patel, V., Koppang, N., Patel, B. and Zeman, W. 1974. p-Phenylenediamine mediated perioxidase deficiency in English Setters with neuronal ceroid-lipofuscinosis. *Lab. Invest.* 30: 366–8.

Patterson, D. F. 1968. Epidemiologic and genetic studies of congenital heart diseases in the dog. *Circ. Res.* 23: 171–202.

Patterson, D. F. 1971. Canine congenital heart disease: epidemiology and etiological hypotheses. *J. small Anim. Pract.* 12: 263–87.

Patterson, D. F. 1974. A catalog of hereditary disease of the dog in *Current Veterinary Therapy V.* (Ed. R. W. Kirk). W. B. Saunders Co, Philadelphia.

Patterson, D. F. 1975. Diseases due to single mutant genes. *J. Am. Anim. Hosp. Ass.* 11: 327–41.

Patterson, D. F. 1976. Congenital defects of the cardiovascular system of dogs: studies in comparative cardiology. *Adv. Vet. Sci. Comp. Med.* 20: 1–37.

Patterson, D. F. and Detweiler, D. K. 1967. Hereditary transmission of patent ductus arteriosus. *Am. Heart J.* 74: 289–90.

Patterson, D. F. and Medway, W. 1966. Hereditary disease of the dog. *J. Am. Vet. Med. Ass.* 149: 1741–54.

Patterson, D. F., Medway, W., Luginbuhl, H. and Chacko, S. 1967. Congenital hereditary lymphodema in the dog. 1. Clinical and genetic studies. *J. Med. Genet.* 4: 145–52.

Patterson, D. F. Pyle, R. L. and Buchanan, J. W. 1972. Hereditary cardiovascular malformations of the dog. In Part XV *The Cardiovascular system* (ed. D. Bergsma) Williams and Wilkins, Baltimore. For the National Foundation March of Dimes. BD: OAS VIII(5).

Patterson, D. F., Pyle, R. L. Buchanan, J. W., Trautvetter, E. and Abt, D. A. 1971. Hereditary patent ductus arteriosus and its sequelae in the dog. *Circ. Res.* 29: 1–13.

Patterson, D. F., Pyle, R. L., Van Mierop, L., Melbin, J. and Olson, M. 1974. Hereditary defects of the conotruncal septum in Keeshond dogs: pathologic and genetic studies. *Am. J. Cardiol.* 34: 187–205.

Pearson, K. and Usher, C. H. 1929. Albinism in dogs. *Biometrika* 21: 144–63.

Pendergrass, T. W. and Hayes, H. M. 1975. Cryptorchidism and related defects in dogs: epidemologic comparisons with man. *Teratology* 12: 51–5.

Persson, F., Persson, S. and Asheim, A. 1961. Renal cortical hypoplasia in dogs. A clinical study of uraemia and secondary hyperparathyroidism. *Acta. Vet. Scand.* 2: 68–84.

Peters, J. A. 1969. Canine mastocytoma excess risk as related to ancestry. *J. Natn. Cancer Inst.* 42: 435–43.

Pettit, G. D. 1974. *Canine surgery.* American Vet. Publ., California.

Pfaffenberger, C. J. 1963. *The new knowledge of dog behavior.* Howell, New York.

Pfaffenberger, C. J., Scott, J. P., Fuller, J. L. Ginsburg, E. E. and Bielfelt, S. W. 1976. *Guide dogs for the blind: their selection, development and training.* Elsevier. Amsterdam. 225pp.

Phillips, J. M. 1938. Sable coat color in Cockers. *J. Hered.* 29: 67–9.

Phillips, J. M. 1945. 'Pig jaw' in Cocker Spaniels. Retrognathia of the mandible in the Cocker Spaniel and its relationship to other deformities of the jaw. *J. Hered.* 36: 177–81.

Phillips, J. M. and Felton, T. M. 1939. Hereditary umbilical hernia in dogs. *J. Hered.* 30: 433–5.

Pick, J. R. 1978. Personal communication.

Pick, J. R., Goyer, R. A., Graham, J. B. and Renwick, J. H. 1967. Subluxation of the carpus in dogs. An X chromosomal defect closely linked with the locus for hemophilia A. *Lab. Invest.* 17: 243–8.

Pidduck, H. and Webbon, P. M. 1978. The genetic control of Perthes' disease in Toy Poodles—a working hypothesis. *J. small Anim. Pract.* 19: 729–33.

Pierce, K. R. and Bridges, C. H. 1967. The role of estrogens and pathogenesis of canine hip dysplasia. Metabolism of exogenous estrogens. *J. small Anim. Pract.* 8: 383–9.

Pierce, K. R., Bridges, C. H. and Banks, W. C. 1965. Hormone induced hip dysplasia in dogs. *J. small Anim. Pract.* 6: 121–6.

Pil'shchikov, Y. N. 1971. (The genetics of behaviour in working dogs.) *Trud. Kazakh. naucho-issled. Inst. Zhivot.* 9: 203–8.

Pinkerton, P. H. and Fletch, S. M. 1972. Inherited haemolytic anaemia with dwarfism (gene symbol—*dan*) in the dog. *Blood* 40: 963 Abstr.

Pinkerton, P. H., Fletch, S. M., Brueckner, P. J. and Miller, D. R. 1974. Hereditary stomatocytosis with hemolytic anaemia in the dog. *Blood* 44: 557–67.

Plott, D. 1964. Congenital laryhngeal-abductor paralysis due to nucleus ambiguus dysgenesis in three brothers. *New. Engl. J. Med. 271*: 593–6.

Pobisch, R. 1980. Zur Röntgendiagnostik der Urolithiasis beim Hund. *Wiener Tierarztliche Monat.* 67: 193–7.

Pobisch, R., Geres, V. and Arbesser, E. 1972. Ellbogengelenkdysplasie beim Hund. *Wien. Tierarzt. Monat.* 59: 297–307.

Poirson, J. 1980. L'hemophile chez le chien a propos de cinq cas rencontres dans la race Berger Allemand. *Point Veterinaire* 10(50): 7–11.

Poller, L., Thomson, J. M., Sear, C. H. J. and Thomas, W. 1971. Identification of a congenital defect of factor VII in a colony of Beagle dogs. The clinical use of plasma. *J. Clin. Pathol.* 24: 626–32.

Poole, C. M. 1974. Unpublished data cited by Fritz *et al* (1976).

Potkay, S. and Bacher, J. D. 1977.   Morbidity and mortality in a closed Foxhound breeding colony. *Lab. Anim. Sci.* 27: 78–84.

Preston, T. R. and Willis, M. B. 1970.   *Intensive Beef Production.* Pergamon, Oxford.

Preu, K. P., Blaurock, H. and Galle, O. 1975.   (Hip dysplasia in Beagles.) *Berliner Munch. Tierz. Wochen.* 58: 271–5.

Priester, W. A. 1967.   Canine lymphoma: relative risk in the Boxer breed. *J. Natnl. Cancer Inst.* 39: 833–45.

Priester, W. A. 1972.   Sex, size and breed as risk factors in canine patellar dislocation. *J. Am. Vet. Med. Ass.* 160: 740–2.

Priester, W. A. 1974.   Canine progressive retinal atrophy: occurrence by age, breed and sex. *Am. J. Vet. Res.* 35: 571–4.

Priester, W. A. 1976.   Canine invertebral disk disease—occurrence by age, breed, and sex among 8117 cases. *Theriogenology* 6: 293–303.

Priester, W. A., Glass, A. G. and Waggoner, N. S. 1970.   Congenital defects in domesticated animals: general considerations. *Am. J. Vet. Res.* 31: 1871–9.

Priester, W. A. and Mulvihill, J. J. 1972.   Canine hip dysplasia: relative risk by sex, size and breed and comparative aspects. *J. Am. Vet. Med. Ass.* 160: 735–9.

Prinzhorn, F. 1921.   Die Haut und die Rückbildung der Haare beim Nackthunde. *Jena Z. Naturw.* 57: 143–98.

Prole, J. H. B. 1973.   Some observations on the physiology of reproduction in the Greyhound bitch. *J. small Anim. Pract.* 14: 781–4.

Pullig, T. 1950.   Inheritance of whorls in Cocker Spaniels. A preliminary report. *J. Hered.* 41: 239–42.

Pullig, T. 1952.   Inheritance of a skull defect in Cocker Spaniels. *J. Hered.* 43: 97–9.

Pullig, T. 1953a.   Anury in Cocker Spaniels. *J. Hered.* 44: 105–7.

Pullig, T. 1953b.   Cryptorchidism in Cocker Spaniels. *J. Hered.* 44: 250, 264.

Pullig, T. 1957.   Brachury in Cocker Spaniels. *J. Hered.* 48: 75–6.

Pyle, R. L., Patterson, D. F. and Chacko, S. 1976.   The genetics and pathology of discrete subaortic stenosis in the Newfoundland dog. *Am. Heart J.* 92: 324–34.

Rahko, T. 1968.   A statistical study of tumours of dogs. *Acta. Vet. Scand.* 9: 328–49.

Rasbridge, W. J. 1944.   *Our Dogs,* 6th May.

Rasmussen, P. G. and Reimann, I. 1977.   Dystosis exchondralis of the ulnar bone in the Basset Hound. *Acta. Vet. Scand.* 18: 31–9.

Rech, H. 1953.   Agressivité chez le chien. *Rev. Méd. Vét. (Toulouse).* 104: 96–110.

Reese, A. B. and Straatsma, B. R. 1958.   *Am. J. Ophthal.* 45. Suppl. 199.

Reetz, J. 1981.   Zur frage der Elternschaftskontrolle dei deutschen Hunderassen. *Dtsch. Tierz. Wochenschrift* 88: 5–8.

Reetz, I., Stecker, M. and Wegner, W. 1977.   Audiometrische Befunde in einer Merlezucht. *Dtsch. Tierärztl. Wschr.* 84: 273–7.

Rehfeld, C. E. 1970.   Definition of relationships in a closed Beagle colony. *A. J. Vet. Res.* 31: 723–32.

Reid, J. B., Chantrey, D. F. and Davie, C. 1984. Eliminatory behaviour of domestic dogs in an urban environment. *App. Anim. Behaviour Sci.* 12: 279–87.

Reinhard, D. W. 1978. Aggressive behaviour associated with hypothyroidism. *Canine Practice* 5(6): 69–70.

Reuterwall, C. and Ryman, N. 1973. An estimate of the magnitude of additive genetic variation of some mental characters in Alsatian dogs. *Hereditas.* 73: 277–84.

Richter, V. 1977. Untersuchungen am Becken des Hundes unter besonderer Berocksichtigung des Hotgelenkes und Rassespezifischer Merkmale. *Thesis. Ludwig Max. Univ. Munich.*

Rickards, E. 1975. Hip dysplasia. *European Spaniel Cong.* Fulda, Germany.

Riser, W. H. 1963. A new look at development, subluxation and dislocation: hip dysplasia in the dog. *J. small Anim. Pract.* 4:421–35.

Riser, W. H. 1964. Radiographic differential diagnosis of skeletal diseases of young dogs. *J. Am. Vet. Radiol. Soc.* 5: 15–27.

Riser, W. H. 1973. Hip dysplasia in military dogs. *J. Am. Vet. Med. Ass.* 162: 644 Abstr.

Riser, W. H. 1974. Canine hip dysplasia: cause and control. *J. Am. Vet. Med. Ass.* 164: 360–2.

Riser, W. H., Cohen, D., Lindquist, S., Mansson, J. and Cheb, S. 1964. Influence of early rapid growth and weight gain on hip dysplasia in the German Shepherd Dog. *J. Am. Vet. Med. Ass.* 145: 661–8.

Riser, W. H., Haskins, M. E., Jezyk, P. F. & Patterson, D. F. 1980. Pseudoachondroplastic dysplasia in Miniature Poodles: clinical, radiologic and pathologic features. *J. Am. Vet. Med. Ass.* 176: 335–41.

Riser, W. H. and Miller, H. 1966. *Canine hip dysplasia and how to control it.* OFA Publ., Philadelphia.

Riser, W. H. and Shirer, J. F. 1967. Correlations between canine hip dysplasia and pelvic muscle mass: a study of 95 dogs. *Am. J. Vet. Res.* 28: 769–77.

Ritter, R. 1937. Können Anomalien des Gebisses gezüchtet werden? *D. Zahn. Mund u Kieferheilk.* 4: 235–57.

Robbins, G. and Grandage, J. 1977. Temporomandibular joint dysplasia and open mouth jaw locking in the dog. *J. Am. Vet. Med. Ass. 171:* 1072–6.

Robbins, G. R. 1965. Unilateral renal agenesis in the Beagle. *Vet. Rec.* 77: 1345–7.

Roberts, S. R. 1959. Detachment of the retina in animals. *J. Am. Vet. Med. Ass.* 5: 423–32.

Roberts, S. R. 1960. Congenital posterior ectasia in the sclera of Collie dogs. *Am. J. Ophthal.* 50: 451–65.

Roberts, S. R. 1967a. Color dilution and hereditary defects in Collie dogs. *Am. J. Ophthal.* 63: 1762–75.

Roberts, S. R. 1967b. Three inherited ocular defects in the dog. *Mod. Vet. Pract.* 48: 30–34.

Roberts, S. R. 1969. The Collie Eye Anomaly. *J. Am. Vet. Med. Ass.* 155: 859–65.

Roberts, S. R. 1973. Hereditary cataracts. *Vet. Clin. North Am.* 3: 433–7.

Roberts, S. R. and Bistner, S. I. 1968. Persistent pupillary membrane in Basenji dogs. *J. Am. Vet. Med. Ass.* 153: 533–42.

Roberts, S. R. and Dellaporta, A. 1965. Congenital posterior ectasia of the sclera in Collie dogs. 1. Clinical features. *Am. J. Ophthal.* 59: 180–6.

Roberts, S. R., Dellaporta, A. and Winter, F. C. 1966a.   The Collie ectasia syndrome. *Am. J. Ophthal.* 62: 728–52.

Roberts, S. R., Dellaporta, A. and Winter, F. C. 1966b.   The Collie ectasia syndrome. Pathology of eyes of pups one to fourteen days of age. *Am. J. Ophthal.* 61: 1458–66.

Roberts, S. R. and Helper, L. C. 1972.   Cataracts in Afghan Hounds. *J. Am. Vet. Med. Ass.* 160: 427–32.

Robertson, A. 1954.   Inbreeding and performance in British Friesian cattle. *Proc. Brit. Soc. Anim. Prod.* 87–92.

Robins, G. M. 1978.   Osteochondritis dissecans in the dog. *Austr. Vet. J.* 54: 272–9.

Robins, G. M. 1980.   Some aspects of the radiographical examination of the canine elbow joint. *J. small Anim. Pract.* 21: 517–28.

Robinson, G. W. 1968.   A comparison of licensed and hospital dog populations. *J. Am. Vet. Med. Ass.* 152: 1383–9.

Robinson, R. 1972.   *Catalogue and bibliography of canine genetic anomalies.* Chart, West Wickham.

Robinson, R. 1973.   Relationship between litter size and weight of dam in the dog. *Vet. Rec.* 92: 221–3.

Robinson, R. 1977.   Genetic aspects of umbilical hernia incidence in cats and dogs. *Vet. Rec.* 100: 9–10.

Robinson, R. 1982.   *Genetics for dog breeders.* Pergamon Press, Oxford.

Robinson, R. 1987.   Inheritance of colour and coat in the Belgian Shepherd Dog. *Genetica* (in press).

Rosinsky, O. E. 1942.   Der Kryptorchismus und seine Behandlung. *Med. Klin.* 38: 843–

Roslin-Williams, M. 1975.   *All about the Labrador.* Pelham, London.

Rowland, M. G. 1978.   German Shepherds and splenic tumours. *Vet. Rec.* 102: 350.

Rowlands, I. W. 1951.   Some observations on the breeding of dogs. *Proc. Soc. Stud. Fert. (Camb.)* 2: 40–55.

Rubin, L. F. 1964.   Heredity retinal detachment in Bedlington Terriers. A preliminary report. *Small Anim. Clin.* 3: 387–9.

Rubin, L. F. 1968.   Heredity of retinal dysplasia in Bedlington Terriers. *J. Am. Vet. Med. Ass.* 152: 260–2.

Rubin, L. F. 1969.   Comments on the paper by Roberts, 1969. *J. Am. Vet. Med. Ass.* 155: 865–6.

Rubin, L. F. 1971a.   Clinical features of hemeralopia in the adult Alaskan Malamute. *J. Am. Vet. Med. Ass.* 158: 1696–8.

Rubin, L. F. 1971b.   Hemeralopia in Alaskan Malamute pups. *J. Am. Vet. Med. Ass.* 158: 1699–701.

Rubin, L. F. 1974.   Cataract in Golden Retrievers. *J. Am. Vet. Med. Ass.* 165: 457

Rubin, L. F., Bourns, T. K. R. and Lord, L. H. 1967.   Hemeralopia in dogs: heredity of hemeralopia in Alaskan Malamutes. *Am. J. Vet. Res.* 28: 355–7.

Rubin, L. F. and Flowers, R. D. 1972.   Inherited cataract in a family of Standard Poodles. *J. Am. Vet. Med. Ass.* 161: 207–8.

Rubin, L. F., Koch, S. A. and Huber, R. J. 1969.   Heredity cataracts in Miniature Schnauzers. *J. Am. Vet. Med. Ass.* 154: 1456–8.

Ruff, A. 1978.   Personal communication.

Russell, E. S. 1946.   A quantitative histological study of the pigment found in the coat colour mutants of the house mouse. 1. Variable attributes of the pigment granules. *Genetics* 31: 327–46.

Russell, S. W. and Griffiths, R. C. 1968.   Recurrence of cervical disc syndrome in surgically and conservatively treated dogs. *J. Am. Vet. Med. Ass.* 153: 1412–17.

Sacher, G. A. 1959.   Relation of life span to brain and body weight in mammals. *CIBA Found. Coll. Ageing.* 115–33.

Sagi, L. 1975.   (Diagnosis and occurrence of hip joint dysplasia in German Shepherd Dogs in Hungary.) *Magyer All. Lapja.* 30: 354–8, 361–2.

Sailer, J. 1954.   Die Stummelschwanzigkeit bei Hunden. *Vet-med. Diss. Ludwig Maximilians Univ., Munich.*

Sande, R. D., Alexander, J. E. and Padgett, G. A. 1974.   Dwarfism in the Alaskan Malamute: its radiographic pathogenesis. *J. Am. Vet. Radiol. Soc.* 15: 10–17.

Sandefeldt, E., Cummings, J. F., deLahunta, A., Bjork, G. and Krook, L. 1973.   Hereditary neuronal abiotrophy in the Swedish Lapland dog. *Cornell Vet.* 63: Supp. No. 3.

Sandefeldt, E. and Nilsson, L. 1986.   Hereditär juvenil neuronal muskelatrof hos lapphund —nuläget. *Svensk Veterinartidning* 38: 162–4.

Sateri, N. 1975.   Investigations on the exocrine pancreatic function in dogs suffering from chronic exocrine pancreatic insufficiency. *Acta. Vet. Scand.* Supp. 53.

Schaer, M. 1979.   A clinicopathologic survey of acute pancreatitis in 30 dogs and 5 cats. *J. Am. Anim. Hosp. Ass.* 15: 681–7.

Schaible, R. H. and Brumbaugh, J. A. 1976.   Electron microscopy of pigment cells in variegated and nonvariegated piebald spotted dogs. *Pigment Cell.* 3: 191–220.

Schalles, O. 1956.   Genetic aspects of dysplasia of the hip joint. *N. Am. Vet.* 37: 476–8.

Schailes, O. 1958.   Genes, the dice of destiny. *The Shepherd Dog Rev.* 36(9): 16.

Schalm, O. W., Jain, N. C. & Carroll, E. J. 1975.   Normal values in blood morphology with comments on species characteristics in response to disease. *Veterinary Hematology* (3rd ed.) Lea & Febiger, Philadelphia.

Schieffer, R. 1968.   Uber Keilwirbel beim Hund. *Berl. Munch. tierarztl.* 81: 149–51.

Schneider, M. 1984.   *Die Huftgelenksdysplasie und ihre Zuchterische Bekampfung beim Leonberger Hund.* Thesis. Fac. Veterinary Med. Freien Univ. Berlin. 47pp.

Schnelle, G. B. 1935.   Some new disease in dogs. *Am. Kennel Gazette* 52(5): 25.

Schnelle, G. B. 1950.   *Radiology in small animal practice.* North Am. Vet. Publ., Evanston, Illinois.

Schnepf, A. 1976.   Evaluation of hip dysplasia in the dog. *Diss. Fachbereits. Tiermed. Munich.*

Schwartz, A., Ravin, C. E., Greenspan, R. H., Schoemann, R. S. and Burt, J. K. 1976.   Congenital neuromuscular esophageal disease in a litter of Newfoundland puppies. *J. Am. Vet. Radiol. Soc.* 17: 101–5.

Scott, J. L. 1958.   *Animal behavior.* Univ. Chicago Press, Chicago.

Scott, J. P. 1964.   Genetics and the development of social behavior in dogs. *Am. Zool.* 4: 161–8.

Scott, J. P. and Fuller, J. L. 1951. Research on genetics and social behavior at the Roscoe B. Jackson Memorial Laboratory 1946–1951: a progress report. *J. Hered.* 42: 191–7.

Scott, J. P. and Fuller, J. L. 1965. *Genetics and the social behavior of the dog.* Univ. Chicago Press, Chicago.

Scott, J. P., Fuller, J. L. and King, J. A. 1959. The inheritance of annual breeding cycles in hybrid Basenji—Cocker Spaniel dogs. *J. Hered.* 50: 254–61.

Searcy, G. P., Miller, D. R. and Tasker, J. B. 1971. Congenital hemolytic anemia in the Basenji dog due to erythrocyte pyruvate kinase deficiency. *Can. J. Comp. Med.* 35: 67–70.

Searle, A. G. 1968. *Comparative genetics of coat colour in mammals.* Logos, London.

Searle, L. V. 1949. The organisation of hereditary maze-brightness and maze-dullness. *Genet. Psychol. Monograph.* 39: 279–325.

Searle, S. R. 1965. The value of indirect selection 1. Mass Selection. *Biometrics.* 21: 682–707.

Selcer, R. R. and Oliver, J. E. Jr. 1975. Cervical spondylopathy—Wobbler syndrome—in dogs. *J. Am. Anim. Hosp. Ass.* 11: 175–9.

Selmanowitz, V. J., Kramer, K. M. and Orentreich, N. 1970. Congenital ectodermal defect in Miniature Poodles. *J. Hered.* 61: 196–9.

Selmanowitz, V. J., Kramer, K. M. and Orentreich, N. 1972. Canine hereditary black hair follicular dysplasia. *J. Hered.* 64: 43–4.

Selmanowitz, V. J., Markofsky, J. and Orentreich, N. 1977a. Heritability of an ectodermal defect. A study of affected dogs. *J. Dermat. Surgery Oncology.* 3: 623–6.

Selmanowitz, V. J., Markofsky, J. and Orentreich, N. 1977b. Black hair follicular dysplasia in dogs. *J. Am. Vet. Med. Ass.* 171: 1079–81.

Sen, S. and Ansari, A. I. 1972. Depigmentation (vitiligo) in animals and its treatment with meladinine. *Indian J. Anim. Health* 10: 249–521.

Sheng, H–P. and Huggins, R. A. 1971. Growth of the Beagle: changes in chemical composition. *Growth* 35: 369–75.

Shupe, J. L., James, L. F., Balls, L. D., Binns, W. and Keeler, R. F. 1967. A probable hereditary skeletal deformity in Hereford cattle. *J. Hered.* 58: 311–13.

Sierts-Roth, U. 1958. Wurfstarke und Geschlechtsproportion bei Ungarischen Hirtenhunden. *Zool. Gart. (Lpz).* 22: 204–8.

Simonsen, W. 1976. Electrophoretic studies on the blood proteins of domestic dogs and other Canidae. *Hereditas.* 82: 7–18.

Sittmann, K. 1976. Inheritance of sexlimited defects. Cryptorchidism in dogs (German Boxers). *8th Int. Cong. Anim. Reprod. Art. Insem. Krakow.* 1: 242.

Sittmann, K. and Woodhouse, B. 1977. Sex-limited and sex-modified genetic defects in swine —cryptorchidism. *Can. J. Genet. Cytol.* 19: 487–502.

Skaggs, S., DeAngelis, M. P. and Rosen, H. 1973. Deformities due to premature closure of the distal ulna in fourteen dogs. A radiographic evaluation. *J. Am. Anim. Hosp. Ass.* 9: 496–500.

Skrentny, T. T. 1964. (Preliminary study on the inheritance of missing teeth in the dog.) *Wien. Tierarztl. Mschr.* 51: 231–45.

Slappendell, R. J. 1975. Hemophilia A and hemophilia B in a family of French Bulldogs. *Tijdschr. Diergeneesk.* 100: 1075–88.

Smart, N. E. and Fletch, S. M. 1971. A hereditary skeletal growth defect in purebred Alaskan Malamutes. *Can. Vet. J.* 12: 21–2.

Smith, G. K. A. and Scammell, L. P. 1968. Congenital abnormalities occurring in a Beagle breeding colony. *Lab. Anim.* 2: 83–8.

Smith, K. W. 1965. *Canine surgery*. Am. Vet. Publ. Wheaton, Illinois.

Smith, W. C. and Reese, W. C. 1968. Characteristics of a Beagle colony. 1. Estrus cycle. *Lab. Anim. Care.* 18: 602–6.

Smythe, R. H. 1945. Recurrent tetany in the dog. *Vet. Rec.* 57: 380.

Smythe, R. H. 1958. *Veterinary ophthalmology*. Balliere Tindall & Co, London.

Smythe, R. H. 1963. The fading syndrome in new-born puppies. *Vet. Rec.* 75: 741.

Snaveley, G. B. 1960. One point of view about hip dysplasia. *The Shepherd Dog Rev.* 38(11): 22.

Snaveley, J. G. 1959. Genetic aspects of hip dysplasia in dogs. *J. Am. Vet. Med. Ass.* 135: 201–7.

Sokolovsky, V. 1972. Achalasia and paralysis of the canine esophagus. *J. Am. Vet. Med. Ass.* 160: 943–55.

Somerfield, E. 1955. *The Popular Boxer*. Popular Dogs, London.

Sommer, O. 1931. Untersuchungen über die Wachstumsvorgänge am Hundeskelett. *Arch. Tierernahr. Tierz.* 6: 439–69.

Sorsby, A. 1970. *Ophthalmic Genetics*. Butterworths, London.

Sorsby, A. and Davey, J. B. 1954. Ocular associations of dappling (or merling) in the coat colour of dogs. 1. Clinical and genetical data. *J. Genet.* 52: 425–40.

Sponenberg, D. P. 1984. Germinal reversion of the merle allele in Australian shepherd dogs. *J. Hered.* 75: 78.

Sponenberg, D. P. 1985. Inheritance of the harlequin color in Great Dane dogs. *J. Hered.* 76: 224–5.

Sponenberg, D. P. and Lamoreux, M. L. 1985. Inheritance of tweed, a modification of merle, in Australian shepherd dogs. *J. Hered.* 76: 303–4.

Spreull, J. S. A. 1949. Some observations on breeding, whelping and rearing. *Vet. Rec.* 61: 579–82.

Spurling, N. W., Burton, L. K., Peacock, R. and Pilling, T. 1972. Hereditary factor VII deficiency in the Beagle. *Brit. J. Haematol.* 23: 59–67.

Spy, G. M. 1963. Megaloesophagus in a litter of Greyhounds. *Vet. Rec.* 75: 853–5.

Stack, W. F., Thomson, J. D. and Suyama, A. 1957. Achalasia of the esophagus with mesaesophagus in a dog. *J. Am. Vet. Med. Ass.* 131: 225–26.

Stades, F. C. 1978. Hereditary retinal dysplasia (RD) in a family of Yorkshire Terriers. *Tijdschr. Diergeneesk.* 103: 1087–90.

Stephan, H. 1954. Die Anwendung der Snell'schen Formel h = ks.p auf Hirn Körpergewichtsbieziehungen bei verschiedenen Hunderassen. *Zool. Anz.* 153: 15–27.

Stern, C. 1973. *Principles of human genetics*. Freeman, San Francisco.

Stewart, R. W., Menges, R. W., Selby, L. A., Rhoades, J. D. and Crenshaw, D. B. 1972. Canine intersexuality in a Pug-breeding kennel. *Cornell Vet.* 62: 464–73.

Stewart, S. J. 1969. Epilepsy. *League Mag.* 7(1): 29.

Stewart, S. J. 1970. Epilepsy: a further report. *League Mag.* 7(8): 18.

Stewart, S. J. 1972. Un-united anconeal process. *Alsatian League & Club Handbook* 21–22.

Stewart, W. C., Baker, G. J. and Lee, R. 1975. Temporomandibular subluxation in the dog. A case report. *J. small Anim. Pract.* 16: 345–9.

Steyn, H. P., Quinlan, J. and Jackson, C. 1939.   A skin condition seen in Rhodesian Ridgeback dogs: report on two cases. *J. S. Afr. Vet. Med. Ass.* 10: 170–4.

Stiern, R. A. 1956.   Ectopic sesamoid bones at the elbow (patella cubiti) of the dog. *J. Am. Vet. Med. Ass.* 128: 498–501.

Stockard, C. R. 1936.   A hereditary lethal for localised moto and preganglionic neurones with resulting paralysis in the dog. *Am. J. Anat.* 59: 1–53.

Stockard, C. R. *et al.* 1941.   The genetic and endocrine basis for differences in form and behavior as elucidated by studies of contrasted pure-line dog breeds and their hybrids. With special contributions on behavior by O. D. Anderson and W. T. James. *Am. Anat. Mem.* No. 19. *Wistar Inst. Anatomy & Biology,* Philadelphia.

Strasser, H. and Schumacher, W. 1968.   Breeding dogs for experimental purposes. II. Assessment of 8-year breeding records for two Beagle strains. *J. small Anim. Pract.* 9: 603–12.

Strating, A. and Clifford, D. H. 1966.   Canine achalasia with special reference to heredity. *S. West. Vet.* 19: 135–7.

Stratton, J. 1964.   Dermoid sinuses in the Rhodesian Ridgeback. *Vet. Rec.* 76: 846.

Studer, T. 1901.   Die prähistorischen Hunde in ihrer Beziehung zu den gegenwärtig lebenden Rassen. *Abh. Schweiz. palont. Ges.* 28: 1–137.

Stunkard, J. A., Schwichtenberg, A. E. and Griffin, T. P. 1969.   Evaluation of hip dysplasia in German Shepherd Dogs. *Mod. Vet. Pract.* 50(4): 40–4.

Subden, R. E., Fletch, S. M., Smart, M. E. and Brown, R. G. 1972.   Genetics of the Alaskan Malamute chondrodysplasia syndrome. *J. Hered.* 63: 149–52.

Suu, S. 1956.   (Studies on short-spined dogs. 1. Their origins and occurrence.) *Res. Bull. Fac. Agric. Gifu Univ.* 7: 127–34.

Suu, S. and Ueshima, T. 1957.   (Studies on short-spined dogs. 2. Somatological observations.) *Res. Bull. Fac. Agric. Gifu Univ.* 8: 112–28.

Suu, S. and Ueshima, T. 1958.   (Studies on short-spined dogs. 3. Postures and movements.) *Res. Bull. Fac. Agric. Gifu Univ.* 9: 178–86.

Suu, S. and Ueshima, T. 1963.   (Studies on short-spined dogs. On the cervial and thoracic organs.) *Res. Bull. Fac. Agric. Gifu Univ.* 18: 159–65.

SV. 1980a.   *Korbuch fur Deutsche Schaferhunde.* 52: iii–v.

SV. 1980b.   *Zeitung.* July p. 642.

Sweeney, P. A. 1972.   Some observations on behaviour of Greyhounds. *J. small Anim. Pract.* 13: 679–85.

Swenson, L. 1986a.   Betydelsen av föraldradjurens egenstatus för uppkomsten av höftledsdysplasi hos avkomman. *Svensk Veterinärtidning.* 38: 64–7.

Swenson, L. 1986b.   What do we know about hip dysplasia today? Proc. Conference Norway.

Swisher, S. N. and Young, L. E. 1961.   The blood grouping systems of dogs. *Physiol. Rev.* 41: 495–520.

Swisher, S. N., Young, L. E. and Trabold, N. 1962.   In vitro and in vivo studies of the behavior of canine erythrocyte-isoantibody systems. *Ann. N.Y. Acad. Sci.* 97: 15–25.

Szczudlowska, M. 1967.   (Dermoid cyst of the eye in relation to heredity and overfeeding.) *Medycyna. Vet.* 23: 567–9.

Tasker, J. B., Young, S. and Gillette, E. L. 1969.   Familial anaemia in the Basenji dog. *J. Am. Vet. Med. Ass.* 154: 158–65.

Teare, J. A., Krook, L., Kallfelz, F. A. and Hintz, H. F. 1979. Ascorbic acid deficiency and hypertrophic osteodystrophy in the dog: A rebuttal. *Cornell Vet.* 69: 384–401.

Telfer, T. P., Denson, K. W. and Wright, D. R. 1956. A 'new' coagulation defect. *Brit. J. Hematol.* 2: 308–16.

Templeton, J. W., Stewart, A. P. and Fletcher, W. S. 1977. Coat color genetics in the Labrador Retriever. *J. Hered.* 68: 134–6.

Theodos, G. 1959a. Breed notes. *Dog World* 5th June.

Theodos, G. 1959b. Breed notes. *Dog World* 17th July.

Thomsen, A. V. Holtet, L., Andresen E., Nilsson, I. M. and Fogh, J. M. 1984. Hemofili hos shaeferhund i Norge. *Norsk veterinaertidsskrift.* 96: 369–74.

Thomsett, L. R. 1961. Congenital hypotrichia in the dog. *Vet. Rec.* 73: 915–17.

Thorne, F. C. 1940. Approach and withdrawal behavior in dogs. *J. Genet. Psychol.* 56: 265–72.

Thorne, F. C. 1944. The inheritance of shyness in dogs. *J. Genet. Psychol.* 65: 275–9.

Thrall, D. E., Badertscher, R. R., Lewis, R. E. and Losonsky, J. M. 1977. Canine bone scanning: its use as a diagnostic tool for canine hip dysplasia. *Am. J. Vet. Res.* 38: 1433–7.

Tontitila, P. and Lindberg, L. A. 1971. ETT fall av cerebellar ataxi hos finsk stovare. *Svomen. Elainlaakarilehti.* 77: 135–8.

Townsend, L. 1973. Hip dysplasia in canine military candidates. *J. Am. Vet. Med. Ass.* 162: 666 Abstr.

Townsend, L. R., Gillette, E. L. and Lebel, J. L. 1971. Progression of hip dysplasia in military working dogs. *J. Am. Vet. Med. Ass.* 159: 1129–33.

Trauner, L. M. 1971. A program for control of progressive retinal atrophy in Poodles. *Mod. Vet. Pract.* 52(7): 29–31.

Treu, H., Reetz, I., Wegner, W. and Krause, D. 1976. Andrologische Befunde in einer Merle-zucht. *Zuchthyg.* 11: 49–61.

Trimble, H. C. and Keeler, C. E. 1938. The inheritance of high uric acid excretion in dogs. *J. Hered.* 29: 280–9.

Trimble, H. C. and Keeler, C. E. 1939. Preference of Dalmatian dogs for particular positions in coach running and inheritance of this character. *Nature.* 144: 671–2.

Trommershausen-Smith, A., Suzuki, Y. and Stormont, C. 1976. Use of blood typing to confirm principles of coat-color genetics in horses. *J. Hered.* 67: 6–10.

Trotter, E. J., deLahunta, A., Geary, J. C. and Brasmer, T. H. 1976. Caudal cervical vertebral malformation-malarticulation in Great Danes and Dobermann Pinschers. *J. Am. Vet. Med. Ass.* 168: 917–30.

Tryon, R. C. 1940. Genetic differences in maze learning ability in rats. *Yearbk. Nat. Soc. Stud. Educ.* 39: 111–19.

Tuch, K. & Matthiesen, T. 1978. Einseitige Anomalie der Niere beim Beagle. *Berliner und Munch. Tierartliche Wochen. 91*: 365–7.

Turba, E. and Willer, S. 1987. Untersuchungen zur Vererbung von Hasenscharten und Wolf-srachen beim Deutschen Boxer. *Monat. fur. Veterinarmedizin.* 42: 897–901.

Tvedten, H. W., Carrig, C. B., Flo, G. L. and Romsos, D. R. 1977. Incidence of hip dysplasia in Beagle dogs fed different amounts of protein and carbohydrate. *J. Am. Anim. Hosp. Ass.* 13: 595–8.

Twedt, D. C., Sternlieb, I. & Gilbertson, S. R. 1979.   Clinical, morphologic and chemical studies on copper toxicosis of Bedlington Terriers. *J. Am. Vet. Med. Ass.* 175: 269–75.

Ueshima, T. 1961.   A pathological study on deformation of the vertebral column in short-spined dogs. *Jap. J. Vet Res.* 9: 155–78.

USKBTC. 1976.   *Report of committee for health and genetics.* US Kerry Blue Terrier Club Inc. mimeo.

Utin, A. V. and Danielov, M. B. 1973.   (Study of heredity in epilepsy under conditions of inbreeding.) *Z.H. Nevropost. Psiklial Korsakov.* 73: 1692–9.

Vanderlip, S. L. 1986.   The Collie skull. A review of its changes during the century. *Int. Collie Handbook.* p. 67–7.

Van der Velden, N. A. 1968.   Fits in Tervueren Shepherd dogs: a presumed hereditary trait. *J. small Anim. Pract.* 9: 63–70.

Van der Velden, N. A., Weerdt, C. J. de, Brooymans-Schallenberg, J. H. C. and Tielen, A. M. 1976.   An abnormal behavioural trait in Bernese Mountain Dogs. (Berner Sennenhund). *Tijdschr. Diergeneesk.* 101: 403–7.

Van Kruiningen, H. J., Montali, R. J., Strandberg, J. D. and Kirk, R. V. 1965.   A granulomatous colitis of dogs with histologic resemblance to Whipples disease. *Vet. Path.* 2: 521–44.

Vaughan, L. C. 1958a.   Studies on invertebral disc protrusion in the dog. 1. Aetiology and pathogenesis. *Brit. Vet. J.* 114: 105–12.

Vaughan, L. C. 1958b.   Studies on invertebral disc protrusion in the dog. 2. Diagnosis of the disease. *Brit. Vet. J.* 114: 203–9.

Vaughan, L. C. 1958c.   Studies on invertebral disc protrusion in the dog. 3. Pathological features. *Brit. Vet. J.* 114: 350–5.

Vaughan, L. C. 1958d.   Studies on invertebral disc protrusion in the dog. 4. Treatment. *Brit. Vet. J.* 114: 458–63.

Vaughan, L. C. 1962.   Congenital detachment of the processus anconeus in the dog. *Vet. Rec.* 74: 309–11.

Vaughan, L. C., Clayton-Jones, D. G. and Lane, J. G. 1975.   Pectineus muscle resection as a treatment for hip dysplasia in dogs. *Vet. Rec.* 96: 145–8.

Veith, I. A. and Gelatt, K. N. 1970.   Persistent pupillary membrane in the dog. *Vet. Med.* 65: 1145–6.

Venker-van Haagen, A. J., Bouw, J. & Hartman, W. 1981.   Hereditary transmission of laryngeal paralysis in Bouviers. *J. Am. Anim. Hosp. Ass.* 17: 75–6.

Venker-van Haagen, A. J., Hartman, W. & Goedegebuure, S. A. 1978.   Spontaneous laryngeal paralysis in young Bouviers. *J. Am. Anim. Hosp. Ass.* 14: 714–20.

Verlinde, J. D. and Ojemann, J. G. 1946.   Eenige aangeboren misvormingen van het centrale zenuwstelsel. *Tijdschr. Diergeneesk.* 71: 557–64.

Verryn, S. D. and Geerthsen, J. M. P. 1987.   Heritabilities of a population of German Shepherd Dogs with a complex interrelationship structure *Theor. Appl. Genet.* 75: 144–6.

Vymetal, F. 1965.   Case reports: renal aplasia in Beagles. *Vet. Rec.* 77: 1344–5.

Wallace, L. J. 1971.   Pectineus tendonectomy or tenotomy for treating clinical hip dysplasia. *Vet. Clin. North Am.* 1: 455–65.

Wallace, M. E. 1975.   Keeshonds: a genetic study of epilepsy and EEG readings. *J. small Anim. Pract.* 16: 1–10.

Wallace, M. E. 1986. Genetic implications of hypomyelinogenesis in Bernese Mountain Dogs. mimeograph of notes from a talk to the BMD clubs. Oxford.

Wallin, B. 1986. Perthes sjukdom hos west highland white terrier en genetisk studie. *Svensk Veterinartidning* 38: 114–18.

Wamberg, K. 1961. Hüftgelenksleiden des Hundes. *Mh. Vet. Med.* 16: 884–91.

Wamberg, K. 1963. Røntgenundersøgelser m.v. af dyr—fortrinsvis hunde—i Danmark vedrørende arvelige hofteledssygdomme. *Beretn. 9 Nord. Vet. Mode (Kbh)* 2: 934–45.

Ward, B. and Hunter, W. M. 1960. The absent testicle: a report on a survey carried out among schoolboys in Nottingham. *Brit. Med. J.* 5179: 110–11.

Warkany, J. 1971a. Male Genitalia in *Congenital Malformations* (Ed. J. Warkany) Year Book. Medical Publ. Chicago. 1098–102.

Warkany, J. 1971b. Congenital dislocation of the hip. In *Congenital Malformations* (Ed. J. Warkany) Year Book. Medical Publ. Chicago. 992–7.

Warner, L. H. 1936. *Comparative psychology* (Eds C. J. Warden, T. N. Jenkins, L. H. Warner) Ronald Press, New York.

Warren, D. C. 1927. Coat color inheritance in Greyhounds. *J. Hered.* 18: 513–22.

Warwick, B. L. 1961. Selection against cryptorchidism in Angora goats. *J. Anim. Sci.* 20: 10–14.

Watters, G. V. & Fitch, N. 1973. Familial laryngeal abductor paralysis and psychomotor retardation. *Clinical Genetics 4*: 429–33.

Waxman, F. J., Clemmons, R. M., Johnson, G., Evermann, J. F., Johnson, M. L., Roberts, C. and Hinrichs, D. J. 1980a. Progressive myelopathy in older German Shepherd Dogs. 1. Depressed response to Thymus-dependent mitogens. *J. Immunol.* 124: 1209–15.

Waxman, F. J., Clemmons, R. M. & Hinrichs, D. J. 1980b. Progressive myelopathy in older German Shepherd Dogs. 11. Presence of circulating suppressor cells. *J. Immunol. 124*: 1216–22.

Weatherford, H. L. and Trimble, H. C. 1940. A further morphological and biochemical study on the intranuclear crystals in the hepatic cells of the dog—the purebred and the hybrid Dalmatian. *Anat. Res.* 77: 487–507.

Weaver, A. D. 1978. Hip dysplasia in beef cattle. *Vet. Rec.* 102: 54–5.

Weaver, A. D. 1983. Survey with follow-up of 67 dogs with testicular sertoli cell tumours. *Vet. Rec.* 113: 105–7.

Weber, W. 1955. Über die mediane Nasenspalte beim Berner Sennenhund. *Arch. Klaus-Stift. VererbForsch.* 30: 139–45.

Weber, W. 1959. Über die Vererbung der medianen Nasenspalte beim Hund. *Schweiz. Arch. Tierheilk.* 101: 378–81.

Weber, W. and Freudiger, U. 1977. Erbanalytische Untersuchungen Über die chronische exocrine Pankreasinsuffizienz beim Deutschen Schäferhunde. *Schweiz. Arch. Tierheilk.* 119: 257–63.

Wegner, W. and Reetz, I. 1975. Aufbau einer Merlezucht. *Tierarztl. prax.* 3: 455–9.

Weiss, G. 1966. (On the growth of various breeds of dog.) *Z. Säugetierk.* 31: 257–82.

Wells, H. G. 1918. The urine metabolism of the Dalmatian Coach Hound. *J. Biol. Chem.* 35: 221.

Wentink, G. H., Van der Linde-Sipman, J. S., Meijer, A. E. F. H., Kamphuisen, H. A. C., Van Vorstenbosch, C. J. A. H., Hartman, W. and Hendriks, H. J. 1972. Myopathy with a possible recessive X-linked inheritance in a litter of Irish Terriers. *Vet. Path.* 9: 328–49.

Westermarck, E. 1980.   The hereditary nature of canine pancreatic degenerative atrophy in the German Shepherd Dog. *Acta Vet. Scand.* 21: 389–94.

Westermarck, E. & Sandholm, M. 1980.   Faecal hydrolase activity as determined by radial enzyme diffusion—a new method for detecting pancreatic dysfunction in the dog. *Res. Vet. Sci.* 28: 341–6.

Westhues, M. 1926.   Der Schichtstar des Hundes. *Arch. f. wiss. u. Prakt. Tierheilk.* 54: 32–83.

Wheat, E. D. 1961.   Cryptorchidism in Hereford cattle. *J. Hered.* 52: 244–6.

White, J., Yeats, A. and Skipworth, G. 1974.   *Tables for statisticians.* Thornes, London.

Whitney, J. C. 1970.   Some aspects of interdigital cysts in the dog. *J. small Anim. Pract.* 11: 83–92.

Whitney, L. F. 1929.   Heredity of trail barking propensity in dogs. *J. Hered.* 20: 561–2.

Whitney, L. F. 1932.   Inheritance of mental aptitudes in dogs. *Proc. 6th Int. Cong. Genet. Ithaca.* 2:211–12.

Whitney, L. F. 1955.   *Bloodhounds and how to train them.* Orange Judd, New York.

Whitney, L. F. 1971.   *How to breed dogs.* Howell, New York.

Wiesner, E. 1960.   *Die Erbschaden der Landwirtschaftlichen Nutztiere*, Fischer, Jena.

Wikstrom, B. 1986.   Retinal dysplasi, R.D. *Svensk. Veterinartidning* 38: 129–30.

Wikstrom, B. and Koch, E. 1974.   Rapport om ögondefekter hos dobermannvalpar. *Svensk. Vet.* 2: 26.

Wilkinson, J. S. 1960.   Spontaneous diabetes mellitus. *Vet. Rec.* 28: 548–58.

Willeberg, P., Kastrup, K. W. and Andresen, E. 1975.   Pituitary dwarfism in German Shepherd Dogs: studies on somatomedin activity. *Nord. Vet. Med.* 27: 448–54.

Williams, L. W., Peiffer, R. L., Gelatt, K. N. & Gum, G. G. 1979.   A survey of ocular findings in the American Cocker Spaniel. *J. Am. Anim. Hosp. Ass.* 15: 603–7.

Willis, M. B. 1963.   Abnormalities and defects in pedigree dogs. V. Cryptorchidism. *J. small Anim. Pract.* 4: 469–74.

Willis, M. B. 1968.   A simple method for calculating Wright's coefficient of inbreeding. *Rev. Cubana Cienc. Agric. (Eng. Ed.).* 2: 171–4.

Willis, M. B. 1976.   *The German Shepherd Dog: its history, development and genetics.* K. & R. Books, Leicester.

Willis, M. B. 1977a.   Unpublished data.

Willis, M. B. 1977b.   The hip dysplasia scheme. *Vet. Rec.* 101: 56–7.

Willis, M. B. 1978a.   *Geneticists report.* German Shepherd Dog Improvement Foundation, Colesden. Mimeo.

Willis, M. B. 1978b.   *Geneticists report to the British Briard Club.*

Willis, M. B. 1979.   Unpublished data.

Willis, M. B. 1981.   The improvement foundation's work during 1980. *GSD League Handbook*: pp. 13–21.

Willis, M. B. 1986a.   Some provisional ideas on hypomeligogenesis in the Bernese Mountain Dog. mimeograph. Bernese Breeders Association.

Willis, M. B. 1986b.   Haemophilia A and Canto vd Wienerau. *German Shepherd Quarterly.* Spring Edition 32–8.

Willis, M. B. 1987. Haemophilia A and Canto vd Wienerau. *GSD League Handbook* 1987.   30–9.

Willis, M. B. 1988a.   Unpublished data.

Willis, M. B. 1988b.   Primary epilepsy in the Welsh Springer Spaniel: A preliminary report on genetic aspects. *Report Welsh Springer Spaniel Club*. 11pp.

Willis, M. B., Curtis, R., Barnett, K. C. and Tempest, W. M. 1979.   Genetic aspects of lens luxation in the Tibetan Terrier. *Vet. Rec.* 104: 409–12.

Willis, M. B. and Cuke, G. 1978.   Unpublished data.

Wilsman, N. J. and Van Sickle, D. C. 1973.   Weight change patterns as a basis for predicting survival of newborn Pointer pups. *J. Am. Vet. Med. Ass.* 163: 971–5.

Wilson, J. G. and Warkany, J. 1948.   Malformations in the genitourinary tract induced by maternal vitamin A deficiency in the rat. *Am. J. Anat.* 83: 357–407.

Wilson, L. C. 1953.   *The Kennel Encyclopaedia*. Virtue, London.

Wilsson, E. 1984.   The social interaction between mothers and offspring during weaning in German Shepherd Dogs: individual differences between mothers and their effects on offspring. *App. Anim. Behaviour Sci.* 13: 101–12.

Winzenburger, W. 1936.   Die Häufigkeitsverteilung der Geschlechtskombination beim Hunde. *Z. Zucht B.* 36: 227–36.

Winge, O. 1950.   *Inheritance in dogs with special reference to hunting breeds.* Comstock, New York.

Wolf, E. D., Vainisi, S. J. and Antos-Anderson, R. 1978.   Rod-Cone dysplasia in the Collie. *J. Am. Vet. Med. Ass.* 173: 1331–3.

Wood, A. K. W., Bath, M. L. and Mason, T. A. 1975.   Osteochondritis dissecans of the digital humerus in a dog. *Vet. Rec.* 96: 489–90.

Woods, C. B. 1977.   Hyperkinetic episodes in two Dalmatian dogs. *J. Am. Anim. Hosp. Ass.* 13: 255–7.

Woods, C. B., Rawlings, C., Barber, D. and Walker, M. 1978.   Esophageal deviation in four English Bulldogs. *J. Am. Vet. Med. Ass.* 172: 934–9.

Wouda, W. and van Nes, J. J. 1986.   Progressive ataxia due to central demyelination in Rottweiler dogs. *Vet. Quarterly* 8: 89–97.

Wriedt, C. 1925.   Letale faktoren. *Z. Tierzucht Zucht Biol.* 3: 223–30.

Wright, D. 1963.   The radiographic diagnosis of hip dysplasia in the dog. *Vet. Rec.* 75: 527–8.

Wright, F. and Palmer, A. C. 1969.   Morphological changes caused by pressure on the spinal cord. *Path. Vet.* 6: 355–68.

Wright, F., Rest, J. R. and Palmer, A. C. 1973.   Ataxia of the Great Dane caused by stenosis of the cervical vertebral canal: comparison with similar conditions in the Basset Hound, Doberman Pinscher, Ridgeback and the Thoroughbred horse. *Vet. Rec.* 92: 1–6.

Wright, J. G. 1934a.   Injures to the dog's eye. *Vet. Rec.* 14: 1435–45.

Wright, P. J. and Mason, T. A. 1977.   Usefulness of palpation of joint laxity in puppies as a predictor of hip dysplasia in a guide dog breeding proramme. *J. small Anim. Pract.* 18: 513–22.

Wright, S. 1922a.   The effects of inbreeding and crossbreeding on guinea pigs. I. Decline in vigor. II. Differentiation among inbred families. *USA BULL.* 1090.

Wright, S. 1922b.   Coefficients of inbreeding and relationship. *Am. Nat.* 56: 330–8.

Wright, S. 1934.   The results of crosses between inbred strains of guinea pigs differing in number of digits. *Genetics* 19: 537–51.

Wright, S. and McPhee, H. C. 1925.   An approximate method of calculating coefficients of inbreeding and relationship from Livestock pedigrees. *J. Agric. Res.* 31: 377–83.

Wyman, M. and Donovan, E. F. 1969.   Eye anomaly of the Collie. *J. Am Vet. Med. Ass.* 155: 866–70.

Wyman, M. and Donovan, E. F. 1971.   *Current Veterinary Therapy IV* (Ed. R. W. Kirk) Saunders, Philadelphia.

Wynne-Davies, R. and Gormley, J. 1978.   The aetiology of Perthes' disease. *J. Bone Joint Surg.* 60–B: 6.

Yakely, W. L. 1972.   Collie Eye Anomaly: decreased prevalance through selective breeding. *J. Am. Vet. Med. Ass.* 161: 1103–7.

Yakely, W. L. 1978.   A study of heritability of cataracts in the American Cocker Spaniel. *J. Am. Vet. Med. Ass.* 172: 814–17.

Yakely, W. L., Hegreberg, G. A. and Padgett, G. A. 1971.   Familial cataracts in the American Cocker Spaniel. *J. Am. Anim. Hosp. Ass.* 7: 127–35.

Yakely, W. L., Wyman, M., Donovan, E. F. and Fechheimer, N. S. 1968.   Genetic transmission of an ocular fundus anomaly in Collies. *J. Am. Vet. Med. Ass.* 152: 457–61.

Yang, T. J. 1978.   Recovery of hair coat color in gray Collie (cyclic neutropenia)—normal bone marrow transplant chimeras. *Am. J. Pathol.* 91: 149–54.

Young, G. B. 1971.   Cryptorchidism in dogs. *Carnivore Genet. Newsl.* 2(2): 38–40.

Young, L. E., Christian, M. R., Ervin, D. M., Davies, W. R., O'Brien, W. A., Swisher, S. N. and Yuille, C. L. 1951.   Hemolytic disease in newborn dogs. *Blood.* 6: 291–313.

Zedler, W., Kostlin, R. and Schnepf, A. 1978.   Zur Frage der sekundären Arthropathia deformans nach Hüftgelenksdysplasie beim Hund. *Tierarz. Umschau.* 33: 370–2.

Zeive, L. 1966.   Pathogenesis of hepatic coma. *Arch. Int. Med.* 118: 221–3.

Zeuner, F. E. 1963.   *The history of domesticated animals.* Hutchinson, London.

Zimmer, E. A. and Stahli, W. 1960.   Erbbedingte Versteifung der Wirbelsäule in einer Familie Deutschen Boxer. *Schweiz. Arch. Tierheilk.* 102: 254–64.

Zulueta, A. De. 1949.   The hairless dogs of Madrid. *Proc. 8th Int. Cong. Genet. Stockholm.*

Glossary

The following terms and abbreviations appear in this book. They are explained at the first stage of use and this list is for ready reference. Definitions are not necessarily dictionary ones but relate to the meaning of the word as used in this book.

Achondroplastic   Dwarfism caused by arrested development of the long bones. In most breeds this is a defect but some breeds (for example Dachshund) are achondroplastic.

Allele   An alternative form of a gene. Thus E^m, E and e are alleles of the extension series gene. A gene may have several alleles (be multi-allelic) but a dog can only have two alleles of any gene and these may be identical or not.

Autosome   Those chromosomes other than the sex chromosomes. There are 76 autosomes in the dog (38 pairs). Any gene carried on these chromosomes is said to be autosomal. It will thus be transmitted to either sex.

Ataxia   Irregularity of bodily functions. In this book generally it refers to lack of locomotory control.

Brachycephalic   Short skulled. Breeds such as the Boxer are of this type.

Breeder's letter   A category used by the BVA/KC in Britain to define a dog whose hips are almost normal as regards hip dysplasia.

BVA   British Veterinary Association.

CEA   Collie Eye Anomaly.

Chi-square   A statistical test much used in deciding whether or not ratios observed agree with those expected.

Chromosome   The gene carrying body in the nucleus of a cell. There are 78 in the dog (39 pairs).

Coefficient of inbreeding   A mathematical term devised by Sewell Wright for measuring the degree of inbreeding. See page 321 for full explanation.

Coefficient of variation   Strictly the standard deviation expressed as a percentage of the mean (see page 22). The higher the value the more variable the population is for the character concerned.

Components of variance   The subdivision of any variation into its sub-units. Thus variation may be divided into that derived from the sire, the dam, age, season of year, type of nutrition, etc.

Continuous variation   Applied to a character that cannot be categorised into distinct parts. Height and weight are typical characters which show a range from one extreme to the other. Usually such traits exhibit a bell-shaped curve.

Correlation   Reciprocally related. Refers to traits which are known to show an association such that when one varies in a certain way the other will also vary either upwards or downwards (see page 26).

Crossing-over   The process by which parts of a chromosome become exchanged for parts of a related chromosome.

Dominant   Relates to an allele of a gene which, when present in a single dose, will mask the presence of another. Usually depicted by upper case letters. Thus B (black) is dominant to b (liver) and hence BB and Bb will appear to be identical in physical appearance.

Dystocia   Whelping trouble or difficult parturition.

ECG   Electrocardiograph—a machine for testing heart performance.

EEG   Electroencephalograph—a machine for testing brain impulses.

Epistasis   The situation whereby a gene at one locus can influence the expression of genes at other loci. Thus BB is black only if at least one D is present. If the animal is BBdd then it will be blue.

ERG   Electroretinograph—a machine for testing the efficiency of the retina of the eye.

Erythrocytes   Red blood cells.

Fitness traits   Those characters associated with fertility and viability of the animal.

Gene   The unit of inheritance.

Generation interval   The average age of parents when their offspring are born. An important aspect of genetic progress (see page 302).

Genotype   The genetic structure of the animal. What the animal carries in its genetic make-up but which may not be apparent in its appearance.

GSDIF   German Shepherd Dog Improvement Foundation—an organisation in Britain aimed at pooling information for the common good.   Now part of the German Shepherd Dog League of Great Britain (GSDL).

Heritability   In the broad sense the proportion of variation that is genetic in origin. In the narrow sense the proportion of the variation that is additive and can thus be transmitted. The heritability can vary from 0 to 100% (0.00 to 1.00). Traits of high heritability are those above 50% while those from 20–50% are medium and those below 20% are low (see page 24).

Heterosis   Strictly the situation when the progeny performance exceeds the mid-parent performance in a cross between two distinct lines.

Heterozygous   Strictly different—used to indicate dogs which carry different alleles of a gene at a specific locus. Thus Aa, BbAa^y, E^{m}E are examples of heterozygous combinations.

Homologous   Refers to chromosomes which are a matching pair, one having come from each parent. The genes on homologous chromosomes may have different alleles but they will be the same genes and thus affect specific traits.

Homozygous   Strictly the same—used to indicate dogs carrying the same allele of a gene in duplicate. Thus AA and aa are homozygous animals.

Hybrid vigour   See *Heterosis*.

Inbreeding   The mating together of animals more closely related than the average of the population from which they come (see page 320).

Incomplete dominance   A situation in which the heterozygote state is different from either homozygote. Thus PK PK is distinguishable from PK pk although not necessarily in physical appearance.

KC   Kennel Club—unless specified refers to the British organisation.

Linkage   The situation when two or more traits are generally transmitted together. Usually this refers to traits controlled by genes situated close together on the same chromosome but it can refer to characters controlled by the same genes (see *pleiotropy*).

Locus (plural *loci*) A particular point on a specific chromosome. Any gene is always found at the same locus.

Meiosis The process during production of ova and sperm whereby the number of chromosomes is halved so that one member of each pair of homologous chromosomes is found in each ovum/sperm.

Melanin The pigment involved in colour of the coat.

Mitosis The process involved in cell division and duplication such as occurs in normal growth. It involves duplication of the chromosomes and then cell division so that each new cell is an exact copy of the original.

Mutation The changing of genetic material (genes) by the action of radiation or certain chemicals. Mutation can also occur naturally but this is very rare.

Non-additive Relating to variation it concerns that part of the variation brought about by dominance or epistasis. Characters with a high non-additive component have a low heritability.

Parity The sequence of litters. Parity 1 is the first litter of a bitch, parity 2 her second and so forth.

PDA Patent ductus arteriosus. A heart defect (see page 233).

Penetrance The extent to which a dominant allele will reveal itself when present in only a single dose. Thus if Bb were always black the B allele would be 100% penetrant. If in 25% of cases Bb was not black then B would be 75% penetrant. (In fact B is 100% penetrant.)

Phenocopy A condition which appears to resemble an inherited trait but which is not genetic in origin.

Phenotype The visible expression of a character. Thus BB and Bb would be different genotypes but the same phenotype (viz, Black). The term visible is used loosely since the X-ray of a ship would also indicate the phenotype, as would the behaviour patterns.

Photoperiodicity The control of ovarian activity by changing day length.

Pituitary A gland situated in the brain that is responsible for the production of various important hormones.

Pleiotropy The situation in which specific genes influence more than one character.

PNA Progressive neuronal abiotrophy (see page 187).

PRA Progressive retinal atrophy. A disease occurring in two forms (see pages 221 and 224).

Polygenic Relates to characters controlled by several genes each of which have a small effect but which have a considerable effect when considered collectively.

Prolificity Fecundity. Usually used in connection with litter size so that prolific bitches or breeds have larger litters than do those of lower prolificity.

Qualitative Usually used in relation to characters of simple inheritance and those concerned with features such as colour.

Quantitative Used in relation to characters that are polygenic and concerned with continuous variation, hence Quantitative genetics is the study of such characters.

Realised heritability The extent to which a selected population will transmit their superiority measures the realised heritability (see page 300).

Recessive Refers to an allele which needs to be present in duplicate in order to indicate its presence. In a single dose it will be masked by a dominant allele.

Regression A statistical term indicating the amount by which one character is influenced by another. The regression of litter size on wither height would indicate number of extra pups likely to result from each unit increase in wither height.

Repeatability   The extent to which a character will be repeated on a subsequent occasion. Thus the repeatability of litter size will measure the extent to which a bitch has similarly-sized litters at each whelping (see page 28).

Selection differential   The extent to which a selected group of breeding animals exceed the average of the population from which they were taken (see page 299).

Sex chromosome   Those chromosomes determining sex. An uneven pair in males (XY) and a matching pair in females (XX).

Sex-controlled   Applies to characters which are influenced by the sex of the individual in which they occur. They can occur in both sexes but may be more prevalent on one sex.

Sex-limited   Characters which are limited to appearing in only one sex even though the genes may appear in both. Thus milk yield and cryptorchidism are sex-limited.

Sex-linkage   Applies to the situation where genes are carried on one of the sex chromosomes (usually the X). Such characters are transmitted from mother to son and sire to daughter.

Sex-ratio   The number of males born per 100 females.

Standard deviation   The square root of the variance. Gives a measure of how far a quantitative character will range either side of the mean (see page 22).

Standard error (SE)   A measure of how accurate a statistical calculation such as the mean has been measured (see page 22).

Strain   An inbred line.

Tail male/female   The top (male) and bottom (female) of a pedigree. Mistakenly believed to be more important than other lines in the pedigree.

Telegony   The belief that if a female is mismated to a male of different breed all subsequent litters from her will be affected. A belief without any scientific basis.

Threshold   Relating to characters which are polygenic in their mode of inheritance but which have a limited number of phenotypic forms. When a certain number of genes are present the phenotype passes the threshold and becomes the next form (see page 30).

Variance   A statistical term measuring the variability of a character (see page 22).

Zygote   The fertilized egg.

Index of Breeds

Every mention of a breed is recorded in this index. Because scientific papers often use generic terms certain procedures have been followed. All types of Dachshund are referred to under the simple heading Dachshund. Similarly both types of Fox Terrier are recorded under that single heading. The term Collie is frequently used to mean Rough Collie and thus reference is made under Collie when not specified and under Rough Collie when specified. Figures in **bold** refer to plate numbers.

General Index